Compiled by
Darryl Smith and Clare Chua
Faculty of Business

BUSINESS STATISTICS

SECOND CUSTOM EDITION FOR RYERSON UNIVERSITY

With material from

Business Statistics: A First Course, Fourth Edition
by David M. Levine, Timothy C. Krehbiel, and Mark L. Berenson

PEARSON
Custom
Publishing

PEARSON
Prentice
Hall

Excerpts taken from:

Business Statistics: A First Course, Fourth Edition
by David M. Levine, Timothy C. Krehbiel, and Mark L. Berenson
Copyright © 2006, 2003, 2000, 1998 by Pearson Education, Inc.
Published by Prentice Hall
Upper Saddle River, New Jersey 07458

Printed in Canada

10 9 8 7 6 5 4 3 2 1

ISBN 0-536-10826-9

2005160169

AG/KW

Please visit our web site at *www.pearsoncustom.com*

PEARSON CUSTOM PUBLISHING
75 Arlington Street, Suite 300, Boston, MA 02116
A Pearson Education Company

BRIEF CONTENTS

Preface xiii

Content provided by Darryl Smith. All other content taken from Business Statistics: A First Course, Fourth Edition, by David M. Levine, Timothy C. Krehbiel, and Mark L. Berenson.

CONTENTS

* Content provided by Darryl Smith. All other content taken from Business Statistics: A First Course, *Fourth Edition, by David M. Levine, Timothy C. Krehbiel, and Mark L. Berenson.*

* Content provided by Darryl Smith. All other content taken from Business Statistics: A First Course, *Fourth Edition*, by David M. Levine, Timothy C. Krehbiel, and Mark L. Berenson.

8 CONFIDENCE INTERVAL ESTIMATION 227

* Content provided by Darryl Smith. All other content taken from Business Statistics: A First Course, *Fourth Edition*, by David M. Levine, Timothy C. Krehbiel, and Mark L. Berenson.

9 FUNDAMENTALS OF HYPOTHESIS TESTING: ONE-SAMPLE TESTS 257

10 TWO-SAMPLE TESTS AND ONE-WAY ANOVA 295

* Content provided by Darryl Smith. All other content taken from Business Statistics: A First Course, Fourth Edition, by David M. Levine, Timothy C. Krehbiel, and Mark L. Berenson.

Content provided by Darryl Smith. All other content taken from Business Statistics: A First Course, Fourth Edition, by David M. Levine, Timothy C. Krehbiel, and Mark L. Berenson.

* Content provided by Darryl Smith. All other content taken from Business Statistics: A First Course, Fourth Edition, by David M. Levine, Timothy C. Krehbiel, and Mark L. Berenson.

Content provided by Darryl Smith. All other content taken from Business Statistics: A First Course, Fourth Edition, by David M. Levine, Timothy C. Krehbiel, and Mark L. Berenson.

PREFACE

Educational Philosophy

In our many years of teaching business statistics, we have continually searched for ways to improve the teaching of these courses. Our active participation in a series of Making Statistics More Effective in Schools and Business, Decision Sciences Institute, and American Statistical Association conferences as well as the reality of serving a diverse group of students at large universities has shaped our vision for teaching these courses. Over the years, our vision has come to include these key principles:

1. Students need to be shown the relevance of statistics.
   - Students need a frame of reference when learning statistics, especially when statistics is not their major. That frame of reference for business students should be the functional areas of business—that is, accounting, economics and finance, information systems, management, and marketing. Each statistical topic needs to be presented in an applied context related to at least one of these functional areas.
   - The focus in teaching each topic should be on its application in business, the interpretation of results, the presentation of assumptions, the evaluation of the assumptions, and the discussion of what should be done if the assumptions are violated.
2. Students need to be familiar with the software used in the business world.
   - Integrating spreadsheet or statistical software into all aspects of an introductory statistics course allows the course to focus on interpretation of results instead of computations.
   - Introductory business statistics courses should recognize that in business, spreadsheet software is typically available on a decision-maker's desktop (and sometimes statistical software is as well).
3. Students need to be given sufficient guidance on using software.
   - Textbooks should provide enough instructions so that students can effectively use the software integrated with the study of statistics, without having the software instruction dominate the course.
4. Students need ample practice in order to understand how statistics is used in business.
   - Both classroom examples and homework exercises should involve actual or realistic data as much as possible.
   - Students should work with data sets, both small and large, and be encouraged to look beyond the statistical analysis of data to the interpretation of results in a managerial context.

New to This Edition

This new fourth edition of *Business Statistics, A First Course* has been improved in a number of important areas.

Improved accessibility for students

- Every chapter in the text has undergone major rewriting and the text now uses a more active, conversational writing style that students will appreciate. Sentences have been shortened and simplified.
- The text now focuses more on those topics typically covered in a first course. Coverage of multiple regression has been reduced and time series forecasting has been deleted.
- The text now includes many more examples from everyday life. Such examples include those on online shopping (Chapter 2), time to get ready in the morning (Chapter 3), and waiting time at a fast-food restaurant (Chapter 9).
- Many problems have been simplified so that they contain no more than four parts.
- Key formulas are now included at the end of each chapter.
- Worked-out solutions to Self-Test Questions are provided in the back of the text.
- A roadmap for selecting the proper statistical method is included at the front of the text to help students select the proper technique and to make connections between topics.

- Many new applied examples and exercises with data from *The Wall Street Journal, USA Today, Consumer Reports,* and other sources have been added to the text.
- A chapter-ending Web case is included for most of the chapters. By visiting Web sites related to the companies and researching the issues raised in the "Using Statistics" scenarios that start each chapter, students learn to identify misuses of statistical information. The Web cases require students to sift through claims and assorted information in order to discover the data most relevant to the case. Students then determine whether the conclusions and claims are supported by the data. (Instructional tips for using the Web cases and solutions to the Web cases are included in the Instructor's Solutions Manual.)

Enhanced software instruction

- End-of-chapter Microsoft Excel appendices now discuss how to use standard Excel worksheets to perform most statistical analyses. Instructors and students who wish to avoid using add-ins will find these new instructions immediately useful. (Those who choose to use the PHStat2 Excel add-in will find that all explanations of PHStat2 commands have been placed together in a new Appendix G for easy reference.)

	A	B	
1	Estimate for the Mean Sales Invoice Amount		
2			
3	Data		
4	Sample Standard Deviation	28.95	
5	Sample Mean	110.27	
6	Sample Size	100	
7	Confidence Level	95%	
8			
9	Intermediate Calculations		
10	Standard Error of the Mean	2.8950	=B4/SQRT(B6)
11	Degrees of Freedom	99	=B6 - 1
12	t Value	1.9842	=TINV(1-B7,B11)
13	Interval Half Width	5.7443	=B12 * B10
14			
15	Confidence Interval		
16	Interval Lower Limit	104.53	=B5 - B13
17	Interval Upper Limit	116.01	=B5 + B13

- Many of the standard Excel worksheets discussed in the Excel appendices are included as in-chapter illustrations. Each illustration (see example above) include a listing of all cell formulas contained in the worksheet. (PHStat2 users will also find these illustrations informative as they are consistent with the worksheets that PHStat2 produces for you.)
- Updated version of PHStat2—PHStat2 version 2.5, the newest version of Prentice Hall's add-in for Microsoft Excel is bundled free with this text. This updated version includes enhancements such as multiple regression with independent variables in noncontiguous columns, improved stem-and-leaf displays and box-and-whisker plots, the Z test for the difference in two means, Levene's test for the homogeneity of variance, and the Marascuilo multiple comparisons procedure for proportions. (Support for PHStat2, including free updates when available, can be found at **www.prenhall.com/phstat**.)
- Use of Minitab Version 14, the latest version of the Minitab statistical software—All Minitab output in the text and all Minitab appendices are from Minitab Version 14, the latest version of the Minitab statistical software.

Reorganization of the hypothesis-testing chapters

- All tests involving the normal and t distribution are covered in Chapters 9 and 10 *prior to* coverage of the F test.
- The Analysis of Variance is covered in Chapter 10.
- All chi-square tests are covered in Chapter 11.

Chapter-by-Chapter Changes in the Fourth Edition

Each chapter has a new opening page that shows the sections and subsections for the chapter.

- *Chapter 1* has rewritten sections 1.1, 1.2, and 1.3. The sections on survey sampling have been moved to Chapter 7.
- *Chapter 2* has a new data set concerning mutual fund returns for 1999–2003. Graphs for categorical variables are discussed prior to graphs for numerical variables. All graphs for one variable are discussed before any graphs for two variables. The examples within the chapter refer to online shopping and the cost of restaurant meals in addition to mutual fund returns.
- *Chapter 3* has a new data set concerning mutual fund returns for 1999–2003. The examples within the chapter refer to the time to get ready in the morning as well as mutual fund returns. Z scores for detecting outliers are now included. The sample covariance is now included along with the coefficient of correlation.
- *Chapter 4* now includes Bayes' theorem and counting rules.
- *Chapter 5* now covers the Poisson distribution. The normal distribution has been moved to Chapter 6.
- *Chapter 6* is entirely devoted to the normal distribution and includes a simplified section on the normal probability plot.
- *Chapter 7* includes sampling distributions and Types of Survey Sampling Methods and Survey Worthiness.
- *Chapter 8* includes confidence interval estimation and sample size determination.
- *Chapter 9* uses a simpler, six-step method to perform hypothesis tests using the critical value approach and a straightforward five-step method to perform hypothesis tests using the *p*-value approach.
- *Chapter 10* is reorganized so that two-sample tests for means and proportions precede the F test for the difference between the variances. The chapter includes the One-Way ANOVA.
- *Chapter 11* includes only the χ^2 tests.
- *Chapter 12* now includes computations for the regression coefficients and sum of squares in chapter examples.
- *Chapter 13* now covers R^2, adjusted R^2, and the overall F test prior to residual analysis. The chapter also includes quadratic regression.
- *Chapter 14* has coverage of Six Sigma Management.

Hallmark Features

We have continued many of the traditions of past editions. We've highlighted some of those features below.

- **"Using Statistics" business scenarios**—Each chapter begins with a "Using Statistics" example that shows how statistics is used in accounting, finance, management, or marketing. Each scenario is used throughout the chapter to provide an applied context for the concepts.

USING STATISTICS

Comparing the Performance of Mutual Funds

Among the many investment choices available today, mutual funds, a market basket of a portfolio of securities, are a common choice for those thinking about their retirement. If you decided to purchase mutual funds for your retirement account, how would you go about making a reasonable choice among the many funds available today?

You first would want to know the strategies of the professionals who manage the funds. Do they invest in high-risk securities or do they make more conservative choices? Does the fund specialize in a certain sized company, one whose outstanding stock totals a large amount (large cap) or one that is quite small (small cap)? Does the fund charge management fees that reduce the percentage return earned by an investor? And, of course, you would want to know how well the fund performed in the past.

All of this is a lot of data to review if you consider several dozen or more mutual funds. How could you "get your hands around" such data and explore it in a comprehensible manner?

- **Emphasis on data analysis and interpretation of computer output**—We believe that the use of computer software is an integral part of learning statistics. Our focus emphasizes analyzing data by interpreting the output from Microsoft Excel and Minitab, while reducing emphasis on doing computations. Therefore, we have included more computer output and integrated this output into the fabric of the text. For example, in the coverage of tables and charts in Chapter 2, the focus is on the interpretation of various charts, not on their construction by hand. In our coverage of hypothesis testing in Chapters 9 through 11, extensive computer output has been included so that focus can be placed on the p-value approach. In our coverage of simple linear regression in Chapter 12, we assume that Microsoft Excel or Minitab will be used. Thus, the focus is on the interpretation of the output, not on hand calculations.
- **Pedagogical aides** such as an active writing style, boxed numbered equations, set-off examples to provide reinforcement for learning concepts, problems divided into Learning the Basics and Applying the Concepts, and key terms are included.
- **End-of-chapter appendices** using standard Microsoft Excel and Minitab Version 14, with illustrations, provide easy-to-follow instructions. PHStat2 instructions are included in Appendix G. SPSS appendices are included on the CD-ROM that accompanies this text.
- **Answers** to most of the even-numbered exercises are provided at the end of the book.
- **PHStat2,** a supplemental add-in program for Microsoft Excel, that enhances the statistical capabilities of Microsoft Excel and executes for you the low-level menu selection and worksheet entry tasks associated with implementing statistical analysis in Excel is included on the student CD-ROMs. When combined with Microsoft Excel's own Data Analysis ToolPak add-in, virtually all statistical methods taught in an introductory statistics course can be illustrated using Microsoft Excel.
- **Case Studies and Team Projects**—Detailed case studies are included at the end of numerous chapters. The *Springville Herald* case is included at the end of virtually all chapters as an integrating theme. A Team Project relating to mutual funds is included at the end of many chapters as an integrating theme.
- **Visual Explorations**—a Microsoft Excel workbook bundled free with this text—allows students to interactively explore important statistical concepts in descriptive statistics, probability, the normal distribution, and regression analysis. For example, in descriptive statistics, students observe the effect of changes in the data on the mean, median, quartiles, and standard deviation. In sampling distributions, students use simulation to explore the effect of sample size on a sampling distribution. With the normal distribution, students get to see the effect of changes in the mean and standard deviation on the areas under the normal curve. In regression analysis, students have the opportunity of fitting a line and observing how changes in the slope and intercept affect the goodness of fit. (Visual Explorations requires a Microsoft Excel security setting of Medium.)

Supplement Package

The supplement package that accompanies this text includes the following:

- **Instructor's Solution Manual**—This manual includes teaching tips for each chapter, extra detail in the problem solutions, and many Excel and Minitab solutions.
- **Student Solutions Manual**—This manual provides detailed solutions to virtually all the even-numbered exercises.
- **Test Item File**—The Test Item File contains true/false, multiple choice, fill-in, and problem-solving questions based on the definitions, concepts, and ideas developed in each chapter of the text.
- **TestGen testing software**—The printed test bank is designed for use with the TestGen test-generating software. This computerized package allows instructors to custom design, save, and generate classroom tests. The test program permits instructors to edit, add, or delete questions from the test banks; edit existing graphics and create new graphics; analyze test results; and organize a database of tests and student results. This software allows for greater flexibility and ease of use. It provides many options for organizing and displaying tests, along with a search and sort feature. The program is available both on the Instructor's CD-ROM and on the Prentice Hall online catalog for download.

- **Instructor's Resource Center**—The Instructor's Resource Center contains the electronic files for the complete Instructor's Solutions Manual (MS Word), the Test Item File (MS Word), the computerized Test Item File (MS Word), TestGen, and PowerPoint presentations.
- **Course and Homework Management Tools**
  - **Prentice Hall's OneKey** offers the best teaching and learning resources all in one place. OneKey for *Business Statistics, A First Course, 4e*, is all you need to plan and administer your course, and is all your students need for anytime, anywhere access to your course materials. Conveniently organized by textbook chapter, the compiled resources include: links to quizzes, PowerPoint presentations, data files, links to Web cases, PHStat2 download, Visual Explorations download, Student Solutions Manual, as well as additional instructor resources.
  - **WebCT and Blackboard**—With a local installation of either course management system, Prentice Hall provides content designed especially for this textbook to create a complete course suite, tightly integrated with the system's course management tools.
  - **PH GradeAssist**—This online homework and assessment system allows the instructor to assign problems for student practice, homework, or quizzes. The problems, taken directly from the text, are algorithmically generated, so each student gets a slightly different problem with a different answer. This feature allows students multiple attempts for more practice and improved competency. PH GradeAssist grades the results and can export them to Microsoft Excel worksheets.
- **Companion Web site**—This site contains
  - An online study guide with true/false, multiple choice, and essay questions designed to test student's comprehension of chapter topics.
  - PowerPoint presentation files with chapter outlines and key formulas.
  - Student data files for text problems in Excel, Minitab, and SPSS.
- **Student version of Minitab**—For a reasonable additional cost, a student version of Minitab Version 14 can be packaged with this text. Please contact your Prentice Hall Sales Representative for ordering information.
- **Student version of SPSS**—For a reasonable additional cost, a student version of SPSS 12 can be packaged with the text. Please contact your Prentice Hall Sales Representative for ordering information.
- **Text Web site**—The text has a home page on the World Wide Web at **www.prenhall.com/levine**. This site provides many resources for both faculty members and students.

  PHStat2 has a home page on the World Wide Web at **www.prenhall.com/phstat**.

  An index page for the supporting material for all the Web cases included in the text can be found at **www.prenhall.com/Springville/Springvillecc.htm**.

Acknowledgments

We are extremely grateful to the many organizations and companies that allowed us to use their data in developing problems and examples throughout the text. We would like to thank *The New York Times*, Consumers Union (publishers of *Consumer Reports*), Mergent's Investor Service (publishers of *Mergent's Handbook of Common Stocks*), and CEEPress.

In addition, we would like to thank the Biometrika Trustees, American Cyanimid Company, the Rand Corporation, the American Society for Testing and Materials (for their kind permission to publish various tables in Appendix E), and the American Statistical Association (for its permission to publish diagrams from the *American Statistician*).

A Note of Thanks

We would like to thank Randy Craig, Salem State University; Mark Eakin, University of Texas–Arlington; Kathy Ernstberger, Indiana University–Southeast; Kimberley Killmer Hollister, Montclair State University; C. P. Kartha, University of Michigan, Flint; Robert Lemke, Lake Forest College; Ram Misra, Montclair State University; Prashant Palvia, University of North Carolina, Greensboro; Susan Pariseau, Merrimack College; Brock Williams, Texas Tech University; Frederick Wiseman, Northeastern University; Reginald Worthley, University of Hawaii, Manoa; and Charles Zimmerman, Robert Morris College, for their comments that have made this a better book.

We would especially like to thank Debbie Clare, Mark Pfaltzgraff, Jeff Shelstad, Alana Bradley, Anne Graydon, Cynthia Regan, Nancy Welcher, and Jane Avery of the editorial, marketing, and production teams at Prentice Hall. It has been our privilege to work with Tom Tucker on this project and many previous ones. As Tom now moves on to a new career, we will greatly miss his insight, encouragement, and dedication. Thank you, Tom, and good luck!

We would like to thank our statistical readers and accuracy checkers Annie Puciloski, Stonehill College, and James Zimmer, Chattanooga State University, for their diligence in checking our work; Robie Grant for her proofreading; Julie Kennedy for her copyediting; and Sandra Krausman of GGS Book Services, Atlantic Highlands, for her work in the production of this text.

We are extremely grateful for the love and support given to us by our families. Our parents Reuben and Lee Levine, Marvin Krehbiel, Roberta Reed, and Nat and Ethel Berenson, have blessed us with a lifetime of encouragement. Finally, we would like to thank our wives and children for their patience, understanding, love, and assistance in making this book a reality. It is to them that we dedicate this book.

Concluding Remarks

We have gone to great lengths to make this text both pedagogically sound and error-free. If you have any suggestions or require clarification about any of the material, or if you find any errors, please contact us at **David_Levine@BARUCH.CUNY.EDU** or **KREHBITC@MUOHIO.EDU**. Include the phrase BSFC—version 4 in the subject line of your e-mail. For more information about using PHStat2, see Appendixes F and G, and the PHStat2 readme file on the CD-ROM packaged with this book.

David M. Levine

Timothy C. Krehbiel

Mark L. Berenson

CHAPTER 1

Introduction and Data Collection

USING STATISTICS: Good Tunes

LEARNING OBJECTIVES

In this chapter, you learn:

- How statistics is used in business
- The sources of data used in business
- The types of data used in business

USING STATISTICS

Good Tunes—Part I

Good Tunes, a privately held online retailer of home entertainment systems, seeks to expand its business by opening several stores. To get the financing necessary to underwrite this expansion, Good Tunes needs to apply for loans at local area banks. The managers of the firm agree to develop an electronic slide show that will explain their business and state the facts that will convince the bankers to loan Good Tunes the money it needs. You have been asked to assist in the process of preparing the slide show. What facts would you include? How would you present those facts?

Every day you use news and information sources to gather the facts that you need to lead your life. You might listen to a weather forecast to decide what clothes to wear, and if you live in a large city, you might listen to a commuter report to learn about the best route for traveling to your job or school.

Your personal likes and dislikes shape some of your decisions, too. In spite of hearing bad reviews of a motion picture that suggest you skip seeing it, you might decide to go anyhow just because you happen to like a particular actor who appears in that film.

Likewise, every day business managers have to make decisions. Although managers sometimes resort to "gut instincts" to make some decisions (this is more formally known as unstructured decision making), they more typically make decisions that are directly influenced by hard facts. As a business student, you cannot really learn how to make unstructured decisions, as such decisions require instincts and insights that require years of experience to form. You can learn, though, the procedures and methods that will help you make better decisions that are based on hard facts. When you begin focusing on the procedures and methods involved in the collecting, presenting, and summarizing of a set of data, or forming conclusions about that data, you have discovered statistics.

In the Good Tunes scenario, you should proceed with the reasonable assumption that the bankers seek to make a decision based on the hard facts you help present, and not on other factors, such as whims or personal likes or dislikes. Presenting the wrong information or the correct information in the wrong fashion could lead the bankers to make a bad business decision, which could jeopardize the future of Good Tunes. You need to know something about statistics to provide the hard facts that are necessary, and to know something about statistics, you first need to know the basic concepts of statistics.

1.1   BASIC CONCEPTS OF STATISTICS

Statistics is the branch of mathematics that examines ways to process and analyze data. Statistics provides procedures to collect and transform data in ways that are useful to business decision-makers. To understand anything about statistics, you need to first understand the definition of a variable.

VARIABLES

Variables are characteristics of items or individuals.

Examples of variables are your gender, your major field of study, the amount of money you have in your wallet, and the amount of time it takes you to get ready to go to school in the morning. The key aspect of the word *variable* is the idea that items differ and people differ. The person next to you may be male rather than female, may be majoring in a different field of study than you, almost certainly has a different amount of money in his or her wallet, and undoubtedly takes a different amount of time to get ready in the morning than you do. You should distinguish between a variable, such as gender, and its *value* for an individual observation (e.g., "male").

All variables should have an **operational definition**, a universally accepted meaning that is clear to all associated with an analysis. Without operational definitions, confusion can occur. A famous example of such confusion that illustrates the importance of operational definitions relates to the 2000 U.S. presidential election and the disputed ballots in the state of Florida (Jackie Calmes and Edward P. Foldessy, "In Election Review, Bush Wins with No Supreme Court Help," *The Wall Street Journal*, November 12, 2001, A1, A14). A review of 175,010 Florida ballots that were rejected for either no presidential votes or votes for two or more candidates was conducted with the help of the National Opinion Research Center of the University of Chicago. Nine standards or operational definitions were used to evaluate these ballots. The nine standards led to different results. Three of the standards (including one pursued by Al Gore) led to margins of victory for George Bush that ranged from 225 to 493 votes. Six of the standards (including one pursued by George Bush) led to margins of victory for Al Gore that ranged from 42 to 171 votes.

Now that variables have been defined, you need to understand the meaning of population, sample, parameter, and statistic.

POPULATION

A **population** consists of all of the members of a group about which you want to draw a conclusion.

SAMPLE

A **sample** is the portion of the population selected for analysis.

PARAMETER

A **parameter** is a numerical measure that describes a characteristic of a population.

STATISTIC

A **statistic** is a numerical measure that describes a characteristic of a sample.

Examples of populations are all the full-time students at a college, all the registered voters in New York, and all the people who went shopping at the local mall this weekend. Samples could be selected from each of the three populations mentioned above. Examples include 10 full-time students selected for a focus group, 500 registered voters in New York who were contacted via telephone for a political poll, and 30 mall shoppers who were asked to complete a customer satisfaction survey. In each case, the people in the sample represent a portion or subset of the people comprising the population.

The average amount spent by all the people who went shopping at the local mall this weekend is a parameter. Information from all the shoppers in the entire population is needed to compute this parameter. The average amount spent by the 30 shoppers completing the customer satisfaction survey is a statistic. Information from only 30 people who went to the local mall this weekend is used in calculating the statistic.

Statistics, itself, is divided into two branches, both of which are applicable to managing businesses. **Descriptive statistics** focuses on collecting, summarizing, and presenting a set of data. **Inferential statistics** uses sample data to draw conclusions about a population.

Descriptive statistics has its roots in the recordkeeping needs of large political and social organizations. For example, every decade since 1790, the United States has conducted a census that collects and summarizes data about its citizens. Through the years, the U.S. Census Bureau has been one of the many groups that have refined the methods of descriptive statistics. The foundation of inferential statistics is based on the mathematics of probability theory. Inferential methods use sample data to calculate statistics that provide estimates of the characteristics of the entire population.

Today, applications of statistical methods can be found in different areas of business. Accounting uses statistical methods to select samples for auditing purposes and to understand the cost drivers in cost accounting. Finance uses statistical methods to choose between alternative portfolio investments and to track trends in financial measures over time. Management uses statistical methods to improve the quality of the products manufactured or the services delivered by an organization. Marketing uses statistical methods to estimate the proportion of customers who prefer one product over another and why they do, and to draw conclusions about what advertising strategy might be most useful in increasing sales of a product.

1.2   THE GROWTH OF STATISTICS AND INFORMATION TECHNOLOGY

During the past century, statistics has played an important role in spurring the use of information technology and, in turn, such technology has spurred the wider use of statistics. At the beginning of the twentieth century, the expanding data-handling requirements associated with the federal census led directly to the development of tabulating machines that were the forerunners of today's business computer systems. Statisticians such as Pearson, Fisher, Gosset, Neyman, Wald, and Tukey established the techniques of modern inferential statistics in response to the need to analyze large sets of population data that had become increasingly costly, time-consuming, and cumbersome to collect. The development of early computer systems permitted others to develop computer programs to ease the calculational and data-processing burdens imposed by those techniques. These first programs, in turn, allowed greater use of statistical methods by business decision-makers, and this greater use, as well as more recent advances in information technology, have completed the cycle by spurring the development of even more sophisticated statistical methods.

Today, when you hear of retailers investing in a "customer-relationship management system" or a packaged goods producer engaging in "data mining" to uncover consumer preferences, you should realize that statistical techniques form the foundations of such cutting-edge applications of information technology. Even though cutting-edge applications might require custom programming, for many years businesses have had access to **statistical packages**, such as Minitab and SPSS, that are standardized sets of programs that help managers use a wide range of statistical techniques by automating the data processing and calculations these techniques require. Whereas such packages were once available only in corporate computing centers, the increasing power and connectivity of personal computers have brought the statistical power of these packages to the desktop, where they have joined such familiar tools as word processing, worksheet, and Web browser programs.

The leasing and training costs associated with statistical packages have led many to consider using some of the graphical and statistical functions of Microsoft Excel. However, you need to be aware of concerns that many statisticians have about the accuracy and completeness of the statistical results that Excel produces. Unfortunately, some investigators have determined that certain Microsoft Excel statistical capabilities contain flaws that can lead to invalid results, especially when the data sets used are very large or have unusual statistical properties (see reference 3). Clearly, when you use Microsoft Excel, you must be careful about the data and the analysis you are undertaking. Whether this complication outweighs the benefits of Excel's attractive features is still an unanswered question in business today.

1.3   HOW THIS TEXT IS ORGANIZED

The primary goal of this text is helping you learn to understand how the methods of statistics can be used in decision-making processes. For business students, this understanding includes the following objectives:

- To properly present and describe business data and information
- To draw conclusions about large populations based solely on information collected from samples
- To make reliable forecasts about business trends
- To improve business processes

This text uses these four objectives listed above as its organizing principle. Figure 1.1 shows how each chapter relates to these objectives. You will explore the methods involved in the collection, presentation, and description of information in the remaining portion of this chapter and

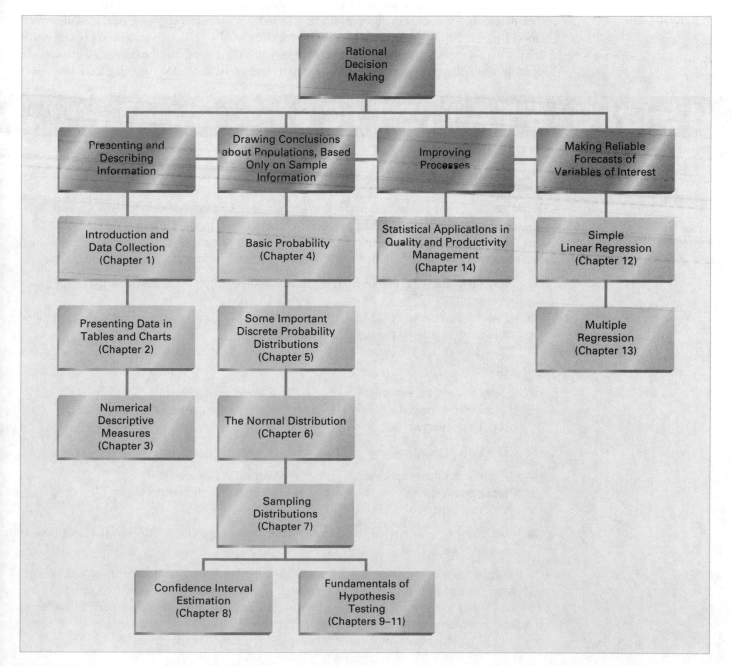

FIGURE 1.1 Structure Chart for This Text

Chapters 2 and 3. In Chapters 4 through 7 you will learn about the basic concepts of probability, and the binomial, normal, and other distributions to better understand, in Chapters 8 through 11, how you can draw conclusions about large populations based solely on information from samples. In Chapters 12 and 13 you will focus on regression analysis that can be used to make forecasts. In Chapter 14 you will learn methods for improving business processes.

Because learning in context enhances comprehension, each chapter begins with a "Using Statistics" scenario, such as the "Good Tunes—Part I" on page 2, that identifies a business problem in which statistics can be applied to change data into the useful information required for a rational decision. Questions raised in the scenarios lead to answers in the form of statistical methods presented in subsequent sections of the text. By thinking about these questions, you will gain an appreciation of how business managers are using statistics today to solve problems and improve the quality of their products and services.

For the "Good Tunes—Part I" scenario, selecting what to present is just as important as selecting the proper method for presentation and summarization. In this case, presumably the bankers themselves would demand some of the data, the "financials" of the business. But what other data could you collect and present that would help win the approval of the loans? (See "Good Tunes—Part II" below.) Of course, having presented your data, you would hope that the bankers would make the right inferences. That is, you would hope that the bankers were knowledgeable about the appropriate statistical methods that assist in the loan-making decision!

USING STATISTICS

Good Tunes—Part II

The owners of Good Tunes have decided to supplement the financial data in their loan application with data concerning customer perceptions about Good Tunes. To help assess these perceptions, Good Tunes has been asking its customers to complete and promptly return a customer satisfaction survey that is included in every order. The survey includes the following questions:

- How many days did it take from the time you ordered your merchandise to the time you received it? _____

- How much money (in U.S. dollars) do you expect to spend on stereo and consumer electronics equipment in the next twelve months? _____

- How do you rate the overall service provided by Good Tunes with respect to your recent purchase?

Much better than expected	☐	Worse than expected	☐
Better than expected	☐	Much worse than expected	☐
About as expected	☐		

- How do you rate the quality of the items you recently purchased from Good Tunes?

Much better than expected	☐	Worse than expected	☐
Better than expected	☐	Much worse than expected	☐
About as expected	☐		

- Are you likely to buy additional merchandise through Good Tunes in the next twelve months? Yes ☐ No ☐

You have been asked to review the survey. What type of data does the survey seek to collect? What type of information can be generated from the data of the completed survey? How can Good Tunes use that information to improve the perceived quality of the service and merchandise? How can Good Tunes use that information to increase its chance of getting a loan approval? What other questions would you suggest to include in the survey?

1.4   COLLECTING DATA

Managing a business effectively requires collecting the appropriate data. In most instances, the data are measurements acquired from items in a sample. The samples are chosen from populations in such a manner that the sample is as representative of the population as possible. The most common technique to ensure proper representation is to use a random sample. (See Chapter 7 for a detailed discussion of sampling techniques.)

Many different types of circumstances require the collection of data:

* A marketing research analyst needs to assess the effectiveness of a new television advertisement.
* A pharmaceutical manufacturer needs to determine whether a new drug is more effective than those currently in use.
* An operations manager wants to monitor a manufacturing process to find out whether the quality of a product is conforming to company standards.
* An auditor wants to review the financial transactions of a company in order to determine whether or not the company is in compliance with generally accepted accounting principles.
* A potential investor wants to determine which firms within which industries are likely to have accelerated growth in a period of economic recovery.

Identifying Sources of Data

Identifying the most appropriate source of data is a critical aspect of statistical analysis. If biases, ambiguities, or other types of errors flaw the data being collected, even the most sophisticated statistical methods will not produce accurate information. Four important sources of data are:

* Data distributed by an organization or an individual
* A designed experiment
* A survey
* An observational study

Data sources are classified as being either **primary sources** or **secondary sources**. When the data collector is the one using the data for analysis, the source is primary. When one organization or individual has compiled the data that are used by another organization or individual, the source is secondary.

Organizations and individuals that collect and publish data typically use that data as a primary source and then let others use it as a secondary source. For example, the United States federal government collects and distributes data in this way for both public and private purposes. The Bureau of Labor Statistics collects data on employment as well as distributing the monthly *Consumer Price Index*. The Census Bureau oversees a variety of ongoing surveys regarding population, housing, and manufacturing and undertakes special studies on topics such as crime, travel, and health care.

Market research firms and trade associations also distribute data pertaining to specific industries or markets. Investment services such as Mergent's provide financial data on a company-by-company basis. Syndicated services such as A. C. Nielsen provide clients with data enabling the comparison of client products with those of their competitors. Daily newspapers are filled with numerical information regarding stock prices, weather conditions, and sports statistics.

As listed above, conducting an experiment is another important data collection source. For example, to test the effectiveness of laundry detergent, an experimenter determines which brands in the study are more effective in cleaning soiled clothes by actually washing dirty laundry instead of asking customers which brand they believe to be more effective. Proper experimental designs are usually the subject matter of more advanced texts, because they often involve sophisticated statistical procedures. However, some fundamental experimental design concepts will be considered in Chapter 10.

Conducting a survey is a third important data source. Here the people being surveyed are asked questions about their beliefs, attitudes, behaviors, and other characteristics. Responses are then edited, coded, and tabulated for analysis.

Conducting an observational study is the fourth important data source. In such a study, a researcher observes the behavior directly, usually in its natural setting. Observational studies take many forms in business. One example is the **focus group**, a market research tool that is used for eliciting unstructured responses to open-ended questions. In a focus group, a moderator leads the discussion, and all the participants respond to the questions asked. Other, more structured types of studies involve group dynamics and consensus building and use various organizational behavior tools such as brainstorming, the Delphi technique, and the nominal-group method. Observational study techniques are also used in situations in which enhancing teamwork, or improving the quality of products and service are management goals.

1.5 TYPES OF DATA

Data are the observed values of variables, for example, the responses to a survey. Statisticians develop surveys to deal with a variety of different variables. As illustrated in Figure 1.2, there are two types of variables—categorical and numerical.

FIGURE 1.2

Types of Variables

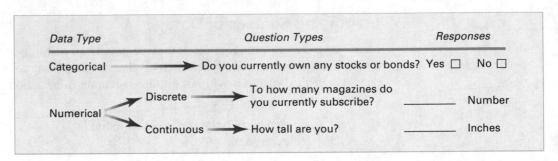

Categorical variables yield categorical responses, such as yes or no answers. An example is the response to the question "Do you currently own any stocks or bonds?" because it is limited to a simple yes or no answer. Another example is the response to the question on the Good Tunes survey (presented on page 6), "Are you likely to buy additional merchandise through Good Tunes in the next 12 months?" Categorical variables can also yield more than two possible responses. For example, "Which day of the week are you most likely to eat dinner in a restaurant?"

Numerical variables yield numerical responses such as your height in inches. Other examples are how much money you expect to spend on stereo equipment in the next 12 months (from the Good Tunes customer satisfaction survey) or the response to the question "To how many magazines do you currently subscribe?" There are two types of numerical variables: discrete and continuous.

Discrete variables produce numerical responses that arise from a counting process. "The number of magazines subscribed to" is an example of a discrete numerical variable, because the response is one of a finite number of integers. You subscribe to zero, one, two, and so on, magazines.

Continuous variables produce numerical responses that arise from a measuring process. Your height is an example of a continuous numerical variable, because the response takes on any value within a continuum or interval, depending on the precision of the measuring instrument. For example, your height may be 67 inches, $67\frac{1}{4}$ inches, $67\frac{7}{32}$ inches, or $67\frac{58}{250}$ inches, depending on the precision of the available instruments.

No two persons are exactly the same height and the more precise the measuring device used, the greater the likelihood of detecting differences between their heights. However, most measuring devices are not sophisticated enough to detect small differences. Hence, *tied observations* are often found in experimental or survey data even though the variable is truly continuous, and theoretically all values of a continuous variable are different.

PROBLEMS FOR SECTION 1.5

Learning the Basics

1.1 Three different beverages are sold at a fast-food restaurant—soft drinks, tea, and coffee. Explain why the type of beverage sold is an example of a categorical variable.

1.2 Soft drinks are sold in three sizes in a fast food restaurant—small, medium, and large. Explain why the size of the soft drink is a categorical variable.

1.3 Suppose that you measure the time it takes to download an MP3 file from the Internet.
a. Explain why the download time is a numerical variable.
b. Is the variable discrete or continuous?

Applying the Concepts

 1.4 For each of the following variables, determine whether the variable is categorical or numerical. If the variable is numerical, determine whether the variable is discrete or continuous.
a. Number of telephones per household
b. Length (in minutes) of the longest long-distance call made per month
c. Whether there is a telephone line connected to a computer modem in the household
d. Whether there is a fax machine in the household

 1.5 The following information is collected from students upon exiting the campus bookstore during the first week of classes:
a. Amount of time spent shopping in the bookstore
b. Number of textbooks purchased
c. Academic major
d. Gender
Classify each of these variables as categorical or numerical. If the variable is numerical, determine whether the variable is discrete or continuous.

 1.6 For each of the following variables, determine whether the variable is categorical or numerical. If the variable is numerical, determine whether the variable is discrete or continuous.
a. Name of Internet provider
b. Amount of time spent surfing the Internet per week
c. Number of e-mails received in a week
d. Number of online purchases made in a month

1.7 For each of the following variables, determine whether the variable is categorical or numerical. If the variable is numerical, determine whether the variable is discrete or continuous.
a. Amount of money spent on clothing in the last month
b. Favorite department store
c. Most likely time period during which shopping for clothing takes place (weekday, weeknight, or weekend)
d. Number of pairs of winter gloves owned

1.8 Suppose the following information is collected from Robert Keeler on his application for a home mortgage loan at the Metro County Savings and Loan Association:
a. Monthly Payments: $1,427
b. Number of Jobs in Past 10 Years: 1
c. Annual Family Salary Income: $86,000
d. Marital Status: Married
Classify each of the responses by type of data.

1.9 One of the variables most often included in surveys is income. Sometimes the question is phrased "What is your income (in thousands of dollars)?" In other surveys, the respondent is asked to "Place an X in the circle corresponding to your income level" and given a number of ranges to choose from.
a. In the first format, explain why income might be considered either discrete or continuous.
b. Which of these two formats would you prefer to use if you were conducting a survey? Why?
c. Which of these two formats would likely bring you a greater rate of response? Why?

1.10 If two students score a 90 on the same examination, what arguments could be used to show that the underlying variable—test score—is continuous?

1.11 The director of market research at a large department store chain wanted to conduct a survey throughout a metropolitan area to determine the amount of time working women spend shopping for clothing in a typical month.
a. Describe both the population and the sample of interest, and indicate the type of data the director might wish to collect.
b. Develop a first draft of the questionnaire needed in (a) by writing a series of three categorical questions and three numerical questions that you feel would be appropriate for this survey.

1.6   MEASUREMENT SCALES

Data can be classified according to the type of measurement scale that is involved. The measurement scale is the set of all the possible values that could result when the data is collected. The type of measurement scale often dictates what calculations can be performed and what type of graphical display will be appropriate.

Qualitative (Categorical) data

a) Nominal: Data indicates a category. The categories have no particular *order* or *ranking*. (Note: Alphabetic order is not a consideration.) The categories may be numeric or non-numeric. In either case, the data is *qualitative*.

Examples:

i. Marital Status: Single, married, divorced or widowed. On a survey the results of this question could be recorded as: 1 = single, 2 = married, etc. Even though the data is recorded as numbers, it is still *qualitative*.

ii. Colour of cars: Blue, red, silver, etc.

iii. Check-out lane used in grocery store: 1, 2, 3, etc. Note: The checkout lanes could have been labelled A, B, C or if the store had various colour schemes, the lanes could have been indicated by their colour.

The only type of **calculations** that can be performed is the number of responses in each category can be *counted*. Bar, pie and Pareto charts may be useful for displaying the results of this type of data collection.

b) Ordinal: Data is similar to nominal in that categories are involved, however, there is a natural *order* to the categories. We can say that one category is higher or better than another. Again the categories can be numeric or non-numeric and are considered as being *qualitative*. Bar and pie charts are appropriate graphs for displaying results.

Examples:

i. Professorial rank: Lecturer, assistant professor, associate professor, and professor.

ii. Rating of a product: Very poor, poor, average, good, and excellent.

iii. Order of finish in a sporting event: 1st, 2nd, 3rd, etc.

iv. Letter grades: A+, A, A–, B+, etc.

Once again, the only type of calculation that can be performed with the data is, the number of values in each category can be counted.

Quantitative (Numerical) Data

c) Interval: The distinguishing feature of interval data, as compared to nominal and ordinal, is the data has *units of measurement*. The data must be numeric and is *quantitative*. As a result, the interval between data values has a meaning. The other characteristic of significance in interval data is that the value "0" (zero) is only an *arbitrary reference point*. In other words, a value of zero does not mean there is no amount of the characteristic being measured.

Examples:

i. Temperature: 0° C does not mean there is no heat.

ii. Calendar scale: The date "0" is just a reference point.

In all cases, with an interval scale, we can subtract data values and get meaningful results.

Example 1: The difference between 10° C and 11° C is the same as the difference between 20° C and 21° C. If one had a container of water at 10° C and a similar sized container at 20° C, then the exact same amount of heat must be added to both containers to increase the temperature to 11° C and 21° C, respectively.

Example 2: The difference between the dates Jan. 1 and Jan. 8 is 7 days, and this is the exact same amount of time as the difference between Feb. 11 and Feb. 18. **Note:** Interval data is *not* of great importance to us in business, because, other than when measuring temperature, we rarely come across this type of data.

d) Ratio: This type of data has the characteristics of interval data, but, in addition, the "0" value does mean the absence of the characteristic being measured, i.e. 0 = 'nothing' and the *ratio* of data values is meaningful. Ratio data is the most common type of numeric data that we will encounter.

Ratio data may be continuous or discrete.
Examples of *discrete* ratio data:

The number of students in this class.
The number of classes you will attend.

Examples of continuous data include data dealing with: time, distance, area, volume, weight, and money.

The name ratio is appropriate because meaningful results occur when two data values are divided. For example:

$$\frac{10\,km}{5\,km} = 2 \quad \text{In other words, 10 km. is twice the distance as 5 km.}$$

Now consider the following:

$$\frac{10\ C}{5\ C} = 2 \quad \text{In other words, 10° C is twice as hot as 5° C ???}$$

(Temperature is measured on an interval scale, thus the result of a division is not meaningful.)

Also, the same is true for discrete data. If you attend 12 classes and your friend attends 6 classes, we can say you attended twice as many classes as your friend.

All types of calculations can be performed with ratio data. Histograms, polygons, ogives, stem-and-leaf displays, and box-whisker plots are all useful graphs of ratio data.

PROBLEMS FOR SECTION 1.6

1.12 Consider the following questions being asked on a survey. The possible responses for each person are given. What is the measurement scale of the response data.

1. What was the rating of the restaurant that you last had dinner out with your partner?
   Answer: **a)** ★
   b) ★★
   c) ★★★
   d) ★★★★
   e) ★★★★★

2. What is the rating of your favourite television show?
   Answer: **a)** TV-G
   b) TV-PG
   c) TV-14
   d) TV-MA

3. On your income tax form: What is your marital status?
   Answer: **a)** Married
   b) Common Law
   c) Widowed
   d) Divorced
   e) Separated
   f) Single

4. What is your level of education?
   Answer: **a)** Elementary School
          b) High School
          c) College
          d) University-Undergrad
          e) University-Post Grad

5. What stock-exchange are the majority of your stock investments listed on?
   Answer: **a)** TSX
          b) NYSE
          c) AMEX
          d) NASDAQ
          e) VSE

6. What type of accommodation do you usually choose for your overnight stay when on a car trip?
   Answer: **a)** Hotel
          b) Motel
          c) Bed & Breakfast
          d) Country Inn
          e) Cabin/Cottage

7. What was the rating of the last motel that you stayed in?
   Answer: **a)** ★
          b) ★★
          c) ★★★
          d) ★★★★
          e) ★★★★★

8. What is your postal code? Answer: _____

9. What was the rating of the last movie that you saw in a theatre:
   Answer: **a)** G
          b) PG
          c) PG-13
          d) R
          e) NC-17
          f) X

10. What is your favourite meat?
    Answer: **a)** Beef
           b) Pork
           c) Chicken
           d) Veal
           e) Lamb

1.13 Refer to the chart below, from the Autumn 1999 issue of Canadian Social Trends, that shows data regarding seniors with driver's licenses who have a health condition. Many seniors were surveyed and much data was obtained from each respondent. The responses to 4 questions were used to obtain the data to allow the researchers to construct the chart shown. What type of measurement scale is used for each type of data? Are the values discrete or continuous?

Source: Statistics Canada, National Population Health Survey, 1996-97.

Question	Measurement Scale	Discrete/Continuous

**Government Travel Survey
of Visitors to Canada**

26

☐ REG   ☐ PERS
☐ CHARTER   ☐ SELF

Confidential when completed
Version française disponible

Dear visitor :

We are currently conducting a travel survey between Canada and overseas countries and we would be interested in knowing about the trip you have taken to Canada. Information from this voluntary survey will be used by members of the Canadian travel industry and government tourism organizations to better understand and serve you, the travelling public.

We would appreciate it if you could spare 10 to 15 minutes of your time to complete this questionnaire. If you require assistance, do not hesitate to ask our Statistics Canada representative. Upon completion, please return the questionnaire to her/him.

This survey is conducted under the authority of the *Statistics Act* (R.S.C. 1985, c. S19) and individual information from your questionnaire will be kept strictly confidential.

Thank you for your co-operation on this important survey and have a nice flight.

---

1. Where do you live? *Usual place of residence*

Country

01 ◯ United Kingdom   03 ◯ Germany   ▶ Other, specify [   ]

02 ◯ France   04 ◯ Japan

If Canada or United States, please return the questionnaire to our representative.

City/Town [   ]   State/Province/Territory [   ]

1a. Are you travelling as a member of i) a crew or ii) a military or diplomatic corps or one of their dependents?

1 ◯ Yes ▶ If «yes», please return the questionnaire to our representative.
2 ◯ No

2a. Where and when did you <u>enter</u> Canada?

Name of Canadian border crossing or airport [   ]   Day Month Year

---

2b. Where will you <u>leave</u> Canada?

01 ◯ Halifax International Airport
02 ◯ Montreal - Dorval / Mirabel Airport
03 ◯ Pearson International Airport, Toronto (T1, T2, T3)
04 ◯ Calgary International Airport
05 ◯ Vancouver International Airport

When will you <u>leave</u> Canada?

Day Month Year   Nights

2c. When <u>entering</u> Canada, did you travel...

1 ◯ From U.S.A. only   2 ◯ Directly from another country   3 ◯ From another country via the U.S.A.

▼ *Please return the questionnaire to our representative.*

2d. When <u>leaving</u> Canada, will you travel...

4 ◯ To U.S.A. only   5 ◯ Directly to another country   6 ◯ To another country via the U.S.A.

8-2200-400.1: 2001-07-16   STC/ECT-250-02797   ☐ COMP   ☐ PART   ☐ OOS

Statistics Canada Statistique Canada   **Canadä**

3. In the next questions we will be referring to a **travelling party**. In your travelling party include only those for whom you feel comfortable reporting **spending** and **activities**. A travelling party usually refers to friends and/or family members travelling together.

How many people including yourself were in the **travelling party**? ☐☐

4. How many people in the **travelling party** were in each of the following groups?

Age groups ▶	Under 2 years	2 to 11	12 to 14	15 to 19	20 to 24	25 to 34	35 to 44	45 to 54	55 to 64	65 to 74	75 and over
Female ▶	01	02	03	04	05	06	07	08	09	10	11
Male ▶	12	13	14	15	16	17	18	19	20	21	22

5. What was the **travelling party's main** reason for taking this trip to Canada?
Check one only.
(e.g. If a person on a business trip took his/her family along to visit relatives, check reason for trip as "business".)

Business
01 ○ Meetings   02 ○ Convention, conference, trade show, seminar   03 ○ Other work

Pleasure
04 ○ Holiday, vacation   05 ○ Visit friends or relatives   06 ○ Visit second home, cottage, condo   07 ○ Attend events, attractions

Other
08 ○ Personal (medical, wedding, etc.)   09 ○ In transit to / from other countries *and* passing through Canada Customs   ○ In transit to / from other countries *without* passing through Canada Customs   ▶ If «In transit to / from other countries *without* passing through Canada Customs », please return the questionnaire to our representative.
10 ○ Educational study   11 ○ Shopping   12 ○ Other – Specify

6. On this trip in Canada did anyone in the **travelling party**...
Check all that apply.
21 ○ Visit friends or relatives
22 ○ Attend a festival or fair
23 ○ Attend a cultural performance (a play, a concert, etc.)
24 ○ Visit a museum or art gallery
25 ○ Visit a historic site
26 ○ Visit a zoo, aquarium or botanical garden
27 ○ Attend a sports event
28 ○ Go shopping
29 ○ Go sightseeing
30 ○ Go to a bar or night club
31 ○ Go to a casino

32 ○ Visit a theme or amusement park
33 ○ Visit a national or provincial nature park
34 ○ Participate in sports or outdoor activities Specify ▼
35 ○ Boating - motor boat, sail boat, kayak, canoe or other
36 ○ Golfing
37 ○ Downhill skiing or snow boarding
38 ○ Hunting
39 ○ Fishing
○ Other sports or outdoor activities Specify ▼

7. How would you rate the following aspects of your trip in Canada?

	Good	Average	Poor	Not applicable
Transportation services	01 ○	06 ○	11 ○	○
Accommodation services	02 ○	07 ○	12 ○	○
Hospitality of local people	03 ○	08 ○	13 ○	○
Value for your money	04 ○	09 ○	14 ○	○
Variety of things to see and do	05 ○	10 ○	15 ○	○

8-2200-400.1

8. While in Canada, what place(s) did the <u>travelling party</u> visit?

Please name all places visited even if you did not stay overnight.
(Exclude stop-overs at airports.)

Please print.

Name of city(ies) / town(s) visited	Name of province(s) / territory(ies) visited	Number of nights spent at each place	Where did the travelling party stay? Check all that apply.					
			Hotel	Motel	Home of friends or relatives	Camping or trailer park	Cottage or cabin	Other
			1○	2○	3○	4○	5○	6○
			1○	2○	3○	4○	5○	6○
			1○	4○	8○	4○	5○	6○
			1○	8○	3○	4○	5○	6○
			1○	2○	3○	4○	5○	6○
			1○	2○	3○	4○	5○	6○
			1○	8○	3○	4○	5○	6○
			1○	7○	3○	4○	5○	6○
			1○	2○	3○	4○	5○	6○
			1○	2○	3○	4○	5○	6○
			1○	2○	3○	4○	5○	6○
			1○	2○	3○	4○	5○	6○

9. Does anyone in the <u>travelling party</u> own any of the accommodations used on this trip?   1○ Yes ▶ Go to Question 11   2○ No ▶ Go to Question 11

For administrative use only

10. When <u>entering</u> Canada, did you travel ...

1○ From U.S.A. only   2○ Directly from another country   3○ From another country via the U.S.A.

When <u>leaving</u> Canada, will you travel ...

4○ To U.S.A. only   5○ Directly to another country   6○ To another country via the U.S.A.

11. For this trip, what means of transportation did you use

	Commercial		Other		
a) ... to <u>enter</u> Canada? *Check one only.*	01○ Plane 03○ Boat		05○ Private automobile 07○ Private plane 09○ Other		
	02○ Train 04○ Bus		06○ Rented automobile 08○ Private boat		
b) ... to <u>leave</u> Canada? *Check one only.*	10⊘ Plane 12○ Boat		14○ Private automobile 16○ Private plane 18○ Other		
	11○ Train 13○ Bus		15○ Rented automobile 17○ Private boat		
c) ... while in Canada? *Check all that apply.*	19○ Plane 21○ Boat		23○ Private automobile 25○ Private plane 27○ Other		
	20○ Train 22○ Bus		24○ Rented automobile 26○ Private boat	*(metro, subway, taxi)*	

12. Please report the routes, carriers and fares (including taxes) to enter and leave Canada.
Please print.
▼

a) From which country did the <u>travelling party</u> come immediately before entering Canada *(excluding stop-overs at airports)?*

Name of airline or other carrier

c) Fares

Round trip fare *(including package tours)* **for <u>entire</u> travelling party**

OR

Entry fare for the <u>travelling party</u>

Currency *(if other than CAN $)*
○ French franc
○ British pound
○ EMU Euro
○ German mark
○ Japanese yen
○ Other, specify

b) To which country the <u>travelling party</u> is going immediately upon leaving Canada *(excluding stop-overs at airports)?*
○ France
○ United Kingdom
○ Germany
○ Japan
○ Other, specify

Name of airline or other carrier

Currency *(if other than CAN $)*
○ French franc
○ British pound
○ EMU Euro
○ German mark
○ Japanese yen
○ Other, specify

Return fare for the <u>travelling party</u>

Currency *(if other than CAN $)*
○ French franc
○ British pound
○ EMU Euro
○ German mark
○ Japanese yen
○ Other, specify

13. What class of fares were used?
Check all that apply.

- ¹○ First class
- ²○ Business class
- ³○ Economy class
- ⁴○ Charter class
- ⁵○ Frequent flyer plan

14. Were these fares part of a package?

○ No   ¹○ Yes ▶

Which of the following item(s) was (were) also included? *Check all that apply.*

- ²○ Accommodation / meals
- ³○ Accommodation only
- ⁴○ Rented car
- ⁵○ Other

15. For this trip, what was the total spending in Canada for all persons in the travelling party?

Include cash/credit transactions for food, accommodation, entertainment, merchandise, gifts, auto operation, local transportation, etc. even if paid for by someone else or a business. Include all taxes and tips. Exclude fares and/or packages reported in Question 12. Estimates appreciated.

Amount
| | | | | | .00

Number of persons included in spending ▶ | | |

Currency *(if other than CAN $)*
- ○ French franc
- ○ British pound
- ○ EMU Euro
- ○ German mark
- ○ Japanese yen
- ○ Other, specify [ ]

16. Please distribute total spending (as reported in Question 15) in each of the following categories. Estimates appreciated.

If estimates can not be provided, report approximate percentages (%) of total spending.

The sums in Questions 15 and 16 should agree.

	Amount	or	%
Accommodation	| | | | .00	or	| | |
Transportation in Canada *(include gasoline expenditures, rented car, intercity plane, bus and train fares, boat tours, local bus, taxi)*	| | | | .00	or	| | |
Food and beverage	| | | | .00	or	| | |
Recreation and entertainment	| | | | .00	or	| | |
Other *(souvenirs, shopping, photos, etc.)* Specify major items. ▼	| | | | .00	or	| | |

17. What percentage of total expenditures *(including fares)* was paid ...

personally? *(including family/friends)* | | | %
by business? | | | %
by government? | | | %

18. After your first arrival to Canada, did you at any time during this trip leave Canada for the U.S.A. and then return?

If yes, please report the place(s) and date(s) of exit and the place(s) of re-entry.

Please print.

¹○ Yes ▶ How many times? | | ²○ No
▼

Place of exit from Canada (border crossing / airport)	Date of exit Day Month Year	Place of re-entry to Canada (border crossing / airport)	Number of nights in U.S.A.

19. If you visited the U.S.A. before entering Canada, how long did you stay in the U.S.A.?

- ¹○ Under 24 hours
- ²○ 1 – 2 nights
- ³○ 3 or more nights
- ⁴○ Not applicable

COMMENTS

We welcome comments on any aspect of your trip including those which would help us to better understand your responses.

_____

_____

_____

_____

THANK YOU VERY MUCH FOR YOUR CO-OPERATION

CHAPTER REVIEW PROBLEMS

Checking Your Understanding

1.12 What is the difference between a sample and a population?

1.13 What is the difference between a statistic and a parameter?

1.14 What is the difference between descriptive and inferential statistics?

1.15 What is the difference between a categorical and a numerical variable?

1.16 What is the difference between a discrete and a continuous variable?

1.17 What is an operational definition and why is it so important?

Applying the Concepts

1.18 The Data and Story Library **lib.stat.cmu.edu/DASL** is an online library of data files and stories that illustrate the use of basic statistical methods. The stories are classified by method and by topic. Go to this site and click on **List all topics**. Pick a story and summarize how statistics are used in the story.

1.19 Go to the official Microsoft Excel Web site **www.microsoft.com/office/excel**. Explain how you think Microsoft Excel could be useful in the field of statistics.

1.20 Go to the official Minitab Web site **www.minitab.com**. Explain how you think Minitab could be useful in the field of statistics.

1.21 Go to the official SPSS Web site **www.spss.com**. Explain how you think SPSS could be useful in the field of statistics.

1.22 The Gallup organization releases the results of recent polls at its Web site **www.gallup.com**. Go to this site and click on an article of interest to you in the "Top Stories" section.
a. Give an example of a categorical variable found in the article.
b. Give an example of a numerical variable found in the article.
c. Is the variable you selected in (b) discrete or continuous?

1.23 The U.S. Census Bureau **www.census.gov** site contains survey information on people, business, geography, and other topics. Go to the site and click on **Housing** in the "People" section. Then click on **American Housing Survey**.
a. Briefly describe the American Housing Survey.
b. Give an example of a categorical variable found in this survey.
c. Give an example of a numerical variable found in this survey.
d. Is the variable you selected in (c) discrete or continuous?

INTRODUCTION TO THE WEB CASES

LEARNING FROM THE WEB CASES IN THIS TEXT

People use statistical techniques to help communicate and present important information to others both inside and outside their businesses. And every day, people misuse these techniques:

- A sales manager working with an "easy-to-use" charting program chooses an inappropriate chart that obscures data relationships.
- The editor of an annual report presents a chart of revenues with an abridged *Y*-axis that creates the false impression of greatly rising revenues.
- An analyst generates meaningless statistics about a set of categorical data using analyses designed for numerical data.

Although much of the misuse of statistics is unintentional, you need to be able to identify all such misuses in order to be an informed manager. The primary goal of the Web Cases throughout this text is to help you develop this type of skill.

Web Cases ask you to visit the Web sites that are related to the companies and issues raised in the "Using Statistics" scenario that starts each chapter or a Web page that supports the continuing story of the *Springville Herald*, a small-city daily newspaper. You review internal documents as well as publicly stated claims, seeking to identify and correct the misuses of statistics. Unlike a traditional text case study, but much like real-world situations, not all of the information you encounter will be relevant to your task, and you may occasionally discover conflicting information that you need to resolve before continuing with the case.

To assist your learning, the Web Case for each chapter begins with the learning objective and a synopsis of the scenario under consideration. You will be directed to a specific Web site or Web page and given a set of questions that will guide your exploration. If you prefer, you can also explore the Web pages for the cases by linking to the Springville Chamber of Commerce page **www.prenhall.com/ Springville/SpringvilleCC.htm**.

Complementing the Web Case in most chapters is a traditional case study exercise in which you are asked to apply your knowledge of statistics to a problem being faced by the management of the *Springville Herald*.

To illustrate how to use a Web Case, link to the Web site for Good Tunes **www.prenhall.com/Springville/ Good_Tunes.htm**, the online retailer mentioned in the "Using Statistics" scenarios for this chapter. Recall that the privately held Good Tunes is seeking financing to expand its business by opening retail locations. Since it is in management's interest to show that Good Tunes is a thriving business, it is not too surprising to discover the "our best sales year ever" claim in the "Good Times at Good Tunes" entry at the top of their home page.

The claim is also a hyperlink, so click on "our best sales year ever" to display the page that supports the claim. How would you support such a claim? With a table of numbers? A chart? Remarks attributed to a knowledgeable source? Good Tunes has used a chart to present "two years ago" and "latest twelve month's" sales data by category. Are there any problems with the choices made on this Web page? *Absolutely*!

First, note that there are no scales for the symbols used, so it is impossible to know what the actual sales volumes are. In fact, as you will learn in section 2.4, charts that incorporate symbols in this way are considered examples of *chartjunk* and would never be used by people seeking to properly use graphs.

This important point aside, another question that arises is whether the sales data represent the number of units sold or something else. The use of the symbols creates the impression that unit sales data are being presented. If the data are unit sales, does such data best support the claim being made—or would something else, such as dollar volumes—be a better indicator of sales at Good Tunes?

Then there are those curious chart labels. "Latest twelve months" is ambiguous—it could include months from the current year as well as months from one year ago and therefore may not be an equivalent time period to "two years ago." Since the business was established in 1997, and the claim being made is "best sales year ever," why hasn't management included sales figures for *every* year?

Is Good Tunes management hiding something or are they just unaware of the proper use of statistics? Either way, they have failed to properly communicate a vital aspect of their "story."

In subsequent Web Cases, you are asked to provide this type of analysis, using the open-ended questions presented in this text as guidance. Not all the cases are as straightforward as this sample and some cases include perfectly appropriate applications of statistics.

REFERENCES

1. Kendall, M. G., and R. L. Plackett, eds., *Studies in the History of Statistics and Probability*, vol. 2 (London: Charles W. Griffin, 1977).
2. Kirk, R. E., ed., *Statistical Issues: A Reader for the Behavioral Sciences* (Monterey, CA: Brooks/Cole, 1972).
3. McCullough, B. D., and B. Wilson, "On the accuracy of statistical procedures in Microsoft Excel 97," *Computational Statistics and Data Analysis*, 31 (1999), 27–37.
4. *Microsoft Excel 2003* (Redmond, WA: Microsoft Corporation, 2002).
5. *Minitab Release 14* (State College, PA: Minitab, Inc., 2004).
6. Pearson, E. S., ed., *The History of Statistics in the Seventeenth and Eighteenth Centuries* (New York: Macmillan, 1978).
7. Pearson, E. S., and M. G. Kendall, eds., *Studies in the History of Statistics and Probability* (Darien, CT: Hafner, 1970).
8. *SPSS® Base 12.0 Brief Guide* (Upper Saddle River, NJ: Prentice Hall, 2003).

CHAPTER 2

Presenting Data in Tables and Charts

USING STATISTICS: Comparing the Performance of Mutual Funds

2.1 TABLES AND CHARTS FOR CATEGORICAL DATA
The Summary Table
The Bar Chart
The Pie Chart

2.2 ORGANIZING NUMERICAL DATA
The Ordered Array
The Stem-and-Leaf Display

2.3 TABLES AND CHARTS FOR NUMERICAL DATA
The Frequency Distribution
The Relative Frequency Distribution and the
    Percentage Distribution
The Histogram
The Polygon
The Cumulative Distribution and Ogives

2.4 MISUSING GRAPHS AND ETHICAL ISSUES
Calculator Lesson 1

LEARNING OBJECTIVES

In this chapter, you learn:

- To develop tables and charts for categorical data
- To develop tables and charts for numerical data
- The principles of properly presenting graphs

USING STATISTICS

Comparing the Performance of Mutual Funds

Among the many investment choices available today, mutual funds, a market basket of a portfolio of securities, is a common choice for those thinking about their retirement. If you decided to purchase mutual funds for your retirement account, how would you go about making a reasonable choice among the many funds available today?

You first would want to know the different categories of mutual funds available. You would want to know the strategies of the professionals who manage the funds. Do they invest in high-risk securities or do they make more conservative choices? Does the fund specialize in a certain sized company, one whose outstanding stock totals a large amount (large cap) or one that is quite small (small cap)? Does the fund charge management fees that reduce the percentage return earned by an investor? And, of course, you would want to know how well the fund performed in the past.

All of this is a lot of data to review if you consider several dozen or more mutual funds. How could you "get your hands around" such data and explore it in a comprehensible manner?

One of the ways you can answer the questions raised in the "Using Statistics" scenario is by studying past data on the performance of mutual funds. The data relating to a sample of 121 mutual funds are in the MUTUALFUNDS2004 file. As an investor you would want to examine both categorical and numerical variables. Did mutual funds with a growth objective have lower returns than mutual funds with a value objective? Do growth funds tend to be riskier investments than value funds? Reading this chapter will help you to select and develop proper tables and charts to try to answer these and other questions.

2.1 TABLES AND CHARTS FOR CATEGORICAL DATA

When you have categorical data, you tally responses into categories and then present the frequency or percentage in each category in tables and charts.

The Summary Table

The **summary table** indicates the frequency, amount, or percentage of items in a set of categories so that you can see differences between categories. A summary table lists the categories in one column and the frequency, amount, or percentage in a different column or columns. Table 2.1 illustrates a summary table based on a recent survey that asked why people shop for holiday gifts online (USA Today Snapshots, "Convenience, Shipping Make Online Appealing," *USA Today*, December 24, 2003, A1). In Table 2.1 the most common reasons for shopping online are free shipping and convenience followed by comparison shopping. Very few respondents shopped online because of larger selection or speed.

TABLE 2.1

Reasons for Shopping for Holiday Gifts Online

Reason	Percentage (%)
Comparison shopping	23
Convenience	33
Free shipping	34
Larger selection	6
Speed	4
Total	100%

EXAMPLE 2.1

SUMMARY TABLE OF LEVELS OF RISK OF MUTUAL FUNDS

The 121 mutual funds that are part of the "Using Statistics" scenario (see page 20) are classified according to the risk level of the mutual funds, categorized as low, average, and high. Construct a summary table of the mutual funds categorized by risk.

SOLUTION
Most of the mutual funds are either low risk or average risk (104 or approximately 86%). Very few of the mutual funds are high-risk funds (14%)

TABLE 2.2

Frequency and Percentage Summary Table Pertaining to Risk Level for 121 Mutual Funds

Fund Risk Level	Number of Funds	Percentage of Funds %
Low	58	47.93
Average	46	38.02
High	17	14.05
Total	121	100.00

The Bar Chart

In a **bar chart**, a bar shows each category, the length of which represents the amount, frequency or percentage of values falling into a category. Figure 2.1 displays the bar chart for the reasons for shopping for holiday gifts online presented in Table 2.1.

FIGURE 2.1

Microsoft Excel Bar Chart of the Reasons for Shopping for Holiday Gifts Online

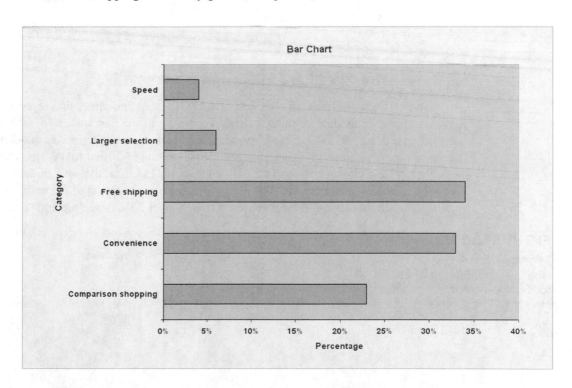

Bar charts allow you to compare percentages in the different categories. In Figure 2.1 the most common reasons for shopping online are free shipping and convenience followed by comparison shopping. Very few respondents shopped online because of larger selection or speed.

EXAMPLE 2.2

BAR CHART OF LEVELS OF RISK OF MUTUAL FUNDS

Construct a bar chart for the levels of risk of mutual funds (based on information in Table 2.2) and interpret the results.

SOLUTION

Most of the mutual funds are either low risk or average risk (104 or 86%). Very few of the mutual funds are high risk funds (17 or 14%).

FIGURE 2.2

Microsoft Excel Bar Chart of the Levels of Risk of Mutual Funds

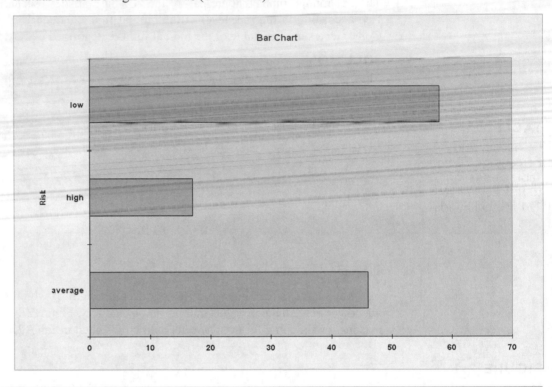

The Pie Chart

The **pie chart** takes a circle and breaks it up into slices that represent the categories. The size of each slice of the pie varies according to the percentage in each category. In Table 2.1 for example, 33% of the respondents stated that convenience was the main reason for online shopping. Thus, in constructing the pie chart, the 360° that makes up a circle is multiplied by 0.33, resulting in a slice of the pie that takes up 118.8° of the 360° of the circle. From Figure 2.3, you can see that the pie chart lets you visualize the portion of the entire pie that is in each category. In this figure, the convenience reason takes 33% of the pie and speed takes only 4%.

FIGURE 2.3

Microsoft Excel Pie Chart of the Reasons for Shopping for Holiday Gifts Online

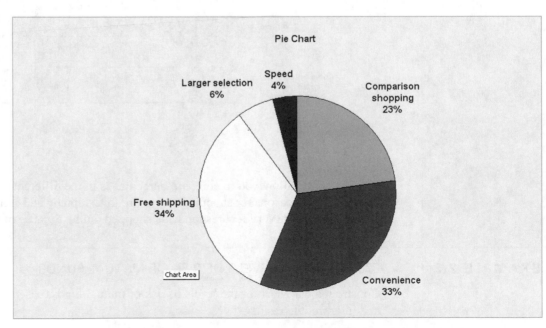

Which chart should you use? The selection of a particular chart often depends on your intention. If a comparison of categories is most important, you should use a bar chart. If observing the portion of the whole that is in a particular category is most important, you should use a pie chart.

EXAMPLE 2.3

PIE CHART OF LEVELS OF RISK OF MUTUAL FUNDS

Construct a pie chart for the levels of risk of mutual funds (see Table 2.2) and interpret the results.

SOLUTION
(See Figure 2.4.) Most of the mutual funds are either low risk or average risk (approximately 86%). Very few of the mutual funds are high-risk funds (approximately 14%).

FIGURE 2.4

Microsoft Excel Pie Chart of the Levels of Risk of Mutual Funds

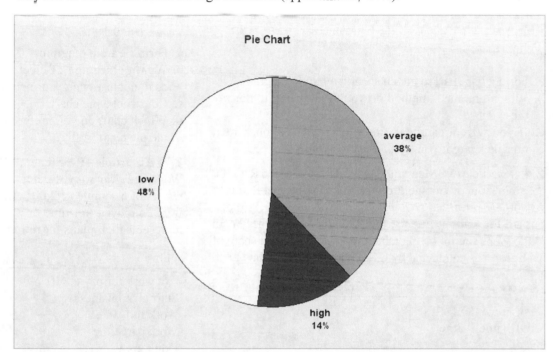

PROBLEMS FOR SECTION 2.1

Learning the Basics

2.1 A categorical variable had three categories with the following frequency of occurrence:

Category	Frequency
A	13
B	28
C	9

a. Compute the percentage of values in each category.
b. Construct a bar chart.
c. Construct a pie chart.
d. Construct a Pareto diagram.

2.2 A categorical variable had four categories with the following percentages of occurrence:

Category	Percentage	Category	Percentage
A	12	C	35
B	29	D	24

a. Construct a bar chart.
b. Construct a pie chart.
c. Construct a Pareto diagram.

Applying the Concepts

You can solve problems 2.3–2.8 manually or by using Microsoft Excel, Minitab or SPSS.

✓SELF Test 2.3 A survey of 150 executives were asked what they think is the most common mistake candidates make during job interviews. The results (*USA Today Snapshots*, November 19, 2001) are as follows:

Reason	%
Little or no knowledge of company	44
Unprepared to discuss career plans	23
Limited enthusiasm	16
Lack of eye contact	5
Unprepared to discuss skills/experience	3
Other reasons	9

a. Form a bar chart, a pie chart, and a Pareto diagram.
b. Which graphical method do you think is best to portray these data?
c. If you were a candidate interviewing for a job, which mistakes might you try hardest to avoid?

2.4 An article (M. Mangalindan, N. Wingfield, and R. Guth, "Rising Clout of Google Prompts Rush by Internet Rivals to Adapt," *The Wall Street Journal*, July 16, 2003, A1, A6) discussed the wide influence that Google had on the World Wide Web. The following table provides the market share of Web searches conducted by U.S. Internet users in May 2003.

Source	Percentage (%)
Ask Jeeves	3
AOL Time Warner	19
Google	32
MSN-Microsoft	15
Yahoo	25
Other	6

a. Form a bar chart, a pie chart, and a Pareto diagram.
b. Which graphical method do you think is best to portray these data?
c. What conclusions can you reach concerning the market share for Web searches in May 2003?

2.5 Americans paid for more than 50 billion dollars in transactions online via credit card in 2000 (Byron Acohido, "Microsoft, Banks Battle to Control Your e-info," *USA Today*, August 13, 2001, 1B–2B). These transactions were broken down as follows:

Credit Card	Amount ($billions)	%
American Express	8.04	15.6
Discover	1.97	3.8
MasterCard	15.57	30.2
Visa	25.96	50.4

a. Form a bar chart, a pie chart, and a Pareto diagram.
b. Which graphical method do you think is best to portray these data?

2.6 The following table represents the U.S. sources of electric energy in a recent year:

Source	%
Coal	51
Hydropower	6
Natural gas	16
Nuclear	21
Oil	3
Other	3

Source: U.S. Department of Energy.

a. Form a Pareto diagram.
b. What percentage of electricity is derived from either coal, nuclear energy, or natural gas?
c. Construct a pie chart.
d. Which chart do you prefer to use, the Pareto diagram or the pie chart? Why?

2.7 An article (P. Kitchen, "Retirement Plan: To Keep Working," *Newsday*, September 24, 2003) discussed the results of a sample of 2,001 Americans ages 50 to 70 who were employed full-time or part-time. The following table represents their plans for retirement.

Plans	Percentage (%)
Not work for pay at all	29
Start own business	10
Work full-time	7
Work part-time	46
Don't know	3
Other	5

a. Form a bar chart and a pie chart.
b. Which graphical method do you think is best to portray these data?

2.8 Junk e-mail or spam has become a serious problem for productivity (J. Hopkins, "Spam Blaster Does Job for Merrill," *USA Today*, January 7, 2004, 7B). The following table concerning company use of anti-spam software is based on a survey of tech executives.

Company Use of Anti-Spam Software	Percentage (%)
Have software for some users	12
Have software for all users	59
Plan for software in the next 12 months	20
Don't plan for software	9

a. Form a bar chart and a pie chart.
b. Which graphical method do you think is best to portray these data?

2.2   ORGANIZING NUMERICAL DATA

When the number of data values is large, you can organize numerical data into an ordered array or a stem-and-leaf display to help you to understand the information you have. Suppose that you decide to undertake a study that compares the cost for a restaurant meal in a major city to the cost of a similar meal in the suburbs outside the city. Table 2.3 shows the data for 50 city restaurants and 50 suburban restaurants. RESTRATE The data are not arranged in order from lowest to highest. This arrangement makes it difficult to draw conclusions about the price of meals in the two geographical areas.

TABLE 2.3

Price per Person at
50 City Restaurants and
50 Suburban Restaurants

City

50	38	43	56	51	36	25	33	41	44
34	39	49	37	40	50	50	35	22	45
44	38	14	44	51	27	44	39	50	35
31	34	48	48	30	42	26	35	32	63
36	38	53	23	39	45	37	31	39	53

Suburban

37	37	29	38	37	38	39	29	36	38
44	27	24	34	44	23	30	32	25	29
43	31	26	34	23	41	32	30	28	33
26	51	26	48	39	55	24	38	31	30
51	30	27	38	26	28	33	38	32	25

The Ordered Array

An **ordered array** is a sequence of the data in rank order from the smallest value to the largest value. Table 2.4 contains ordered arrays for the price of meals at city restaurants and suburban restaurants. RESTRATE From Table 2.4 you can see that the price of a meal at the city restaurants is between $14 and $63, and the price of a meal at the suburban restaurants is between $23 and $55.

TABLE 2.4

Ordered Array
of Price per Person at
50 City Restaurants and
50 Suburban Restaurants

City

14	22	23	25	26	27	30	31	31	32
33	34	34	35	35	35	36	36	37	37
38	38	38	39	39	39	39	40	41	42
43	44	44	44	44	45	45	48	48	49
50	50	50	50	51	51	53	53	56	63

Suburban

23	23	24	24	25	25	26	26	26	26
27	27	28	28	29	29	29	30	30	30
30	31	31	32	32	32	33	33	34	34
36	37	37	37	38	38	38	38	38	38
39	39	41	43	44	44	48	51	51	55

Stem-and-Leaf Display

EXAMPLE 2.4

The following data appeared in the Education Quarterly Review—Vol. 5, No. 2, 1998.

The table shows the percentage of the population in various age groups that have post-secondary education.

TABLE 2.5

Country	Age Group	
	26 to 35	46 to 55
United States	45.1	41.6
Canada	41.2	34.9
New Zealand	31.5	26.6
Australia	29.0	28.4
Sweden	28.6	32.4
Belgium	35.0	20.2
United Kingdom	25.3	23.0
Switzerland	23.2	23.3
Ireland	22.4	14.9
Netherlands	23.5	22.5
Poland	16.8	17.9

Suppose we would like to compare the data for each age group.

One graphical tool that can be used to organize the data is a **STEM-and-LEAF** display. This diagram should be considered when the number of data values is not more than 50.

The recommended Stem-and-Leaf display for the 26 to 35 age group data is as follows:

% of Population with Postsecondary Education for people aged 26 to 35 years	
Stem (tens)	Leaf
1	6
2	2 3 3
2	5 8 9
3	1
3	5
4	1
4	5

Rules and Conventions

There is more than one set of rules and conventions regarding the drawing of a stem-and-leaf display. The purpose of a stem-and-leaf display is to organize a small amount of data in an easy-to-understand diagram. We will use the following set of rules and conventions.

Stems:
1. Should be from 6 to 13 stems.
2. Should be consecutive numbers or repeated numbers. The numbers may each be repeated twice or 5 times.
3. Units must be indicated if stem not to be taken at face value
4. There must be at least one leaf associated with the first and last stem

Leaves: 1. The leaf for each data value is the next single digit after the stem
Note: When the stems are repeated twice, the leaves 0–4 go with the first stem and the leaves 5–9 go with the second. (This order is reversed when the stems are negative values.)
When the stems are repeated 5 times, the leaves 0–1 go with the first stem, 2–3 with the second, etc. (This order is reversed when the stems are negative values.)
2. There is no rounding off.
3. They are written in ascending order.
4. They must be evenly spaced.
5. No commas or dashes between the numbers are allowed.

In order to compare the two sets of data, we will set up the stem-and-leaf display for the second age group. (Note: When comparing data, you should try to use a similar set-up for each stem-and-leaf display.)

% of Population with Postsecondary Education for people aged 46 to 55 years	
Stem (tens)	Leaf
1	4
1	7
2	0 2 3 3
2	6 8
3	2 4
3	
4	1

Conclusion: Both age groups have the most data in the 20 - 30 percent range. The percentages are generally lower for the higher age group.

EXAMPLE 2.5

The following data represents the selling price ($ 000's) of 2 bedroom homes in Cartersville for the month of December:

96 93   88 107 125 127 112 127 117
95 113 96 135 132 111 148 156 139

The following stem-and-leaf display would be appropriate:

Prices of 2-bedroom Homes ($ 000's)	
Stem (tens)	Leaf
8	8
9	3 5 6 6
10	7
11	1 2 3 7
12	5 7 7
13	2 5 9
14	8
15	6

EXAMPLE 2.6

The following data represents the management expense ratio (MER) in percent for a group of Canadian balanced mutual funds:

2.13   2.25   2.25   2.26   2.26   2.41   2.36   2.50   2.08
2.53   2.48   2.04   2.18

The following stem-and-leaf display would be appropriate:

MER (%)	
Stem	Leaf
2.0	4 8
2.1	3 8
2.2	5 5 6 6
2.3	6
2.4	1 8
2.5	0 3

EXAMPLE 2.7

Suppose a survey of employees for a certain department of a certain company reveal that they paid the following amounts of income taxes last year:

$20,130 $20,161 $20,207 $20,175 $20,213 $20,147
$20,189 $20,215 $20,264 $20,219 $20,252 $20,173
$20,209 $20,155 $20,128

The following stem-and-leaf display would be appropriate.

Annual Taxes ($)	
Stem (00's)	Leaf
201	2 3
201	4 5
201	6 7 7
201	8
202	0 0 1 1 1
202	
202	5
202	6

EXAMPLE 2.8

Suppose the tax data is:

$20,130 $20,161 $20,207 $20,175   **$20,213** $20,147
$20,189 $20,215 $20,264 $20,219 $20,252 $20,173
$20,209 $20,155 $20,128 $20,312   **$20,364**

The following stem-and-leaf display would be appropriate.

Annual Taxes ($)

Stem (00's)	Leaf
201	2 3 4
201	5 6 7 7 8
202	0 0 1 1 1
202	5 6
203	1
203	6

EXAMPLE 2.9

Suppose the tax data is:

$20,130 $20,161 $20,207 $20,175 $20,213 $20,147
$20,189 $20,215 $20,264 $20,219 $20,252 $20,173
$20,209 $20,155 $20,128 $20,312 $20,364   **$20,438**
$20,567 $20,619

The following stem-and-leaf display would be appropriate.

Annual Taxes ($)

Stem (00's)	Leaf
201	2 3 4 5 6 7 7 8
202	0 0 1 1 1 5 6
203	1 6
204	3
205	6
206	1

EXAMPLE 2.10

The following data shows the precipitation (in cm.) for 30 Canadian cities for a certain year.

64.6	53.2	7.1	99.2	12.1	15.3	44.4	41.4	57.6
148.6	23.5	11.7	33.3	39.1	30.8	28.6	43.6	79.7
41.8	83.8	31.0	29.7	52.8	33.9	115.2	30.3	
7.5	36.5	41.9						

The following stem-and-leaf display would be appropriate:

Precipitation (cm) for Canadian cities

Stem (00's)	Leaf
0	0 0 1 1 1
0	2 2 2 3 3 3 3 3 3
0	4 4 4 4 4 4 5 5 5
0	6 7
0	8 9
1	1
1	
1	4

PROBLEMS FOR SECTION 2.2

Learning the Basics

 2.9 Form an ordered array given the following data from a sample of $n = 7$ midterm exam scores in accounting:

68 94 63 75 71 88 64

 2.10 Form a stem-and-leaf display given the following data from a sample of $n = 7$ midterm exam scores in finance:

80 54 69 98 93 53 74

 2.11 Form an ordered array given the following data from a sample of $n = 7$ midterm exam scores in marketing:

88 78 78 73 91 78 85

 2.12 Form an ordered array given the following stem-and-leaf display from a sample of $n = 7$ midterm exam scores in information systems:

```
5 | 0
6 |
7 | 446
8 | 19
9 | 2
```

Applying the Concepts

 2.13 The following is a stem-and-leaf display representing the amount of gasoline purchased in gallons (with leaves in tenths of gallons) for a sample of 25 cars that use a particular service station on the New Jersey Turnpike:

```
 9 | 147
10 | 02238
11 | 125566777
12 | 223489
13 | 02
```

a. Place the data into an ordered array.
b. Which of these two displays seems to provide more information? Discuss.
c. What amount of gasoline (in gallons) is most likely to be purchased?
d. Is there a concentration of the purchase amounts in the center of the distribution?

 2.14 The following data represent the bounced check fee in dollars for a sample of 23 banks for direct-deposit customers who maintain a $100 balance. BANKCOST1

26 28 20 20 21 22 25 25 18 25 15 20
18 20 25 25 22 30 30 30 15 20 29

Source: "The New Face of Banking," Copyright © 2000 by Consumers Union of U.S., Inc., Yonkers, NY 10703–1057. Adapted with permission from Consumer Reports, *June 2000.*

a. Place the data into an ordered array.
b. Set up a stem-and-leaf display for these data.
c. Which of these two displays seems to provide more information? Discuss.
d. Around what value, if any, are the bounced check fees concentrated? Explain

 2.15 The following data represent the monthly service fee in dollars if a customer's account falls below the minimum required balance for a sample of 26 banks for direct-deposit customers who maintain a $1,500 balance. BANKCOST2

12 8 5 5 6 6 10 10 9 7 10 7 7
 5 0 10 6 9 12 0 5 10 8 5 5 9

Source: "The New Face of Banking," Copyright © 2000 by Consumers Union of U.S. Inc., Yonkers, NY 10703–1057. Adapted with permission from Consumer Reports, *June 2000.*

a. Place the data into an ordered array.
b. Set up a stem-and-leaf display for these data.
c. Which of these two displays seems to provide more information? Discuss.
d. Around what value, if any, are the monthly service fees concentrated? Explain.

2.16 The following data represent the total fat for burgers and chicken items from a sample of fast-food chains. FASTFOOD

BURGERS
19 31 34 35 39 39 43

CHICKEN
7 9 15 16 16 18 22 25 27 33 39

Source: "Quick Bites," Copyright © 2001 by Consumers Union of U.S., Inc., Yonkers, NY 10703–1057. Adapted with permission from Consumer Reports, *March 2001.*

a. Place the data for burgers and chicken into two ordered arrays.
b. Construct stem-and-leaf displays for burgers and chicken.
c. Does the ordered array or the stem-and-leaf display provide more information? Discuss.
d. Compare the burgers and chicken items in terms of the total fat. What conclusions can you make?

2.17 The following data represent the daily average hotel cost and rental car cost for 20 U.S. cities during a week in October 2003. HOTEL-CAR

City	Hotel	Cars
San Francisco	205	47
Los Angeles	179	41
Seattle	185	49
Phoenix	210	38
Denver	128	32
Dallas	145	48
Houston	177	49
Minneapolis	117	41
Chicago	221	36
St. Louis	159	41
New Orleans	205	50
Detroit	128	32
Cleveland	165	34
Atlanta	180	46
Orlando	198	41
Miami	158	40
Pittsburgh	132	39
Boston	283	67
New York	269	69
Washington D.C.	204	40

Source: Extracted from The Wall Street Journal, *October 10, 2003, W4.*

a. Place the data for hotel cost and rental car cost into two ordered arrays.

b. Construct stem-and-leaf displays for hotel cost and rental car cost.

c. Does the ordered array or the stem-and-leaf display provide more information? Discuss.

d. Around what value, if any, are the hotel cost and rental car cost concentrated? Explain.

Stem-and-Leaf

Refer to Table 2.6 that shows data regarding the first 20 companies taken from The FP500 'Canada's 500 Largest Corporations table that appeared in the June 2003 issue of National Post Business.

2.18 Construct stem-and-leaf displays for the following data:

a. Profit rank

b. Asset rank

c. Revenues for 2002

d. Assets for 2002

e. Number of Employees

f. Share Price Change—1 year percent

g. Profits as a percent of Assets

h. Profits as a percent of Equity

Table 2.6

FP500 CANADA'S 500 LARGEST CORPORATIONS

RANK BY REVENUE 2002 2001			Industry	REVENUES 2002 $'000s	% Change	% Sales Outside Canada	ASSETS 2002 $'000s	% Change	Rank
1	1	General Motors of Canada Ltd., Oshawa, ON	Vehicle	37,000,000	n.a.	n.a.	n.a.	n.a.	n.a.
2	4	George Weston Ltd., Toronto	Conglom	27,446,000	11.3	n.a.	16,630,000	2.2	34
3	7	Bombardier Inc., Montreal (Ja03)	High-tech	23,664,900	9.4	n.a.	29,009,400	4.5	20
4	8	Ford Motor Co. of Canada, Ltd., Oakville, ON	Vehicle	23,328,700	8.1	n.a.	11,398,000	8.0	48
5	3	Royal Bank of Canada, Montreal (Oc02)	Bank	23,234,000	(9.0)	n.a.	376,956,000	4.9	1
6	18	Sun Life Financial Services of Canada, Toronto	Life	23,101,000	38.4	72	123,438,000	53.7	6
7	5	Onex Corp., Toronto	Conglom	22,653,000	(4.8)	85	19,890,000	(4.7)	27
8	17	Magna International Inc.*, Aurora, ON	Vehicle	20,364,470	19.3	70	16,004,076	27.1	35
9	6	BCE Inc., Montreal	Telecom	19,768,000	(8.9)	n.a.	39,563,000	(27.2)	14
10	13	Alcan Inc.*, Montreal	Mining	19,687,800	0.7	94	27,674,964	(0.4)	21
11	12	DaimlerChrysler Canada Inc., Windsor, ON	Vehicle	19,353,000	(5.2)	n.a.	n.a.	n.a.	n.a.
12	14	Power Corp. of Canada, Montreal	Conglom	19,017,000	3.6	30	70,136,000	2.0	11
13	10	The Bank of Nova Scotia, Toronto (Oc02)	Bank	18,310,000	(13.0)	n.a.	296,380,000	4.2	2
14	9	Canadian Imperial Bank of Commerce, Toronto (Oc02)	Bank	17,055,000	(20.3)	n.a.	273,293,000	(4.9)	4
15	16	Imperial Oil Ltd., Toronto	Energy	16,890,000	(1.5)	13	11,868,000	10.3	44
16	11	The Toronto-Dominion Bank, Toronto (Oc02)	Bank	16,680,000	(20.3)	n.a.	278,040,000	(3.4)	3
17	2	Nortel Networks Corp.*, Brampton, ON	High-tech	16,538,380	(39.1)	n.a.	23,382,804	(27.5)	24
18	19	Manulife Financial Corp., Toronto	Life	16,532,000	1.9	80	81,195,000	3.3	9
19	15	Bank of Montreal, Montreal (Oc02)	Bank	13,059,000	(24.2)	n.a.	252,864,000	5.6	5
20	20	Hydro-Québec, Montreal	Utility	13,002,000	3.4	28	59,078,000	(1.3)	12

PROFITS 2002 $'000s	% Change	Rank	EPS $0.00	PROFITS AS % OF... Revenue	Assets	Equity	GROWTH 5-Year % Profit Growth	Share Price Change 1 Year %	5 Year %	EMPLOYEES & OWNERSHIP Employees	Symbol	Exchange	Major Shareholder(s)	% Foreign	RANK 2002
n.a.	n.a.	n.a.	n.a.	n.a.	n.a.	n.a.	n.a.	n.a.	n.a.	24,500	(Pr)		General Motors, US	100	1
690,000	18.6	24	5.05	2.5	4.2	17.2	182.8	(19.4)	106.9	139,000	WN	T	W. Galen Weston 62%		2
(615,200)	(257.4)	569	(0.47)	(2.6)	(2.2)	(18.0)	(246.4)	(81.1)	(68.8)	75,000	BBD.B	T	Bombardier family 63%		3
n.a.	n.a.	n.a.	n.a.	n.a.	n.a.	n.a.	n.a.	n.a.	n.a.	15,074	(Pr)		Ford Motor Co., US	100	4
2,762,000	14.6	3	3.96	11.9	0.8	15.0	64.5	9.2	36.7	59,549	RY	T,NY	Widely held	20	5
997,000	13.2	15	1.84	4.3	1.0	8.8	95.1	(17.6)	n.a.	11,800	SLF	T,NY	Widely held		6
(145,000)	(118.2)	546	(0.90)	(0.6)	(0.7)	(8.9)	(366.4)	(36.9)	55.0	98,000	OCX	T	Gerald Schwartz 67% voting		7
869,780	(3.1)	19	9.15	4.3	6.1	11.1	44.1	(32.8)	(26.8)	73,000	MG.A	T,NY	Stronach Trust 58%		8
2,475,000	373.2	4	2.74	12.5	5.3	16.6	259.4	(2.3)	(53.7)	66,266	BCE	T,NY	Widely held	14	9
587,180	7,486.3	31	1.81	3.0	2.1	4.3	(9.4)	(33.1)	(8.5)	50,000	AL	T,NY	Widely held		10
n.a.	n.a.	n.a.	n.a.	n.a.	n.a.	n.a.	n.a.	n.a.	n.a.	n.a.	(Pr)		DaimlerChrysler Corp., US	100	11
645,000	4.4	27	2.81	3.4	0.9	12.8	94.9	(5.9)	31.1	28,000	POW	T	Paul Desmarais Sr. 65%		12
1,797,000	(17.2)	7	3.36	9.8	0.6	12.2	18.7	(0.5)	39.6	49,000	BNS	T,NY	Widely held		13
653,000	(61.3)	26	1.37	3.8	0.2	5.4	(57.9)	(15.7)	(3.3)	42,552	CM	T, NY	Widely held		14
1,210,000	(2.7)	14	3.19	7.2	10.7	25.1	42.9	(0.7)	73.4	6,460	IMO	T,AM	Exxon Mobil Corp., US	70	15
(76,000)	(105.5)	533	(0.25)	(0.5)	n.a.	(0.6)	(107.0)	(24.3)	5.9	42,817	TD	T	Widely held		16
(5,549,950)	86.9	574	(1.43)	(33.6)	(19.9)	(106.6)	n.a.	(56.3)	(86.4)	52,600	NT	T,NY	Widely held		17
1,370,000	17.4	12	2.90	8.3	1.7	16.1	(65.8)	(18.5)	n.a.	32,400	MFC	T,NY	Widely held		18
1,417,000	(3.7)	11	2.73	10.9	0.6	12.6	8.6	4.9	4.4	33,000	BMO	T,NY	Widely held		19
1,526,000	37.7	9	n.a.	11.7	2.6	10.5	94.1	n.a.	n.a.	20,972	(Cr)		Quebec government		20

2.3 TABLES AND CHARTS FOR NUMERICAL DATA

When you have a data set that contains a large number of values, reaching conclusions from an ordered array or stem-and-leaf is often difficult. You need to use tables and charts in such circumstances. There are many different tables and charts to visually present numerical data. These include the frequency and percentage distributions, histogram, polygon, and cumulative percentage polygon (ogive).

The Frequency Distribution

The frequency distribution helps you draw conclusions from a large set of data.

A **frequency distribution** is a summary table in which the data are arranged into numerically ordered class groupings.

The following scenario is just one of many reasons why one would want to make a frequency distribution.

In most production or manufacturing situations quality is related to variability. Specifically,

the lower the variability—the higher the quality.

Ideally, the goal is to have a production process with NO variability. Unfortunately, most production processes use machines, and people who are not perfect, and thus there usually is some level of variability in the items being produced.

In Chapter 14 we will learn about some Statistical Process Control Charts, which are used to control variable measures. These charts would not be necessary if there was no variability in the variable being controlled.

To use the control charts correctly, it is necessary that the variable being controlled fit a Normal Distribution (Bell-Curve). Simply put, most of the measurements should be near the target value, with fewer and fewer measurements occurring the farther we go from the target value.

EXAMPLE 2.11

The high-voltage output of a certain power supply that is to be used in copying machines must be 300 ± 50 volts, i.e. from 250 to 350 volts. In setting up a control chart, data from a sample of 125 power supplies is to be used. The results are given as follows:

TABLE 2.7

333	297	285	300	279	311	298	300	305	262
289	315	305	302	273	282	313	330	300	271
303	330	290	291	300	290	340	293	309	287
292	312	295	296	302	308	268	296	294	306
295	320	322	328	326	316	290	291	320	315
301	292	291	299	298	308	295	296	325	333
309	304	306	292	327	295	302	302	276	331
293	306	286	310	277	309	307	304	323	288
285	292	342	311	316	297	304	316	305	320
303	296	332	336	313	282	294	341	334	317
296	312	307	328	326	301	309	313	275	328
326	303	308	310	285	317	318	319	314	325
284	289	312	319	298					

The first question that needs to be answered is:

Does the data appear to fit a bell-curve?

In order to get a picture of the **SHAPE** of the distribution of data, we need to *GROUP* the data into a ***FREQUENCY DISTRIBUTION***.

Rules and Conventions for a Frequency Distribution:

The data is grouped in **classes**.

Number of classes: It is recommended to use from 5 to 10 classes (i.e. not too few and not too many.)

Notation for indicating classes: Use format   _____ and under _____

                                          or   _____ to _____

Note: In our course, we will use the "and under" notation.

Class width (CW): 1, 2, 2.5 (if the data has at least one decimal), 5, 10, 20, 25, 50, 100, 200, 250 etc.

or

0.1, 0.2, 0.25 (if data has at least 2 decimals), 0.5, etc. for smaller classes

Note: 1. Unless you have a specific reason to do otherwise, the class width should be an 'easy' number to work with.
   2. In this course, when you are asked to group data into classes, all classes must have the *same class width*.

Boundaries: They must *look like* the data, i.e. have the same number of decimal places.

Each boundary must be a **multiple** of the chosen class width.

There must be *no gaps* between the classes, i.e. the upper boundary of one class will also be the lower boundary of the next class.

Example. If CW = 20 is chosen and the data ranges from L = 112 to H = 196 then use:

         Classes
100 and under 120
120 "   "   140
140 "   "   160
160 "   "   180
180 "   "   200

Frequency: f = # of data values which belong to the class

Referring back to our voltage data, an appropriate frequency distribution that follows all the rules and conventions mentioned above is shown below:

Power Supply Voltage (Volts)	# of power supplies
260 and under 270	2
270 " " 280	6
280 " " 290	11
290 " " 300	29
300 " " 310	31
310 " " 320	21
320 " " 330	14
330 " " 340	8
340 " " 350	3

Looking at the frequencies, we can see that most of the data is close to the target value of 300, and there are fewer and fewer data values as we move further away from the target on the high and low sides.

Frequency distributions are often used to summarize data and give a general idea of where the data values are located. They also give an indication as to the 'shape' of a set of data.

EXAMPLE 2.12   Suppose that for a particular process we are filling cereal boxes. The boxes are labelled as having 450 gm. We have set the filling machine to make sure that all boxes weigh at least 450 grams. There are two machines used to fill these cereal boxes. The results of a random sample of 16 boxes from each machine are shown below. The numbers indicate the amount over 450 grams.

Machine A: 1.8   5.3   7.4   9.1   7.5   8.6   5.7   9.6   2.2   1.6   6.9   5.2   9.4   9.0   3.6   7.8
Machine B: 8.4   1.2   7.2   9.8   6.5   5.1   4.0   6.9   7.8   5.5   7.4   6.3   7.1   6.8   7.3   8.5

Make a frequency distribution of each set of results.

Amount of cereal over 450 grams in a box (grams)	Machine A # boxes	Machine B # boxes
1.0 and under 2.0	2	1
2.0 " " 3.0	1	0
3.0 " " 4.0	1	0
4.0 " " 5.0	0	1
5.0 " " 6.0	3	2
6.0 " " 7.0	1	4
7.0 " " 8.0	3	5
8.0 " " 9.0	1	2
9.0 " " 10.0	4	1

The frequency distribution shows that machine B appears to be doing a better job of producing a more consistent product.

EXAMPLE 2.13   Consider the following set of measurements:

TABLE 2.8

3.56	3.46	3.48	3.50	3.42	3.43	3.52
3.49	3.44	3.50	3.48	3.56	3.50	3.52
3.47	3.48	3.46	3.50	3.56	3.38	3.41
3.37	3.47	3.49	3.45	3.44	3.50	3.49
3.46	3.46	3.55	3.52	3.44	3.50	3.45
3.44	3.48	3.46	3.52	3.46	3.48	3.48
3.32	3.40	3.52	3.34	3.46	3.43	**3.30**
3.46	3.59	3.63	3.59	3.47	3.38	3.52
3.45	3.48	3.31	3.46	3.40	3.54	3.46
3.51	3.48	3.50	**3.68**	3.60	3.46	3.52
3.48	3.50	3.56	3.50	3.52	3.46	3.48
3.46	3.52	3.56	3.52	3.48	3.46	3.45
3.46	3.54	3.54	3.48	3.49	3.41	3.41
3.45	3.34	3.44	3.47	3.47	3.41	3.48

$$L = 3.30 \quad H = 3.68$$

An appropriate frequency distribution would be as follows:

Classes	f
3.30 and under 3.35	4
3.35 " " 3.40	3
3.40 " " 3.45	15
3.45 " " 3.50	42
3.50 " " 3.55	23
3.55 " " 3.60	8
3.60 " " 3.65	2
3.65 " " 3.70	1

EXAMPLE 2.14   Refer to the following table from the July 2000 Report on Business.

TABLE 2.9

RETAILERS

COMPANY AND YEAR END	REVENUE $000	% CH'GE	PROFIT $000	% CH'GE	RETURN ON CAPITAL 1-YR %	5-YR %	INVENTORY TURNOVER CURRENT	PREVIOUS	DAYS RECEIVABLE CURRENT	PREVIOUS	OPERATING REVENUE PER STORE $000
DEPARTMENT STORES											
Hudson's Bay Co.(Ja00)	7,295,751	3	96,035	132	8.04	4.94	4.5	4.6	30	35	14,592
Sears Canada(Ja00)	6,131,200	12	199,600	36	20.64	14.05	7.9	8.0	30	43	55,738
Zellers Inc.(Ja00)	4,598,000	2	na	na	na	na	na	na	na	na	14,018
Costco Canada(Au99)	3,087,962	7	na	na	na	na	na	na	na	na	102,932
Jean Coutu Group (PJC)(My99)	2,289,370	18	74,307	18	19.25	18.78	7.5	7.2	21	23	4,156
North West Co. Fund(Ja00)	626,469	0	27,957	73	11.72	9.64	5.5	5.1	28	32	3,539
Industry Average		4		41	11.65	9.41	10.3	10.3	24	29	25,234
CLOTHING STORES											
Dylex Ltd.(Ja00)	1,081,767	0	-36,387	-283	-17.14	11.01	6.6	6.9	3	3	1,685
Reitmans (Canada)(Ja00)	526,811	19	51,707	273	38.88	12.92	15.7	14.2	2	2	812
Suzy Shier(Ja00)	357,733	7	6,070	-55	9.09	14.06	7.9	6.9	5	5	754
Mark's Work Wearhouse(Ja00)	321,187	11	6,387	11	18.53	21.94	4.0	4.1	16	17	1,815
Boutiques San Francisco(Ja00)	226,769	12	5,555	-15	15.24	16.47	7.3	7.2	3	4	1,271
Château Stores of Canada(Ja00)	168,666	5	5,269	-10	17.71	16.02	na	23.1	na	2	na
Industry Average		6		-19	16.48	15.31	6.8	11.7	7	5	1,437
SPECIALITY STORES											
Canadian Tire Corp.(Ja00)	4,728,259	9	145,929	-13	12.72	13.68	10.7	10.6	63	64	10,996
Future Shop(Ap99)[3]	1,960,274	11	-82,245	-2,176	-118.93	6.63	9.5	7.1	4	3	22,531
Katz Group(Ja00)	1,700,000	113	na	na	na	na	na	na	na	na	3,400
Rona Inc.(De99)	988,385	21	14,706	9	17.18	18.98	14.0	15.3	20	15	2076
Hartco Enterprises(Ja00)	850,279	5	-4,774	-156	-1.64	11.90	7.7	13.4	10	12	15,184
Reno-Depot Inc.(De99)	588,000	na	na	na	na	na	na	na	na	na	na
Chapters Inc.(Ap99)	577,880	24	10,301	20	15.16	na	3.1	3.5	4	4	1,829
Grand & Toy Ltd.(De99)	568,195	19	na	na	na	na	na	na	na	na	na
Industry Average		72		-463.2	-15.10	14.98	10.0	8.2	23	18	9,386

a) Make a frequency distribution of the previous inventory turnover data.

Previous Inventory Turnover	# of Companies
0.0 and under 5.0	3
5.0 " " 10.0	7
10.0 " " 15.0	3
15.0 " " 20.0	1
20.0 " " 25.0	1

Since the L = 3.5 H = 23.1

b) Make a frequency distribution for the return on capital 1-yr % data.

Return on Capital — 1yr %	# of Companies
−125.00 and under −100.00	1
−100.00 " " −75.00	0
−75.00 " " −50.00	0
−50.00 " " −25.00	0
−25.00 " " 0.00	2
0.00 " " 25.00	11
25.00 " " 50.00	1

Since the L = −118.93 H = 38.80

EXAMPLE 2.15

FREQUENCY DISTRIBUTION OF THE 2003 RETURN FOR GROWTH AND VALUE MUTUAL FUNDS

In the "Using Statistics" scenario, you are interested in comparing the 2003 return of growth and value mutual funds. MUTUALFUNDS2004 Construct frequency distributions for the growth funds and for the value funds.

SOLUTION

The 2003 percentage returns of the growth funds are highly concentrated between 30 and 50, with some concentration between 20 and 30 (see Table 2.10). The 2003 percentage returns of the value funds are concentrated between 30 and 50, with some also between 20 and 30 and 50 and 70. You should not directly compare the frequencies of the growth funds and the value funds since there are 49 growth funds and 72 value funds in the sample.

TABLE 2.10

Frequency Distribution of the 2003 Return for Growth and Value Mutual Funds

2003 Percentage Return	# of Growth Funds	# of Value Funds
10 and under 20	2	2
20 and under 30	9	9
30 and under 40	13	20
40 and under 50	15	20
50 and under 60	5	10
60 and under 70	5	9
70 and under 80	0	2
Total	49	72

Relative Frequency or Percentage Distributions

Consider the following frequency distributions of manufacturing personnel salaries at ABC Inc. and XYZ Inc.

TABLE 2.11

Salary ($000's)	ABC Inc. # Employees	XYZ Inc. # Employees
20 and under 25	24	10
25 " " 30	41	23
30 " " 35	44	31
35 " " 40	29	14
40 " " 45	15	8
45 " " 50	7	2

Notice that there is a large difference in the number of manufacturing employees in the two companies, therefore it is difficult to *compare* the salary distributions by looking at the frequencies.

If we were to set up a **relative frequency** or **percentage** distribution for the two sets of salaries, it would be much easier to make comparisons.

TABLE 2.12

	ABC Inc.			XYZ Inc.		
Salary ($000's)	f	rf	%	f	rf	%
20 and under 25	24	0.150	15.0	10	0.114	11.4
25 " " 30	41	0.256	25.6	23	0.261	26.1
30 " " 35	44	0.275	27.5	31	0.352	35.2
35 " " 40	29	0.181	18.1	14	0.159	15.9
40 " " 45	15	0.094	9.4	8	0.091	9.1
45 " " 50	7	0.044	4.4	2	0.023	2.3
Total	160	1.000	100.0	88	1.000	100.0

Relative Frequency: rf = f/n   where: f = frequency   n = sample size
Note: We will use a maximum of 3 decimals for rf and thus 1 decimal for %.

The following graphs were produced by SPSS.

FIGURE 2.5
Percentage Histogram

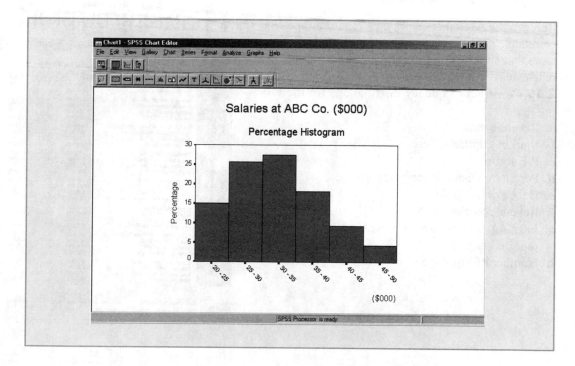

FIGURE 2.6
Percentage Polygons

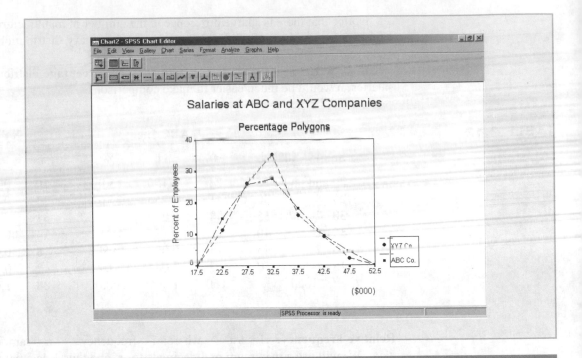

PROBLEM FOR SECTION 2.3

Frequency Distributions

Refer to the table that shows data regarding the first 32 companies taken from The Top 1000 Ranking by Profits table that appeared in the July 2003 issue of the Report on Business.

2.19 Construct frequency distributions for the following data:

a. Revenue rank
b. Market Capitalization
c. P/E Ratio
d. Per Share Data—Price/Sales
e. Debt/Equity Ratio
f. Revenue % change
g. Earnings per Share—Latest Year (Exclude values reported in $US)
h. Number of Employees

Table 2.13

▶ Ranking by profits

PROFIT RANK 2002 2001	COMPANY AND YEAR END	PROFIT		REVENUE			MARKET CAP	DIV YIELD	P/E RATIO	PER SHARE DATA	
		$000	% CH'GE	$000	RANK	%CH'GE	$ MIL	%		PRICE/ SALES	CASH FLOW
	Royal Bank of Canada(Oc02) ON	2,762,000	15	23,234,000	3	-9	36,197	2.79	13.74	1.58	6.59
	BCE Inc.(De02) QC	2,475,000	382	19,809,000	8	2	26.102	4.21	10.40	1.22	6.04
	Bank of Nova Scotia(Oc02) ON	1,797,000	-17	18,310,000	12	-13	23,129	3.16	13.66	1.26	8.44
	Bell Canada(De02) QC	1,504,000	-5	15,685,000	20	7	nm	nm	nm	nm	13.43
	Bank of Montreal(Oc02) ON	1,417,000	-4	13,059,000	21	-24	18,764	3.15	13.96	1.43	4.45
	Manulife Financial(De02) ON	1,378,000	19	16,532,000	18	2	15,923	1.74	11.86	1.03	4.84
	EnCana Corp.(De02) AB	1,224,000	-5	11,031,000	25	112	23,361	.82	16.71	1.85	9.04
	Imperial Oil(De02) ON	1,210,000	2	15,821,000	19	-2	16,996	1.87	14.06	1.09	4.64
	Sun Life Financial Services(De02) ON	998,000	13	23,101,000	4	37	16,517	2.10	14.52	.63	9.38
	Power Financial(De02) QC	988,000	12	18,700,000	11	3	12,591	2.87	13.35	.68	5.16
	Petro-Canada(De02) AB	974,000	15	9,917,000	28	14	12,892	.82	13.18	1.30	8.66
	Thomson Corp.(De02) ON¹	¹US7,768,000	-21	¹US7.768,000	23	7	27,348	2.64	28.77	2.21	¹US4.32
	Great-West Lifeco(De02) MB	962,000	76	16,632,000	16	4	13,648	2.54	14.72	.84	3.79
	Magna International(De02) ON¹	¹US554,000	-4	¹US13,044,000	7	17	8,417	2.43	9.62	.38	20.25
	TransCanada PipeLines(De02) AB	805,000	17	5,300,000	48	-1	10.990	4.36	14.69	2.10	3.82
	Husky Energy(De02) AB	804,000	23	6,385,000	40	-3	6.882	2.19	8.76	1.08	¹US5.02
	Suncor Energy(De02) AB	761,000	96	4,913,000	52	17	11,090	.69	15.06	2.26	3.21
	Loblaw Companies(De02) ON	728,000	29	23,099,000	5	7	14.905	.89	20.46	.65	4.05
	George Weston Ltd.(De02) ON	690,000	19	27,464,000	1	11	11,938	1.06	17.87	.43	12.25
	Cdn. Imp. Bank of Commerce(Oc02) ON	653,000	-61	17,055,000	¹13	-20	13.914	4.13	28.29	.82	4.78
	Power Corp.(De02) QC	645,000	4	19,011,000	10	3	7,997	2.21	12.81	.53	8.65
	Enbridge Inc.(De02) AB	610,100	26	4,830.600	54	13	7,233	3.57	11.84	1.50	4.57
	Alcan Inc.(De02) QC¹	¹US374,000	nm	¹US12,553,000	9	-1	14,894	2.03	25.65	.76	¹US6.39
	Cdn. Natural Resources(De02) AB	574,800	-12	4,114,900	59	15	6,261	1.07	10.49	1.47	17.71
	Canadian National Railway Co.(De02) QC	571,000	-21	6,173,000	41	8	12,891	1.32	22.74	2.10	8.14
	Shell Canada(De02) AB	561,000	-44	7,314,000	35	-5	13,575	1.63	24.24	1.88	4.45
	Talisman Energy(De02) AB	524,000	-29	5,379,000	47	5	7,450	1.06	15.24	1.42	19.74
	Investors Group(De02) MB	511,759	87	1,940,036	102	10	7,058	3.21	14.35	3.63	3.02
	Canada Life Financial(De02) ON	499,000	46	8,598,000	32	7	6,463	1.49	13.21	.77	4.68
	Canadian Pacific Railway Ltd.(De02) AB	496,000	33	3,692,600	62	-1	4,937	1.64	9.95	1.35	5.98
	Great-West Life Assurance(De02) MB	475,000	68	10,766,000	26	7	nm	nm	nm	nm	1,180.76
	Nexen Inc.(De02) AB	452,000	0	3,102,000	77	1	4,212	.88	10.25	1.35	9.75

DEBT/ EQUITY	EARNINGS PER SHARE			RETURN ON COMMON EQUITY				NUMBER OF EMPLOYEES	INDUSTRY	MAJOR SHAREHOLDER
	LATEST YEAR	PREVIOUS YEAR	2 YEARS AGO	ONE-YEAR %	RANK	FIVE-YEAR %	RANK			
0.4	3.96	3.55	3.53	15.96	159	17.16	99	59,770	banks	Widely held
1.2	2.74	0.56	7.43	17.99	127	26.69	23	66,266	tele	Widely held
0.4	3.36	4.12	3.67	12.85	230	15.64	118	44,633	banks	Widely held
1.6	3.90	4.18	4.09	19.00	111	21.38	55	54,258	tele	BCE Inc. 100%
0.3	2.73	2.72	3.30	13.37	218	14.92	138	33,912	banks	Widely held
0.2	2.90	2.40	2.22	16.17	154	14.74	143	13,000	insur	Widely held
0.6	2.92	5.02	4.09	13.94	194	19.13	67	3,646	oilprd	Widely held
0.3	3.19	3.15	3.40	25.35	62	22.24	50	6,460	integ	Exxon Mobil Corp. (U.S.) 69.6%
0.2	1.84	2.08	1.49	8.82	355	na	nr	14,905	insur	Widely held
0.3	2.72	2.44	2.18	17.33	136	18.89	72	18.300	fin	Power Corp. of Canada 67.4%
0.5	3.71	3.19	3.28	18.29	123	13.00	180	4.470	integ	Government of Canada 18.74%
0.5	¹US0.93	¹US1.19	¹US1.96	7.32	397	15.34	131	44.000	serv	Woodbridge Company Ltd.69%
0.2	2.53	1.39	1.72	22.86	74	17.53	96	14.000	insur	Power Financial Corp.64.99%
0.1	¹US5.83	¹US6.55	¹US7.04	11.85	262	12.45	195	70,800	auto	Stronach Trust 66.3%
1.6	1.56	1.30	1.50	13.37	219	8.63	309	2,767	pipeline	Widely held
0.5	1.88	1.49	1.39	16.73	146	nm	nr	2.753	integ	Li Ka-sning 71.5%
0.8	1.64	0.79	0.79	28.25	51	17.72	93	3.422	integ	Widely held
1.0	2.64	2.04	1.71	18.93	113	15.58	122	122,000	food	George Weston Ltd. 61%
1.4	5.05	4.42	3.66	18.27	124	21.10	57	142,850	food	W. Galen Weston 62.13%
0.3	1.37	4.19	4.97	5.22	461	12.58	189	42,552	banks	Widely held
0.4	2.81	2.74	2.93	13.66	205	15.74	117	19,000	mgt	Paul Desmarais and associates 65%
1.8	3.60	2.91	2.54	20.08	101	16.94	103	4,000	pipeline	Widely held
0.4	¹US1.15	¹US-0.02	¹US2.45	4.32	486	5.76	373	48,100	mining	Widely held
0.8	4.46	5.30	6.70	13.51	211	16.29	107	1,573	oilprd	Widely held
0.8	2.87	3.72	3.91	8.93	352	10.29	250	23,190	trans	Widely held
0.3	2.03	3.67	3.04	11.45	271	17.54	95	3,825	integ	Shell Investments (1996) Ltd. 78%
0.7	3.73	5.25	6.41	12.88	229	11.17	226	1,565	oilprd	Widely held
0.5	1.86	1.05	1.35	20.01	103	22.45	48	3,285	fin	Power Financial Corp. 56.2%
0.1	3.05	2.13	2.22	13.80	200	nm	nr	6,768	insur	Widely held
1.0	3.13	2.35	3.36	15.60	165	11.38	217	16,116	trans	Widely held
0.2	na	na	na	14.39	185	12.63	187	7,000	insur	Great-West Lifeco Inc. 100%
0.8	3.34	3.40	4.52	29.17	45	26.11	26	2,767	oilprd	Ontario Teachers' Pension Plan 20%

EXAMPLE 2.16

RELATIVE FREQUENCY DISTRIBUTION AND PERCENTAGE DISTRIBUTION OF THE 2003 RETURN FOR GROWTH AND VALUE MUTUAL FUNDS

In the "Using Statistics" scenario, you are interested in comparing the 2003 return for growth and value mutual funds. MUTUALFUNDS2004 Construct relative frequency distributions and percentage distributions for the growth funds and for the value funds.

SOLUTION

You conclude (see Table 2.14) that the 2003 return for the growth funds is slightly lower than for the value funds and that 18.37% of growth funds have returns between 20 and 30 as compared to 12.5% of the value funds. Slightly more of the value funds have higher returns (between 50 and 60, and 60 and 70) than the growth funds.

TABLE 2.14

Relative Frequency Distribution and Percentage Distribution of the 2003 Return for Growth and Value Mutual Funds

Annual Percentage Return in 2003	Growth		Value	
	Proportion	Percentage	Proportion	Percentage
10 and under 20	0.0408	4.08	0.0278	2.78
20 and under 30	0.1837	18.37	0.1250	12.50
30 and under 40	0.2653	26.53	0.2778	27.78
40 and under 50	0.3061	30.61	0.2778	27.78
50 and under 60	0.1020	10.20	0.1389	13.89
60 and under 70	0.1020	10.20	0.1250	12.50
70 and under 80	0.0000	0.00	0.0278	2.78
Total	1.0000	100.0	1.0000	100.0

Graphing Frequency Distributions

HISTOGRAM

A histogram is a graph of 'touching rectangles.' The horizontal axis represents the class boundaries. No other values are shown on this axis. The vertical axis shows the class frequencies.

(The above rules only apply to histograms where the classes are all of *equal width*. We are not concerned in this course with how to draw other types of histograms.)

FIGURE 2.7

Frequency Histogram— Power Supply Voltages (using SPSS version 12).

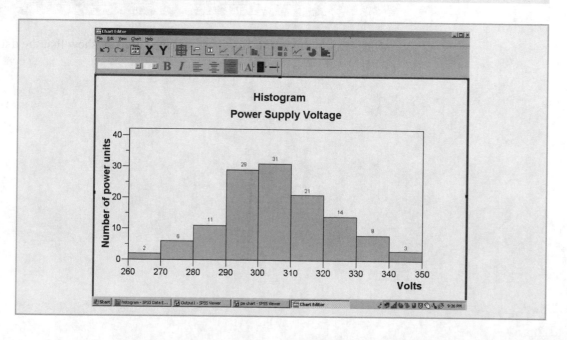

POLYGON

A polygon is a graph in the shape of a many-sided closed figure. (Some texts show a smooth curve, but this is technically not a polygon.) The horizontal axis shows the class **midpoints**. No other values are shown on this axis. The vertical axis shows the class frequencies. In order to *close* the polygon, an extra class midpoint on the left and right side is used.

The class midpoints may be calculated as follows:

$$m = \frac{lower\ boundary + upper\ boundary}{2} \tag{2.1}$$

(The above rules only apply to polygons where the classes are all of *equal_width*. We are not concerned with how to draw other types of polygons.)

FIGURE 2.8

Frequency Polygon—
Power Supply Voltages
(using SPSS version 12)

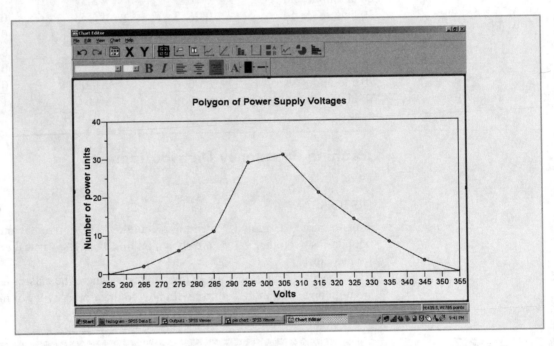

Note: Both graphs, the histogram and the polygon, show that the data has roughly a bell-curve shape.

Constructing multiple histograms on the same graph when comparing two or more sets of data is difficult and confusing. Superimposing the vertical bars of one histogram on another histogram causes difficulty in interpretation. When there are two or more groups, you should use a percentage polygon.

Figure 2.9 displays the percentage polygons for the cost of meals for city and suburban restaurants. The polygon for the suburban restaurants is concentrated to the left of (corresponding to lower cost) the polygon for city restaurants. The highest percentages of cost for the suburban restaurants are for class midpoints of $27.50 and $32.50, while the highest percentages of cost for the city restaurants are for a class midpoint of $37.50.

FIGURE 2.9

Percentage Polygons for the Cost of Restaurant Meals for City and Suburban Restaurants

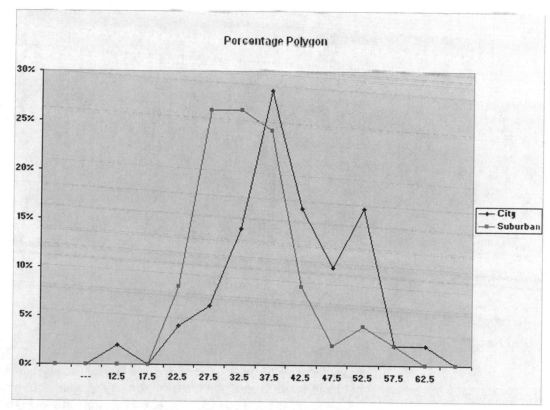

The polygons in Figure 2.9 have points whose values on the X axis represent the midpoint of the class interval. For example, look at the points plotted on the X axis at 22.5 ($22.50). The point for the suburban restaurants (the higher one) represents the fact that 8% of these restaurants have meal costs between $20 and $25. The point for the city restaurants (the lower one) represents the fact that 4% of these restaurants have meal costs between $20 and $25.

When you construct polygons or histograms, the vertical (Y) axis should show the true zero or "origin" so as not to distort the character of the data. The horizontal (X) axis does not need to specify the zero point for the variable of interest, although the range of the variable should constitute the major portion of the axis.

EXAMPLE 2.18   PERCENTAGE POLYGONS OF THE 2003 RETURN FOR GROWTH AND VALUE MUTUAL FUNDS

In the "Using Statistics" scenario, you are interested in comparing the 2003 return of growth and value mutual funds. MUTUALFUNDS2004 Construct percentage polygons for the growth funds and for the value funds.

SOLUTION

Figure 2.10 shows that the distribution of the growth funds has more lower annual returns as compared to the value funds, which have more higher returns.

FIGURE 2.10

Percentage Polygons of 2003 Percentage Return

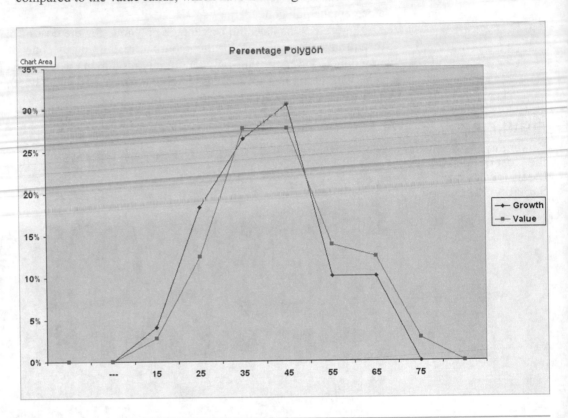

PIE CHART

Occasionally a pie chart is necessary to graph a frequency distribution. The situations that would make it difficult, if not impossible, to draw either a histogram or polygon would include the existence of: 1) open-ended classes or 2) classes of unequal width.

Consider the following example:

The grades of students in a QMS102 class have been summarized in the following table.

TABLE 2.15

Grades	# students	%
Less than 50	5	10
50 and under 60	12	24
60 " " 70	17	34
70 " " 80	10	20
80 " " 100	6	12

The following pie chart was produced using SPSS.

FIGURE 2.11

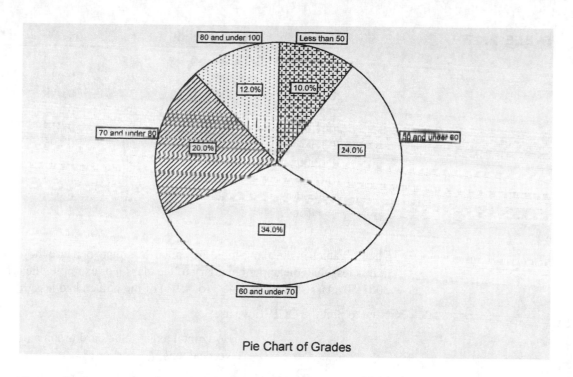

Pie Chart of Grades

Cumulative Distributions and OGIVES

EXAMPLE 2.19

A soft-drink bottling machine is periodically tested to determine if it is functioning within certain limits. The frequency distribution below is a summary of the measurements for 255 bottles, where the data shows how much soft-drink was in each bottle.

TABLE 2.16

Amount in a 2 litre bottle(ml)	# of bottles
1999.00 and under 1999.50	5
1999.50　"　"　2000.00	10
2000.00　"　"　2000.50	20
2000.50　"　"　2001.00	35
2001.00　"　"　2001.50	55
2001.50　"　"　2002.00	50
2002.00　"　"　2002.50	40
2002.50　"　"　2003.00	30
2003.00　"　"　2003.50	10
Total	255

Suppose this frequency distribution is the only data we have available and we would like to know the answers to the following questions.

a. What percent of the bottles had less than 2000.00 ml?
b. What percent of the bottles had less than 2002.70 ml?
c. What percent of the bottles had more than 2001.25 ml?
d. Thirty percent of the bottles have at most _____ ml.
e. 25% of the bottles have at least _____ ml.

To answer these questions, we must plot an **OGIVE**. But first we will have to determine the *cumulative relative 'less-than' frequency* (crf) for each class as follows:

$$crf = rf \text{ of the class} + rf \text{ of all previous classes}$$

TABLE 2.17

Amount in a 2 litre bottle(ml)	f	rf	crf	c%
1999.00 and under 1999.50	5	0.020	0.020	2.0
1999.50 " " 2000.00	10	0.039	0.059	5.9
2000.00 " " 2000.50	20	0.078	0.137	13.7
2000.50 " " 2001.00	35	0.137	0.274	27.4
2001.00 " " 2001.50	55	0.216	0.490	49.0
2001.50 " " 2002.00	50	0.196	0.686	68.6
2002.00 " " 2002.50	40	0.157	0.843	84.3
2002.50 " " 2003.00	30	0.118	0.961	96.1
2003.00 " " 2003.50	10	0.039	1.000	100.0
Total	255	1.000		

The crf values in the above table are called 'less-than' because they show the fraction of the data that is less than the upper boundary of the class. For example, the crf of the '2001.00 and under 2001.50' class shows that 0.490 (or 49%) of the bottles had less than 2001.50 ml.

Now to plot the OGIVE we use:

Horizontal axis: Standard graph axis
Vertical axis: crf or c%

Plot the crf for each class at the *upper* boundary.

Join the points with straight lines. (Start the graph at the 1st boundary)

For our example, we get the OGIVE shown below:

FIGURE 2.12

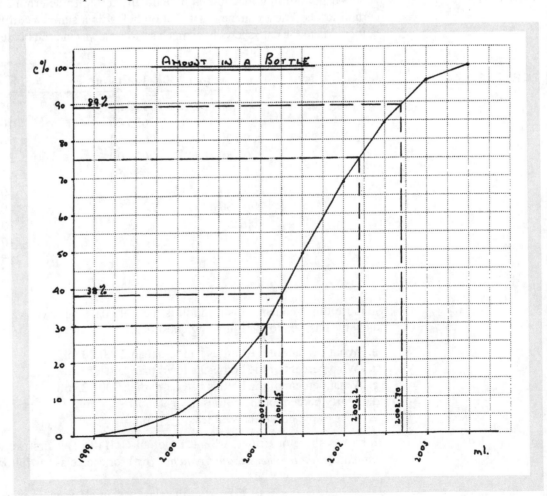

The answers to the questions posed at the beginning of this discussion are:

a. 5.9% (from c%)
b. 89%
c. 62%
d. 2001.1 ml
e. 2002.2 ml

The rules given on the previous page for constructing an Ogive apply to *any* cumulative relative frequency distribution, i.e. even those where there are classes of *unequal width* or *open-ended* classes.

EXAMPLE 2.20

A survey of employees in a large company revealed the following results regarding the amount of time employees had been in their current job position. The results were summarized as follows:

TABLE 2.18

Time in Current Position (years)	Percent
less than 1	15.0
1 and under 3	27.4
3 " " 6	22.2
6 " " 10	13.9
10 " " 20	15.5
20 and over	6.0
Total	100

Based on these results:

a. Approximately what percent of quality professionals had been in the current position for 5 years or more?
b. Seventy percent of quality professionals had been in their current position for less than _____ years.

The calculations necessary to construct a Percentage Ogive from the above data are shown below.

TABLE 2.19

Time in current position (years)	Percent	Cumulative Percent
less than 1	15.0	15.0
1 and under 3	27.4	42.4
3 " " 6	22.2	64.6
6 " " 10	13.9	78.5
10 " " 20	15.5	94.0
20 and over	6.0	100.0
Total	100	

The Ogive is plotted on the following page.

FIGURE 2.13

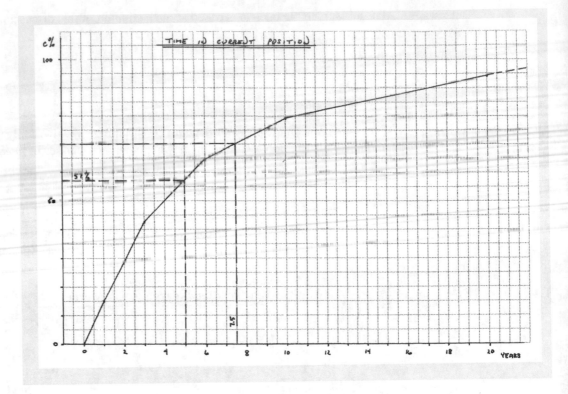

The answers to the questions are:

   a. 43%

   b. 7.5 years

PROBLEMS FOR SECTION 2.3

Ogive

2.20 The National Association of Real Estate Agents has collected the following data on a sample of 170 salespersons. The classes represent their total annual commission.

Total Annual Commission	# people	rf	crf
$ 0 and under $ 5,000	5		
5,000 " " 10,000	9		
10,000 " " 15,000	11		
15,000 " " 20,000	48		
20,000 " " 30,000	62		
30,000 " " 40,000	19		
40,000 " " 50,000	9		
50,000 and over	7		
Total	170		

Construct an ogive that will help you answer the following questions:

a. Approximately what percentage of the salespeople earn more than $27,000 ?

b. Approximately how much is earned by the 'middle' salesperson?

c. Approximately how much would a salesperson have to earn to be in the top 25% ?

2.21 A Pharmaceutical company sells 78 different products. The distribution of the annual sales amounts last year for these products is shown below:

Annual Sales ($ 000)	Number of Products
0 and under 10	17
10 " " 50	20
50 " " 100	24
100 " " 150	13
150 " " 250	4
Total	78

Construct an ogive and use it to determine:

a. How many products had annual sales of less than $80,000 last year?

b. What percentage of the products had sales of $120,000 or more last year?

2.22 The distribution of a company's stock according to the number of shares held is shown below:

Number of Shares Held	% of Shareholders
0 and under 50	25
50 " " 100	19
100 " " 500	41
500 " " 1000	12
1000 " " 2000	3
Total	100

Construct an ogive and use it to determine:

a. What percentage of shareholders held 200 or more shares?

b. The 20 percent of shareholders with the most shares each held how many shares or more?

Learning the Basics

PH Grade ASSIST **2.23** The values for a set of data vary from 11.6 to 97.8.

a. If these values are grouped into classes, indicate the class boundaries.

b. What class-interval width did you choose?

c. What are the class midpoints?

PH Grade ASSIST **2.24** In constructing an ogive (i.e., a cumulative percentage polygon) pertaining to the GMAT scores from a sample of 50 applicants to an MBA program, previous data indicated that none of the applicants scored below 450. The frequency distribution was formed by choosing class intervals 450 to 499, 500 to 549, and so on, with the last class grouping being 700 to 749. If two applicants scored in the interval 450 to 499 and 16 applicants scored in the interval 500 to 549:

a. What percentage of applicants scored below 500?

b. What percentage of applicants scored between 500 and 549?

c. What percentage of applicants scored below 550?

d. What percentage of applicants scored below 750?

Applying the Concepts

You can solve problems 2.25–2.30 manually or by using Microsoft Excel, Minitab, or SPSS.

PH Grade ASSIST **2.25** The data displayed below represent the cost of electricity during July 2004 for a random sample of 50 one-bedroom apartments in a large city. UTILITY

Raw Data on Utility Charges ($)

96	171	202	178	147	102	153	197	127	82
157	185	90	116	172	111	148	213	130	165

141	149	206	175	123	128	144	168	109	167
95	163	150	154	130	143	187	166	139	149
108	119	183	151	114	135	191	137	129	158

a. Form a frequency distribution and a percentage distribution that have class intervals with the upper class limits $99, $119, and so on.

b. Plot a histogram and a percentage polygon.

c. Form the cumulative percentage distribution and plot the ogive (cumulative percentage polygon).

d. Around what amount does the monthly electricity cost seem to be concentrated?

 2.26 One operation of a mill is to cut pieces of steel into parts that will later be used as the frame for front seats in an automobile. The steel is cut with a diamond saw and requires the resulting parts to be within ±0.005 inch of the length specified by the automobile company. The following table comes from a sample of 100 steel parts. The measurement reported is the difference in inches between the actual length of the steel part, as measured by a laser measurement device, and the specified length of the steel part. For example, the first value, −0.002, represents a steel part that is 0.002 inch shorter than the specified length. STEEL

−0.002	0.002	0.0005	−0.0015	−0.001
0.0005	0.001	0.001	−0.0005	−0.001
0.0025	0.001	0.0005	−0.0015	0.0005
0.001	0.001	0.001	−0.0005	−0.0025
0.002	−0.002	0.0025	−0.0005	0.0025
0.001	−0.003	0.001	−0.001	0.002
0.005	−0.0015	0	−0.0015	0.0025
−0.002	−0.0005	−0.0025	0.0025	−0.002
0	0	−0.001	0.001	0
0.001	−0.0025	0.0035	0.0005	−0.0005
−0.0025	−0.003	0	0	−0.001
−0.003	−0.001	−0.003	0.002	0
0.001	0.002	−0.002	−0.0005	−0.002
−0.0005	−0.001	−0.001	0.0005	0
0	0	−0.0015	0.0005	0
−0.003	0.003	−0.0015	0	0.002
−0.001	0.0015	−0.002	−0.0005	−0.003
0.0005	0	0.001	0.002	−0.0005
0.0025	0	−0.0025	0.001	−0.002
−0.0025	−0.0025	−0.0005	−0.0015	−0.002

a. Construct the frequency distribution and the percentage distribution.
b. Plot a histogram and a percentage polygon.
c. Plot the cumulative percentage polygon.
d. Is the steel mill doing a good job in meeting the requirements set by the automobile company? Explain.

2.27 A manufacturing company produces steel housings for electrical equipment. The main component part of the housing is a steel trough that is made out of a 14-gauge steel coil. It is produced using a 250-ton progressive punch press with a wipe-down operation putting two 90-degree forms in the flat steel to make the trough. The distance from one side of the form to the other is critical because of weatherproofing in outdoor applications. The company requires that the width of the trough be between 8.31 inches and 8.61 inches. The following are the widths of the troughs in inches for a sample of $n = 49$. TROUGH

8.312	8.343	8.317	8.383	8.348	8.410	8.351	8.373
8.481	8.422	8.476	8.382	8.484	8.403	8.414	8.419
8.385	8.465	8.498	8.447	8.436	8.413	8.489	8.414
8.481	8.415	8.479	8.429	8.458	8.462	8.460	8.444
8.429	8.460	8.412	8.420	8.410	8.405	8.323	8.420
8.396	8.447	8.405	8.439	8.411	8.427	8.420	8.498
8.409							

a. Construct the frequency distribution and the percentage distribution.
b. Plot a histogram and a percentage polygon.
c. Plot the cumulative percentage polygon.
d. What can you conclude about the number of troughs that will meet the company's requirements of troughs being between 8.31 and 8.61 inches wide?

2.28 The manufacturing company in problem 2.24 also produces electric insulators. If the insulators break when in use, a short circuit is likely to occur. To test the strength of the insulators, destructive testing in high-powered labs is carried out to determine how much *force* is required to break the insulators. Force is measured by observing how many pounds must be applied to the insulator before it breaks. The strength of 30 insulators tested are as follows. FORCE

1,870	1,728	1,656	1,610	1,634	1,784	1,522	1,696
1,592	1,662	1,866	1,764	1,734	1,662	1,734	1,774
1,550	1,756	1,762	1,866	1,820	1,744	1,788	1,688
1,810	1,752	1,680	1,810	1,652	1,736		

a. Construct the frequency distribution and the percentage distribution.
b. Plot a histogram and a percentage polygon.
c. Plot the cumulative percentage polygon.

d. What can you conclude about the strength of the insulators if the company requires a force measurement of at least 1,500 pounds before breaking?

2.29 The ordered arrays in the accompanying table deal with the life (in hours) of a sample of forty 100-watt lightbulbs produced by manufacturer A and a sample of forty 100-watt lightbulbs produced by manufacturer B. BULBS

Manufacturer A					Manufacturer B				
684	697	720	773	821	819	836	888	897	903
831	835	848	852	852	907	912	918	942	943
859	860	868	870	876	952	959	962	986	992
893	899	905	909	911	994	1,004	1,005	1,007	1,015
922	924	926	926	938	1,016	1,018	1,020	1,022	1,034
939	943	946	954	971	1,038	1,072	1,077	1,077	1,082
972	977	984	1,005	1,014	1,096	1,100	1,113	1,113	1,116
1,016	1,041	1,052	1,080	1,093	1,153	1,154	1,174	1,188	1,230

a. Form the frequency distribution and percentage distribution for each manufacturer using the following class-interval widths for each distribution:
(1)   Manufacturer A: 650 but less than 750, 750 but less than 850, and so on.
(2)   Manufacturer B: 750 but less than 850, 850 but less than 950, and so on.
b. Plot the percentage histograms on separate graphs and plot the percentage polygons on one graph.
c. Form the cumulative percentage distributions and plot the ogives on one graph.
d. Which manufacturer has bulbs with a longer life— manufacturer A or manufacturer B? Explain.

2.30 The following data represent the amount of soft drink in a sample of 50 2-liter bottles. DRINK

2.109	2.086	2.066	2.075	2.065	2.057	2.052	2.044
2.036	2.038	2.031	2.029	2.025	2.029	2.023	2.020
2.015	2.014	2.013	2.014	2.012	2.012	2.012	2.010
2.005	2.003	1.999	1.996	1.997	1.992	1.994	1.986
1.984	1.981	1.973	1.975	1.971	1.969	1.966	1.967
1.963	1.957	1.951	1.951	1.947	1.941	1.941	1.938
1.908	1.894						

a. Construct the frequency distribution and the percentage distribution.
b. Plot a histogram and a percentage polygon.
c. Form the cumulative percentage distribution and plot the cumulative percentage polygon.
d. On the basis of the results of (a) through (c), does the amount of soft drink filled in the bottles concentrate around specific values?

Stem-and-Leaf and Frequency Distributions

Refer to the mutual fund data shown below that appeared in the Canadian Mutual Funds table of the June 3, 2004 issue of The Globe and Mail.

2.31 Construct stem-and-leaf displays for the following data:
a. Equitable Life Valuation data
b. Equitable Life Change data
c. Equitable Life Percent Change data
d. MD Management Valuation data
e. MD Management Percent Change data

2.32 Construct frequency distributions for the following data:
a. Manulife Mix Funds Valuation data
b. Manulife Mix Funds Change data
c. Manulife Mix Funds Percent Change data
d. CI-Clarica Mutual Funds Valuation data
e. Transamerica Growsafe 75/100 Valuation data
f. Transamerica Growsafe 75/100 Percent Change data

Table 2.20

fund	valuation	chg	% chg
EQUITABLE LIFE			
AIM Cdn Premier 06/01	10.01	+.01	+.07
Accum Income 06/01	23.26	-.03	-.15
American Gwth 06/01	10.48	+.04	+.37
Asian-Pacific 06/01	6.38	+.01	+.17
Asset Allocat 06/01	16.72	-.01	-.06
Bissett Div Inc 06/01	10.19	-.01	-.10
Cdn Bond 06/01	15.55	-.02	-.15
Cdn Stock 06/01	20.17	-.01	-.05
CommonStock 06/01	29.96	-.02	-.05
European Equity 06/01	7.23	-.02	-.22
International 06/01	11.49	+.02	+.17
MB Cdn Eq Value 06/01	18.21	-.04	-.24
Mack US Em Grth 06/01	10.15	+.09	+.84
Templeton Grwth 06/01	9.39	+.02	+.17
Tmplton Glo Bnd 06/01	12.32	+.04	+.36
Trimark Europis 06/01	10.51	+.02	+.15
Trimark Glo Bal 06/01	10.48	+.02	+.17
US Equity 06/01	6.30	+.02	+.32

fund	valuation	chg	% chg
MD MANAGEMENT			
MD Balanced	18.08	-.06	-.33
MD Bnd & Mtg	10.39	-.01	-.10
MD Bond	7.10	-.03	.42
MD Dividend	16.66	-.03	-.18
MD Equity	19.03	-.03	-.16
MD Glo Bond	11.27	-.03	-.27
MD Glo Equ RSP	7.07	unch	unch
MD Growth	10.37	unch	unch
MD Growth RSP	9.82	unch	unch
MD Int'l Growth	6.64	unch	unch
MD Int'l Value	10.13	unch	unch
MD Intl Gr RSP	6.46	unch	unch
MD Select	15.39	-.04	-.26
MD US LgCpGrRSP	6.07	unch	unch
MD US LrCap Val	8.42	unch	unch
MD US LrCpVlRSP	8.25	unch	unch
MD US Lrg Cp Gr	4.79	unch	unch
MD US Sml Cp Gr	3.68	-.01	-.27
MDPIM Cdn Equ-A	11.01	-.04	-.36
MDPIM US Equ-A	7.39	-.02	-.27

fund	valuation	chg	% chg
MANULIFE MIX FUNDS			
AIM Am MidCp Gw	12.26	-.04	-.33
AIM Cd First Cl	12.25	-.05	-.41
Cd Lg Cap Gw Cl	12.85	-.07	-.54
Cd Lg Cap ValCl	12.12	-.02	-.16
Cd Lg Cp CoreCl	12.05	-.02	-.17
Cdn Equ Val Cl	12.65	-.02	-.16
E&P Gw Opp Cl	14.38	-.04	-.28
E&P US MidCapCl	11.81	-.05	-.42
FI Can DiscEqCl	13.07	-.08	-.61
FI Gwth Amer Cl	11.09	-.03	-.27
FI Intl Port Cl	11.60	-.02	-.17
Global Equ Cl	10.86	-.01	-.09
Global Sect Cl	11.31	-.06	-.53
Global SectCl-H	11.31	-.05	-.44
Global Val Cl	12.48	-.01	-.08
Int'l Growth Cl	11.29	-.01	-.09
Int'l Value Cl	12.27	+.01	+.08
Japanese Class	12.63	-.12	-.94
SM Tot Cd Eq Cl	13.26	+.02	+.15
SM Total Glo Cl	12.00	-.04	-.33
SM Total USEqCl	11.33	-.03	-.26
SMTotal Gl Cl-H	12.00	-.04	-.33
Sht Term Yld Cl	10.21	unch	unch
Str Bond Class	10.30	-.03	-.29
Tri Sel Cdn Cl	12.13	-.03	-.25
Trimark Glo Cl	11.41	+.04	+.35
US Lg Cap Gw Cl	10.40	-.01	-.10
US Lg Cp CoreCl	10.77	-.01	-.09
US Lg Cp Val Cl	10.92	-.02	-.18
US MidCp Val Cl	11.51	-.03	-.26

fund	valuation	chg	% chg
CI - CLARICA MUTUAL FUNDS			
Alpine CdnRes	10.35	-.08	-.77
Alpine CdnRes A	10.46	-.07	-.66
Alpine GrthEq	13.09	-.04	-.30
Alpine GrthEq A	13.28	-.05	-.38
Cdn Blu Chip Z	11.35	-.04	-.35
Cdn BlueChip	16.34	-.06	-.37
Cdn BlueChip A	16.51	-.07	-.42
Cdn Div Cl Z	10.86	-.04	-.37
Cdn Divers	14.71	-.05	-.34
Cdn Divers A	14.96	-.05	-.33
Cdn Equity	12.80	-.02	-.16
Cdn Equity A	12.82	-.02	-.16
Cdn Lrg Cap Val	10.55	+.01	+.09
Cdn Small/Mid A	21.02	-.04	-.19
Cdn Sml/Mid Cap	18.40	-.03	-.16
Clarica Balance	11.64	-.02	-.17
Glo Lrg Cap Val	10.52	+.04	+.38
Global Bond	9.91	-.04	-.40
Global Bond A	9.91	-.03	-.30
Prem Bond	11.34	-.04	-.35
Prem Bond A	11.49	-.04	-.35
Prem Int'l	12.43	-.03	-.24
Prem Int'l A	12.78	-.03	-.23
Prem Mtg	10.34	-.02	-.19
Prem Mtg A	10.46	-.02	-.19
Sig Corp Bond	9.83	-.02	-.20
Sum Cdn Equ	15.37	-.05	-.32
Sum Cdn Equ A	15.50	-.05	-.32
Sum Div Gwth	15.18	-.02	-.13
Sum Div Gwth A	14.91	-.02	-.13
Sum For Equ	14.46	-.03	-.21
Sum For Equ A	14.96	-.03	-.20
Sum Gwth&Inc	14.09	-.03	-.21
Sum Gwth&Inc A	14.50	-.03	-.21
US Small Cap	8.44	-.02	-.24
US Small Cap A	8.54	-.01	-.12

fund	valuation	chg	% chg
TRANSAMERICA GROWSAFE 75/100			
AGF Int Val7510 06/01	4.51	+.00	+.02
AIC AmFoc 7510 06/01	5.07	-.01	-.19
AIC DivCan 7510 06/01	5.38	-.00	-.01
Agg AA GIF 7510	3.63	-.00	-.03
Bal AA GIF 7510	4.47	-.01	-.12
CI Gl Boom 7510 06/01	4.82	-.00	-.10
CI Global 7510 06/01	5.46	-.00	-.01
CanAsian 7510	4.21	-.01	-.14
CanEuro 7510	3.14	+.02	+.75
CanUS 21st 7510	2.86	-.01	-.24
CanUS L Cap7510	4.16	+.02	+.38
Cdn Bal 7510	4.77	-.02	-.46
Cdn Bond 7510	5.91	-.02	-.34
Cdn Equity 7510	3.40	-.03	-.79
Cdn Lg Cap 7510	4.17	-.01	-.35
Cdn MMF 7510	5.29	+.00	+.00
CdnEqVal 7510 06/01	5.62	+.00	+.04
CdnFixPay 7510 06/01	5.67	-.01	-.18
Con AA GIF 7510	4.88	-.01	-.20
Fid Can AA 7510 06/01	5.66	+.03	+.46
Fid IntPort7510 06/01	4.78	-.06	-1.19
Fid TrueNrt7510 06/01	5.75	+.01	+.19
Grow AA GIF7510	4.11	-.00	-.06
MacIvyGwinc7510 06/01	5.68	+.01	+.17
TD Div Inc 7510 06/01	6.12	-.00	-.03
TOP AggrGw 7510 06/01	3.66	+.01	+.24
TOP Bal 7510 06/01	4.50	+.01	+.19
TOP CdnMgr 7510 06/01	5.75	+.00	+.02
TOP Cons 7510 06/01	5.00	+.01	+.14
TOP GloMgr 7510 06/01	4.89	+.01	+.13
TOP GloSect7510 06/01	4.90	+.01	+.29
TOP Growth 7510 06/01	4.24	+.01	+.20
TOP USMgrs 7510 06/01	4.80	+.02	+.39
US EqVal 7510 06/01	5.74	+.03	+.47
US Equity 7510	3.68	-.00	-.01

2.4 MISUSING GRAPHS AND ETHICAL ISSUES

Good graphical displays reveal what the data are conveying. Unfortunately many graphs presented in newspapers and magazines as well as graphs that can be developed using the Chart Wizard of Microsoft Excel either are incorrect, misleading, or are so unnecessarily complicated that they never should be used. To illustrate the misuse of graphs, the first graph presented is one that was printed in *Time* magazine as part of an article on increasing exports of wine from Australia to the United States.

FIGURE 2.14

Figure 2.14 "Improper" Display of Australian Wine Exports to the United States in Millions of Gallons

Source: *Adapted from S. Watterson, "Liquid Gold— Australians Are Changing the World of Wine. Even the French Seem Grateful," Time, November 22, 1999, 68.*

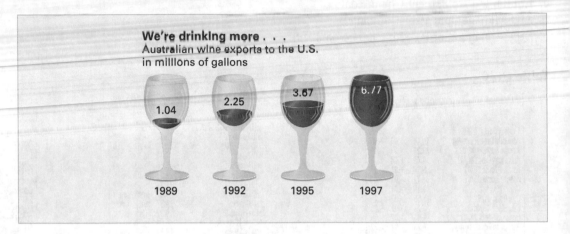

In Figure 2.14, the wineglass icon representing the 6.77 million gallons for 1997 does not appear to be almost twice the size of the wineglass icon representing the 3.67 million gallons for 1995, nor does the wineglass icon representing the 2.25 million gallons for 1992 appear to be twice the size of the wineglass icon representing the 1.04 million gallons for 1989. Part of the reason for this is that the three-dimensional wineglass icon is used to represent the two dimensions of exports and time. Although the wineglass presentation may catch the eye, the data should be presented in a summary table or a time-series plot.

In addition to the type of distortion created by the wineglass icons in the *Time* magazine graph displayed in Figure 2.14, improper use of the vertical and horizontal axes leads to distortions. Figure 2.15 presents another graph used in the same *Time* magazine article.

FIGURE 2.15

"Improper" Display of Amount of Land Planted with Grapes for the Wine Industry

Source: *Adapted from S. Watterson, "Liquid Gold— Australians Are Changing the World of Wine. Even the French Seem Grateful," Time, November 22, 1999, 68–69.*

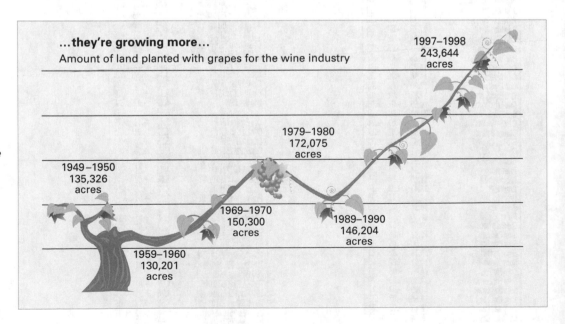

There are several problems in the graph. First, there is no zero point on the vertical axis. Second, the acreage of 135,326 for 1949 to 1950 is plotted above the acreage of 150,300 for 1969 to 1970. Third, it is not obvious that the difference between 1979 to 1980 and 1997 to 1998 (71,569 acres) is approximately three and a half times the difference between 1979–1980 and 1969–1970 (21,775 acres). Fourth, there are no scale values on the horizontal axis. Years are plotted next to the acreage totals, not on the horizontal axis. Fifth, the values for the time dimension are not properly spaced along the horizontal axis. The value for 1979–1980 is much closer to 1990 than it is to 1969–1970.

Other types of eye-catching displays that you typically see in magazines and newspapers often include information that is not necessary and just add excessive clutter. Figure 2.16 represents one such display. The graph in Figure 2.16 shows those products with the largest market share for soft drinks in 1999. The graph suffers from too much clutter although it is designed to show the differences in market share among the soft drinks. The display of the fizz for each soft drink takes up too much of the graph relative to the data. The same information could have been conveyed with a bar chart or pie chart.

FIGURE 2.16

Plot of Market Share of Soft Drinks in 1999

Source: *Adapted from Anne B. Carey and Sam Ward, "Coke Still Has Most Fizz," USA Today, May 10, 2000, 1B.*

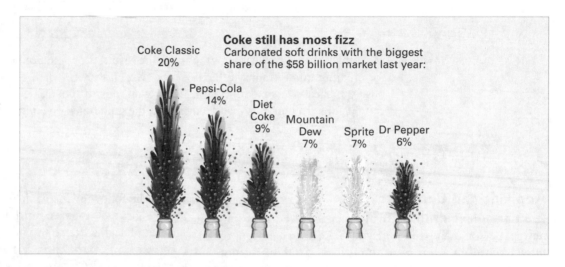

Some guidelines for developing good graphs are as follows:

- The graph should not distort the data.
- The graph should not contain unnecessary adornments (sometimes referred to as **chartjunk**).
- Any two-dimensional graph should contain a scale for each axis.
- The scale on the vertical axis should begin at zero.
- All axes should be properly labeled.
- The graph should contain a title.
- The simplest possible graph should be used for a given set of data.

One of the biggest sources of improper graphs is the Chart Wizard of Microsoft Excel. Figure 2.17 represents the Step 1 dialog box of the Chart Wizard. You can select from among column, bar, line, pie, and area charts as well as more complicated types such as doughnut, radar, surface, bubble, stock, cylinder, cone, and pyramid charts. These more complicated charts should rarely be used since they are harder to interpret than the simpler charts covered in this chapter.

FIGURE 2.17

Step 1 Dialog Box of
the Microsoft Excel
Chart Wizard

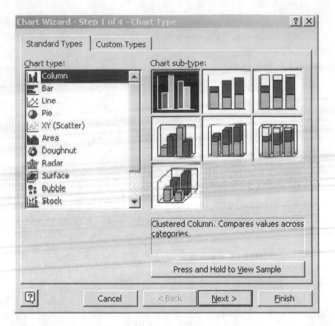

Most instances of misleading graphs are the result of people not being aware of the guidelines for creating good graphs. Ethical issues arise, however, when charts are constructed to purposely mislead the reader. In either case, you must use extreme caution when trying to draw conclusions from graphs that deviate from the guidelines given in this chapter.

PROBLEMS FOR SECTION 2.4

Applying the Concepts

2.33 (Student Project) Bring a chart to class from a newspaper or magazine that you believe to be a poorly drawn representation of a numerical variable. Be prepared to submit the chart to the instructor with comments as to why you believe it is inappropriate. Do you believe that the intent of the chart is to purposely mislead the reader? Also, be prepared to present and comment on this in class.

2.34 (Student Project) Bring a chart to class from a newspaper or magazine that you believe to be a poorly drawn representation of a categorical variable. Be prepared to submit the chart to the instructor with comments as to why you consider it inappropriate. Do you believe that the intent of the chart is to purposely mislead the reader? Also, be prepared to present and comment on this in class.

2.35 (Student Project) Bring a chart to class from a newspaper or magazine that you believe to contain too many unnecessary adornments (i.e., chartjunk) that may cloud the message given by the data. Be prepared to submit the chart to the instructor with comments about why you think it is inappropriate. Also, be prepared to present and comment on this in class.

2.36 The following visual display contains an overembellished chart that appeared in *USA Today* dealing with the number of deaths from lightning strikes in the United States.

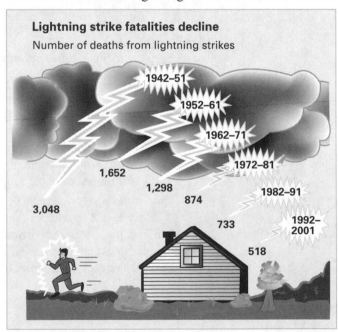

Source: Adapted from USA Today, *November 12, 2002.*

a. Describe at least one good feature of this visual display.
b. Describe at least one bad feature of this visual display.
c. Redraw the graph, using the guidelines given on page 51.

2.37 The following visual display concerning the relative size of police departments in major U.S. cities appeared in *USA Today*:

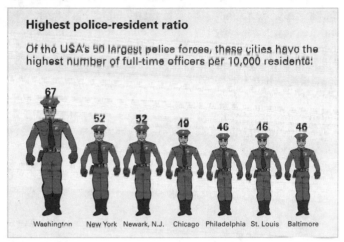

Highest police-resident ratio

Of the USA's 50 largest police forces, these cities have the highest number of full-time officers per 10,000 residents:

67 Washington   52 New York   52 Newark, N.J.   49 Chicago   46 Philadelphia   46 St. Louis   46 Baltimore

Source: Adapted from USA Today, February 2000.

a. Indicate a feature of this chart that violates the principles of good graphs.

b. Set up an alternative graph for the data provided in this figure.

2.38 The following visual display concerning where the United States gets its electricity appeared in *USA Today*:

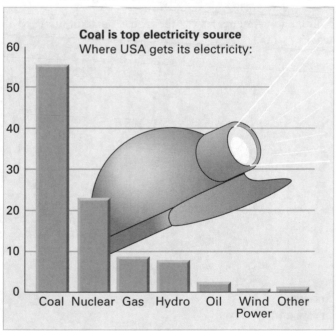

Coal is top electricity source
Where USA gets its electricity:

Coal Nuclear Gas Hydro Oil Wind Power Other

Source: Adapted from USA Today, January 30, 2002.

a. Describe at least one good feature of this visual display.

b. Describe at least one bad feature of this visual display.

c. Redraw the graph using the guidelines given on page 51.

2.39 An article in *The New York Times* (Donna Rosato, "Worried about the Numbers? How about the Charts?" *The New York Times*, September 15, 2002, Business 7) reported on research done on annual reports of corporations by Professor Deanna Oxender Burgess of Florida Gulf Coast University. Professor Burgess found that even slight distortions in a chart changed readers' perception of the information. The article displayed sales information from the annual report of Zale Corporation and showed how results were exaggerated.

Go to the World Wide Web or the library and study the most recent annual report of a selected corporation. Find at least one chart in the report that you think needs improvement and develop an improved chart. Explain why you believe the improved chart is better than the one included in the annual report.

2.40 Figures 2.1 and 2.3 consist of a bar chart and a pie chart for the online shopping data.

a. Use the Chart Wizard of Microsoft Excel to develop a doughnut chart, a cone chart, and a pyramid chart for the online shopping data.

b. Which graphs do you prefer—the bar chart, the pie chart, and the Pareto diagram or the doughnut chart, a cone chart, and a pyramid chart? Explain.

2.41 Figures 2.2 and 2.4 consist of a bar chart and a pie chart for the risk level for the mutual fund data. MUTUAL-FUNDS2004

a. Use the Chart Wizard of Microsoft Excel to develop a doughnut chart, a cone chart, and a pyramid chart for the risk level of the mutual funds.

b. Which graphs do you prefer—the bar chart and pie chart or the doughnut chart, a cone chart, and a pyramid chart? Explain.

TABLE 2.21

Roadmap for Selecting
Tables and Charts

Type of Analysis	Type of Data	
	Numerical	**Categorical**
Tabulating, organizing, and graphically presenting the values of a variable	Ordered array, stem-and-leaf display, frequency distribution, relative frequency distribution, percentage distribution, cumulative percentage distribution, histogram, polygon, cumulative percentage polygon **(sections 2.2 and 2.3)**	Summary table, bar chart, pie chart, Pareto diagram **(section 2.1)**

CALCULATOR LESSON 1

CASIO FX-9750G OR CFX-9850GB CALCULATOR

Introduction

To install the batteries and make the initial adjustments follow the instructions on the PINK pages inside the front cover of the owner's manual.

The GFX-9850GB has three keyboards:

i. The Primary keyboard
      –indicated on the keys

ii. The **Shift** keyboard
      –indicated in *yellow* above the keys

iii. The **ALPHA** keyboard
      –indicated in *red* above the keys

Common Operations

Clear screen	**AC**/**ON**
Insert	**SHIFT INS**
Delete	**DEL**
Move cursor	**Use cursor arrows**
Erase the last entry	**Use cursor arrow and typeover**
Power (exponent)	^

The function keys F1, F2 . . . F6 directly under the display are used to select functions shown at the bottom of the display at various times.

Calculations

RUN Mode:

Highlight the RUN icon and press **EXE**

or press **1 EXE** when the main menu screen is visible.

Note: If you change your mind about which *mode* you want to select, just press the menu key and this will always return you to the main menu screen.

EXAMPLE 2.21

To calculate the average of 38, 20, 18 and 23:

Enter the following into the calculator:
(38+20+18+23)÷4 EXE   You should get the result 24.75   Try it.

Correcting errors

Inserting: Suppose we should have entered 148 instead of 18 in the example above. Use the replay arrows, i.e. ◄ or ► , to position the cursor at the end or beginning of the previously entered calculation. Move the cursor until it is located under the 8 in 18. The 8 will flash on and off. Press **SHIFT INS**. A square blank cursor will now be flashing on and off. Press **4** followed by **EXE**.

We now have the following calculation:
(38+20+148+23)÷4 EXE   You should get the result 57.25   Try it.

Note: You may insert several digits consecutively without pressing **SHIFT INS** each time. The cursor will be insert mode any time that it appears as a square blank cursor.

Deleting

If, in fact, the original value of 18 is correct, we can delete the 4 as follows. Use the replay cursor followed by any cursor key to position the cursor under the 4. The 4 will flash on and off. Press the **DEL** key followed by **EXE**. We will now get the answer 24.75 of the original calculation.

Using the ANSWER of the Previous Calculation

Suppose we want to add 10 to the previously calculated average. Press + (the word Ans will appear on the display) and **10 EXE**. The result 34.75 will appear.

Now suppose we want to calculate 30/34.75 . Press **30 ÷ SHIFT Ans EXE** and the result 0.8633093525 appears.

Note: The calculator displayed 10 decimals for the answer above, however, it keeps 15 digits internally in case this number is to be used in further calculations. In this way round off errors are not likely to have occurred in the digits shown on the display.

Note: Suppose the calculator has shut off due to being inactive for several minutes, use the **AC/ON** key to turn the calculator back on. Choose the RUN icon and press **EXE** . The screen will be blank. Now press the ▲ cursor key followed by **EXE** and the screen will return to the last calculation that was done when the calculator was last on.

Working with DATA LISTS

LIST Mode:

Press the **MENU** key.

Highlight the LIST icon and press **EXE**

You will now have 6 blank lists set up on the screen. You can only see the Lists 1 to 4 at first, but if you move the ► cursor key you will be able to scroll over to the other 2 lists.

You can enter the data from the first example in List 1 as follows:

38 EXE
20 EXE
18 EXE
23 EXE

Note: If you make a mistake, use the following options on the bottom of the display: (If you are in **STAT mode**, use the F6 key ($\triangleright$) to bring up these options.)

DEL	DEL-A	INS
F3	F4	F5

Now, if you press **F3** you can *delete* a highlighted data value. If you press **F5** you can create a space to *insert* a data value into the list. All other values will shift downward. To *change* a data value just highlight and typeover the old value and then key **EXE**.

Sorting a List

When on the list screen press the **F1** key (if you want to sort a list in ascending order). The calculator will ask you how many lists you want to sort. Answer this and press **EXE** . The calculator will now ask which list(s). Answer this and press **EXE** .

The calculator will immediately sort the list(s) specified.

Deleting a List

To delete a list, place the cursor on any entry in the list and press the **F4** key. The calculator will give you one last chance to change your mind. Delete the highlighted list by answering YES (**F1**).

Error Messages

When you make a syntax error, i.e. you key something that the calculator cannot understand, it tries to point out where the error has occurred. Key in the following:

2 ÷ × 5 – 3 ENTER

The calculator will respond **Syn ERROR** at the bottom of the screen.

Press the left or right cursor arrow and the calculator will return to the calculation and the cursor will be flashing on the entry that is causing the problem.

The SET-UP menu

The SET UP menu allows you to modify the default settings for the calculator. For example, you may want your answer to a series of calculations to have only 2 decimal places (possibly because the numbers represent dollars and cents). In order to FIX the number of decimal places to any calculation result you would get on the main calculation (RUN) screen and press:

SHIFT SETUP then scroll to **DISPLAY** and choose F1 (Fix) then choose the appropriate number of decimal places, in this case **F3** (for 2 decimals). Now press the **EXIT** key to return to the previous screen.

Now key in the following calculation: **2 ÷ 3 EXE** The calculator shows **.67**

To return to the normal 10 digits with floating point, you will have to reenter the **NORM1** setting from the SETUP menu.

CHAPTER REVIEW PROBLEMS

Checking Your Understanding

2.42 How do histograms and polygons differ with respect to their construction and use?

2.43 Why would you construct a summary table?

2.44 What are the advantages and/or disadvantages of using a bar chart, a pie chart, or a Pareto diagram?

2.45 Compare and contrast the bar chart for categorical data with the histogram for numerical data.

2.46 What is the difference between a time-series plot and a scatter diagram?

2.47 Why is it said that the main feature of the Pareto diagram is its ability to separate the "vital few" from the "trivial many"? Discuss.

2.48 What percentage breakdowns can help you interpret the results found in a cross-classification table?

Applying the Concepts

You can solve problems 2.49–2.53 manually or by using Microsoft Excel, Minitab, or SPSS.

2.49 The data below represent the breakdown of the price of a new college textbook.

Revenue Categories	Percentage
Publisher	64.8
Manufacturing costs	32.3
Marketing and promotion	15.4
Administrative costs and taxes	10.0
After-tax profit	7.1
Bookstore	22.4
Employee salaries and benefits	11.3
Operations	6.6
Pretax profit	4.5
Author	11.6
Freight	1.2

Source: Extracted from T. Lewin, "When Books Break the Bank,"
The New York Times, *September 16, 2003, B1, B4.*

a. Using the four categories of publisher, bookstore, author, and freight, construct a bar chart, a pie chart, and a Pareto diagram.

b. Using the four subcategories of publisher and three subcategories of bookstore along with the author and freight categories, construct a Pareto diagram.

c. Based on the results of (a) and (b), what conclusions can you reach concerning who gets the revenue from the sales of new college textbooks? Do any of these results surprise you? Explain.

2.50 The following data represent the market share for the repair of cars and light trucks in 1992 and 2002.

Source	1992 Percentage	2002 Percentage
Foreign specialists	3.9	6.0
Parts stores with service bays	7.3	6.4
Repair specialists	12.7	16.2
Service stations, garages	39.1	29.5
Tire stores	8.1	8.9
Vehicle dealers	21.6	26.6
Others	7.3	6.4

Source: Extracted from A. Frangos, " Corner Garages Battle Dealers to Fix Your Car," The Wall Street Journal, *June 3, 2003, B1, B4.*

a. For each year, construct a bar chart, a pie chart, and a Pareto diagram.

b. Construct a side-by-side bar chart of the market share in 1992 and in 2002.

c. Based on the results of (a) and (b), what changes in market share have occurred between 1992 and 2002?

2.51 The following data represent how consumers made in-store payments in 1999, 2001, and 2003.

Type of Payment	1999 Percentage	2001 Percentage	2003 Percentage
Cash	39	33	32
Check	18	18	15
Debit	21	26	31
Credit	22	21	21
Other	0	2	1

Source: Extracted from M. Ingebretsen and M. Ballinger, "Charge It," The Wall Street Journal, *February 9, 2004, R2.*

a. Construct a side-by-side bar chart of the types of payment in 1999, 2001, and 2003.

b. Based on the results of (a), what changes in the types of payment have occurred in 1999, 2001, and 2003?

2.52 The following data represent the per-capita consumption of beverages (in gallons) sold at retail stores in 1998, 2000, and 2002.

Type of Drink	1998 Consumption	2000 Consumption	2002 Consumption
Bottled water	2.5	4.1	6.7
Dairy/other	0.3	0.3	0.3
Juice drinks	3.1	3.7	4.0
Soft drinks	54.0	53.0	52.5
Sports drinks	1.9	2.2	2.5
Tea	1.9	2.0	1.9
Total	63.7	65.3	67.9

Source: Extracted from T. Howard, "Coke, Pepsi Sales Up, but Core Colas Flat," USA Today, July 21, 2003, 3B.

a. For each year, form a percentage summary table for the types of drinks.
b. For each year, construct a bar chart, a pie chart, and a Pareto diagram.
c. Construct a side-by-side bar chart of the market share of the types of drinks in 1998, 2000, and 2002.
d. Based on the results of (a) through (c), what changes in market share have occurred between 1998 and 2002?

2.53 Brazil is the second-largest coffee consuming country in the world. Unlike most major markets where a handful of corporations dominate the coffee roasting and selling market, over 2,000 small roasters are active in Brazil. The Sara Lee Corporation has become the leading coffee retailer in Brazil by acquiring several Brazilian coffee roasters (Miriam Jordan, "Sara Lee Wants to Percolate through All of Brazil," *The Wall Street Journal*, May 8, 2002, A14). Consumption by the seven largest coffee-consuming nations and a breakdown of the market leaders in Brazil are given below.

Coffee Consumption in Major Markets in 2000	
Country	Consumption (in Millions of 60-Kg Bags)
United States	18.6
Brazil	12.8
Germany	9.2
Japan	6.7
France	5.4
Netherlands	1.8
Finland	0.9

Source: Extracted from The Wall Street Journal.

Leading Coffee Brands in Brazil	
Brand	Market Share
Sara Lee owned brands	27.6%
Nescafe	6.1%
Tres Coracoes	4.8%
Melitta	4.0%
All Others	57.5%

Source: Extracted from The Wall Street Journal.

a. Construct a graph for the data concerning the major coffee-consuming countries. Which type of graph is most appropriate? Explain.
b. Construct a graph for the data concerning the market share of coffee in Brazil. Which type of graph is most appropriate? Explain.

WEB CASE

In the "Using Statistics" scenario, you were asked to gather information that would help you make wise investment choices. Sources for such information include brokerage firms and investment counselors. Apply your knowledge about the proper use of tables and charts in this Web Case about the claims of foresight and excellence by a Springville investment service.

Visit the StockTout Investing Service Web site **www. prenhall.com/Springville/StockToutHome.htm**. Review their investment claims and supporting data and then answer the following.

1. How does the presentation of the general information about StockTout on its home page affect your perception of their business?

2. Is their claim about having more winners than losers a fair and accurate reflection about the quality of their investment service? If you do not think that the claim is a fair and accurate one, provide an alternate presentation that you think is fair and accurate.

3. StockTout's "Big Eight" mutual funds are part of the sample found in the MUTUALFUNDS2004 file. Is there any other relevant data from that file that could have been included in the Big Eight table? How would that new data alter your perception of StockTout's claims?

4. StockTout is proud that all "Big Eight" funds have gained in value over the past five years. Do you agree that they should be proud of their selections? Why or why not?

REFERENCES

1. Huff, D., *How to Lie with Statistics* (New York: Norton, 1954).
2. *Microsoft Excel 2003* (Redmond, WA: Microsoft Corporation, 2002).
3. *Minitab for Windows Version* 14 (State College; PA: Minitab Inc., 2004).
4. *SPSS ® Base 12.0 Brief Guide* (Upper Saddle River, NJ: Prentice Hall, 2003).
5. Tufte, E. R., *Envisioning Information* (Cheshire, CT: Graphics Press, 1990).
6. Tufte, E. R., *The Visual Display of Quantitative Information*, 2nd ed (Cheshire, CT: Graphics Press, 2002).
7. Tufte, E. R., *Visual Explanations* (Cheshire, CT: Graphics Press, 1997).
8. Wainer, H., *Visual Revelations: Graphical Tales of Fate and Deception from Napoleon Bonaparte to Ross Perot* (New York: Copernicus/Springer Verlag, 1997)

TABLE 2.22

2001 Census of Population (46 Large Urban Centres, Census Tracts (neighbourhoods))

2001 Population by Age and Sex—Toronto (932 areas)		
Characteristic:	**0001.00**	**0002.00**
Population, 1996 (100% data)	695	563
Population, 2001 (100% data)	626	658
Male, total population	345	320
0–4 years, Male population	15	10
5–9 years, Male population	25	20
10–14 years, Male population	20	40
15–19 years, Male population	20	30
20–24 years, Male population	30	10
25–29 years, Male population	40	10
30–34 years, Male population	40	15
35–39 years, Male population	40	15
40–44 years, Male population	30	25
45–49 years, Male population	35	35
50–54 years, Male population	15	50
55–59 years, Male population	15	30
60–64 years, Male population	10	10
65–69 years, Male population	5	5
70–74 years, Male population	10	10
75–79 years, Male population	0	10
80–84 years, Male population	0	0
85+ years, Male population	0	0

TABLE 2.23

Profile of Income of Individuals, Families and Households, Social and Economic Characteristics of Individuals, Families and Households, Housing Costs, and Religion, for Census Metropolitan Areas[1] and Census Agglomerations, 2001 Census

Toronto	
Title	**Count**
Census family income in 2000 of all families—20% Sample Data	1,280,960
Under $10,000	64,190
$ 10,000–$19,999	66,645
$ 20,000–$29,999	112,350
$ 30,000–$39,999	120,075
$ 40,000–$49,999	119,000
$ 50,000–$59,999	113,210
$ 60,000–$69,999	111,850
$ 70,000–$79,999	100,170
$ 80,000–$89,999	86,690
$ 90,000–$99,999	73,065
$100,000 and over	313,720
Average family income $	81,245
Median family income $	63,700

TABLE 2.24

Profile of Income of Individuals, Families and Households, Social and Economic Characteristics of Individuals, Families and Households, Housing Costs, and Religion, for Census Metropolitan Areas[1] and Census Agglomerations, 2001 Census

Title	Count
Total income in 2000 of population 15 years and over—20% Sample Data	3,728,980
Without income	214,230
With income	3,514,750
Under $1,000	168,025
$ 1,000–$ 2,999	159,175
$ 3,000–$ 4,999	132,710
$ 5,000–$ 6,999	136,835
$ 7,000–$ 9,999	188,715
$10,000–$11,999	142,605
$12,000–$14,999	223,650
$15,000–$19,999	288,290
$20,000–$24,999	262,395
$25,000–$29,999	247,090
$30,000–$34,999	267,745
$35,000–$39,999	217,710
$40,000–$44,999	198,250
$45,000–$49,999	141,795
$50,000–$59,999	228,750
$60,000 and over	511,015

TABLE 2.25

Number of Children at Home (8) and Family Structure (7) for Census Families in Private Profile of Marital Status, Common-law Status, Families, Dwellings and Households, for Census Metropolitan Areas and Census Agglomerations, 2001 Census

Toronto	
Title	**Count**
Total number of children at home—20% Sample Data	1,641,660
Under 6 years of age	351,595
6–14 years	560,230
15–17 years	178,705
18–24 years	326,785
25 years and over	224,345
Total number of private households by household size—100% Data	1,634,755
1 person	360,870
2 persons	448,290
3 persons	288,305
4-5 persons	451,485
6 or more persons	85,805

TABLE 2.26

Family units' by net worth group and age

	1999					
Data including employer-sponsored registered pension plans	**Age of the individual/family unit member with the highest pre-tax income**					
	Total	**Under 35**	**35–44**	**45–54**	**55–64**	**65 and older**
	%					
All family units' net worth groups	**100.0**	**100.0**	**100.0**	**100.0**	**100.0**	**100.0**
Negative	5.9	15.2	4.8	x	x	x
Less than $5,000	9.3	17.0	7.7	5.6	7.1	6.3
$5,000 to $14,999	8.0	15.3	7.3	4.5	x	5.1
$15,000 to $29,999	5.7	9.2	6.6	3.7	x	3.4
$30,000 to $49,999	6.4	9.2	7.5	4.8	x	4.5
$50,000 to $74,999	7.3	9.1	9.1	5.7	x	6.0
$75,000 to $99,999	5.6	5.7	7.2	5.3	x	4.3
$100,000 to $149,999	8.9	6.5	12.8	9.0	6.2	8.6
$150,000 to $249,999	13.4	5.9	16.4	15.8	13.0	17.7
$250,000 to $499,999	16.1	4.6	13.8	24.3	20.5	23.9
$500,000 to $999,999	9.3	x	5.0	13.4	21.3	13.7
$1,000,000 and over	4.0	x	1.8	5.0	10.5	6.0

x Data unavailable, not applicable or confidential.
1. Family units: economic families (a group of two or more persons who live in the same dwelling and are related to each other by blood, marriage, common law or adoption) and unattached individuals (a person living either alone or with others to whom he or she is unrelated).
Source: Statistics Canada, Survey of Financial Security.

TABLE 2.27

Profile of Labour Force Activity, Class of Worker, Occupation, Industry, Place of Work, Mode of Transportation, Language of Work and Unpaid Work, for Census Metropolitan Areas and Census Agglomerations, 2001 Census

Title	Count
Total population 15 years and over by hours spent doing unpaid housework—20% Sample Data	3,728,980
No hours of unpaid housework	439,155
Less than 5 hours of unpaid housework	977,565
5 to 14 hours of unpaid housework	1,205,890
15 to 29 hours of unpaid housework	662,550
30 to 59 hours of unpaid housework	315,790
60 hours or more of unpaid housework	128,030

CHAPTER 3

Numerical Descriptive Measures

USING STATISTICS: Evaluating the Performance of Mutual Funds

LEARNING OBJECTIVES

In this chapter, you learn:

- To describe the properties of central tendency, variation, and shape in numerical data
- To calculate descriptive summary measures for a population
- To construct and interpret a box-and-whisker plot
- To describe the covariance and the coefficient of correlation

USING STATISTICS

Evaluating the Performance of Mutual Funds

Return to the study of mutual funds introduced in Chapter 2. You want to decide which types of mutual funds to invest in. In the last chapter you learned how to *present* data in tables and charts. However, when dealing with numerical data, such as the return on investments in mutual funds in 2003, you also need to summarize the data, and ask statistical questions. What is the central tendency for returns of the various funds? For example, what is the mean return in 2003 for the low-risk, average-risk, and high-risk mutual funds? How much variability is present in the returns? Are the returns for high-risk funds more variable than for average-risk funds or low-risk funds? How can you use this information when deciding what mutual funds to invest in?

F̲or numerical variables, you need more than just the visual picture of what a variable looks like than you get from the graphs discussed in Chapter 2. For example, for the 2003 returns, you would like to determine not only whether the riskier funds had a higher 2003 return, but whether they also had greater variation, and how the returns for each risk group were distributed. You also want to examine whether there is a relationship between the expense ratio and the 2003 return. Reading this chapter will allow you to learn about some of the methods to measure:

- **central tendency**, the extent to which all of the data values group around a central value
- **variation**, the amount of dispersion or scattering of values away from a central value
- **shape**, the pattern of the distribution of values from the lowest value to the highest value

You will also learn about the covariance and the coefficient of correlation that help measure the strength of the association between two numerical variables.

3.1 DESCRIPTIVE STATISTICS 1: MEASURES OF CENTRAL TENDENCY

You can characterize any set of numerical data by measuring its central tendency, variation, and shape. Most sets of data show a distinct central tendency to group around a central value. When people talk about an "average value" or the "middle value" or the most popular or frequent value, they are talking informally about the mean, median, and mode, three measures of central tendency.

Variation measures the **spread** or **dispersion** of values in a data set. One simple measure of variation is the range, the difference between the highest and lowest value. More commonly used in statistics are the standard deviation and variance, two measures explained later in this section. The shape of a data set represents a pattern of all the values from the lowest to highest value. As you will learn later in this section, many data sets have a pattern that looks approximately like a bell, with a peak of values somewhere in the middle.

Descriptive statistics are numbers calculated to describe various aspects of a data set. The two most important types of descriptive statistics are:

Measures of Central Tendency: A single value to represent the data set.
Measures of Variability: A single value to describe how spread out the data is.

In this section we will learn how to calculate various measures of central tendency and also how to calculate a measure of position, which is a related topic.

Mean

I: Arithmetic Mean (Average)

Symbol: Sample $\bar{x}$ Population μ

Formula: $\bar{x} = \dfrac{\sum x}{n}$ $\mu = \dfrac{\sum x}{N}$

where: x = data

n = sample size

N = population size

$\sum$ = summation   therefore $\sum x$ = add up the data

EXAMPLE 3.1

A fast food franchise has many outlets across the country. One small restaurant in the city where you live has seven full-time employees who earn $38, 20, 20, 18, 18, 18 and 23 thousand annually. Calculate the average salary of these employees.

Solution: $\bar{x} = \dfrac{\sum x}{n} = \dfrac{38 + 20 + 20 + 18 + 18 + 18 + 23}{7} = \$22.1$ thou. per employee

Note: Regarding the form of the answer, use one more figure than the data if the data has 1 or 2 figures. Otherwise, the answer should look like the data.

e.g. If data is: 234, 315 and 484   then $\bar{x} = 344$

II: Weighted Mean

EXAMPLE 3.2

The salaries of all the employees in the outlets in the city where you live can be summarized in the following table:

TABLE 3.1

Job Classification	Number of Employees	Annual Salary ($000's)
Senior Management	3	52
Middle Management	10	38
Cooking Staff	45	20
Serving Staff	74	18
Maintenance Staff	7	23

Calculate the average salary of these employees.

Solution: In this example the salary figures again need to be averaged. However, we realize that it would be incorrect to add the figures and divide by 5 since this would only be correct if there were an equal number of employees in each category. To take into account the differing number of employees in each category, we must use the **Weighted** method to calculate the mean salary. Many textbooks call the result of this calculation, the **Weighted Mean.**

The formula for the weighted mean is as follows:

$$\bar{x} = \frac{\sum wx}{\sum w}$$

where x = data

w – weights i.e. numbers to indicate the relative importance of each data value in the overall result

In this example:

x = the salaries

w = the number of employees.

$$\bar{x} = \frac{\sum wx}{\sum w} = \frac{3 \times 52 + 10 \times 38 + 45 \times 20 + 74 \times 18 + 7 \times 23}{3 + 10 + 45 + 74 + 7}$$

$$= \frac{2929}{139} = \$21.1 \text{ thou. per employee}$$

Note: This formula also is 'logical' in that the denominator is 139, which is the total number of employees.

Sometimes the *relative frequency* or *percentages* are used as weights.

EXAMPLE 3.3

A Cruise ship does several week-long cruises during a year. The ship is not always fully occupied. There are three types of cabins on this particular ship: interior (no port hole), deluxe exterior (porthole), and luxury exterior (private balcony). The price for each type of cabin and estimated percent of passengers in each type of cabin for the next cruise is shown below.

TABLE 3.2

Cabin Style	Price for each Person ($)	Percent of Passengers
Interior	1900	40
Deluxe exterior	2400	45
Luxury exterior	3200	15

Calculate the average revenue per person earned by the cruise company.

Solution: In this example:

$$x = \text{the price for each person}$$

$$w = \text{the percentages.}$$

$$\bar{x} = \frac{\sum wx}{\sum w} = \frac{40 \times 1900 + 45 \times 2400 + 15 \times 3200}{40 + 45 + 15}$$

$$= \frac{232000}{100} = \$2,320 \text{ per person.}$$

There are two other common scenarios where the weighted mean is necessary.

a) Data to be averaged are themselves *averages*.
b) Data to be averaged are *percentages*.

EXAMPLE 3.4

ILLUSTRATION OF (A)

A car manufacturing company has assembly lines in four plants. Some data regarding the car production on these assembly lines for the past week are shown below.

TABLE 3.3

Production Line	Number of Cars Produced	Average time per car (minutes)
Toronto	134	257
Montreal	105	248
Calgary	97	272
Vancouver	82	286

Calculate the overall average production time for all these cars.

Solution: In this example:

$$x = \text{the average times}$$

$$w = \text{the number of cars.}$$

$$\bar{x} = \frac{\sum wx}{\sum w} = \frac{134 \times 257 + 105 \times 248 + 97 \times 272 + 82 \times 286}{134 + 105 + 97 + 82}$$

$$= \frac{110314}{418} = 264 \text{ min. per car}$$

EXAMPLE 3.5   ILLUSTRATION OF (B)

The following data refers to three divisions of a medium sized business.

TABLE 3.4

Division	Profit Margin (%)	Sales ($ millions)
A	5	10
B	6	5
C	7	35

Calculate the overall average profit margin for the three divisions.

Solution: In this example:

$$x = \text{the profit margin}$$
$$w = \text{the sales.}$$

$$\bar{x} = \frac{\sum wx}{\sum w} = \frac{10 \times 5 + 5 \times 6 + 35 \times 7}{10 + 5 + 35}$$

$$= \frac{325}{50} = 6.5\% \ \ (\text{per division})$$

One final scenario involving the calculating of a mean is also common.

III: Another Type of Mean

EXAMPLE 3.6   In a particular province there are three provincial parks. The Ministry of Natural Resources is interested in the concentration of moose in these parks. The results of a survey yielded the following data.

TABLE 3.5

Provincial Park	Number of Moose	Area of park (km^2)
Moose Forest	134	2575
Moose Swamp	105	2037
Moosonee	97	2892

Calculate the overall average number of moose per square kilometer.

Solution

$$\bar{x} = \frac{\sum moose}{\sum area} = \frac{134 + 105 + 97}{2575 + 2037 + 2892}$$

$$= \frac{336}{7504} = 0.0448 \ \text{moose per km}^2.$$

Note: When no other rule applies to the result of a particular calculation, we will use a general rule of **3 significant digits** (or more if the zeros are to the left of the decimal point).

The arithmetic mean is by far the most important measure of central tendency.

IV: Grouped data—Mean
Suppose the only data available to us is in the form of a frequency or relative frequency (or percentage) distribution. Then in order to estimate the mean of the data we need to use the **class midpoints** to represent all the values in each class. We then use the weighted method to calculate the mean where the frequencies or relative frequencies will be the appropriate weights.

EXAMPLE 3.7   On a particular Saturday the amount paid for parking in a small downtown parking lot has been summarized in the following table:

TABLE 3.6

Cost of Parking ($)	f	%	m
2.00 and under 4.00	20	18.3	3.00
4.00 " " 6.00	37	33.9	5.00
6.00 " " 10.00	29	26.6	8.00
10.00 " " 15.00	15	13.8	12.50
15.00 " " 20.00	8	7.3	17.50
Total	109	99.9	

Estimate the mean amount paid for parking.

Solution:

a) Using the frequencies as weights: (Note the symbols in the formula)

$$\bar{x} = \frac{\sum fm}{\sum f} = \frac{20 \times 3.00 + 37 \times 5.00 + 29 \times 8.00 + 15 \times 12.50 + 8 \times 17.50}{20 + 37 + 29 + 15 + 8}$$

$$= \frac{804.50}{109} = \$7.38 \text{ per customer.}$$

b) Using the percentages as weights:

$$\bar{x} = \frac{\sum \%m}{\sum \%}$$

$$= \frac{18.3 \times 3.00 + 33.9 \times 5.00 + 26.6 \times 8.00 + 13.8 \times 12.50 + 7.3 \times 17.50}{18.3 + 33.9 + 26.6 + 13.8 + 7.3}$$

$$= \frac{737.45}{99.9} = \$7.38 \text{ per customer.}$$

CALCULATOR LESSON 2

CASIO FX-9750G OR CFX-9850GB CALCULATOR

Lesson 2—Calculations using Lists

STAT Mode:

Press the **MENU** key

Highlight the STAT Icon and press **EXE**

You will now have 6 blank lists set up on the screen. You can only see List 1 to List 4 at first, but if you move the ▶ cursor key you will be able to scroll over to the other 2 lists.

You can enter the data from the Example 3.1 in Section 3.1 in List 1 as follows:

38 EXE
20 EXE
20 EXE
18 EXE
18 EXE
18 EXE
23 EXE

EXAMPLE 3.1
(Revisited)

To calculate the average of the salary data, use the **F6** key (▷) if necessary to get the following menu choices at the bottom of the display:

GRPH	CALC	TEST	INTR	DIST	▷
F1	F2	F3	F4	F5	F6

Now press **F2** (CALC) and you will get the following on-screen menu items:

1 VAR	2 VAR	REG			SET
F1	F2	F3			F6

Now press **F6** (SET) and you will get the following display:

1 Var	XList	:	List1
1 Var	Freq	:	1
2 Var	Xlist	:	List1
2 Var	YList	:	List2
2 Var	Freq	:	1

List 1	List 2	List 3	List 4	List 5	List 6

The first row will be highlighted. Use the appropriate **F** key to select the desired list for your 1Var XList. In this case you want **F1** (List 1). (As you are just starting, List 1 should already be indicated next to 1Var XList.) You also want to have the 1Var Freq as **F1** (1). (As you are just starting, 1 (one) should already be indicated next to 1Var Freq.) Now press **EXIT** to return to the display of the data.

Now press **F1** (1 VAR) and a full range of 1-variable statistics will appear. The result $\bar{x} = 22.1428$ will be at the top of the list.

Now press **EXIT** to return to the data list display.

Weighted Data

Recall from the Measures of Central Tendency lecture notes that in example 3.2 we needed to calculate the mean salary for the following group of people:

TABLE 3.7

Job Classification	Number of Employees	Annual Salary ($000's)
Senior Management	3	52
Middle management	10	38
Cooking Staff	45	20
Serving Staff	74	18
Maintenance Staff	7	23

Enter the values for the annual salary in List 1 and the corresponding values for the number of employees in List 2. The following keystrokes will calculate the **weighted** statistics:

Now enter the salaries **52 EXE** **38 EXE** **20 EXE** **18 EXE** **23 EXE** under List 1.

Position the cursor at the top of List 2. Now enter the weights (frequencies)
3 EXE **10 EXE** **45 EXE** **74 EXE** **7 EXE**

Now press **F2** (CALC) **F6** (SET)

Highlight 1Var XList: and choose List 1 (**F1** if necessary). Then highlight 1Var Freq: and choose List 2 (**F3** if necessary). Now press **EXIT**.

Press **F1** (1 VAR) and a full range of 1-variable weighted statistics will appear. The result $\bar{x} = 21.0719$ will be at the top of the list. That is, the average salary is $21.1 thou as we saw in the notes on measures of central tendency.

EXAMPLE 3.9

THE MEAN 2003 RETURN FOR SMALL CAP MUTUAL FUNDS WITH HIGH RISK

The 121 mutual funds that are part of the "Using Statistics" scenario (see page 64) are classified according to the risk level of the mutual funds (low, average, and high) and type (small cap, mid cap, and large cap). Compute the mean 2003 return for the small cap mutual funds with high risk.

SOLUTION The mean 2003 return for the small cap mutual funds with high risk (MUTUALFUNDS2004) is 51.53, calculated as follows:

$$\bar{X} = \frac{\text{sum of the values}}{\text{number of values}}$$

$$= \frac{\sum_{i=1}^{n} X_i}{n}$$

$$= \frac{463.8}{9} = 51.53$$

The ordered array for the nine small cap mutual funds with high risk is:

37.3 39.2 44.2 44.5 53.8 56.6 59.3 62.4 66.5

Four of these returns are below the mean of 51.53 and five of these returns are above the mean.

Median

Symbol: Sample or population $\tilde{x}$

The technical definition of the median is that it is the value such that at most 50% of the data values are less than the median and at most 50% of the data values are more than the median In other words, the median occupies the *middle position* of the data after it is sorted into an **order array,** either ascending or descending

Let i = the position of the median

To calculate i we use: $i = \dfrac{n+1}{2}$

Once 'i' is calculated there are two possibilities regarding how to determine the median of a data set.

EXAMPLE 3.10   THERE IS AN EVEN NUMBER OF DATA VALUES

The following data represents the ages, in years, of 20 employees working at a retail outlet

63, 52, 38, 20, 21, 18, 29, 28, 45, 40, 24, 25, 22, 20, 29, 20, 18, 20, 18, 22

The corresponding **data array** in ascending order is:

18, 18, 18, 20, 20, 20, 20, 21, 22, 22, 24, 25, 28, 29, 29, 38, 40, 45, 52, 63

The **position** of the median is: $i = \dfrac{n+1}{2} = \dfrac{20+1}{2} = 10.5$ th position

Therefore, the median is: $\tilde{x} = \dfrac{10\text{th value} + 11\text{th value}}{2} = \dfrac{22+24}{2} = 23$ years

Note: The mean is $\bar{x} = 28.6$ years. The mean is higher than the median because most of the data is in the 18 to 29 range, with a few larger values which will have the effect of increasing the mean.

EXAMPLE 3.11   THERE IS AN ODD NUMBER OF DATA VALUES

The following data represents the ages, in years, of 17 employees working at a retail outlet

63, 52, 38, 20, 21, 18, 29, 28, 45, 40, 24, 25, 22, 20, 29, 20, 18

The corresponding **data array** in ascending order is:

18, 18, 20, 20, 20, 21, 22, 24, 25, 28, 29, 29, 38, 40, 45, 52, 63

The **position** of the median is: $i = \dfrac{n+1}{2} = \dfrac{17+1}{2} = 9$th position

Therefore, the median is: $\tilde{x} = 9$ th value $= 25$ years

---

The following examples show situations that illustrate when the median might be the preferred number to represent a data set, i.e. when the median is preferred over the mean.

EXAMPLE 3.12

The following data represents the prices of houses sold last week in a particular neighbourhood. The data has been put into an array.

$200,000   205,000   210,000   220,000   225,000

a) If you read that the mean house price in this neighbourhood was

$$\bar{x} = \$212,000$$

then you would get a certain impression as to the size, and type of the *typical* house in the neighbourhood.

b) If you read that the median house price in this neighbourhood was

$$\tilde{x} = \$210,000$$

then you would get the same impression as to the size and type of the *typical* house in the neighbourhood.

Conclusion: If the mean and median are **close**, then the **mean** will give the correct impression and is the preferred measure.

EXAMPLE 3.13

The following data represents the prices of houses sold last week in a particular neighbourhood. The data has been put into an array.

$200,000   205,000   210,000   220,000   425,000

a) If you read that the mean house price in this neighbourhood was

$$\bar{x} = \$252,000$$

then you would get a certain impression as to the size and type of the *typical* house in the neighbourhood.

b) If you read that the median house price in this neighbourhood was

$$\tilde{x} = \$210,000$$

then you would get a different impression as to the size and type of the *typical* house in the neighbourhood.

Conclusion: If the mean and median are **not close**, then the **median** will give the correct impression. The reason why the mean and the median were not close, was the fact that the data set had **unbalanced extreme values.**

10% rule:

To help you determine if the mean and median are really different use the following rule:

Calculate the 'difference' between the mean and median.
Calculate '10% of the smaller' of the mean or median.
If Difference < 10% of smaller conclude $\bar{x} = \tilde{x}$ in which case the *mean* is the preferred measure.
If Difference > 10% of smaller conclude $\bar{x} \neq \tilde{x}$ in which case the *median* is the preferred measure.

EXAMPLE 3.12 *(revisit)*	DIFFERENCE = 2,000 < 10% OF SMALLER = 21,000
EXAMPLE 3.13 *(revisit)*	DIFFERENCE = 42,000 > 10% OF SMALLER = 21,000

The Mode

The **mode** is the value in a set of data that appears most frequently. Like the median and unlike the mean, extreme values do not affect the mode. You should use the mode only for descriptive purposes as it is more variable from sample to sample than either the mean or the median. Often there is no mode or there are several modes in a set of data. For example, consider the time to get ready data shown below.

$$29 \quad 31 \quad 35 \quad 39 \quad 39 \quad 40 \quad 43 \quad 44 \quad 44 \quad 52$$

There are two modes, 39 minutes and 44 minutes, since each of these values occurs twice.

EXAMPLE 3.14

COMPUTING THE MODE

A systems manager in charge of a company's network keeps track of the number of server failures that occur in a day. Compute the mode for the following data that represents the number of server failures in a day for the past two weeks.

$$1 \quad 3 \quad 0 \quad 3 \quad 26 \quad 2 \quad 7 \quad 4 \quad 0 \quad 2 \quad 3 \quad 3 \quad 6 \quad 3$$

SOLUTION The ordered array for these data is

$$0 \quad 0 \quad 1 \quad 2 \quad 2 \quad 3 \quad 3 \quad 3 \quad 3 \quad 3 \quad 4 \quad 6 \quad 7 \quad 26$$

Because 3 appears five times, more times than any other value, the mode is 3. Thus, the systems manager can say that the most common occurrence is having three server failures in a day. For this data set, the median is also equal to 3 while the mean is equal to 4.5. The extreme value 26 is an outlier. For these data, the median and the mode better measure central tendency than the mean.

A set of data will have no mode if none of the values is "most typical." Example 3.15 presents a data set with no mode.

EXAMPLE 3.15

DATA WITH NO MODE

Compute the mode for the 2003 return for the small cap mutual funds with high risk.
MUTUALFUNDS2004

SOLUTION The ordered array for these data is

$$37.3 \quad 39.2 \quad 44.2 \quad 44.5 \quad 53.8 \quad 56.6 \quad 59.3 \quad 62.4 \quad 66.5$$

These data have no mode. None of the values is most typical because each value appears once.

Measures of Position

So far we have seen several measures of the 'centre' of a data set. Sometimes we are interested in the relative 'position' of a data value in a data set. There are several ways to determine position in a data set. One way involves the calculation of a percentile.

Percentiles:

$$\text{Symbol} \qquad P_k = k^{th} \text{ percentile}$$

The kth percentile in a data set is the value such that at most k% of the data is lower than the value and at most $(100 - k)\%$ of the data is higher than the value.

There are three steps involved in calculating percentile value.

i.   Arrange the data into an *ascending* data array.
ii. Calculate the position of the kth percentile using $i - \dfrac{nk}{100}$ and then making certain adjust-ments

At this point it would beneficial to demonstrate the calculation of various percentiles by refer-ring to a specific example.

EXAMPLE 3.16

The following data represents the ages, in years, of 20 employees working at a retail outlet. The data has already been arranged in an ascending data array.

18, 18, 18, 20, 20, 20, 20, 21, 22, 22, 24, 25, 28, 29, 29, 38, 40, 45, 52, 63

a) Determine the 80th percentile.

$$i = \frac{nk}{100} = \frac{(20)(80)}{100} = 16 \quad \text{therefore } i = 16.5 \qquad \text{(i.e. add 0.5 when (nk/100) is a whole number.)}$$

$$\text{therefore } P_{80} = \frac{16th \text{ value} + 17th \text{ value}}{2} = \frac{38 + 40}{2} = 39 \text{ years}$$

b) Determine the 34th percentile.

$$i = \frac{nk}{100} = \frac{(20)(34)}{100} = 6.8 \quad \text{therefore } i = 7 \qquad \text{(i.e. round \textbf{UP} when (nk/100) is a fraction.)}$$

$$\text{therefore } P_{34} = 7th \text{ value} = 20 \text{ years}$$

c) Determine the 61st percentile.

$$i = \frac{nk}{100} = \frac{(20)(61)}{100} = 12.2 \quad \text{therefore } i = 13 \qquad \text{(i.e. round \textbf{UP} when (nk/100) is a fraction.)}$$

$$\text{therefore } P_{61} = 13th \text{ value} = 28 \text{ years}$$

Quartiles:

Some of the percentiles have special names. These are

$$P_{25} = Q_1 = 1^{st} \text{ quartile}$$
$$P_{50} = Q_2 = 2^{nd} \text{ quartile} = \text{the median}$$
$$P_{75} = Q_3 = 3^{rd} \text{ quartile}$$

We will use the calculator to give us the values of the quartiles. (Note: The calculator does NOT use the same method of calculating percentiles as shown above.)

Refer to Example 3.16:

From the calculator we get:

$$Q_1 = 20 \text{ years} \quad \text{and} \quad Q_3 = 33.5 \text{ years}$$

PROBLEMS FOR SECTION 3.1

Descriptive Statistics: Set 1

3.1 A company has invited its entire human resources staff from each office across the country to attend a conference at the head office in Toronto. The following information is available:

Office	Return Airfare	# of Offices	# of HR Staff per Office
Calgary	$400	2	4
Halifax	350	1	2
Montreal	330	2	3
Ottawa	300	2	3
Vancouver	500	3	5

a. What is the median return airfare per office?
b. What is the mean return airfare per person?

3.2 The following sample data was obtained at 8:00 pm at a popular downtown restaurant. There were 15 tables occupied at that time.

Number of guests at the table	Food Bill for the table ($)	Liquor Bill for the table ($)
2	48.75	15.75
2	36.75	26.00
4	90.55	22.90
4	87.45	42.45
2	41.25	14.00
4	83.30	29.75
6	109.40	44.05
4	88.25	21.55
4	93.45	22.00
2	36.50	16.45
2	42.60	18.00
4	105.80	37.57
4	84.65	18.95
5	110.35	43.95
4	83.55	22.50

a. What is the 40th percentile table liquor bill?
b. What was the average food bill for the 15 tables?
c. How much did the average person spend on food?
d. In order to be in the top 32% of the amount spent on food, a table would have to spend at least what amount?

3.3 A referendum was held on a particular issue affecting the GTA Megacity. The following table shows the results.

Municipality	Number of votes	% in Favour
City of Toronto	482,000	45
East York	152,000	63
North York	365,000	27
Etobicoke	298,000	48
Scarborough	456,000	33

a. What was the overall percent in favour of the issue?

3.4 A specialty bookstore concentrates mainly on selling used books and magazines. Paperbacks sell for $1.00 each, hardcover books are $5.00 each and magazines sell for $0.50 each. Of the 50 books sold on Tuesday, 40 were paperback and the remainder were hardcover. They also sold 15 magazines. What was the mean price per item sold?

3.5 Rye Pizza sells soft drinks in three sizes: small, medium and large. The small size costs $0.75, the medium is $0.90 and the large is $1.15 . On a typical weekday 25% of the soft drinks sold are small, 45% are medium and 30% are large. What is the typical daily mean price per soft drink sold?

3.6 A particular oak dining table requires time in three manufacturing stages: 2 hours of cutting, 4 hours of assembly, and 6 hours of finishing. The wood-cutters are paid $10 per hour, the assemblers get $15 per hour and the finishers get $20 per hour. What is the average hourly labour cost to manufacture one table?

3.7 The personnel director at recovery Hospital wanted a study made of overtime hours and associated costs of the nurses. Ten(10) nurses were randomly selected and the following data was obtained for August.

Nurse	O/T Hours	Pay ($/hr)	Nurse	O/T Hours	Pay ($/hr)
1	13	35	6	15	25
2	13	35	7	5	30
3	12	20	8	12	35
4	15	25	9	6	30
5	7	30	10	7	25

a. What was the average number of hours of overtime worked per nurse?
b. What was the average hourly overtime pay rate per nurse?
c. What was the average pay per hour of overtime?

3.8 The following table shows some data regarding the top 4 chains of toy stores. For the chains and stores in this table:

Chain	# of Stores	Average Sales/Store ($ 000)
Toys 'R' Us	144	7,236
Child World	79	3,582
Kay bee	361	507
Lionel	56	3,232

a. What is the average sales of a toy store?
b. What is the mean sales of the 4 toy store chains?
c. Data regarding several retail chains is shown in the table below. What is the overall % gain in sales for the chains shown?

Company/ Chain	Sales (000,000)	% Gain (Loss)	Number of Stores	% Gain (Loss)
Radio Shack	$1,515	28	4,398	7
Mervyn's	1,336	26	92	15
Toys 'R' Us	1,042	33	144	20
Marshall's	830	35	137	27
Saks Fifth Avenue	710	2	34	6
Lerners	682	(4)	790	3
Nordstrum	613	17	36	6

3.9 The table below shows data dealing with product liability.

Liability Category Claim	Injured Party	# of persons receiving Payment	% of persons receiving Payment	% of total Payment	Average payment per person
Bodily Injury	Employee	875	10.6	42.0	$97,884
	Purchaser	5,562	67.5	28.7	10,544
	User	1,441	17.5	22.5	31,836
	Other	364	4.4	6.8	38,016
Property Damage	Employee	12	0.2	0.0	$ 325
	Purchaser	3,928	78.7	64.3	4,372
	User	359	7.2	22.8	22,468
	Employee	695	3.9	12.9	6,176

a. What was the average payment to a person who suffered bodily injury?
b. What was the average payment to a purchaser involved in all type of claims?

3.10 An extensive study was conducted to determine whether there are differences in the characteristics of holiday travellers that are less than 50 years old as compared to those that are more than 50 years old. One of the items of interest was the amount spent for a one-day trip. The results are shown below:

Cost of One-day Trip	Under 50 years old (n = 480)	Over 50 years old (n = 325)
$ 0 and under 50	2%	1%
50 " " 100	7	5
100 " " 200	12	9
200 " " 300	20	13
300 " " 400	29	20
400 " " 500	18	17
500 " " 750	6	14
750 " " 1000	3	10
1000 " " 2000	2	7
2000 " " 3000	1	4

a. For which group of travellers, if any, would the median be a better measure of central tendency than the mean?

b. For the under 50 group, 360 of those surveyed would have spent less than $____.?

3.11 Based on the data in the following table:

a. What is the overall average tobacco sales revenue per person?

b. What is the mean amount of federal tax per state?

c. Would the mean or median better represent the state tobacco taxes?

d. Which state(s) had the 60th percentile federal tobacco taxes?

	Under-Age Smoking			
	Number of smokers under 18 years old	State tobacco taxes ($millions)	Federal tobacco taxes ($millions)	Sales revenue ($millions)
California	300,000	20.6	11.8	125.0
New York	190,000	14.6	7.4	78.2
Texas	200,000	16.6	8.0	76.0
Illinois	130,000	7.8	5.2	49.2
Florida	125,000	8.4	5.0	49.2
Pennsylvania	130,000	8.0	5.2	47.8
Ohio	125,000	4.6	5.0	43.6
Michigan	110,000	5.6	4.4	41.0
New Jersey	85,000	6.6	3.4	33.2
Alabama	50,000	2.8	3.4	31.4

3.12 The following is a portion of a table that appeared in the Dec. 1, 2002 issue of the Toronto Star.

Cancer surgery wait Times

In 2002, the average wait time for cancer surgery at the Princess Margaret Hospital and University Health Network was 54 days. This is an increase from 43 days in 2000.

Average wait time from the decision to operate to the date of surgery:

Hospital	Days	Cases
Princess Margaret Hospital	35	144
Toronto General Hospital	33	537
Toronto Western Hospital	5	10

What is the overall average wait time per patient for the three hospitals shown?

3.13 Based on the following table that appeared in Globe and Mail, Classroom Edition, of March 1994:

a. Was the overall mean price per room higher for 3 star hotels than 2 star hotels?

b. What is the median number of rooms for all the hotels in the table?

c. It would be reported that 40% of the hotels had a selling price higher than $____ ?

Eastern Canada

Hotel	Level of quality	Location	Number of rooms	Selling price $million	Buyer origin
Hotel Strata, Mississauga	2-star	Toronto	129	$2.7	Domesti
Royal Connaught	3-star	Hamilton	206	$4.5	Domesti
Chestnut Park	3-star	Toronto	520	$28.4	Hong Kon
Carlton Place	2-star	Toronto	528	$8.5	Indonesia/Singapo
Howard Johnson, Scarborough	2-star	Toronto	192	$5.6	China
Howard Johnson	2-star	Ottawa	108	$3.7	Domesti
Best Western, Rose City Inn	1-star	Windsor	147	$2.5	Domesti
Sutton Place	4-star	Toronto	280*	$29.2	Hong Kon
Hotel Aurora	2-star	Aurora	98	$3.5	Domesti
Rock Haven Motor Inn	1-star	Peterborough	86	$1.0	Iranian
Skyline Triumph	2-star	Toronto	380	$9.5	Domest

Western Canada

Hotel	Level of quality	Location	Number of rooms	Selling price $million	Buyer origin
Delta River Inn	4-star	Vancouver	416	$30.0	Domestic/Hong Ko
Skyline Hotel	3-star	Calgary	385	$26.0	Domest
Cherrywood Inn	2-star	Edmonton	136	$2.9	Domest
Coast Lakeside Inn	3-star	Penticton	200	$13.5	Domestic
Best Western, Port O'Call	3-star	Calgary	201	$8.5	East Africa

*Plus 161 apartment units.   Source: Colliers Macaulay Nico

3.14 The following data came from the Sales & Marketing Management, Survey of Buying Power, 1998. For the states shown in the table below:

a. What is the projected overall average retail sales per household in 2002?

b. What is the projected overall % increase in the number of households from 1998 to 2003?

Survey of Buying Power (Regional and State Summaries for 5-year Projections)

	POPULATION					RETAIL SALES	
	1/1/2003	%	1/1/2003	%	2002	
	1/1/98	TOTAL	CHANGE	TOTAL	CHANGE	TOTAL RETAIL	
	TOTAL POP.	POP.	1998-	HSHLDS.	1998-	SALES	% CHANGE
REGION STATE	(000s)	(000s)	2003	(000s)	2003	($000)	1997-2002
NEW ENGLAND							
Connecticut	3,271.1	3,275.2	.1	1,246.1	1.4	39,848,761	15.0
Maine	1,243.7	1,266.1	1.8	466.2	6.9	10,666,671	16.6
Massachusetts	6,133.5	6,241.1	1.8	2,384.6	3.3	66,722,629	12.6
New Hampshire	1,179.1	1,242.3	5.4	472.5	7.0	17,284,399	18.6
Rhode Island	987.0	978.5	−.9	372.5	.1	8,590,400	9.4
Vermont	590.4	601.6	1.9	235.4	4.3	6,407,914	11.4

3.15 A survey of 300 prize winners of a certain contest revealed the following results:

a. What was their mean prize value?

b. How many won prizes of less than $500?

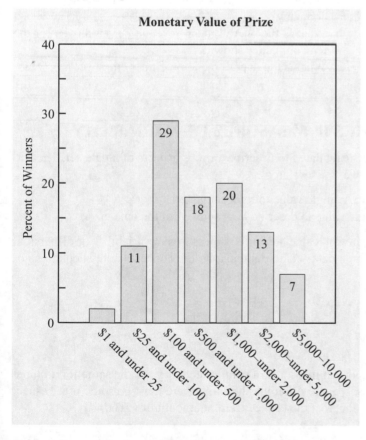

3.16 Based on the following table, what is the mean size of institutions that make extensive use of TQM (Total Quality Management)?

Breakdown by Size of Institution

Student Population	Number of Institutions Responding	Percent of Institutions Responding	Number of Institutions Extensively using TQM	Percent of Institutions Extensively using TQM
0 and under 2,000	19	8	3	7
2,000 " " 5,000	58	24	7	17
5,000 " " 10,000	65	27	13	31
10,000 " " 15,000	41	17	6	14
15,000 " " 25,000	35	14	9	22
25,000 " " 35,000	15	6	3	7
35,000 " " 50,000	10	4	1	2

3.17 The following table appeared in the June 19, 2003 issue of the Toronto Star.

Auto productivity

Top 10 assembly plants in North America by labour-hours per vehicle.

Nissan, Smyrna, Tenn.
Midsize car   **15.74**

GM, Oshawa #1
Midsize car   **16.44**

GM, Oshawa #2
Midsize car   **17.08**

Ford, Chicago
Midsize car   **17.71**

Ford, Atlanta
Midsize car   **17.78**

Nissan, Smyrna
Small pickup   **18.23**

Nissan, Smyrna
Small SUV   **18.35**

GM, Lansing, Mich
Compact car   **18.59**

GM, Lansing
Midsize car   **18.64**

Toyota Georgetown #1
Midsize car   **20.06**

SOURCE: Harbour and Associates

Last month their were 2400 cars produced at Oshawa #1, 3000 cars produced at Oshawa #2, 1800 midsize cars produced at Lansing and 1500 compact cars produced at Lansing. What was the overall average labour hours per car for these four GM plants?

3.18 The following is a portion of a chart that appeared in the May 25, 2003 issue of the Toronto Star.

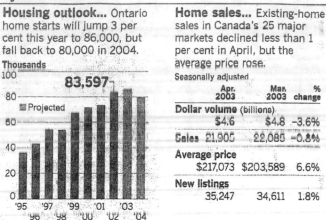

By the numbers

Housing outlook... Ontario home starts will jump 3 per cent this year to 86,000, but fall back to 80,000 in 2004.

Home sales... Existing-home sales in Canada's 25 major markets declined less than 1 per cent in April, but the average price rose.

Seasonally adjusted

	Apr. 2003	Mar. 2003	% change
Dollar volume (billions)	$4.6	$4.8	-3.6%
Sales	21,905	22,085	-0.8%
Average price	$217,073	$203,589	6.6%
New listings	35,247	34,611	1.8%

What was the overall average price of houses sold in Canada's 25 major markets for the 2 months March and April 2003?

3.19 The table below appeared in the Financial Post of December 2, 1998.

World oil giants

		Profit US$billion	Rev. per employee US$	Employees
1	Exxon Corp./Mobil Corp. (U.S.)	11.8	96,170	122,700
2	Royal Dutch/Shell Group (Britain/Netherlands)	7.8	74,286	105,000
3	British Petroleum/Amoco (Britain)	4.0	70,859	56,450
4	Total SA/Petrofina SA (France)	2.9	67,391	69,066
5	Texaco Inc. (U.S.)	2.7	92,109	29,313
6	Elf Aquitaine (France)	0.96	11,469	83,700
7	ENI (Italy)	3.0	37,417	80,178
8	Chevron Corp. (U.S.)	3.3	84,615	39,362
9	PDVSA (Venezuela)	4.8	84,818	56,592
10	SK (South Korea)	0.125	4,086	30,595

SOURCE: COMPANY REPORTS

a. For the 10 companies shown, what is the mean profit per company?

b. What is the overall mean revenue per employee for the ten companies shown?

c. What is the overall mean profit per employee?

3.2 DESCRIPTIVE STATISTICS II: MEASURES OF VARIABILITY

Descriptive statistics are numbers calculated to describe various aspects of a data set. The two most important types of descriptive statistics are:

Measures of Central Tendency: A single value to represent the data set.
Measures of Variability: A single value to describe how spread out the data is.

In this section we will learn how to calculate various measures of variability or dispersion.

We will use the following three data sets to demonstrate the concepts and calculations of variability measures:

Data set A: 1, 2, 3, 4, 5
Data set B: 1, 1, 3, 3, 5, 5
Data set C: 1, 1, 1, 5, 5, 5

It should be noted for each data set: $\bar{x} = \tilde{x} = 3$

In other words, the most important measures of central tendency are the same for all three data sets, but the data sets themselves are different, therefore there must be some other aspect of them that is different. It is the fact that they have different amount of **variability**.

Range

Symbol: R for sample or population

Formula: $R = High - Low$

EXAMPLE 3.17

Data set A: $R = 5 - 1 = 4$
Data set B: $R = 5 - 1 = 4$
Data set C: $R = 5 - 1 = 4$

These results would seem to indicate that the three data sets had the same amount of variability. This would appear not to be true, since our intuition would seem to indicate that the three data sets would have different amounts of variability.

From this example we can see why the range has limited use. It only considers the high and low values of a data set and ignores the values in between. These in-between values should have some input in determining the variability of a data set.

It should be noted, however, that the range can be useful to measure variability in some cases. For many years the range has been the preferred way to measure variability when setting up quality control charts which are used to monitor the mean and the variability of repeated processes.

In this course, you will only calculate the range if you are told to do so.

EXAMPLE 3.18

COMPUTING THE RANGE IN THE 2003 RETURN OF SMALL CAP HIGH-RISK MUTUAL FUNDS

The 121 mutual funds that are part of the "Using Statistics" scenario (see page 64) are classified according to the risk level of the mutual funds (low, average, and high) and type (small cap, mid cap, and large cap). Compute the range of the 2003 return for the small cap mutual funds with high risk. MUTUALFUNDS2004

SOLUTION Ranked from the smallest to the largest, the 2003 return for the nine small cap mutual funds with high risk is:

37.3   39.2   44.2   44.5   53.8   56.6   59.3   62.4   66.5

Therefore, using Equation (3.7), the range = 66.5 – 37.3 = 29.2.
    The largest difference between any two returns for the small cap mutual funds with high risk is 29.2.

The range measures the *total spread* in the set of data. Although the range is a simple measure of total variation in the data, it does not take into account *how* the data are distributed between the smallest and largest values. In other words, the range does not indicate if the values are evenly distributed throughout the data set, clustered near the middle, or clustered near one or both extremes. Thus, using the range as a measure of variation when at least one value is an extreme value is misleading.

Interquartile Range

Symbol: IQR for sample or population

Formula: $IQR = Q_3 - Q_1$

EXAMPLE 3.19
Data set A: $IQR = 4.5 - 1.5 = 3$
Data set B: $IQR = 5 - 1 = 4$
Data set C: $IQR = 5 - 1 = 4$

These results would seem to indicate that data set A has less variability than data sets B and C. This is an improvement over the previous results based on the range (as we shall see shortly). However, data sets B and C do not have the same amount of variability.

The interquartile range is often preferred over the range as a measure of variability since the range can easily be influenced by one extreme value.

Consider the following example:

EXAMPLE 3.20
Data set D: 1, 3, 3, 4, 4, 4, 5, 5, 5, 5, 6, 6, 6, 7, 7, 7, 8, 8, 9, 10
Data set E: 1, 3, 3, 4, 4, 4, 5, 5, 5, 5, 6, 6, 6, 7, 7, 7, 8, 8, 9, 20

Suppose we use the *range* to measure the variability of these two data sets:

Data set D: $R = 10 - 1 = 9$ Data set E: $R = 20 - 1 = 19$

Intuitively, we would not expect that data set E would have twice as much variability as data set E, i.e. the range does not seem to be a good measure of variability in this case.

Now, suppose we use the *interquartile range* to measure the variability:

Data set D: $IQR = 7 - 4 = 3$ Data set E: $IQR = 7 - 4 = 3$

Intuitively, we would not say that both data sets have exactly the same variability. However, this appears to be closer to the truth that the conclusion that the range results lead us to. The IQR is not affected by one or two extreme values as the range is.

EXAMPLE 3.21
COMPUTING THE INTERQUARTILE RANGE FOR THE 2003 RETURN OF SMALL CAP HIGH-RISK MUTUAL FUNDS

The 121 mutual funds that are part of the "Using Statistics" scenario (see page 64) are classified according to the risk level of the mutual funds (low, average, and high) and type (small cap, mid cap, and large cap). Compute the interquartile range of the 2003 return for the small cap mutual funds with high risk. MUTUALFUNDS2004

SOLUTION Ranked from smallest to largest, the 2003 return for the nine small cap mutual funds with high risk is:

37.3   39.2   44.2   44.5   53.8   56.6   59.3   62.4   66.5

Using Equation (3.8) and the earlier results, $Q_1 = 41.7$ and $Q_3 = 60.85$.

Interquartile range $= 60.85 - 41.7 = 19.15$

Therefore, the interquartile range in the 2003 return is 19.15.

Because the interquartile range does not consider any value smaller than Q_1 or larger than Q_3, it cannot be affected by extreme values. Summary measures such as the median, Q_1, Q_3, and the interquartile range, which cannot be influenced by extreme values, are called **resistant measures**.

Variance

Symbol: Sample s^2 Population σ^2

Formula: Sample $s^2 = \dfrac{\sum (x-\bar{x})^2}{n-1}$ Population $\sigma^2 = \dfrac{\sum (x-\mu)^2}{N}$

Note: For the first time, we will get a different result for a descriptive measure if a data is a sample instead of a population. Previously, only the symbol was different (if anything was different).

We now have a measure of variability that takes into account all the values in a data set.

EXAMPLE 3.22   **Data set A:**

x	$x-\bar{x}$ or $x-\mu$	$(x-\bar{x})^2$ or $(x-\mu)^2$
1	−2	4
2	−1	1
3	0	0
4	1	1
5	2	4
		10

Sample: $s^2 = \dfrac{10}{5-1} = 2.5$ Population: $\sigma^2 = \dfrac{10}{5} = 2$

Data set B:

x	$x-\bar{x}$ or $x-\mu$	$(x-\bar{x})^2$ or $(x-\mu)^2$
1	-2	4
1	-2	4
3	0	0
3	0	0
5	2	4
5	2	4
		16

Sample: $s^2 = \dfrac{16}{6-1} = 3.2$ Population: $\sigma^2 = \dfrac{16}{6} = 2.67$

Data set C:

x	$x - \bar{x}$ or $x - \mu$	$(x - \bar{x})^2$ or $(x - \mu)^2$
1	-2	4
1	-2	4
1	-2	4
5	2	4
5	2	4
5	2	4
		24

Sample: $s^2 = \dfrac{24}{6-1} = 4.8$ Population: $\sigma^2 = \dfrac{24}{6} = 4$

Conclusion: Based on these results, data set A has the least amount of variability, while data set C has the most. These results are reasonable when we understand that variability in statistics has nothing to do with 'how many different values are there' but instead has to do with 'does the data seem to be close to the mean or does the data tend to be further from the mean'.

Variance is a good measure of variability in that it takes into account all values. However, variance has major practical disadvantage: the units don't make sense. The units of variance = (data units)². For example, if the data in data set A is \$, then the variance is 2.5\$² ??? If the data is people, the variance is 2.5 people² ??? Because of this problem, variance cannot have a *practical* interpretation. In statistics, variance is used almost exclusively in the theoretical development of formulas.

Standard Deviation

Symbol: Sample s Population σ

Formula: Sample $s = \sqrt{s^2} = \sqrt{\dfrac{\sum (x - \bar{x})^2}{n-1}}$ Population $\sigma = \sqrt{\sigma^2}$

EXAMPLE 3.23

Data set A: $s = \sqrt{2.5} = 1.58$

Data set B: $s = \sqrt{3.2} = 1.79$

Data set B: $s = \sqrt{4.8} = 2.19$

We can see that the conclusions regarding which data set is the most variable and which is the least variable is the same as when we compared variances.

The main advantage of standard deviation, for practical purposes, is that the units are the *same* as the data.

Rounding rule for standard deviation   Regarding the form of the answer when calculating standard deviation (when rounding is obviously necessary): use three(3) figures or a number that looks like the data, whichever has the most figures. This rule also applies to the use of standard deviation in further calculations, although it is sometimes easier to use results stored in memory of your calculator or computer.

Ex. 1: If data is: 10,   11,   13,   15   then $s = 2.22$
Ex. 2: If data is: 2,315   4,156   7,542   9,587 then $s = 3,275$
Ex. 3: If data is: 2,315   2,320   2,325   2,330 then $s = 6.45$
Ex. 4: If data is: 23.46   56.82   83.47   92.61 then $s = 31.05$

EXAMPLE 3.24

COMPUTING THE VARIANCE AND STANDARD DEVIATION OF THE 2003 RETURN OF SMALL CAP HIGH-RISK MUTUAL FUNDS

The 121 mutual funds that are part of the "Using Statistics" scenario (see page 64) are classified according to the risk level of the mutual funds (low, average, and high) and type (small cap, mid cap, and large cap). Compute the variance and standard deviation of the 2003 return for the small cap mutual funds with high risk. MUTUALFUNDS2004

SOLUTION Table 3.8 illustrates the computation of the variance and standard deviation for the return in 2003 for the small cap mutual funds with high risk. Using Equation (3.9)

$$S^2 = \frac{\sum_{i=1}^{n}(X_i - \bar{X})^2}{n-1}$$

$$= \frac{(44.5 - 51.53)^2 + (39.2 - 51.53)^2 + \cdots + (66.5 - 51.53)^2}{9-1}$$

$$= \frac{891.16}{8}$$

$$= 111.395$$

Using Equation (3.10), the sample standard deviation S is

$$S = \sqrt{S^2} = \sqrt{\frac{\sum_{i=1}^{n}(X_i - \bar{X})^2}{n-1}} = \sqrt{111.395} = 10.55$$

The standard deviation of 10.55 indicates that the 2003 returns for the small cap mutual funds with high risk are clustering within 10.55 around the mean of 51.53 (i.e., clustering between $\bar{X} - 1S = 40.98$ and $\bar{X} + 1S = 62.08$). In fact, 55.6% (5 out of 9) of the 2003 returns lie within this interval.

TABLE 3.8

Computing the Variance of the 2003 Return for the Small Cap Mutual Funds with High Risk

$\bar{X} = 51.5333$

Return 2003	Step 1: $(X_i - \bar{X})$	Step 2: $(X_i - \bar{X})^2$
44.5	−7.0333	49.4678
39.2	−12.3333	152.1111
62.4	10.8667	118.0844
59.3	7.7667	60.3211
56.6	5.0667	25.6711
53.8	2.2667	5.1378
37.3	−14.2333	202.5878
44.2	−7.3333	53.7778
66.5	14.9667	224.0011

	Step 3: Sum:	Step 4: Divide by $(n - 1)$:
	891.16	111.395

The following summarizes the characteristics of the range, interquartile range, variance, and standard deviation.

- The more spread out, or dispersed, the data are, the larger the range, interquartile range, variance, and standard deviation.
- The more concentrated, or homogeneous the data are, the smaller the range, interquartile range, variance, and standard deviation.
- If the values are all the same (so that there is no variation in the data), the range, interquartile range, variance, and standard deviation will all equal zero.
- None of the measures of variation (the range, interquartile range, standard deviation, and variance) can *ever* be negative.

Coefficient of Variation

All of the above measures of variability are **absolute** measures. It is often better (i.e. you get more meaningful results) to compare factors using **relative** measures. The coefficient of variation is a relative measure of variability.

Symbol: CV

Formula: Sample $CV = \dfrac{s}{\bar{x}} \times 100$ Population $CV = \dfrac{\sigma}{\mu} \times 100$

EXAMPLE 3.25   THE FOLLOWING INFORMATION FOR 4 STOCKS IS TO BE ANALYZED.

TABLE 3.9

Stock	Price	Dividend
ABC Company	$25	$0.70
DEF Company	47	1.50
HIJ Company	78	2.00
XYZ Company	92	3.00

Compare the variability of the prices and dividends.

Solution: Since the sizes of the numbers in the two data sets are quite a bit different, it will be best to use a relative measure to compare the variability.

$$\text{Price:} \qquad CV = \frac{s}{\bar{x}} \times 100 = \frac{30.23}{60.50} \times 100 = 50\%$$

$$\text{Dividend:} \quad CV = \frac{s}{\bar{x}} \times 100 = \frac{0.963}{1.80} \times 100 = 54\%$$

Using the *10% rule* to compare CV's: Diff = 4 < 10% of the smaller = 5

Conclusion: The dividends and the prices have approximately the same amount of variability.

Note: If we had just looked at the standard deviation, we would have concluded (rather obviously because of the size of the numbers) that the prices were more variable.

Rounding rule for CV   One decimal if < 10%. No decimals if > 10%.

EXAMPLE 3.26

The following table shows data for the houses that are being built on a short street in a new subdivision.

TABLE 3.10

House number	Size Square ft.	Price ($000's)
1002	2400	269
1004	2650	289
1006	2200	225
1008	2150	219
1010	2500	249

Compare the variabilty of the sizes and the prices.

Solution: Since the *units* of the data are *different*, the only way to compare the variability of these two sets of data is to use the coefficient of variation.

$$\text{Size:} \quad CV = \frac{s}{\bar{x}} \times 100 = \frac{208}{2380} \times 100 = 8.7\%$$

$$\text{Price:} \quad CV = \frac{s}{\bar{x}} \times 100 = \frac{29.4}{250} \times 100 = 12\%$$

Using the 10% rule to compare CV's: Diff = 3.3 > 10% of the smaller = 0.87

Conclusion: The prices are relatively more variable than the sizes.

EXAMPLE 3.27   COMPARING TWO COEFFICIENTS OF VARIATION WHEN TWO VARIABLES HAVE DIFFERENT UNITS OF MEASUREMENT

The operations manager of a package delivery service is deciding on whether to purchase a new fleet of trucks. When packages are stored in the trucks in preparation for delivery, you need to consider two major constraints—the weight (in pounds) and the volume (in cubic feet) for each item.

The operations manager samples 200 packages, and finds that the mean weight is 26.0 pounds, with a standard deviation of 3.9 pounds, and the mean volume is 8.8 cubic feet, with a standard deviation of 2.2 cubic feet. How can the operations manager compare the variation of the weight and the volume?

SOLUTION Because the measurement units differ for the weight and volume constraints, the operations manager should compare the relative variability in the two types of measurements.

For weight, the coefficient of variation is

$$CV_W = \left(\frac{3.9}{26.0}\right)100\% = 15.0\%$$

For volume, the coefficient of variation is

$$CV_V = \left(\frac{2.2}{8.8}\right)100\% = 25.0\%$$

Thus, relative to the mean, the package volume is much more variable than the package weight.

PROBLEMS FOR SECTION 3.1

Descriptive Statistics Set 2

3.20 Last year's travel expenditures ($) by the 12 members of a university's business council were as follows:

     0   0   173   378   441   733   759
   857 958 985 1434 2063

a. Calculate the mean travel expenditure per member.
b. Determine the median travel expenditure per member.
c. Determine the 80th percentile of this data.
d. Determine the range and the interquartile range of the data.
e. Calculate the coefficient of variation of the data.

3.21 The number of defective items in 12 recent production lots of 1000 items each from Plant A were as follows:

   3   1   0   0   2   21   4   1   1   0   2   5

a. Calculate the mean number of defective per lot.
b. The mean number of defectives per lot in a group of 16 lots from Plant B was 3.5. What was the total number of defective items in these 16 lots?
c. What is the median number of defective items per lot?

d. Why does the median differ substantially from the mean of this data?
e. The median number of defectives per lot for 20 lots from Plant C was 4. What was the total number of defectives in these 20 lots?
f. What is the standard deviation of the number of defectives per lot for Plant A?

3.22 The change in enrollment between this year and last year in seven programs at a particular university are:

   −614   −103   41   258   313   387   490

a. Calculate the mean enrollment change per program. Does the fact that the mean is positive imply that the combined total enrollment in the seven programs has increased? Explain.
b. Determine the median enrollment change per program.
c. Calculate the standard deviation of enrollment change. Does the fact that the standard deviation is positive relate to the fact that the mean was positive? Explain.

3.23 Refer to problem 3.2 in Descriptive Statistics Exercises—Set 1:
What is the standard deviation of the liquor bill for a table?

3.24 Refer to problem 3.7 in Descriptive Statistics Exercises—Set 1:
What is the standard deviation of the sales of a toy store?

3.25 Refer to problem 3.10 in Descriptive Statistics Exercises—Set 1:
What is the standard deviation of the cost of a one-day trip for people under 50 years old?

3.26 Refer to problem 3.15 in Descriptive Statistics Exercises—Set 1:
What is the standard deviation of the monetary value of the prizes?

3.27 Refer to problem 3.17 in Descriptive Statistics Exercises—Set 1:
What is the standard deviation of the labour hours per car for the four GM plants?

3.28 Refer to problem 3.19 in Descriptive Statistics Exercises—Set 1:
What is the standard deviation of the company profits?

3.29 A suburban farm grows strawberries in a large field where prospective customers go to pick-their-own. A survey of 200 customers showed that 30% picked one basket, 50% picked two baskets and the remainder picked three baskets. What is the mean number of baskets of strawberries per customer? What is the standard deviation?

3.30 The means and standard deviations of revenue per farm ($000) and volume harvested per farm (Thou. kg.) for two farm products in Western Canada are as follows:

Grain	Revenue per Farm		Volume per Farm	
	Mean	Std. Dev.	Mean	Std. Dev.
Wheat	12.56	4.03	76.7	22.9
Barley	14.49	5.89	106.3	35.4

Is revenue or volume relatively more variable for wheat? Is the same true for barley?

3.31 The table below appeared in the May 1995 issue of the Report on Business.
a. What is the overall average selling space per store for all 469 stores?
b. What is the overall average sales per store for all 469 stores?

Can Brooks Catch Up

Coutu's current stores outperform its newly acquired Brooks outlets

Coutu stores averaged sales of $6 million in 94

Number of franchises 227
Selling space per store .... 7,700 sq.ft.
System-wide retail sales 1994 .... $1.34 billion

...and the U.S. Maxi outlets averaged $4 million

Number of stores 21
Selling space per store .... 12,000 sq.ft.
1994 sales .... $85 million

...while Brooks lagged far behind at $1.9 million

Number of stores 221
Selling space per store .... 6,000 sq.ft.
1994 sales .... $425.8 million

3.32 The percentage distribution of hourly earnings for the 2100 plant employees of the ABC Corp. is shown below:

Hourly Earnings ($)	Percent of Employees
14.00 and under 16.00	12
16.00 " " 18.00	24
18.00 " " 20.00	44
20.00 " " 25.00	15
25.00 " " 30.00	5

Calculate the mean and standard deviation of hourly earnings of the employees at ABC Corp.

3.33 Refer to the table 'Who works the hardest' and determine if the five countries indicated were more variable in terms of average hours worked or gross domestic product in 2000?

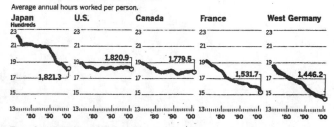

Who works the hardest

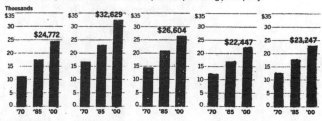

Buying power

Shape

A third important property that describes a set of numerical data is shape. Shape is the pattern of the distribution of data values throughout the entire range of all the values. A distribution will either be **symmetrical**, when low and high values balance each other out, or **skewed**, not symmetrical and showing an imbalance of low values or high values.

Shape influences the relationship of the mean to the median in the following ways:

- Mean < median; negative or left-skewed
- Mean = median; symmetric or zero skewness
- Mean > median; positive or right-skewed

Figure 3.1 depicts three data sets, each with a different shape.

FIGURE 3.1

A Comparison of Three Data Sets Differing in Shape

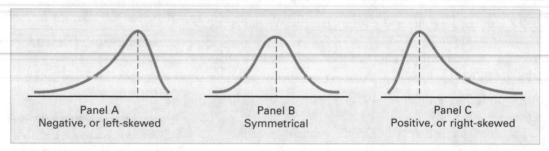

The data in panel A are negative, or **left-skewed**. In this panel, most of the values are in the upper portion of the distribution. There is a long tail and distortion to the left that is caused by some extremely small values. These extremely small values pull the mean downward so that the mean is less than the median.

The data in panel B are symmetrical. Each half of the curve is a mirror image of the other half of the curve. The low and high values on the scale balance, and the mean equals the median.

The data in panel C are positive, or **right-skewed**. In this panel, most of the values are in the lower portion of the distribution. There is a long tail on the right of the distribution and a distortion to the right that is caused by some extremely large values. These extremely large values pull the mean upward so that the mean is greater than the median.

Z Scores

An **extreme value** or **outlier** is a value located far away from the mean. Z scores are useful in identifying outliers. The larger the Z score, the farther the distance from the value to the mean. The **Z score** is the difference between the value and the mean, divided by the standard deviation.

Z SCORES

$$Z = \frac{X - \bar{X}}{S} \tag{3.12}$$

For the time to get ready in the morning data, the mean is 39.6 minutes and the standard deviation is 6.77 minutes. The time to get ready on the first day is 39.0 minutes. You compute the Z score for day 1 from

$$Z = \frac{X - \bar{X}}{S}$$

$$= \frac{39.0 - 39.6}{6.77}$$

$$= -0.09$$

Table 3.11 shows the Z scores for all 10 days. The largest Z score is 1.83 for day 4 on which the time to get ready was 52 minutes. The lowest Z score was −1.57 for day 2 on which the time to get ready was 29 minutes. As a general rule, a Z score is considered an outlier if it is less than −3.0 or greater than +3.0. None of the times met that criterion to be considered outliers.

TABLE 3.11

Z Scores for the 10 Get-Ready Times

	Time (X)	Z Score
	39	−0.09
	29	−1.57
	43	0.50
	52	1.83
	39	−0.09
	44	0.65
	40	0.06
	31	−1.27
	44	0.65
	35	−0.68
Mean	39.6	
Standard deviation	6.77	

EXAMPLE 3.28

COMPUTING THE Z SCORES OF THE 2003 RETURN OF SMALL CAP HIGH-RISK MUTUAL FUNDS

The 121 mutual funds that are part of the "Using Statistics" scenario (see page 64) are classified according to the risk level of the mutual funds (low, average, and high) and type (small cap, mid cap, and large cap). Compute the Z scores of the 2003 return for the small cap mutual funds with high risk. **MUTUALFUNDS2004**

SOLUTION Table 3.12 illustrates the Z scores of the 2003 return for the small cap mutual funds with high risk. The largest Z score is 1.42 for a percentage return of 66.5. The lowest Z score is −1.35 for a percentage return of 37.3. As a general rule, a Z score is considered an outlier if it is less than -3.0 or greater than +3.0. None of the percentage returns met that criterion to be considered outliers.

TABLE 3.12

Z Scores of the 2003 Return for the Small Cap Mutual Funds with High Risk

	Return 2003	Z Scores
	44.5	−0.67
	39.2	−1.17
	62.4	1.03
	59.3	0.74
	56.6	0.48
	53.8	0.21
	37.3	−1.35
	44.2	−0.69
	66.5	1.42
Mean	51.53	
Standard Deviation	10.55	

PROBLEMS FOR SECTION 3.1

Learning the Basics

 3.34 The following is a set of data from a sample of $n = 5$:

$$7 \quad 4 \quad 9 \quad 8 \quad 2$$

a. Compute the mean, median, and mode.
b. Compute the range, interquartile range, variance, standard deviation, and coefficient of variation.
c. Compute the Z scores. Are there any outliers?
d. Describe the shape of the data set.

3.35 The following is a set of data from a sample of $n = 6$:

$$7 \quad 4 \quad 9 \quad 7 \quad 3 \quad 12$$

a. Compute the mean, median, and mode.
b. Compute the range, interquartile range, variance, standard deviation, and coefficient of variation.
c. Compute the Z scores. Are there any outliers?
d. Describe the shape of the data set.

3.36 The following set of data is from a sample of $n = 7$:

$$12 \quad 7 \quad 4 \quad 9 \quad 0 \quad 7 \quad 3$$

a. Compute the mean, median, and mode.
b. Compute the range, interquartile range, variance, standard deviation, and coefficient of variation.
c. Describe the shape of the data set.

3.37 The following is a set of data from a sample of $n = 5$:

$$7 \quad -5 \quad -8 \quad 7 \quad 9$$

a. Compute the mean, median, and mode.
b. Compute the range, interquartile range, variance, standard deviation, and coefficient of variation.
c. Describe the shape of the data set.

3.38 Suppose that the rate of return for a particular stock during the past two years was 10% and 30%. Compute the geometric mean rate of return. (*Note:* A rate of return of 10% is recorded as 0.10 and a rate of return of 30% is recorded as 0.30.)

Applying the Concepts

Problems 3.39–3.49 can be solved manually or by using Microsoft Excel, Minitab, or SPSS.

 **3.39** The operations manager of a plant that manufactures tires wants to compare the actual inner diameter of two grades of tires, each of which is expected to be 575 millimeters. A sample of five tires of each grade was selected, and the results representing the inner diameters of the tires, ranked from smallest to largest, are as follows:

Grade X					Grade Y				
568	570	575	578	584	573	574	575	577	578

a. For each of the two grades of tires, compute the mean, median, and standard deviation.
b. Which grade of tire is providing better quality? Explain.
c. What would be the effect on your answers in (a) and (b) if the last value for grade Y were 588 instead of 578? Explain.

 3.40 The following data represent the total fat for burgers and chicken items from a sample of fast-food chains. FASTFOOD

Burgers

$$19 \quad 31 \quad 34 \quad 35 \quad 39 \quad 39 \quad 43$$

Chicken

$$7 \quad 9 \quad 15 \quad 16 \quad 16 \quad 18 \quad 22 \quad 25 \quad 27 \quad 33 \quad 39$$

Source: Extracted from "Quick Bites," Copyright © 2001 by Consumers Union of U.S., Inc., Yonkers, NY 10703–1057. Adapted with permission from Consumer Reports, *March 2001, 46.*

For the burgers and chicken items separately:
a. Compute the mean, median, first quartile, and third quartile.
b. Compute the variance, standard deviation, range, interquartile range, and coefficient of variation.
c. Are the data skewed? If so, how?
d. Based on the results of (a) through (c), what conclusions can you reach concerning the differences in total fat of burgers and chicken items?

3.41 The median price of a home in December 2003 rose to $173,200, an increase of 6.7% from December 2002. For the full year, sales hit a record 6.1 million homes (James R. Hagerty, "Housing Prices Continue to Rise," *The Wall Street Journal*, January 27, 2004, D1).
a. Describe the shape of the distribution of the price of homes sold.
b. Why do you think the article reports the median home price and not the mean home price?

3.42 In the 2002–2003 academic year, many public universities in the United States raised tuition and fees due to a decrease in state subsidies (Mary Beth Marklein, "Public Universities Raise Tuition, Fees—and Ire," *USA Today*, August 8, 2002, 1A–2A). The following represents the change in the cost of tuition, a shared dormitory room, and the most popular meal plan between the 2001–2002 academic year and the 2002–2003 academic year for a sample of 10 public universities. COLLEGECOST

University	Change in Cost ($)
University of California, Berkeley	1,589
University of Georgia, Athens	593
University of Illinois, Urbana–Champaign	1,223
Kansas State University, Manhattan	869
University of Maine, Orono	423
University of Mississippi, Oxford	1,720
University of New Hampshire, Durham	708
Ohio State University, Columbus	1,425
University of South Carolina, Columbia	922
Utah State University, Logan	308

a. Compute the mean, median, first quartile, and third quartile.
b. Compute the variance, standard deviation, range, interquartile range, coefficient of variation, and Z scores.
c. Are the data skewed? If so, how?
d. Based on the results of (a) through (c), what conclusions can you reach concerning the change in costs between the 2001–2002 and 2002–2003 academic years?

3.43 The following data COFFEEDRINK represent the calories and fat (in grams) of 16-ounce iced coffee drinks at Dunkin' Donuts and Starbucks.

Product	Calories	Fat
Dunkin' Donuts Iced Mocha Swirl latte (whole milk)	240	8.0
Starbucks Coffee Frappuccino blended coffee	260	3.5
Dunkin' Donuts Coffee Coolatta (cream)	350	22.0
Starbucks Iced Coffee Mocha Expresso (whole milk and whipped cream)	350	20.0
Starbucks Mocha Frappuccino blended coffee (whipped cream)	420	16.0
Starbucks Chocolate Brownie Frappuccino blended coffee (whipped cream)	510	22.0
Starbucks Chocolate Frappuccino Blended Crème (whipped cream)	530	19.0

Source: Extracted from "Coffee as Candy at Dunkin' Donuts and Starbucks," Copyright © 2004 by Consumers Union of U.S., Inc., Yonkers, NY 10703–1057, a nonprofit organization. Adapted with permission from Consumer Reports, *June 2004, 9, for educational purposes only. No commercial use or reproduction permitted.* www.ConsumerReports.org

For each variable (calories and fat),
a. Compute the mean, median, first quartile, and third quartile.
b. Compute the variance, standard deviation, range, interquartile range, coefficient of variation, and Z scores. Are there any outliers? Explain.
c. Are the data skewed? If so, how?

d. Based on the results of (a) through (c), what conclusions can you reach concerning the calories and fat in iced coffee drinks at Dunkin' Donuts and Starbucks?

3.44 The following data represent the daily hotel cost and rental car cost for 20 U. S. cities during a week in October 2003. HOTEL-CAR

City	Hotel	Cars
San Francisco	205	47
Los Angeles	179	41
Seattle	185	49
Phoenix	210	38
Denver	128	32
Dallas	145	48
Houston	177	49
Minneapolis	117	41
Chicago	221	56
St. Louis	159	41
New Orleans	205	50
Detroit	128	32
Cleveland	165	34
Atlanta	180	46
Orlando	198	41
Miami	158	40
Pittsburgh	132	39
Boston	283	67
New York	269	69
Washington, D.C.	204	40

Source: Extracted from The Wall Street Journal, *October 10, 2003, W4.*

For each variable (hotel cost and rental car cost),
a. Compute the mean, median, first quartile, and third quartile.
b. Compute the variance, standard deviation, range, interquartile range, coefficient of variation, and Z scores. Are there any outliers? Explain.
c. Are the data skewed? If so, how?
d. Based on the results of (a) through (c), what conclusions can you reach concerning the daily cost of a hotel and rental car?

3.45 The cost of 14 models of 3-megapixel digital cameras at a camera specialty store during 2003 was as follows. CAMERA

340 450 450 280 220 340 290
370 400 310 340 430 270 380

a. Compute the mean, median, first quartile, and third quartile.
b. Compute the variance, standard deviation, range, interquartile range, coefficient of variation, and Z scores. Are there any outliers? Explain.
c. Are the data skewed? If so, how?

d. Based on the results of (a) through (c), what conclusions can you reach concerning the price of 3-megapixel digital cameras at a camera specialty store during 2003?

3.46 A software development and consulting firm located in the Phoenix metropolitan area develops software for supply chain management systems using systematic software reuse. Instead of starting from scratch when writing and developing new custom software systems, the firm uses a database of reusable components totaling more than 2,000,000 lines of code collected from 10 years of continuous reuse effort. Eight analysts at the firm were asked to estimate the reuse rate when developing a new software system. The following data are given as a percentage of the total code written for a software system that is part of the reuse database. REUSE

> 50.0   62.5   37.5   75.0   45.0   47.5   15.0   25.0

Source: M. A. Rothenberger, and K. J. Dooley, "A Performance Measure for Software Reuse Projects," Decision Sciences, 30(Fall 1999), 1131–1153.

a. Compute the mean, median, and mode.
b. Compute the range, variance, and standard deviation.
c. Interpret the summary measures calculated in (a) and (b).

3.47 A manufacturer of flashlight batteries took a sample of 13 batteries from a day's production and used them continuously until they were drained. The number of hours they were used until failure were: BATTERIES

> 342   426   317   545   264   451
> 1,049   631   512   266   492   562   298

a. Compute the mean, median, and mode. Looking at the distribution of times to failure, which measures of location do you think are most appropriate and which least appropriate to use for these data? Why?
b. Calculate the range, variance, and standard deviation.
c. What would you advise if the manufacturer wanted to be able to say in advertisements that these batteries "should last 400 hours"? (*Note:* There is no right answer to this question; the point is to consider how to make such a statement precise.)
d. Suppose that the first value was 1,342 instead of 342. Repeat (a) through (c), using this value. Comment on the difference in the results.

3.48 A bank branch located in a commercial district of a city has developed an improved process for serving customers during the noon to 1:00 P.M. lunch period. The waiting time in minutes (defined as the time the customer enters the line to when he or she reaches the teller window) of all customers during this hour is recorded over a period of one week. A random sample of 15 customers is selected, and the results are as follows: BANK1

> 4.21   5.55   3.02   5.13   4.77   2.34   3.54
> 3.20   4.50   6.10   0.38   5.12   6.46   6.19   3.79

a. Compute the mean, median, first quartile, and third quartile.
b. Compute the variance, standard deviation, range, interquartile range, coefficient of variation, and Z scores. Are there any outliers? Explain.
c. Are the data skewed? If so, how?
d. As a customer walks into the branch office during the lunch hour, she asks the branch manager how long she can expect to wait. The branch manager replies, "Almost certainly less than five minutes." On the basis of the results of (a) and (b), evaluate the accuracy of this statement.

3.49 Suppose that another branch, located in a residential area, is also concerned with the noon to 1 P.M. lunch hour. The waiting time in minutes (defined as the time the customer enters the line to the time he or she reaches the teller window) of all customers during this hour is recorded over a period of one week. A random sample of 15 customers is selected, and the results are as follows: BANK2

> 9.66   5.90   8.02   5.79   8.73   3.82   8.01
> 8.35   10.49   6.68   5.64   4.08   6.17   9.91   5.47

a. Compute the mean, median, first quartile, and third quartile.
b. Compute the variance, standard deviation, range, interquartile range, and coefficient of variation. Are there any outliers? Explain.
c. Are the data skewed? If so, how?
d. As a customer walks into the branch office during the lunch hour, he asks the branch manager how long he can expect to wait. The branch manager replies, "Almost certainly less than five minutes." On the basis of the results of (a) and (b), evaluate the accuracy of this statement.

The Empirical Rule

In most data sets, a large portion of the values tend to cluster somewhat near the median. In right-skewed data sets, this clustering occurs to the left of the mean, that is, at a value less than the mean. In left-skewed data sets, the values tend to cluster to the right of the mean, that is, at a value greater than the mean. In symmetrical data sets, where the median and mean are the same, the values often tend to cluster around the median and mean producing a bell-shaped distribution. You can use the **empirical rule** to examine the variability in bell-shaped distributions:

- Approximately 68% of the values are within a distance of ±1 standard deviation from the mean.
- Approximately 95% of the values are within a distance of ±2 standard deviations from the mean.
- Approximately 99.7% are within a distance of ±3 standard deviations from the mean.

The empirical rule helps you measure how the values distribute above and below the mean. This can help you to identify outliers when analyzing a set of numerical data. The empirical rule implies that for bell-shaped distributions only about one out of 20 values will be beyond two standard deviations from the mean in either direction. As a general rule, you can consider values not found in the interval $\mu \pm 2\sigma$ as potential outliers. The rule also implies that only about three in 1,000 will be beyond three standard deviations from the mean. Therefore, values not found in the interval $\mu \pm 3\sigma$ are almost always considered outliers. For heavily skewed data sets, or those not appearing bell-shaped for any other reason, the Chebyshev rule discussed below should be applied instead of the empirical rule.

EXAMPLE 3.29

USING THE EMPIRICAL RULE

A population of 12-ounce cans of cola is known to have a mean fill-weight of 12.06 ounces and a standard deviation of 0.02. The population is also known to be bell-shaped. Describe the distribution of fill-weights. Is it very likely that a can will contain less than 12 ounces of cola?

SOLUTION $\mu \pm \sigma = 12.06 \pm 0.02 = (12.04, 12.08)$

$$\mu \pm 2\sigma = 12.06 \pm 2(0.02) = (12.02, 12.10)$$

$$\mu \pm 3\sigma = 12.06 \pm 3(0.02) = (12.00, 12.12)$$

Using the empirical rule, approximately 68% of the cans will contain between 12.04 and 12.08 ounces, approximately 95% will contain between 12.02 and 12.10 ounces, and approximately 99.7% will contain between 12.00 and 12.12 ounces. Therefore, it is highly unlikely that a can will contain less than 12 ounces.

The Chebyshev Rule

The **Chebyshev rule** (reference 1) states that for any data set, regardless of shape, the percentage of values that are found within distances of k standard deviations from the mean must be at least

$$(1 - 1/k^2) \times 100\%$$

You can use this rule for any value of k greater than 1. Consider $k = 2$. The Chebyshev rule states that at least $[1 - (1/2)^2] \times 100\% = 75\%$ of the values must be found within ±2 standard deviations of the mean.

The Chebyshev rule is very general and applies to any type of distribution. The rule indicates *at least* what percentage of the values fall within a given distance from the mean. However, if the data set is approximately bell-shaped, the empirical rule will more accurately reflect the greater concentration of data close to the mean. Table 3.13 compares the Chebyshev and empirical rules.

TABLE 3.13

How Data Vary Around the Mean

	% of Values Found in Intervals Around the Mean	
Interval	Chebyshev (for any distribution)	Empirical Rule (bell-shaped distribution)
$(\mu - \sigma, \mu + \sigma)$	At least 0%	Approximately 68%
$(\mu - 2\sigma, \mu + 2\sigma)$	At least 75%	Approximately 95%
$(\mu - 3\sigma, \mu + 3\sigma)$	At least 88.89%	Approximately 99.7%

EXAMPLE 3.30   USING THE CHEBYSHEV RULE

As in Example 3.31, a population of 12-ounce cans of cola is known to have a mean fill-weight of 12.06 ounces and a standard deviation of 0.02. However, the shape of the population is unknown and you cannot assume that it is bell-shaped. Describe the distribution of fill-weights. Is it very likely that a can will contain less than 12 ounces of cola?

SOLUTION $\mu \pm \sigma = 12.06 \pm 0.02 = (12.04, 12.08)$

$\mu \pm 2\sigma = 12.06 \pm 2(0.02) = (12.02, 12.10)$

$\mu \pm 3\sigma = 12.06 \pm 3(0.02) = (12.00, 12.12)$

Because the distribution may be skewed, you cannot use the empirical rule. Using the Chebyshev rule, you cannot say anything about the percentage of cans containing between 12.04 and 12.08 ounces. You can state that at least 75% of the cans will contain between 12.02 and 12.10 ounces, and at least 88.89% will contain between 12.00 and 12.12 ounces. Therefore, between 0 and 11.11% of the cans contain less than 12 ounces.

You can use these two rules for understanding how data are distributed around the mean when you have sample data. In each case, use the value you calculated for $\overline{X}$ in place of μ and the value you calculated for S in place of σ. The results you compute using the sample statistics are approximations since you used sample statistics $(\overline{X}, S)$ and not population parameters (μ, σ).

PROBLEMS FOR SECTION 3.2

Learning the Basics

 3.50 The following is a set of data for a population with $N = 10$:

   7   5   11   8   3   6   2   1   9   8

a. Compute the population mean.
b. Compute the population standard deviation.

 3.51 The following is a set of data for a population with $N = 10$:

   7   5   6   6   6   4   8   6   9   3

a. Compute the population mean.
b. Compute the population standard deviation.

Applying the Concepts

 3.52 The following data represent the quarterly sales tax receipts (in thousands of dollars) submitted to the comptroller of the Village of Fair Lake for the period ending March 2004 by all 50 business establishments in that locale: TAX

10.3	11.1	9.6	9.0	14.5
13.0	6.7	11.0	8.4	10.3
13.0	11.2	7.3	5.3	12.5
8.0	11.8	8.7	10.6	9.5
11.1	10.2	11.1	9.9	9.8
11.6	15.1	12.5	6.5	7.5
10.0	12.9	9.2	10.0	12.8
12.5	9.3	10.4	12.7	10.5
9.3	11.3	10.7	11.6	7.8
10.5	7.6	10.1	8.9	8.6

a. Compute the mean, variance, and standard deviation for this population.

b. What proportion of these businesses have quarterly sales tax receipts within ±1, ±2, or ±3 standard deviations of the mean?

c. Compare and contrast your findings with what would be expected on the basis of the empirical rule. Are you surprised at the results in (b)?

 3.53 Consider a population of 1,024 mutual funds that primarily invested in large companies. You determined that μ, the mean one-year total percentage return achieved by all the funds, is 8.20 and that σ, the standard deviation, is 2.75. In addition, suppose you determined that the range in the one-year total returns is from −2.0 to 17.1 and that the quartiles are, respectively, 5.5 (Q_1) and 10.5 (Q_3). According to the empirical rule, what percentage of these funds is expected to be

a. within ±1 standard deviation of the mean?

b. within ±2 standard deviations of the mean?

c. According to the Chebyshev rule, what percentage of these funds are expected to be within ±1, ±2, or ±3 standard deviations of the mean?

d. According to the Chebyshev rule, at least 93.75% of these funds are expected to have one-year total returns between what two amounts?

3.54 The following table ASSETS represents the assets in billions of dollars of the five largest bond funds.

Bond Fund	Assets (Billions $)
Vanguard GNMA	19.5
Vanguard Total Bond Mkt. Index	16.8
Bond Fund of America A	13.7
Franklin Calif. Tax-Free Inc. A	12.8
Vanguard Short-Term Corp.	10.9

a. Compute the mean for this population of the five largest bond funds. Interpret this parameter.

b. Compute the variance and standard deviation for this population. Interpret these parameters.

c. Is there a lot of variability in the assets of the bond funds?

3.55 The data in the file ENERGY contains the per capita energy consumption in kilowatt hours for each of the 50 states and the District of Columbia during 1999.

a. Compute the mean, variance, and standard deviation for the population.

b. What proportion of these states has average per capita energy consumption within ±1 standard deviation of the mean, within ±2 standard deviations of the mean, and within ±3 standard deviations of the mean?

c. Compare and contrast your findings versus what would be expected based on the empirical rule. Are you surprised at the results in (b)?

d. Do (a) through (c) with the District of Columbia removed. How have the results changed?

3.56 The data in the file DOWRETURN give the 10-year annualized return (1994–2003) for the 30 companies in the Dow Jones Industrials.

a. Compute the mean for this population. Interpret this number.

b. Compute the variance and standard deviation for this population. Interpret the standard deviation.

c. Use the empirical rule or the Chebyshev rule, whichever is appropriate, to further explain the variation in this data set.

d. Using the results in (c), are there any outliers? Explain.

Box-Whisker Plot

The box-whisker plot is a graphical display that is used to get a general picture of a set of data. The main conceptual difference from the box-whisker plot and previous graphical displays that we have discussed is that the box-whisker plot shows some the values of descriptive statistics.

EXAMPLE 3.31

The following data shows the number of days absent from work for 50 employees in a large company. The data has been arranged into an ascending data array.

1	2	4	4	5	5	5	10	10	11
12	13	13	14	19	20	22	23	25	26
26	26	27	27	27	28	29	29	29	30
31	31	32	33	35	35	36	52	54	61
68	74	81	84	95	123	126	137	152	173

The following statistics have been calculated using the Sharp EL-9600 calculator.

Mean: 40.7   Min: 1
Median: 27.5   Max: 173
Q_1: 13
Q_3: 52
IQR: 39

The first step in drawing the box whisker plot is to lay out an appropriate horizontal scale.

The box is then formed with the first and third quartiles determining the location of the sides. The *mean* may be indicated with a '+' sign. The *median* is indicated by a line across the box.

The **inner left and right fences** are then calculated, but are *not* plotted on the diagram.

$$LIF = Q_1 - 1.5 \times IQR \qquad RIF = Q_3 + 1.5 \times IQR$$

The whiskers may now be drawn using the following procedure:

i. Imagine plotting all the data between the edge of the box and the inner fences (including data that falls on the fence) as points.
ii. Two(2) rules now apply for the whisker. Each whisker is as long as possible, but
    a) They can't go past the inner fence.
    b) They must end at a data point.

Now we can calculate the location of the **left and right outer fences** as follows:

$$LOF = LIF - 1.5 \times IQR \qquad ROF = RIF + 1.5 \times IQR$$

All data values that fall between the fences are called **outliers** and are plotted individually using a special symbol. SPSS uses a 'o' symbol to indicate outliers. Outliers are values that are *somewhat unusual* in that they lie away from the majority of the data.

All data values that lie beyond the outer fences are called **extremes** and are also plotted using a special symbol. SPSS uses an '*' symbol to indicate extremes. Extremes are *unusual* values that are often of extreme interest to the statistical analyst.

EXAMPLE 3.32

$LIF = Q_1 - 1.5 \times IQR = 13 - 1.5 \times 39 = -45.5$
$RIF = Q_3 + 1.5 \times IQR = 52 + 1.5 \times 39 = 110.5$
$LOF = RIF + 1.5 \times IQR = 110.5 + 1.5 \times 39 = 169$

The complete box-whisker plot is shown below.

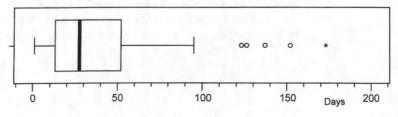

BOX-WHISKER PLOT—EXERCISES

3.57 The following data was obtained by taking a sample of stocks listed in the Financial Times. All of these stocks have had recent trends of price increases.

Stock	Closing Price	Volume ($00's)	Yield %	P/E Ratio
Abitibi-Price	20.25	31435	0.7	67.5
Agnico Eagle	19.38	7529	na	55.4
Air Canada	7.75	13010	na	na
Alberta Energy	20.75	9934	1.9	15.6
Arbor Me	18.50	770	0.3	21.8
Atlantis	1.90	3896	na	14.6
Brascan Cl	19.38	2616	5.4	57.5
Brunswick	11.12	749	3.1	na
Canadex j	33.30	62	na	20.6
Donohue Sv	16.75	1938	1.6	23.8
Electrohom	10.38	920	1.0	7.7
Finning	21.62	1658	1.5	19.3
Gennum	18.50	4	0.4	14.6
Hemlo gold	15.38	3091	1.3	24.4
Ipsco	26.25	1873	1.8	17.5
Jordan Petrol	10.62	356	na	31.3
Kerr Addison	24.50	292	2.5	37.1
Lynx Energy	11.00	10	na	13.6
MDS Helth	14.38	60	1.0	13.2
Noranda	27.50	26426	3.6	32.5
Okanaga	3.30	46	0.6	33.0
Pagurian nv	4.50	3898	6.7	13.6
Rio Algom	25.75	24697	2.3	21.6
Shaw Ind	13.75	557	1.0	16.0
Tombill A	5.50	2	3.3	7.6
Versa Services	10.12	699	2.2	21.5
Wetsmin	5.62	388	3.5	na
XL Foods	0.78	1315	na	7.8

a. Draw the box-whisker plot for the VOLUME data.
b. Draw the box-whisker plot for the YIELD data.

3.58 Refer to problem 3.20 in Descriptive Statistics Exercises—Set 2:

Draw the box-whisker plot for the travel expense data?

3.59 Refer to problem 3.21 in Descriptive Statistics Exercises—Set 2:

Draw the box-whisker plot for the number of defectives data?

3.60 Refer to problem 3.22 in Descriptive Statistics Exercises—Set 2:

Draw the box-whisker plot for the university enrolment data?

3.3   EXPLORATORY DATA ANALYSIS

Section 3.1 discussed sample statistics for numerical data that are measures of central tendency, variation, and shape. Another way of describing numerical data is through exploratory data analysis that includes the five-number summary and the box-and-whisker plot (references 5 and 6).

The Five-Number Summary

A **five-number summary** that consists of

$$X_{smallest} \quad Q_1 \quad Median \quad Q_3 \quad X_{largest}$$

provides a way to determine the shape of the distribution. Table 3.14 explains how the relationships among the "five numbers" allows you to recognize the shape of a data set.

TABLE 3.14

Relationships among the Five-Number Summary and the Type of Distribution

	Type of Distribution		
Comparison	**Left-Skewed**	**Symmetric**	**Right-Skewed**
Distance from $X_{smallest}$ to the median versus the distance from the median to $X_{largest}$.	The distance from $X_{smallest}$ to the median is greater than the distance from the median to $X_{largest}$.	Both distances are the same.	The distance from $X_{smallest}$ to the median is less than the distance from the median to $X_{largest}$.
Distance from $X_{smallest}$ to Q_1 versus the distance from Q_3 to $X_{largest}$.	The distance from $X_{smallest}$ to Q_1 is greater than the distance from Q_3 to $X_{largest}$.	Both distances are the same.	The distance from $X_{smallest}$ to Q_1 is less than the distance from Q_3 to $X_{largest}$.
Distance from Q_1 to the median versus the distance from the median to Q_3.	The distance from Q_1 to the median is greater than the distance from the median to Q_3.	Both distances are the same.	The distance from Q_1 to the median is less than the distance from the median to Q_3.

For the sample of 10 get-ready times, the smallest value is 29 minutes and the largest value is 52 minutes. Calculations done previously in section 3.1 show that the median = 39.5, the first quartile = 35, and the third quartile = 44. Therefore, the five-number summary is

$$29 \quad 35 \quad 39.5 \quad 44 \quad 52$$

The distance from $X_{smallest}$ to the median ($39.5 - 29 = 10.5$) is slightly less than the distance from the median to $X_{largest}$ ($52 - 39.5 = 12.5$). The distance from $X_{smallest}$ to Q_1 ($35 - 29 = 6$) is slightly less than the distance from Q_3 to $X_{largest}$ ($52 - 44 = 8$). Therefore, the get-ready times are slightly right-skewed.

EXAMPLE 3.33

COMPUTING THE FIVE-NUMBER SUMMARY OF THE 2003 PERCENTAGE RETURN OF SMALL CAP HIGH-RISK MUTUAL FUNDS

The 121 mutual funds that are part of the "Using Statistics" scenario (see page 64) are classified according to the risk level of the mutual funds (low, average, and high) and type (small cap, mid cap, and large cap). Compute the five-number summary of the 2003 return for the small cap mutual funds with high risk. MUTUALFUNDS2004

SOLUTION From previous computations for the 2003 return for the small cap mutual funds with high risk, the median = 53.8, the first quartile = 41.7, and the third quartile = 60.85. In addition, the smallest value in the data set is 37.3 and the largest value is 66.5. Therefore, the five-number summary is

$$37.3 \quad 41.7 \quad 53.8 \quad 60.85 \quad 66.5$$

The distance from $X_{smallest}$ to the median ($53.8 - 37.3 = 16.5$) is greater than the distance from the median to $X_{largest}$ ($66.5 - 53.8 = 12.7$). This indicates left skewness. The distance from $X_{smallest}$ to Q_1 ($41.7 - 37.3 = 4.4$) is slightly less than the distance from Q_3 to $X_{largest}$ ($66.5 - 60.85 = 5.65$). This indicates slight right-skewness. Therefore, the results are inconsistent.

The Box-and-Whisker Plot

A **box-and-whisker plot** provides a graphical representation of the data based on the five-number summary. Figure 3.2 illustrates the box-and-whisker plot for the get-ready times.

FIGURE 3.2

Box-and-Whisker Plot of the Time to Get Ready

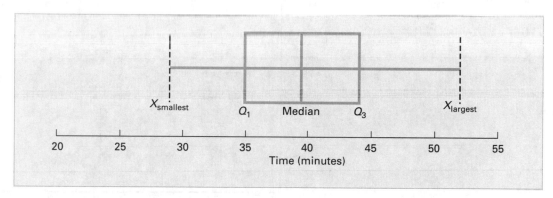

The vertical line drawn within the box represents the median. The vertical line at the left side of the box represents the location of Q_1 and the vertical line at the right side of the box represents the location of Q_3. Thus, the box contains the middle 50% of the values in the distribution. The lower 25% of the data are represented by a line (i.e., a *whisker*) connecting the left side of the box to the location of the smallest value, $X_{smallest}$. Similarly, the upper 25% of the data are represented by a whisker connecting the right side of the box to $X_{largest}$.

The box-and-whisker plot of the get-ready times in Figure 3.2 indicates very slight right-skewness since the distance between the median and the highest value is slightly more than the distance between the lowest value and the median. The right whisker is slightly longer than the left whisker.

EXAMPLE 3.34

THE BOX-AND-WHISKER PLOT OF THE 2003 PERCENTAGE RETURN OF LOW-RISK, AVERAGE RISK, AND HIGH-RISK MUTUAL FUNDS

The 121 mutual funds that are part of the "Using Statistics" scenario (see page 64) are classified according to the risk level of the mutual funds (low, average, and high) and type (small cap, mid cap, and large cap). Construct the box-and-whisker plot of the 2003 return for low-risk, average-risk, and high-risk mutual funds. MUTUALFUNDS2004

SOLUTION Figure 3.3 is the Minitab box-and-whisker plot of the 2003 return for low-risk, average-risk, and high-risk mutual funds. Minitab displays the box-and-whisker plot vertically from bottom (low) to top (high). The asterisk (*) for the average-risk fund represents the pres-

[2]If there are outliers, the whiskers in the Minitab box-and-whisker plot extend to 1.5 times the interquartile range beyond the quartiles or to the highest value.

ence of outlier values.[2] The median percentage return and the quartiles are higher for the high-risk funds than for the low-risk and average-risk funds. The average-risk funds are right-skewed due to the extremely large return of one fund (78). The high-risk funds appear left-skewed because of the long lower whisker, but the median return is closer to the first quartile than to the third quartile. The low-risk funds appear to be slightly right-skewed since the upper whisker is longer than the lower whisker.

FIGURE 3.3

Minitab Box-and-Whisker Plot of the 2003 Return for Low-Risk, Average-Risk, and High-Risk Mutual Funds

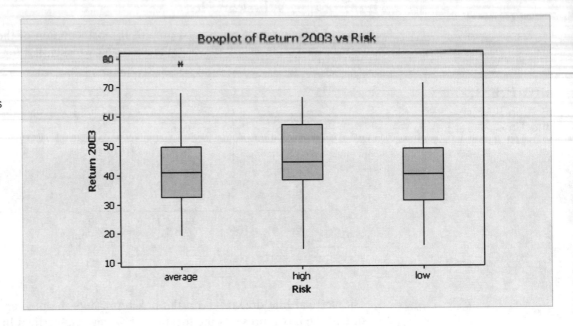

Figure 3.4 demonstrates the relationship between the box-and-whisker plot and the polygon for four different types of distributions. (*Note:* The area under each polygon is split into quartiles corresponding to the five-number summary for the box-and-whisker plot.)

FIGURE 3.4

Box-and-Whisker Plots and Corresponding Polygons for Four Distributions

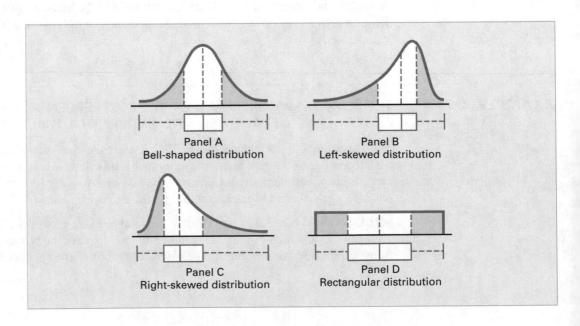

Panels A and D of Figure 3.4 are symmetric. In these distributions, the mean and median are equal. In addition, the length of the left whisker is equal to the length of the right whisker, and the median line divides the box in half.

Panel B of Figure 3.4 is left-skewed. The few small values distort the mean toward the left tail. For this left-skewed distribution, the skewness indicates that there is a heavy clustering of values at the high end of the scale (i.e., the right side); 75% of all values are found between the left edge of the box (Q_1) and the end of the right whisker ($X_{largest}$). Therefore, the long left whisker contains the smallest 25% of the values, demonstrating the distortion from symmetry in this data set.

Panel C of Figure 3.4 is right-skewed. The concentration of values is on the low end of the scale (i.e., the left side of the box-and-whisker plot). Here, 75% of all data values are found between the beginning of the left whisker ($X_{smallest}$) and the right edge of the box (Q_3), and the remaining 25% of the values are dispersed along the long right whisker at the upper end of the scale.

PROBLEMS FOR SECTION 3.3

Learning the Basics

 3.61 The following is a set of data from a sample of $n = 6$:

$$7 \quad 4 \quad 9 \quad 7 \quad 3 \quad 12$$

a. List the five-number summary.
b. Construct the box-and-whisker plot and describe the shape.
c. Compare your answer in (b) with that from problem 3.35(d). Discuss.

 3.62 The following is a set of data from a sample of $n = 7$:

$$12 \quad 7 \quad 4 \quad 9 \quad 0 \quad 7 \quad 3$$

a. List the five-number summary.
b. Construct the box-and-whisker plot and describe the shape.
c. Compare your answer in (b) with that from problem 3.36(c). Discuss.

3.63 The following is a set of data from a sample of $n = 5$:

$$7 \quad -5 \quad -8 \quad 7 \quad 9$$

a. List the five-number summary.
b. Construct the box-and-whisker plot and describe the shape.
c. Compare your answer in (b) with that from problem 3.37(c). Discuss.

Applying the Concepts

Problems 3.64–3.69 can be solved manually or by using Microsoft Excel, Minitab, or SPSS.

  3.64 A manufacturer of flashlight batteries took a sample of 13 batteries from a day's production and used them

continuously until they were drained. The number of hours until failure are in the file. **BATTERIES**

$$342 \quad 426 \quad 317 \quad 545 \quad 264 \quad 451$$
$$1{,}049 \quad 631 \quad 512 \quad 266 \quad 492 \quad 562 \quad 298$$

a. List the five-number summary.
b. Construct the box-and-whisker plot and describe the shape.

3.65 In the 2002–2003 academic year, many public universities in the United States raised tuition and fees due to a decrease in state subsidies (Mary Beth Marklein, "Public Universities Raise Tuition, Fees—and Ire," *USA Today*, August 8, 2002, 1A–2A). The following represents the change in the cost of tuition, a shared dormitory room, and the most popular meal plan from the 2001–2002 academic year to the 2002–2003 academic year for a sample of 10 public universities. **COLLEGECOST**

University	Change in Cost ($)
University of California, Berkeley	1,589
University of Georgia, Athens	593
University of Illinois, Urbana–Champaign	1,223
Kansas State University, Manhattan	869
University of Maine, Orono	423
University of Mississippi, Oxford	1,720
University of New Hampshire, Durham	708
Ohio State University, Columbus	1,425
University of South Carolina, Columbia	922
Utah State University, Logan	308

a. List the five-number summary.
b. Construct the box-and-whisker plot and describe the shape.

3.66 A software development and consulting firm located in the Phoenix metropolitan area develops software for supply chain management systems using systematic software reuse. Instead of starting from scratch when writing and developing new custom software systems, the firm uses a database of reusable components totaling more than 2,000,000 lines of code collected from 10 years of continuous reuse effort. Eight analysts at the firm were asked to estimate the reuse rate when developing a new software system. The following data are given as a percentage of the total code written for a software system that is part of the reuse database. **REUSE**

50.0 62.5 37.5 75.0 45.0 47.5 15.0 25.0

Source: M. A. Rothenberger, and K. J. Dooley, "A Performance Measure for Software Reuse Projects," Decision Sciences, 30(Fall 1999), 1131–1153.

a. List the five-number summary.
b. Construct the box-and-whisker plot and describe the shape of the data.

3.67 The following data represent the bounced check fee (in dollars) for a sample of 23 banks for direct-deposit customers who maintain a $100 balance and the monthly service fee (in dollars) for direct-deposit customers if their accounts fall below the minimum required balance of $1500 for a sample of 26 banks. **BANKCOST1 BANKCOST2**

Bounced Check Fee

26 28 20 20 21 22 25 25 18 25 15 20 18 20 25 25 22 30 30 30 15 20 29

Monthly Service Fee

12 8 5 5 6 6 10 10 9 7 10 7 7 5 0 10 6 9 12 0 5 10 8 5 5 9

Source: Extracted from "The New Face of Banking," Copyright © 2000 by Consumers Union of U.S., Inc., Yonkers, NY 10703–1057. Adapted with permission from Consumer Reports, June 2000.

a. List the five-number summary of the bounced check fee and of the monthly service fee.
b. Construct the box-and-whisker plot of the bounced check fee and the monthly service fee.
c. What similarities and differences are there in the distributions for the bounced check fee and the monthly service fee?

3.68 The following data represent the total fat for burgers and chicken items from a sample of fast-food chains. **FASTFOOD**

Burgers

19 31 34 35 39 39 43

Chicken

7 9 15 16 16 18 22 25 27 33 39

Source: Extracted from "Quick Bites," Copyright © 2001 by Consumers Union of U.S., Inc., Yonkers, NY 10703–1057. Adapted with permission from Consumer Reports, March 2001, 46.

a. List the five-number summary for the burgers and for the chicken items.
b. Construct the box-and-whisker plot for the burgers and the chicken items, and describe the shape of the distribution for the burgers and chicken items.
c. What similarities and differences are there in the distributions for the burgers and the chicken items?

3.69 A bank branch located in a commercial district of a city has developed an improved process for serving customers during the noon to 1:00 P.M. lunch period. The waiting time in minutes (operationally defined as the time the customer enters the line to the time he or she reaches the teller window) of all customers during this hour is recorded over a period of one week. A random sample of 15 customers is selected, and the results are as follows: **BANK1**

4.21 5.55 3.02 5.13 4.77 2.34 3.54
3.20 4.50 6.10 0.38 5.12 6.46 6.19 3.79

Another branch, located in a residential area, is also concerned with the noon to 1 P.M. lunch hour. The waiting time in minutes (defined as the time the customer enters the line until he or she reaches the teller window) of all customers during this hour is recorded over a period of one week. A random sample of 15 customers is selected, and the results are as follows: **BANK2**

9.66 5.90 8.02 5.79 8.73 3.82 8.01
8.35 10.49 6.68 5.64 4.08 6.17 9.91 5.47

a. List the five-number summary of the waiting time at the two bank branches.
b. Construct the box-and-whisker plot and describe the shape of the distribution of the two bank branches.
c. What similarities and differences are there in the distribution of the waiting time at the two bank branches?

Descriptive Statistics: Set 3

3.70 The following table appeared in the May 28th, 1998 issue of the Toronto Star.

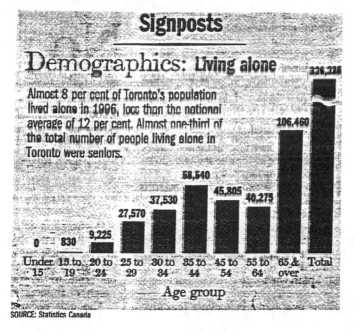

Signposts

Demographics: Living alone

Almost 8 per cent of Toronto's population lived alone in 1996, less than the national average of 12 per cent. Almost one-third of the total number of people living alone in Toronto were seniors.

SOURCE: Statistics Canada

In 1996, excluding seniors (aged 65 and over), what was the average age of people who lived alone in Toronto?

3.71 The following ad appeared in the Feb. 7th, 1997 issue of the Real Estate News. It shows the rental costs for various condos in Harbour Square.

HARBOUR SQUARE RENTALS

250 Queens Quay W.#806   2br $1,200 mo.

270 Queens Quay W.#1301 1br $1,295 mo.

270 Queens Quay W.#602   1br $1,295 mo.

270 Queens Quay W.#2302 1br   Furnished
                              $1,595 mo.

77 Harbour Sq.   #2611 1br $1,500 mo.

401 Queens Quay W.#204   1br $1,950 mo.

105 Victoria   #305   1br $1,150 mo.

                #306   2br $1,450 mo.

                #807   1br $1,200 mo.

                #1007 1br $1,200 mo.

Carrie Bynford 203-6636.
Harry Stinson R.E. Ltd.

What is the mean monthly rent for an unfurnished one bedroom condo?

3.72 Ryerson Memorial Hospital wants to compare its annual patient turnover rate per bed with other similar hospitals. The turnover rates for a sample of 80 beds at Ryerson were summarized and organized in the following frequency distribution. (An annual turnover of 21 per bed indicates that, during the year, 21 patients occupied the same hospital bed.)

Annual turnover rate patients per bed	Number of beds
10 and under 15	4
15 " " 20	9
20 " " 25	13
25 " " 30	25
30 " " 35	15
35 " " 40	7
40 " " 50	5
50 " " 60	2

a. What is the mean turnover rate?
b. What is the median turnover rate?
c. What is the standard deviation of the turnover rate?

3.73 The following table shows room rates for a resort hotel in Nova Scotia for the time period Jan.1 to Dec. 31, 2003.

2003 Room Rates	1/1– 7/3	8/3– 30/3	31/3– 31/5	1/6– 30/6	1/7– 1/9	2/9– 8/10	9/10– 1/12	2/12– 20/12	21/12– 31/12
A Oceanfront									
1 double bed	75	125	85	100	150	95	85	75	125
B Oceanfront									
2 double beds	85	135	95	110	160	105	95	85	135
C Oceanfront Effic.									
2 double beds	105	155	115	130	180	125	115	105	155
D 2 room suite									
3 double beds	120	175	130	150	200	140	130	120	175
E Oceanfront Suite									
3 double beds	140	200	150	175	225	165	150	140	200
Extra Person	5	8	5	5	10	7	5	5	10

a. For the 9 time periods, what was the mean extra person rate?
b. This hotel has 20% type A rooms, 15% type B, 30% type C, 25% type D and the remainder are type E. If the hotel was fully booked (with no extra people in any room) on Oct. 1st, then what was the mean revenue per room? What was the standard deviation?
c. On April 20th the only rooms occupied were 25 type A, 13 type B and 5 type E. What was the average revenue per bed on that day? If every bed was occupied by 2 people, what was the mean and standard deviation of the number of people per rented room on that day?

3.74 The following data refers to the OAC average grades of students being accepted into first year of several Ontario universities.

Grade Distribution of New 1st Year Students

University	60–70	70–75	75–80	80–85	85–90	≥ 90
Brock	5.8	22.1	26.7	26.0	13.1	6.3
Guelph	0	0.2	27.6	37.9	21.4	12.9
McMaster	0.1	10.5	24.2	32.4	19.7	13.1
Queen's	0	0.2	3.2	21.9	36.8	37.9
Ryerson	0.5	23.0	31.0	29.3	12.4	3.8
Toronto	0	1.2	8.9	26.0	36.6	27.3

a. Based on the above data, is the average entering grade higher for Brock or Ryerson, or is the average about the same? How do the standard deviations compare?

b. What about Ryerson compared to Queen's?

KEY FORMULAS

Sample Mean

$$\bar{X} = \frac{\sum\limits_{i=1}^{n} X_i}{n} \quad \text{(3.1)}$$

Median

$$\text{Median} = \frac{n+1}{2} \text{ ranked value} \quad \text{(3.2)}$$

First Quartile Q_1

$$Q_1 = \frac{n+1}{4} \text{ ranked value} \quad \text{(3.3)}$$

Third Quartile Q_3

$$Q_3 = \frac{3(n+1)}{4} \text{ ranked value} \quad \text{(3.4)}$$

Geometric Mean

$$\bar{X}_G = (X_1 \times X_2 \times \cdots \times X_n)^{1/n} \quad \text{(3.5)}$$

Geometric Mean Rate of Return

$$\bar{R}_G = [(1 + R_1) \times (1 + R_2) \times \cdots \times (1 + R_n)]^{1/n} - 1 \quad \text{(3.6)}$$

Range

$$\text{Range} = X_{\text{largest}} - X_{\text{smallest}} \quad \text{(3.7)}$$

Interquartile Range

$$\text{Interquartile range} = Q_3 - Q_1 \quad \text{(3.8)}$$

Sample Variance

$$S^2 = \frac{\sum\limits_{i=1}^{n}(X_i - \bar{X})^2}{n-1} \quad \text{(3.9)}$$

Sample Standard Deviation

$$S = \sqrt{S^2} = \sqrt{\frac{\sum\limits_{i=1}^{n}(X_i - \bar{X})^2}{n-1}} \quad \text{(3.10)}$$

Coefficient of Variation

$$CV = \left(\frac{S}{\bar{X}}\right)100\% \quad \text{(3.11)}$$

Z Scores

$$Z = \frac{X - \bar{X}}{S} \quad \text{(3.12)}$$

Population Mean

$$\mu = \frac{\sum\limits_{i=1}^{N} X_i}{N} \quad \text{(3.13)}$$

Population Variance

$$\sigma^2 = \frac{\sum\limits_{i=1}^{N}(X_i - \mu)^2}{N} \quad \text{(3.14)}$$

Population Standard Deviation

$$\sigma = \sqrt{\frac{\sum\limits_{i=1}^{N}(X_i - \mu)^2}{N}} \quad \text{(3.15)}$$

Sample Covariance

$$\text{cov}(X,Y) = \frac{\sum\limits_{i=1}^{n}(X_i - \bar{X})(Y_i - \bar{Y})}{n-1} \quad \text{(3.16)}$$

Sample Coefficient of Correlation

$$r = \frac{\text{cov}(X,Y)}{S_X S_Y} \quad \text{(3.17)}$$

CHAPTER REVIEW PROBLEMS

Checking Your Understanding

3.75 What are the properties of a set of numerical data?

3.76 What is meant by the property of central tendency?

3.77 What are the differences among the mean, median, and mode, and what are the advantages and disadvantages of each?

3.78 How do you interpret the first quartile, median, and third quartile?

3.79 What is meant by the property of variation?

3.80 What does the Z score measure?

3.81 What are the differences among the various measures of variation such as the range, interquartile range, variance, standard deviation, and coefficient of variation, and what are the advantages and disadvantages of each?

3.82 How does the empirical rule help explain the ways in which the values in a set of numerical data cluster and distribute?

3.83 How do the empirical rule and the Chebychev rule differ?

3.84 What is meant by the property of shape?

3.85 How do the covariance and the coefficient of correlation differ?

Applying the Concepts

You can solve problems 3.86–3.92 manually or by using Microsoft Excel, Minitab, or SPSS. We recommend that you solve problem 3.93 using Microsoft Excel, Minitab, or SPSS.

3.86 A quality characteristic of interest for a tea-bag-filling process is the weight of the tea in the individual bags. If the bags are underfilled, two problems arise. First, customers may not be able to brew the tea to be as strong as they wish. Second, the company may be in violation of the truth-in-labeling laws. For this product, the label weight on the package indicates that, on average, there are 5.5 grams of tea in a bag. If the mean amount of tea in a bag exceeds the label weight, the company is giving away product. Getting an exact amount of tea in a bag is problematic because of variation in the temperature and humidity inside the factory, differences in the density of the tea, and the extremely fast filling operation of the machine (approximately 170 bags a minute). The following table provides the weight in grams of a sample of 50 tea bags produced in one hour by a single machine. **TEABAGS**

5.65	5.44	5.42	5.40	5.53	5.34	5.54	5.45	5.52	5.41
5.57	5.40	5.53	5.54	5.55	5.62	5.56	5.46	5.44	5.51
5.47	5.40	5.47	5.61	5.53	5.32	5.67	5.29	5.49	5.55
5.77	5.57	5.42	5.58	5.58	5.50	5.32	5.50	5.53	5.58
5.61	5.45	5.44	5.25	5.56	5.63	5.50	5.57	5.67	5.36

a. Compute the mean, median, first quartile, and third quartile.
b. Compute the range, interquartile range, variance, standard deviation, and coefficient of variation.
c. Interpret the measures of central tendency and variation within the context of this problem. Why should the company producing the tea bags be concerned about the central tendency and variation?
d. Construct a box-and-whisker plot. Are the data skewed? If so, how?
e. Is the company meeting the requirement set forth on the label that, on average, there are 5.5 grams of tea in a bag? If you were in charge of this process, what changes, if any, would you try to make concerning the distribution of weights in the individual bags?

3.87 In New York State, savings banks are permitted to sell a form of life insurance called Savings Bank Life Insurance (SBLI). The approval process consists of underwriting, which includes a review of the application, a medical information bureau check, possible requests for additional medical information and medical exams, and a policy compilation stage during which the policy pages are generated and sent to the bank for delivery. The ability to deliver approved policies to customers in a timely manner is critical to the profitability of this service to the bank. During a period of one month, a random sample of 27 approved policies was selected and the following total processing time in days was recorded: **INSURANCE**

73	19	16	64	28	28	31	90	60	56	31	56	22	18
45	48	17	17	17	91	92	63	50	51	69	16	17	

a. Compute the mean, median, first quartile, and third quartile.
b. Compute the range, interquartile range, variance, standard deviation, and coefficient of variation.
c. Construct a box-and-whisker plot. Are the data skewed? If so, how?
d. What would you tell a customer who enters the bank to purchase this type of insurance policy and asks how long the approval process takes?

3.88 One of the major measures of the quality of service provided by any organization is the speed with which it responds to customer complaints. A large family-held department store selling furniture and flooring, including carpet, had undergone a major expansion in the past several years. In particular, the flooring department had expanded from 2 installation crews to an installation supervisor, a measurer, and 15 installation crews. A sample of 50 complaints concerning carpet installation was selected during a recent year. The following data represent the number of days between the receipt of the complaint and the resolution of the complaint. FURNITURE

54	5	35	137	31	27	152	2	123	81	74	27
11	19	126	110	110	29	61	35	94	31	26	5
12	4	165	32	29	28	29	26	25	1	14	13
13	10	5	27	4	52	30	22	36	26	20	23
33	68										

a. Compute the mean, median, first quartile, and third quartile.
b. Compute the range, interquartile range, variance, standard deviation, and coefficient of variation.
c. Construct a box-and-whisker plot. Are the data skewed? If so, how?
d. On the basis of the results of (a) through (c), if you had to tell the president of the company how long a customer should expect to wait to have a complaint resolved, what would you say? Explain.

3.89 A manufacturing company produces steel housings for electrical equipment. The main component part of the housing is a steel trough that is made out of a 14-gauge steel coil. It is produced using a 250-ton progressive punch press with a wipe-down operation putting two 90-degree forms in the flat steel to make the trough. The distance from one side of the form to the other is critical because of weatherproofing in outdoor applications. The company requires that the width of the trough be between 8.31 inches and 8.61 inches. The following are the widths of the troughs in inches for a sample of $n = 49$. TROUGH

8.312 8.343 8.317 8.383 8.348 8.410 8.351 8.373 8.481 8.422

8.476 8.382 8.484 8.403 8.414 8.419 8.385 8.465 8.498 8.447

8.436 8.413 8.489 8.414 8.481 8.415 8.479 8.429 8.458 8.462

8.460 8.444 8.429 8.460 8.412 8.420 8.410 8.405 8.323 8.420

8.396 8.447 8.405 8.439 8.411 8.427 8.420 8.498 8.409

a. Calculate the mean, median, range, and standard deviation for the width. Interpret these measures of central tendency and variability.
b. List the five-number summary.
c. Construct a box-and-whisker plot and describe the shape.
d. What can you conclude about the number of troughs that will meet the company's requirements of troughs being between 8.31 and 8.61 inches wide?

3.90 The manufacturing company in problem 3.89 also produces electric insulators. If the insulators break when in

use, a short-circuit is likely to occur. To test the strength of the insulators, destructive testing is carried out to determine how much *force* is required to break the insulators. Force is measured by observing how many pounds must be applied to the insulator before it breaks. The data from 30 insulators from this experiment are as follows: FORCE

1,870 1,728 1,656 1,610 1,634 1,784 1,522 1,696 1,592 1,662

1,866 1,764 1,734 1,662 1,734 1,774 1,550 1,756 1,762 1,866

1,820 1,744 1,788 1,688 1,810 1,752 1,680 1,810 1,652 1,736

a. Calculate the mean, median, range, and standard deviation for the force variable.
b. Interpret the measures of central tendency and variability in (a).
c. Construct a box-and-whisker plot and describe the shape.
d. What can you conclude about the strength of the insulators if the company requires a force measurement of at least 1,500 pounds?

3.91 Problems with a telephone line that prevent a customer from receiving or making calls are disconcerting to both the customer and the telephone company. The following data represent samples of 20 problems reported to two different offices of a telephone company and the time to clear these problems (in minutes) from the customers' lines: PHONE

Central Office I Time to Clear Problems (minutes)

1.48 1.75 0.78 2.85 0.52 1.60 4.15 3.97 1.48 3.10

1.02 0.53 0.93 1.60 0.80 1.05 6.32 3.93 5.45 0.97

Central Office II Time to Clear Problems (minutes)

7.55 3.75 0.10 1.10 0.60 0.52 3.30 2.10 0.58 4.02

3.75 0.65 1.92 0.60 1.53 4.23 0.08 1.48 1.65 0.72

For each of the two central office locations:
a. Compute the mean, median, first quartile, and third quartile.
b. Compute the range, interquartile range, variance, standard deviation, and coefficient of variation.
c. Construct a side-by-side box-and-whisker plot. Are the data skewed? If so, how?
d. On the basis of the results of (a) through (c), are there any differences between the two central offices? Explain.

3.92 In many manufacturing processes the term "work-in-process" (often abbreviated WIP) is used. In a book manufacturing plant the WIP represents the time it takes for sheets from a press to be folded, gathered, sewn, tipped on end sheets, and bound. The following data represent samples of 20 books at each of two production plants and the processing time (operationally defined as the time in days from when the books came off the press to when they were packed in cartons) for these jobs. WIP

Plant A

5.62 5.29 16.25 10.92 11.46 21.62 8.45 8.58 5.41 11.42

11.62 7.29 7.50 7.96 4.42 10.50 7.58 9.29 7.54 8.92

Plant B

9.54 11.46 16.62 12.62 25.75 15.41 14.29 13.13 13.71 10.04

5.75 12.46 9.17 13.21 6.00 2.33 14.25 5.37 6.25 9.71

For each of the two plants:

a. Compute the mean, median, first quartile, and third quartile.

b. Compute the range, interquartile range, variance, standard deviation, and coefficient of variation.

c. Construct a side-by-side box-and-whisker plot. Are the data skewed? If so, how?

d. On the basis of the results of (a) through (c), are there any differences between the two plants? Explain.

3.93 The data contained in the file CEREALS consists of the cost in dollars per ouce, calories, fiber in grams, and sugar in grams for 33 breakfast cereals.

Source: Extracted from Copyright 1999 by Consumers Union of U.S., Inc., Yonkers, NY 10703-1057. Adapted with permission from Consumer Reports, October 1999, 33–34.

For each variable:

a. Compute the mean, median, first quartile, and third quartile.

b. Compute the range, interquartile range, variance, standard deviation, and coefficient of variation.

c. Construct a box-and-whisker plot. Are the data skewed? If so, how?

d. What conclusions can you reach concerning the cost per ounce in cents, calories, giber in grams, and the sugar in grams for the 44 breakfast cereals?

RUNNING CASE
MANAGING THE *SPRINGVILLE HERALD*

For what variable in the Chapter 2 Managing the *Springville Herald* case are numerical descriptive measures needed? For the variable you identify:

1. Compute the appropriate numerical descriptive measures, and generate a box-and-whisker plot.

2. Identify another graphical display that might be useful and construct it. What conclusions can you form from that plot that cannot be made from the box-and-whisker plot? Summarize your findings in a report that can be included with the task force's study.

WEB CASE

Apply your knowledge about the proper use of numerical descriptive measures in this continuing Web Case from Chapter 2.

Visit the StockTout Investing Service Web site **www.prenhall.com/Springville/StockToutHome.htm** a second time and reexamine their supporting data and then answer the following:

1. Reexamine the data you inspected when working on the Web Case for Chapter 2. Can descriptive measures be computed for any variables? How would such summary statistics support StockTout's claims? How would those summary statistics affect your perception of StockTout's record?

2. Evaluate the methods StockTout used to summarize the results of its customer survey **www.prenhall.com/Springville/ST_Survey.htm**. Is there anything you would do differently to summarize these results?

3. Note that the last question of the survey has fewer responses. What factors may have limited the number of responses to that question?

REFERENCES

1. Kendall, M. G., and A. Stuart, *The Advanced Theory of Statistics*, vol. 1 (London: Charles W. Griffin, 1958).
2. *Microsoft Excel 2003* (Redmond, WA: Microsoft Corporation, 2002).
3. *Minitab Version 14* (State College, PA: Minitab Inc., 2004).
4. *SPSS Base 12.0 Brief Guide* (Upper Saddle River, NJ: Prentice Hall, 2003).
5. Tukey, J., *Exploratory Data Analysis* (Reading, MA: Addison-Wesley, 1977).
6. Velleman, P. F., and D. C. Hoaglin, *Applications, Basics, and Computing of Exploratory Data Analysis* (Boston, MA: Duxbury Press, 1981).

Profile of School Attendance, Education, Field of Study, Highest Level of Schooling and Earnings, for Census Metropolitan Areas[1] and Census Agglomerations, 2001 Census

Toronto	
Title	Count
Total population 15 years and over with employment income, by sex and work activity—20% Sample Data	2,659,225
Average employment income $	38,598
Standard error of average employment income $	95
Worked full year, full time	1,508,125
Average employment income $	51,112
Standard error of average employment income $	145
Worked part year or part time	1,083,230
Average employment income $	22,655
Standard error of average employment income $	106

Number of Children at Home (8) and Family Structure (7) for Census Families in Private Households, for Canada, Provinces, Territories and Federal Electoral Districts (1996 Representation Order), 2001 Census—20% Sample Data

Title	Canada				
Family Structure (7)	Total—Family structure	Total couple families	Married couples	Common-law couples	Total lone-parent families
Total families without children at home	3,059,225	3,059,225	2,431,725	627,505	0
Total families with children at home	5,311,795	4,000,605	3,469,700	530,905	1,311,185
1 child at home	2,285,110	1,483,435	1,229,055	254,375	801,675
2 children at home	2,087,355	1,716,265	1,518,475	197,790	371,085
3 or more children at home	939,325	800,905	722,170	78,730	138,425
Total children at home	9,582,615	7,579,255	6,666,195	913,060	2,003,360
Average number of children at home per family	1.1	1.1	1.1	0.8	1.5

Number of Children at Home (8) and Family Structure (7) for Census Families in Private Profile of Marital Status, Common-law Status, Families, Dwellings and Households, for Census Metropolitan Areas and Census Agglomerations, 2001 Census

Toronto	
Title	**Count**
Total number of children at home—20% Sample Data	1,641,660
Average number of children at home per census family	1.3
Number of family persons	3,993,575
Average number of persons per census family	3.1
Total number of occupied private dwellings—20% Sample Data	1,634,755
Average number of rooms per dwelling	6.1
Average number of bedrooms per dwelling	2.6

Family units[1] by income group and by net worth quintile

	1999				
	Net worth quintile[2]				
	Lowest quintile ($10,000 or less)	Second quintile ($10,000 to $65,700)	Middle quintile ($65,700 to $166,500)	Fourth quintile ($166,500 to $372,600)	Highest quintile ($372,600 and more)
	%				
All family units' income groups[3]	**100.0**	**100.0**	**100.0**	**100.0**	**100.0**
Less than $10,000	29.0	6.9	3.1	x	x
$10,000 to $19,999	37.3	22.0	15.0	9.7	4.9
$20,000 to $29,999	18.9	25.9	17.2	18.2	9.2
$30,000 to $39,999	8.3	19.4	19.6	15.8	15.3
$40,000 to $49,999	3.8	13.0	17.0	15.0	13.2
$50,000 to $74,999	x	11.6	21.5	25.7	26.6
$75,000 and more	x	x	6.6	13.3	29.6

x Data unavailable, not applicable or confidential.
1. Family units: economic families (a group of two or more persons who live in the same dwelling and are related to each other by blood, marriage, common law or adoption) and unattached individuals (a person living either alone or with others to whom he or she is unrelated).
2. All family units, whether individuals or families, are ranked from lowest to highest by the value of their net worth. The ranked family units are then divided into five groups, each containing an equal number of family units. Net worth was calculated with employer-sponsored registered pension plans included as an asset.
3. Total family income after tax.
Source: Statistics Canada, Survey of Financial Security.

Private pension assets of family units by selected characteristics

	1999			
	All family units	Family units with private pension assets		
			Average amount	Median[1] amount
	%	%	$	$
All ages[4]	**100.0**	**100.0**	**118,100**	**50,000**
Under 35	25.5	4.8	26,600	10,000
35–44	24.7	14.2	63,600	36,700
45–54	19.6	26.8	141,800	89,100
55–64	11.9	27.7	247,400	160,300
65 and older	18.3	26.6	185,300	115,700
All education levels[5]	**100.0**	**100.0**	**118,100**	**50,000**
Less than high school	26.9	16.6	94,400	47,000
Graduated high school	23.4	20.3	105,200	42,400
Non-university certificate[6]	28.3	24.0	92,500	40,500
University certificate or bachelor's degree	14.5	22.3	153,700	73,000
Degree or certificate above bachelor's[7]	6.8	16.8	228,100	125,000

1. The value at which half of all family units have lower net worth and half have higher net worth.
4. Age of the individual/family member with the highest pre-tax income.
5. Education level of the individual/family member with the highest pre-tax income.
6. Includes certificates or diplomas from trade or vocational schools, community colleges, CEGEPs, technical institutes and hospital schools of nursing.
7. Includes certificate above bachelor's degree, master's degree, doctorate, degrees in law, medicine, dentistry, veterinary medicine and optometry.
Source: Statistics Canada, Survey of Financial Security.
Last modified: November 30, 2001.

CHAPTER 4

Basic Probability

USING STATISTICS: The Consumer Electronics Company

LEARNING OBJECTIVES

In this chapter, you learn:

- Basic probability concepts
- Conditional probability
- To use Bayes' theorem to revise probabilities
- Various counting rules

USING STATISTICS

The Consumer Electronics Company

You are the marketing manager for the Consumer Electronics Company. You are analyzing the survey results of 1,000 households concerning their intentions to purchase a big-screen television set (defined as 31 inches or larger) in the next 12 months. Investigations of this type are known as intent to purchase studies. As a follow-up, you will survey the same households 12 months later to see whether they actually purchased the television set. In addition, for those who did purchase a big-screen television set, you are interested in whether they purchased a high-definition television (HDTV) set, whether they also purchased a DVD player in the last 12 months, and whether they were satisfied with their purchase of the big-screen television set. Some of the questions you would like to answer include the following:

- What is the probability that a household is planning to purchase a big-screen television set in the next year?
- What is the probability that the household will actually purchase a big-screen television set?
- What is the probability that a household is planning to purchase a big-screen television set and actually purchases the television set?
- Given that the household is planning to purchase a big-screen television set, what is the probability that the purchase is made?
- Does knowledge of whether the household *plans* to purchase the television set change the likelihood of predicting whether the household *will* purchase the television set?
- What is the probability that a household that purchases a big-screen television set will purchase an HDTV?
- What is the probability that a household that purchases a big-screen television set will also purchase a DVD player?
- What is the probability that a household that purchases a big-screen television set will be satisfied with their purchase?

Answers to these questions and others can help you develop future sales and marketing strategies. For example, should marketing campaigns for your big-screen television sets target those customers indicating intent to purchase? Are those individuals purchasing big-screen television sets easily persuaded to buy a higher-priced HDTV and/or a DVD player?

The principles of probability help bridge the worlds of descriptive statistics and inferential statistics. Reading this chapter will help you learn about different types of probabilities and how to revise probabilities in light of new information. These topics are the foundation for the probability distribution, the concept of mathematical expectation, and the binomial and Poisson distributions (topics that will be covered in Chapter 5).

4.1 BASIC PROBABILITY CONCEPTS

What is meant by the word *probability*? A **probability** is the numeric value representing the chance, likelihood, or possibility a particular event will occur, such as the price of a stock increasing, a rainy day, a nonconforming unit of production, or the outcome five in one toss of a die. In all these instances, the probability attached is a proportion or fraction whose value ranges between 0 and 1 inclusively. An event that has no chance of occurring (i.e., the **impossible event**) has a probability of 0. An event that is sure to occur (i.e., the **certain event**) has a probability of 1. There are three approaches to the subject of probability:

- *a priori* classical probability
- empirical classical probability
- subjective probability

In *a priori* **classical probability**, the probability of success is based on prior knowledge of the process involved. In the simplest case, where each outcome is equally likely, the chance of occurrence of the event is defined in Equation (4.1)

PROBABILITY OF OCCURRENCE

$$\text{Probability of occurrence} = \frac{X}{T} \qquad\qquad \textbf{(4.1)}$$

where
X = number of ways in which the event occurs
T = total number of possible outcomes

Consider a standard deck of cards that has 26 red cards and 26 black cards. The probability of selecting a black card is $26/52 = 0.50$ since there are $X = 26$ black cards and $T = 52$ total cards. What does this probability mean? If each card is replaced after it is selected, does it mean that one out of the next two cards selected will be black? No, because you cannot say for certain what will happen on the next several selections. However, you can say that in the long run, if this selection process is continually repeated, the proportion of black cards selected will approach 0.50.

EXAMPLE 4.1	FINDING *A PRIORI* PROBABILITIES

A standard six-sided die has six faces. Each face of the die contains either one, two, three, four, five, or six dots. If you roll a die, what is the probability you will get a face with five dots?

SOLUTION Each face is equally likely to occur. Since there are six faces, the probability of getting a face with five dots is $\frac{1}{6}$.

The above examples use the *a priori* classical probability approach because the number of ways the event occurs and the total number of possible outcomes are known from the composition of the deck of cards or the faces of the die.

In the **empirical classical probability** approach, the outcomes are based on observed data, not on prior knowledge of a process. Examples of this type of probability are the proportion of individuals in the "Using Statistics" scenario who actually purchase a television, the proportion of registered voters who prefer a certain political candidate, or the proportion of students who have a part-time job. For example, if you take a survey of students and 60% state that they have a part-time job, then there is a 0.60 probability that an individual student has a part-time job.

The third approach to probability, **subjective probability**, differs from the other two approaches because subjective probability differs from person to person. For example, the development team for a new product may assign a probability of 0.6 to the chance of success for the product while the president of the company is less optimistic and assigns a probability of 0.3. The assignment of subjective probabilities to various outcomes is usually based on a combination of an individual's past experience, personal opinion, and analysis of a particular situation. Subjective probability is especially useful in making decisions in situations in which you cannot use *a priori* classical probability or empirical classical probability.

Events and Sample Spaces

The basic elements of probability theory are the individual outcomes of a variable under study. You need the following definitions to understand probabilities.

Each possible outcome of a variable is referred to as an **event**.

A **simple event** is described by a single characteristic.

For example, when you toss a coin, the two possible outcomes are heads and tails. Each of these represents a simple event. When you roll a standard six-sided die in which the six faces of the die contain either one, two, three, four, five, or six dots, there are six possible simple events. An event can be any one of these simple events, a set of them, or a subset of all of them. For example, the event of an *even number of dots* consists of three simple events (i.e., two, four, or six dots).

A **joint event** is an event that has two or more characteristics.

Getting two heads on the toss of two coins is an example of a joint event since it consists of heads on the toss of the first coin and heads on the toss of the second coin.

The **complement** of event A (given the symbol A') includes all events that are not part of A.

The complement of a head is a tail since that is the only event that is not a head. The complement of face five is not getting face five. Not getting face five consists of getting face one, two, three, four, or six.

The collection of all the possible events is called the **sample space**.

The sample space for tossing a coin consists of heads and tails. The sample space when rolling a die consists of one, two, three, four, five, and six dots.

EXAMPLE 4.2

EVENTS AND SAMPLE SPACES

The "Using Statistics" scenario on page 114 concerns The Consumer Electronics Company. Table 4.1 presents the results of the sample of 1,000 households in terms of purchase behavior for big-screen television sets.

TABLE 4.1

Purchase Behavior for Big-Screen Television Sets

	ACTUALLY PURCHASED		
PLANNED TO PURCHASE	Yes	No	Total
Yes	200	50	250
No	100	650	750
Total	300	700	1,000

What is the sample space? Give examples of simple events and joint events.

SOLUTION The sample space consists of the 1,000 respondents. Simple events are "planned to purchase," "did not plan to purchase," "purchase," and "did not purchase." The complement of the event "planned to purchase" is "did not plan to purchase." The event "planned to purchase and actually purchased" is a joint event because the respondent must plan to purchase the television set *and* actually purchase it.

Contingency Tables and Venn Diagrams

There are several ways to present a sample space. Table 4.1 uses a **table of cross-classifications** to present a sample space. This table is also called a **contingency table**. You get the values in the cells of the table by subdividing the sample space of 1,000 households according to whether someone planned to purchase and actually purchased the big-screen television set. For example, 200 of the respondents planned to purchase a big-screen television set and subsequently did purchase the big-screen television set.

A **Venn diagram** is a second way to present a sample space. This diagram graphically represents the various events as "unions" and "intersections" of circles. Figure 4.1 presents a typical Venn diagram for a two-variable situation, with each variable having only two events (A and A', B and B'). The circle on the left (the red one) represents all events that are part of A. The circle on the right (the yellow one) represents all events that are part of B. The area contained within circle A and circle B (center area) is the **intersection** of A and B (written as $A \cap B$), since it is part of A and also part of B. The total area of the two circles is the **union** of A and B (written as $A \cup B$) and contains all outcomes that are just part of event A, just part of event B, or part of both A and B. The area in the diagram outside of $A \cup B$ contains outcomes that are neither part of A nor part of B.

You must define A and B in order to develop a Venn diagram. You can define either event as A or B, as long as you are consistent in evaluating the various events. For the consumer electronics example, you can define the events as follows:

A = planned to purchase	B = actually purchased
A' = did not plan to purchase	B' = did not actually purchase

In drawing the Venn diagram (see Figure 4.2), you must determine the value of the intersection of A and B in order to divide the sample space into its parts. $A \cap B$ consists of all 200 households who planned to purchase and actually purchased a big-screen television set. The remainder of event A (planned to purchase) consists of the 50 households who planned to purchase a big-screen television set but did not actually purchase one. The remainder of event B (actually purchased) consists of the 100 households who did not plan to purchase a big-screen television set but actually purchased one. The remaining 650 households represent those who neither planned to purchase nor actually purchased a big-screen television set.

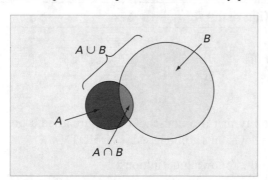

FIGURE 4.1

Venn Diagram for Events A and B

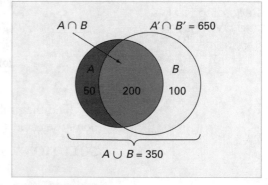

FIGURE 4.2

Venn Diagram for the Consumer Electronics Example

Simple (Marginal) Probability

Now you can answer some of the questions posed in the "Using Statistics" scenario. Since the results are based on data collected in a survey (see Table 4.1), you can use the empirical classical probability approach.

As stated previously, the most fundamental rule for probabilities is that they range in value from 0 to 1. An impossible event has a probability of 0, and an event that is certain to occur has a probability of 1.

Simple probability refers to the probability of occurrence of a simple event, $P(A)$. A simple probability in the "Using Statistics" scenario is the probability of planning to purchase a big-screen television set. How can you determine the probability of selecting a household that planned to purchase a big-screen television set? Using Equation (4.1):

$$\text{Probability of occurrence} = \frac{X}{T}$$

$$P(\text{planned to purchase}) = \frac{\text{number who planned to purchase}}{\text{total number of households}}$$

$$= \frac{250}{1,000} = 0.25$$

Thus, there is a 0.25 (or 25%) chance that a household planned to purchase a big-screen television set.

Simple probability is also called **marginal probability**, because you can compute the total number of successes (those who planned to purchase) from the appropriate margin of the contingency table (see Table 4.1). Example 4.3 illustrates another application of simple probability.

EXAMPLE 4.3	**COMPUTING THE PROBABILITY THAT THE BIG-SCREEN TELEVISION SET PURCHASED WILL BE AN HDTV**

In the "Using Statistics" follow-up survey, additional questions were asked of the 300 households that actually purchased a big-screen television set. Table 4.2 indicates the consumers' responses to whether the television set purchased was an HDTV and whether they also purchased a DVD player in the last 12 months.

TABLE 4.2

Purchase Behavior Regarding HDTVs and DVD Players

	PURCHASED DVD		
PURCHASED HDTV	**Yes**	**No**	**Total**
HDTV	38	42	80
Not HDTV	70	150	220
Total	108	192	300

Find the probability that if a household that purchased a big-screen television set is randomly selected, the television set purchased is an HDTV.

SOLUTION Using the following definitions:

A = purchased an HDTV B = purchased a DVD player

A' = did not purchase an HDTV B' = did not purchase a DVD player

$$P(\text{HDTV}) = \frac{\text{number of HDTV television sets}}{\text{total number of television sets}}$$

$$= \frac{80}{300} = 0.267$$

There is a 26.7% chance that a randomly selected big-screen television set purchase is an HDTV.

Joint Probability

Marginal probability refers to the probability of occurrence of simple events. **Joint probability** refers to the probability of an occurrence involving two or more events. An example of joint probability is the probability that you will get heads on the first toss of a coin and heads on the second toss of a coin.

Referring to Table 4.1, those individuals who planned to purchase and actually purchased a big-screen television set consist only of the outcomes in the single cell "yes—planned to purchase *and* yes—actually purchased." Because this group consists of 200 households, the probability of picking a household that planned to purchase *and* actually purchased a big-screen television set is

$$P(\text{planned to purchase } and \text{ actually purchased}) = \frac{\text{planned to purchase } and \text{ actually purchased}}{\text{total number of respondents}}$$

$$= \frac{200}{1,000} = 0.20$$

Example 4.4 also demonstrates how to determine joint probability.

EXAMPLE 4.4

DETERMINING THE JOINT PROBABILITY THAT A BIG-SCREEN TELEVISION SET CUSTOMER PURCHASED AN HDTV AND A DVD PLAYER

In Table 4.2, the purchases are cross-classified as HDTV or not HDTV and whether or not the household purchased a DVD player. Find the probability that a randomly selected household that purchased a big-screen television set also purchased an HDTV and a DVD player.

SOLUTION Using Equation (4.1),

$$P(\text{HDTV } and \text{ DVD player}) = \frac{\text{number that purchased an HDTV } and \text{ a DVD player}}{\text{total number of big-screen television set purchasers}}$$

$$= \frac{38}{300} = 0.127$$

Therefore, you have a 12.7% chance that a randomly selected household that purchased a big-screen television set purchased an HDTV and a DVD player.

You can view the marginal probability of a particular event using the concept of joint probability just discussed. The marginal probability of an event consists of a set of joint probabilities. For example, if B consists of two events, B_1 and B_2, then $P(A)$, the probability of event A, consists of the joint probability of event A occurring with event B_1 and the joint probability of event A occurring with event B_2. Use Equation (4.2) to compute marginal probabilities.

MARGINAL PROBABILITY

$$P(A) = P(A \text{ and } B_1) + P(A \text{ and } B_2) + \cdots + P(A \text{ and } B_k) \qquad (4.2)$$

where $B_1, B_2, \ldots, B_k$ are k mutually exclusive and collectively exhaustive events.

Mutually exclusive events and collectively exhaustive events are defined as follows.

Two events are **mutually exclusive** if both the events cannot occur simultaneously.

Heads and tails in a coin toss are mutually exclusive events. The result of a coin toss cannot simultaneously be a head and a tail.

A set of events is **collectively exhaustive** if one of the events must occur.

Heads and tails in a coin toss are collectively exhaustive events. One of them must occur. If heads does not occur, tails must occur. If tails does not occur, heads must occur.

Being male and being female are mutually exclusive and collectively exhaustive events. No one is both (they are mutually exclusive), and everyone is one or the other (they are collectively exhaustive).

You can use Equation (4.2) to compute the marginal probability of planned to purchase a big-screen television set.

$$P(\text{planned to purchase}) = P(\text{planned to purchase } and \text{ purchased})$$
$$+ P(\text{planned to purchase } and \text{ did not purchase})$$

$$= \frac{200}{1,000} + \frac{50}{1,000}$$

$$= \frac{250}{1,000} = 0.25$$

You will get the same result if you add the number of outcomes that make up the simple event "planned to purchase."

General Addition Rule

The general addition rule allows you to find the probability of event "*A or B*." This rule considers the occurrence of either event *A* or event *B* or both *A* and *B*. How can you determine the probability that a household planned to purchase *or* actually purchased a big-screen television set? The event "planned to purchase *or* actually purchased" includes all households who planned to purchase and all households who actually purchased the big-screen television set. You examine each cell of the contingency table (Table 4.1) to determine whether it is part of this event. From Table 4.1, the cell "planned to purchase *and* did not actually purchase" is part of the event, because it includes respondents who planned to purchase. The cell "did not plan to purchase *and* actually purchased" is included because it contains respondents who actually purchased. Finally, the cell "planned to purchase *and* actually purchased" has both characteristics of interest. Therefore, the probability of planned to purchase *or* actually purchased is:

$$P(\text{planned to purchase } or \text{ actually purchased}) = P(\text{planned to purchase } and \text{ did not actually}$$
$$\text{purchase}) + P(\text{did not plan to purchase } and$$
$$\text{actually purchased}) + P(\text{planned to purchase}$$
$$and \text{ actually purchased})$$

$$= \frac{50}{1,000} + \frac{100}{1,000} + \frac{200}{1,000} = \frac{350}{1,000} = 0.35$$

Often you will find it easier to determine $P(A \text{ or } B)$, the probability of the event *A or B*, by using the **general addition rule** defined in Equation (4.3).

GENERAL ADDITION RULE

The probability of *A or B* is equal to the probability of *A* plus the probability of *B* minus the probability of *A and B*.

$$P(A \text{ or } B) = P(A) + P(B) - P(A \text{ and } B) \qquad \textbf{(4.3)}$$

Applying this equation to the previous example produces the following result:

$$P(\text{planned to purchase } or \text{ actually purchased}) = P(\text{planned to purchase}) + P(\text{actually purchased})$$
$$- P(\text{planned to purchase } and \text{ actually purchased})$$

$$= \frac{250}{1,000} + \frac{300}{1,000} - \frac{200}{1,000}$$

$$= \frac{350}{1,000} = 0.35$$

The general addition rule consists of taking the probability of *A* and adding it to the probability of *B*, and then subtracting the joint event of *A and B* from this total because the joint event has already been included both in computing the probability of *A* and the probability of *B*. Referring to Table 4.1, if the outcomes of the event "planned to purchase" are added to those of the event "actually purchased," the joint event "planned to purchase *and* actually purchased" has been included in each of these simple events. Therefore, because this joint event has been double-counted, you must subtract it to provide the correct result. Example 4.5 illustrates another application of the general addition rule.

EXAMPLE 4.5

USING THE GENERAL ADDITION RULE FOR THE HOUSEHOLDS THAT PURCHASED BIG-SCREEN TELEVISION SETS

In Example 4.3, the purchases were cross-classified as an HDTV or not HDTV and whether or not the household purchased a DVD player. Find the probability that among households that purchased a big-screen television set, that they purchased an HDTV or a DVD player.

SOLUTION Using Equation (4.3) above,

$$P(\text{HDTV } or \text{ DVD player}) = P(\text{HDTV}) + P(\text{DVD player}) - P(\text{HDTV } and \text{ DVD player})$$

$$= \frac{80}{300} + \frac{108}{300} - \frac{38}{300}$$

$$= \frac{150}{300} = 0.50$$

Therefore, you have a 50.0% chance that a randomly selected household that purchased a big-screen television set purchased an HDTV or a DVD player.

PROBLEMS FOR SECTION 4.1

Learning the Basics

 4.1 Two coins are tossed.
a. Give an example of a simple event.
b. Give an example of a joint event.
c. What is the complement of a head on the first toss?

4.2 An urn contains 12 red balls and 8 white balls. One ball is to be selected from the urn.
a. Give an example of a simple event.
b. What is the complement of a red ball?

4.3 Given the following contingency table:

	B	*B'*
A	10	20
A'	20	40

What is the probability of
a. event *A*?
b. event *A'*?
c. event *A and B*?
d. event *A or B*?

 4.4 Given the following contingency table:

	B	*B'*
A	10	30
A'	25	35

What is the probability of
a. event *A'*?
b. event *A and B*?
c. event *A' and B'*?
d. event *A' or B'*?

Applying the Concepts

4.5 For each of the following, indicate whether the type of probability involved is an example of *a priori* classical probability, empirical classical probability, or subjective probability.
a. The next toss of a fair coin will land on heads.
b. Italy will win soccer's World Cup the next time the competition is held.
c. The sum of the faces of two dice will be 7.
d. The train taking a commuter to work will be more than 10 minutes late.

4.6 For each of the following, state whether the events created are mutually exclusive and collectively exhaustive. If they are not mutually exclusive and collectively exhaustive, either reword the categories to make them mutually exclusive and collectively exhaustive or explain why this would not be useful.
a. Registered voters in the United States were asked whether they registered as Republicans or Democrats.
b. Respondents were classified by type of car he or she drives: American, European, Japanese, or none.
c. People were asked, "Do you currently live in (i) an apartment or (ii) a house?"
d. A product was classified as defective or not defective.

4.7 The probability of each of the following events is zero. For each, state why.
a. A voter in the United States who is registered as a Republican and a Democrat

b. A product that is defective and not defective
c. An automobile that is a Ford and a Toyota

 4.8 A U.S. Census American Housing Survey studied how U.S. homeowners get to work ("How People Get to Work," *USA Today* Snapshots, February 25, 2003, 1A). Suppose that the survey consisted of a sample of 1,000 homeowners and 1,000 renters.

Drives to Work	Homeowner	Renter	Total
Yes	824	681	1,505
No	176	319	495
Total	1,000	1,000	2,000

a. Give an example of a simple event.
b. Give an example of a joint event.
c. What is the complement of "drives to work"?
d. Why is "drives to work and is a homeowner" a joint event?

4.9 Referring to the contingency table in problem 4.8, if a respondent is selected at random, what is the probability that he or she
a. drives to work?
b. drives to work and is a homeowner?
c. drives to work or is a homeowner?
d. Explain the difference in the results in (b) and (c).

4.10 A yield improvement study at a semiconductor manufacturing facility provided defect data for a sample of 450 wafers. The following table presents a summary of the responses to two questions: "Was a particle found on the die that produced the wafer?" and "Is the wafer good or bad?"

QUALITY OF WAFER	CONDITION OF DIE		
	No Particles	Particles	Totals
Good	320	14	334
Bad	80	36	116
Totals	400	50	450

Source: S. W. Hall, Analysis of Defectivity of Semiconductor Wafers by Contingency Table, Proceedings Institute of Environmental Sciences, Vol. 1 (1994), 177–183.

a. Give an example of a simple event.
b. Give an example of a joint event.
c. What is the complement of a good wafer?
d. Why is a "good wafer" and a die "with particles" a joint event?

4.11 Referring to the contingency table in problem 4.10, if a wafer is selected at random, what is the probability that
a. it was produced from a die with no particles?
b. it is a bad wafer and was produced from a die with no particles?

c. it is a bad wafer or was produced from a die with particles?

d. Explain the difference in the results in (b) and (c).

 4.12 Are large companies less likely to offer board members stock options than small- to mid-sized companies? A survey conducted by the Segal Company of New York found that in a sample of 189 large companies, 40 offered stock options to their board members as part of their non-cash compensation packages. For small to mid sized companies, 13 of the 180 surveyed indicated that they offer stock options as part of their non cash compensation packages to their board members (Kemba J. Dunham, "The Jungle: Focus on Recruitment, Pay and Getting Ahead," *The Wall Street Journal*, August 21, 2001, B6). Construct a contingency table or a Venn diagram to evaluate the probabilities. If a company is selected at random, what is the probability that the company

a. offered stock options to their board members?

b. is small- to mid-sized and did not offer stock options to their board members?

c. is small- to mid-sized or offered stock options to their board members?

d. Explain the difference in the results in (b) and (c).

4.13 Are whites more likely to claim bias? A survey conducted by Barry Goldman ("White Fight: A Researcher Finds Whites Are More Likely to Claim Bias," *The Wall Street Journal*, Work Week, April 10, 2001, A1) found that of 56 white workers terminated, 29 claimed bias. Of 407 black workers terminated, 126 claimed bias. Construct a contingency table or a Venn diagram to evaluate the probabilities. If a worker is selected at random, what is the probability that he or she

a. claimed bias?

b. is black and did not claim bias?

c. is black or claimed bias?

d. Explain the difference in the results in (b) and (c).

4.14 A sample of 500 respondents was selected in a large metropolitan area to study consumer behavior. Among the questions asked was "Do you enjoy shopping for clothing?" Of 240 males, 136 answered yes. Of 260 females, 224 answered yes. Construct a contingency table or a Venn diagram to evaluate the probabilities. What is the probability that a respondent chosen at random

a. enjoys shopping for clothing?

b. is a female and enjoys shopping for clothing?

c. is a female or enjoys shopping for clothing?

d. is a male or a female?

4.15 Each year, ratings are compiled concerning the performance of new cars during the first 90 days of use. Suppose that the cars have been categorized according to whether the car needs warranty-related repair (yes or no) and the country in which the company manufacturing the car is based (United States or not United States). Based on the data collected, the probability that the new car needs a warranty repair is 0.04, the probability that the car is manufactured by a U.S.-based company is 0.60, and the probability that the new car needs a warranty repair *and* was manufactured by a U.S.-based company is 0.025. Construct a contingency table or a Venn diagram to evaluate the probabilities of a warranty-related repair. What is the probability that a new car selected at random

a. needs a warranty-related repair?

b. needs a warranty repair and is manufactured by a company based in the United States?

c. needs a warranty repair or was manufactured by a U.S.-based company?

d. needs a warranty repair or was not manufactured by a U.S.-based company?

4.2 CONDITIONAL PROBABILITY

Computing Conditional Probabilities

Each example in section 4.1 involved finding the probability of an event when sampling from the entire sample space. How do you determine the probability of an event if certain information about the events involved are already known?

Conditional probability refers to the probability of event *A*, given information about the occurrence of another event *B*.

CONDITIONAL PROBABILITY

The probability of *A* given *B* is equal to the probability of *A and B* divided by the probability of *B*

$$P(A|B) = \frac{P(A \text{ and } B)}{P(B)} \qquad \textbf{(4.4a)}$$

The probability of *B* given *A* is equal to the probability of *A and B* divided by the probability of *A*

$$P(B\mid A) = \frac{P(A\ and\ B)}{P(A)} \qquad \textbf{(4.4b)}$$

where

$$P(A\ and\ B) = \text{joint probability of } A \text{ and } B$$

$$P(A) = \text{marginal probability of } A$$

$$P(B) = \text{marginal probability of } B$$

Referring to the "Using Statistics" scenario involving the purchase of big-screen television sets, suppose you were told that a household planned to purchase a big-screen television set. Now, what is the probability that the household actually purchased the television set? In this example the objective is to find *P* (actual purchase | planned to purchase). Here you are given the information that the household planned to purchase the big-screen television set. Therefore, the sample space does not consist of all 1,000 households in the survey. It consists of only those households that planned to purchase the big-screen television set. Of 250 such households, 200 actually purchased the big-screen television set. Therefore, (see Table 4.1 or Figure 4.2) the probability that a household actually purchased the big-screen television set given that he or she planned to purchase is

$$P(\text{actually purchased}\mid\text{planned to purchase}) = \frac{\text{planned to purchase } and \text{ actually purchased}}{\text{planned to purchase}}$$

$$= \frac{200}{250} = 0.80$$

You can also use Equation (4.4b) to compute this result.

$$P(B\mid A) = \frac{P(A\ and\ B)}{P(A)}$$

where

$$\text{event } A = \text{planned to purchase}$$

$$\text{event } B = \text{actually purchased}$$

Then

$$P(\text{actually purchased}\mid\text{planned to purchase}) = \frac{200/1{,}000}{250/1{,}000}$$

$$= \frac{200}{250} = 0.80$$

Example 4.6 further illustrates conditional probability.

EXAMPLE 4.6

FINDING A CONDITIONAL PROBABILITY CONCERNING THE HOUSEHOLDS THAT ACTUALLY PURCHASED A BIG-SCREEN TELEVISION SET

Table 4.2 is a contingency table for whether the household purchased an HDTV and a DVD player. Of the households that purchased an HDTV, what is the probability that they also purchased a DVD player?

SOLUTION Because you know that the household purchased an HDTV, the sample space is reduced to 80 households. Of these 80 households, 38 also purchased a DVD player. Therefore, the probability that a household purchased a DVD player, given that the household purchased an HDTV, is:

$$P(\text{purchased DVD player} \mid \text{purchased HDTV}) = \frac{\text{number purchasing HDTV } and \text{ DVD player}}{\text{number purchasing HDTV}}$$

$$= \frac{38}{80} = 0.475$$

If you use Equation (4.4a):

$$A = \text{purchased DVD player} \qquad B = \text{purchased HDTV}$$

then

$$P(A \mid B) = \frac{P(A \text{ and } B)}{P(B)} = \frac{38/300}{80/300} = 0.475$$

Therefore, given that the household purchased an HDTV, there is a 47.5% chance that the household also purchased a DVD player. You can compare this conditional probability to the marginal probability of purchasing a DVD player, which is $108/300 = 0.36$, or 36%. These results tell you that households that purchased an HDTV are more likely to purchase a DVD player than are households that purchased a big-screen television set that is not an HDTV.

Decision Trees

In Table 4.1 households are classified according to whether they planned to purchase and whether they actually purchased a big-screen television set. A **decision tree** is an alternative to the contingency table. Figure 4.3 represents the decision tree for this example.

FIGURE 4.3

Decision Tree for the Consumer Electronics Example

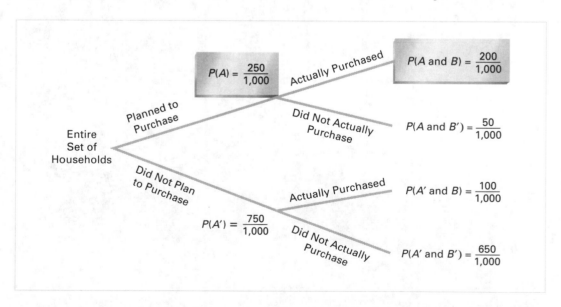

In Figure 4.3, beginning at the left with the entire set of households, there are two "branches" for whether or not the household planned to purchase a big-screen television set. Each of these branches has two subbranches, corresponding to whether the household actually purchased or did not actually purchase the big-screen television set. The probabilities at the end of the initial branches represent the marginal probabilities of A and A'. The probabilities at the end of each of the four subbranches represent the joint probability for each combination of events A and B. You compute the conditional probability by dividing the joint probability by the appropriate marginal probability.

For example, to compute the probability that the household actually purchased given that the household planned to purchase the big-screen television set, take P (planned to purchase *and* actually purchased) and divide by P (planned to purchase). From Figure 4.3

$$P(\text{actually purchased}\mid\text{planned to purchase}) = \frac{200/1,000}{250/1,000}$$

$$= \frac{200}{250} = 0.80$$

Example 4.7 illustrates how to construct a decision tree.

EXAMPLE 4.7

FORMING THE DECISION TREE FOR THE HOUSEHOLDS THAT PURCHASED BIG-SCREEN TELEVISION SETS

Using the cross-classified data in Table 4.2, construct the decision tree. Use the decision tree to find the probability that a household purchased a DVD player, given that the household purchased an HDTV.

SOLUTION The decision tree for purchased a DVD player and an HDTV is displayed in Figure 4.4. Using Equation (4.4b) and the following definitions:

$$A = \text{purchased HDTV} \quad B = \text{purchased DVD player}$$

$$P(B\mid A) = \frac{P(A \text{ and } B)}{P(A)} = \frac{38/300}{80/300} = 0.475$$

FIGURE 4.4

Decision Tree for Purchased a DVD Player and an HDTV

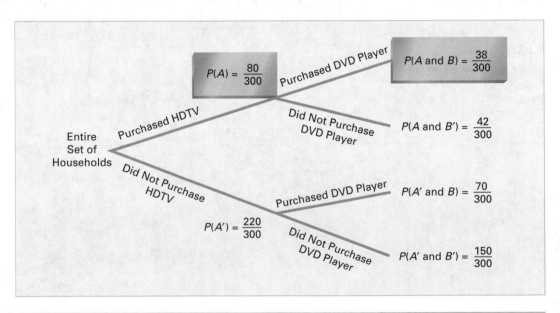

Statistical Independence

In the example concerning the purchase of big-screen television sets, the conditional probability is 200/250 = 0.80 that the selected household actually purchased the big-screen television set, given that the household planned to purchase. The simple probability of selecting a household that actually purchased is 300/1,000 = 0.30. This result shows that the prior knowledge that the household planned to purchase affected the probability that the household actually purchased the television set. In other words, the outcome of one event is *dependent* on the outcome of a second event.

When the outcome of one event does *not* affect the probability of occurrence of another event, the events are said to be statistically independent. **Statistical independence** can be determined by using Equation (4.5).

STATISTICAL INDEPENDENCE

Two events A and B are statistically independent if and only if

$$P(A \mid B) = P(A) \tag{4.5}$$

where

$$P(A \mid B) = \text{conditional probability of } A \text{ given } B$$

$$P(A) = \text{marginal probability of } A$$

Example 4.8 demonstrates the use of Equation (4.5).

EXAMPLE 4.8

DETERMINING STATISTICAL INDEPENDENCE

In the follow-up survey of the 300 households that actually purchased big-screen television sets, the households were asked if they were satisfied with their purchase. Table 4.3 cross-classifies the responses to the satisfaction question with their responses to whether the television set was an HDTV.

TABLE 4.3

Satisfaction with Purchase of Big-Screen Television Sets

	SATISFIED WITH PURCHASE?		
TYPE OF TELEVISION	Yes	No	Total
HDTV	64	16	80
Not HDTV	176	44	220
Total	240	60	300

Determine whether being satisfied with the purchase and type of television set purchased are statistically independent.

SOLUTION For these data,

$$P(\text{satisfied} \mid \text{HDTV}) = \frac{64/300}{80/300} = \frac{64}{80} = 0.80$$

which is equal to

$$P(\text{satisfied}) = \frac{240}{300} = 0.80$$

Thus, being satisfied with the purchase and type of television set purchased are statistically independent. Knowledge of one event does not affect the probability of the other event.

Multiplication Rules

By manipulating the formula for conditional probability, you can determine the joint probability $P(A \text{ and } B)$ from the conditional probability of an event. The **general multiplication rule** is derived using Equation (4.4a),

$$P(A|B) = \frac{P(A \text{ and } B)}{P(B)}$$

and solving for the joint probability $P(A \text{ and } B)$.

GENERAL MULTIPLICATION RULE

The probability of A and B is equal to the probability of A given B times the probability of B.

$$P(A \text{ and } B) = P(A \mid B)P(B) \qquad \textbf{(4.6)}$$

Example 4.9 demonstrates the use of the general multiplication rule.

EXAMPLE 4.9

USING THE MULTIPLICATION RULE

Consider the 80 households that purchased an HDTV. In Table 4.3 you see that 64 households are satisfied with their purchase and 16 households are dissatisfied. Suppose two households are randomly selected from the 80 customers. Find the probability that both households are satisfied with their purchase.

SOLUTION Here you can use the multiplication rule in the following way. If:

$$A = \text{second household selected is satisfied}$$

$$B = \text{first household selected is satisfied}$$

then, using Equation (4.6)

$$P(A \text{ and } B) = P(A \mid B)P(B)$$

The probability that the first household is satisfied with the purchase is 64/80. However, the probability that the second household is also satisfied with the purchase depends on the result of the first selection. If the first household is not returned to the sample after the satisfaction level is determined (sampling without replacement), then the number of households remaining will be 79. If the first household is satisfied, the probability that the second is also satisfied is 63/79, because 63 satisfied households remain in the sample. Therefore,

$$P(A \text{ and } B) = \left(\frac{63}{79}\right)\left(\frac{64}{80}\right) = 0.6380$$

There is a 63.80% chance that both of the households sampled will be satisfied with their purchase.

The **multiplication rule for independent events** is derived by substituting $P(A)$ for $P(A \mid B)$ in Equation (4.6).

MULTIPLICATION RULE FOR INDEPENDENT EVENTS

If A and B are statistically independent, the probability of A and B is equal to the probability of A times the probability of B.

$$P(A \text{ and } B) = P(A)P(B) \qquad \textbf{(4.7)}$$

If this rule holds for two events, A and B, then A and B are statistically independent. Therefore, there are two ways to determine statistical independence.

1. Events A and B are statistically independent if and only if $P(A \mid B) = P(A)$.
2. Events A and B are statistically independent if and only if $P(A \text{ and } B) = P(A)P(B)$.

Marginal Probability Using the General Multiplication Rule

In section 4.1 marginal probability was defined using Equation (4.2). You can state the formula for marginal probability using the general multiplication rule. If

$$P(A) = P(A \text{ and } B_1) + P(A \text{ and } B_2) + \cdots + P(A \text{ and } B_k)$$

then, using the general multiplication rule, Equation (4.8) defines the marginal probability.

> **MARGINAL PROBABILITY USING THE GENERAL MULTIPLICATION RULE**
>
> $$P(A) = P(A \mid B_1)P(B_1) + P(A \mid B_2)P(B_2) + \cdots + P(A \mid B_k)P(B_k) \quad \textbf{(4.8)}$$
>
> where $B_1, B_2, \ldots, B_k$ are the k mutually exclusive and collectively exhaustive events.

To illustrate this equation, refer to Table 4.1. Using Equation (4.8), the probability of planning to purchase is:

$$P(A) = P(A \mid B_1)P(B_1) + P(A \mid B_2)P(B_2)$$

where

$P(A)$ = probability of "planned to purchase"

$P(B_1)$ = probability of "actually purchased"

$P(B_2)$ = probability of "did not actually purchase"

$$P(A) = \left(\frac{200}{300} \right)\left(\frac{300}{1,000} \right) + \left(\frac{50}{700} \right)\left(\frac{700}{1,000} \right)$$

$$= \frac{200}{1,000} + \frac{50}{1,000} = \frac{250}{1,000} = 0.25$$

PROBLEMS FOR SECTION 4.2

Learning the Basics

PH Grade ASSIST

4.16 Given the following contingency table:

	B	B'
A	10	20
A'	20	40

What is the probability of
a. $A \mid B$?
b. $A \mid B'$?
c. $A' \mid B'$?
d. Are events A and B statistically independent?

4.17 Given the following contingency table:

	B	B'
A	10	30
A'	25	35

What is the probability of
a. $A \mid B$?
b. $A' \mid B'$?
c. $A \mid B'$?
d. Are events A and B statistically independent?

PH Grade **4.18** If $P(A \text{ and } B) = 0.4$ and $P(B) = 0.8$, find
ASSIST $P(A \mid B)$.

PH Grade **4.19** If $P(A) = 0.7$ and $P(B) = 0.6$, and if A and
ASSIST B are statistically independent, find $P(A \text{ and } B)$.

PH Grade **4.20** If $P(A) = 0.3$ and $P(B) = 0.4$, and if $P(A \text{ and } B) = 0.2$, are A and B statistically independent?

Applying the Concepts

SELF **4.21** A U.S. Census American Housing Survey
Test studied how U.S. homeowners get to work ("How People Get to Work," *USA Today* Snapshots, February 25, 2003, 1A). Suppose that the survey consisted of a sample of 1,000 homeowners and 1,000 renters.

Drives to Work	Homeowner	Renter	Total
Yes	824	681	1,505
No	176	319	495
Total	1,000	1,000	2,000

a. Given that the respondent drives to work, what then is the probability that he or she is a homeowner?
b. Given that the respondent is a homeowner, what then is the probability that he or she drives to work?
c. Explain the difference in the results in (a) and (b).
d. Are the two events, driving to work and whether the respondent is a homeowner or a renter, statistically independent?

4.22 A yield improvement study at a semiconductor manufacturing facility provided defect data for a sample of 450 wafers. The following table presents a summary of the responses to two questions: "Were particles found on the die that produced the wafer?" and "Is the wafer good or bad?"

	CONDITION OF DIE		
QUALITY OF WAFER	**No Particles**	**Particles**	**Totals**
Good	320	14	334
Bad	80	36	116
Totals	400	50	450

Source: S. W. Hall, Analysis of Defectivity of Semiconductor Wafers by Contingency Table, Proceedings Institute of Environmental Sciences, *Vol. 1 (1994), 177–183.*

a. Suppose you know that a wafer is bad. What then is the probability that it was produced from a die that had particles?
b. Suppose you know that a wafer is good. What then is the probability that it was produced from a die that had particles?
c. Are the two events, a good wafer and a die with no particle, statistically independent? Explain.

PH Grade **4.23** Are large companies less likely to offer
ASSIST board members stock options than small- to mid-sized companies? A survey conducted by the Segal Company of New York found that in a sample of 189 large companies, 40 offered stock options to their board members as part of their non-cash compensation packages. For small- to mid-sized companies, 43 of the 180 surveyed indicated that they offer stock options as part of their non-cash compensation packages to their board members (Kemba J. Dunham, "The Jungle: Focus on Recruitment, Pay and Getting Ahead," *The Wall Street Journal*, August 21, 2001, B6).

a. Given that a company is large, what then is the probability that the company offered stock options to their board members?
b. Given that a company is small- to mid-sized, what then is the probability that the company offered stock options to their board members?
c. Is the size of the company statistically independent of whether stock options are offered to their board members? Explain.

4.24 Are whites more likely to claim bias? A survey conducted by Barry Goldman ("White Fight: A Researcher Finds Whites Are More Likely to Claim Bias," *The Wall Street Journal*, Work Week, April 10, 2001, A1) found that of 56 white workers terminated, 29 claimed bias. Of 407 black workers terminated, 126 claimed bias.

a. Given that a worker is white, what then is the probability that the worker has claimed bias?
b. Given that a worker has claimed bias, what then is the probability that the worker is white?
c. Explain the difference in the results in (a) and (b).
d. Are the two events, "being white" and "claiming bias," statistically independent? Explain.

4.25 A sample of 500 respondents was selected in a large metropolitan area to study consumer behavior with the following results:

	GENDER		
ENJOYS SHOPPING FOR CLOTHING	**Male**	**Female**	**Total**
Yes	136	224	360
No	104	36	140
Total	240	260	500

a. Suppose the respondent chosen is a female. What, then, is the probability that she does not enjoy shopping for clothing?
b. Suppose the respondent chosen enjoys shopping for clothing. What, then, is the probability that the individual is a male?
c. Are enjoying shopping for clothing and the gender of the individual statistically independent? Explain.

4.26 Each year, ratings are compiled concerning the performance of new cars during the first 90 days of use. Suppose that the cars have been categorized according to whether or not the car needs warranty-related repair (yes or no) and the country in which the company manufacturing the car is based (United States or not United States). Based on the data collected, the probability that the new car needs a warranty repair is 0.04, the probability that the car is manufactured by a U.S. based company is 0.60, and the probability that the new car needs a warranty repair *and* was manufactured by a U.S.-based company is 0.025.

a. Suppose you know that a company based in the United States manufactured the car. What, then, is the probability that the car needs a warranty repair?

b. Suppose you know that a company based in the United States did not manufacture the car. What, then, is the probability that the car needs a warranty repair?

c. Are need for a warranty repair and location of the company manufacturing the car statistically independent?

4.27 In 34 of the 54 years from 1950 to 2003, the S&P 500 finished higher after the first five days of trading. In 29 of those 34 years the S&P 500 finished higher for the year. Is a good first week a good omen for the upcoming year? The following table gives the first-week and annual performance over this 54-year period.

FIRST WEEK	S & P 500'S ANNUAL PERFORMANCE	
	Higher	Lower
Higher	29	5
Lower	10	10

Source: Adapted from Aaron Luchetti, "Stocks Enjoy a Good First Week," The Wall Street Journal, January 12, 2004, C1.

a. If a year is selected at random, what is the probability that the S&P finished higher for the year?

b. Given that the S&P 500 finished higher after the first five days of trading, what then is the probability that it finished higher for the year?

c. Are the two events, first-week performance and annual performance, statistically independent? Explain.

d. In 2004, the S&P 500 was up 0.9% after the first five days. Look up the 2004 annual performance of the S&P 500 at **finance.yahoo.com**. Comment on the results.

4.28 A standard deck of cards is being used to play a game. There are four suits (hearts, diamonds, clubs, and spades), each having 13 faces (ace, 2, 3, 4, 5, 6, 7, 8, 9, 10, jack, queen, and king), making a total of 52 cards. This complete deck is thoroughly mixed, and you will receive the first two cards from the deck without replacement.

a. What is the probability that both cards are queens?

b. What is the probability that the first card is a 10 and the second card is a 5 or 6?

c. If you were sampling with replacement, what would be the answer in (a)?

d. In the game of blackjack, the picture cards (jack, queen, king) count as 10 points and the ace counts as either 1 or 11 points. All other cards are counted at their face value. Blackjack is achieved if your two cards total 21 points. What is the probability of getting blackjack in this problem?

 4.29 A box of nine golf gloves contains two left-handed gloves and seven right-handed gloves.

a. If two gloves are randomly selected from the box without replacement, what is the probability that both gloves selected will be right-handed?

b. If two gloves are randomly selected from the box without replacement, what is the probability there will be one right-handed glove and one left-handed glove selected?

c. If three gloves are selected with replacement, what is the probability that all three will be left-handed?

d. If you were sampling with replacement, what would be the answers to (a) and (b)?

4.3 BAYES' THEOREM

Bayes' theorem is used to revise previously calculated probabilities when you have new information. Developed by the Rev. Thomas Bayes in the eighteenth century (see reference 1), Bayes' theorem is an extension of what you previously learned about conditional probability.

You can apply Bayes' theorem to the following situation. The Consumer Electronics Company is considering marketing a new model of television set. In the past, 40% of the television sets introduced by the company have been successful and 60% have been unsuccessful. Before introducing the television set to the marketplace, the marketing research department conducts an extensive study and releases a report, either favorable or unfavorable. In the past, 80% of the successful television sets had received a favorable market research report and 30% of the unsuccessful television sets had received a favorable report. For the new model of television set under consideration, the marketing research department has issued a favorable report. What is the probability that the television set will be successful?

Bayes' theorem is developed from the definition of conditional probability. To find the conditional probability of B given A, consider Equation (4.4b) [originally presented on page 124 and given below]:

$$P(B|A) = \frac{P(A \text{ and } B)}{P(A)} = \frac{P(A|B)P(B)}{P(A)}$$

Bayes' theorem is derived by substituting Equation (4.8) for $P(A)$ in the above equation.

BAYES' THEOREM

$$P(B_i|A) = \frac{P(A|B_i)P(B_i)}{P(A|B_1)P(B_1) + P(A|B_2)P(B_2) + \cdots + P(A|B_k)P(B_k)} \quad (4.9)$$

where B_i is the ith event out of k mutually exclusive and collectively exhaustive events.

To use Equation (4.9) for the television marketing example, let

event S = successful television set   event F = favorable report

event S' = unsuccessful television set   event F' = unfavorable report

and

$$P(S) = 0.40 \qquad P(F|S) = 0.80$$
$$P(S') = 0.60 \qquad P(F|S') = 0.30$$

Then, using Equation (4.9),

$$P(S|F) = \frac{P(F|S)P(S)}{P(F|S)P(S) + P(F|S')P(S')}$$

$$= \frac{(0.80)(0.40)}{(0.80)(0.40) + (0.30)(0.60)}$$

$$= \frac{0.32}{0.32 + 0.18} = \frac{0.32}{0.50}$$

$$= 0.64$$

The probability of a successful television set, given that a favorable report was received, is 0.64. Thus, the probability of an unsuccessful television set, given that a favorable report was received, is $1 - 0.64 = 0.36$. Table 4.4 summarizes the computation of the probabilities and Figure 4.5 presents the decision tree.

TABLE 4.4 Bayes' Theorem Calculations for the Television-Marketing Example

Event S_i	Prior Probability $P(S_i)$	Conditional Probability $P(F \mid S_i)$	Joint Probability $P(F \mid S_i)P(S_i)$	Revised Probability $P(S_i \mid F)$
S = successful television set	0.40	0.80	0.32	$0.32/0.50 = 0.64 = P(S \mid F)$
S' = unsuccessful television set	0.60	0.30	0.18	$0.18/0.50 = 0.36 = P(S' \mid F)$
			0.50	

FIGURE 4.5

Decision Tree for
Marketing a New
Television Set

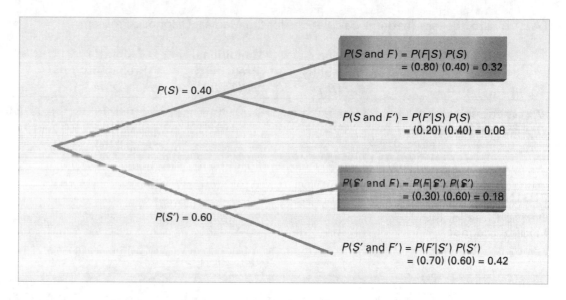

$P(S) = 0.40$

$P(S \text{ and } F) = P(F|S)\, P(S)$
$= (0.80)\,(0.40) = 0.32$

$P(S \text{ and } F') = P(F'|S)\, P(S)$
$= (0.20)\,(0.40) = 0.08$

$P(S' \text{ and } F) = P(F|S')\, P(S')$
$= (0.30)\,(0.60) = 0.18$

$P(S') = 0.60$

$P(S' \text{ and } F') = P(F'|S')\, P(S')$
$= (0.70)\,(0.60) = 0.42$

Example 4.10 applies Bayes' theorem to a medical diagnosis problem.

EXAMPLE 4.10

USING BAYES' THEOREM IN A MEDICAL DIAGNOSIS PROBLEM

The probability that a person has a certain disease is 0.03. Medical diagnostic tests are available to determine whether the person actually has the disease. If the disease is actually present, the probability that the medical diagnostic test will give a positive result (indicating that the disease is present) is 0.90. If the disease is not actually present, the probability of a positive test result (indicating that the disease is present) is 0.02. Suppose that the medical diagnostic test has given a positive result (indicating that the disease is present). What is the probability that the disease is actually present? What is the probability of a positive test result?

SOLUTION

Let   event D = has disease   event T = test is positive

            event D' = does not have disease   event T' = test is negative

and

$$P(D) = 0.03 \qquad P(T\,|\,D) = 0.90$$
$$P(D') = 0.97 \qquad P(T\,|\,D') = 0.02$$

Using Equation (4.9),

$$P(D\,|\,T) = \frac{P(T|D)P(D)}{P(T|D)P(D) + P(T|D')P(D')}$$

$$= \frac{(0.90)(0.03)}{(0.90)(0.03) + (0.02)(0.97)}$$

$$= \frac{0.0270}{0.0270 + 0.0194} = \frac{0.0270}{0.0464}$$

$$= 0.582$$

The probability that the disease is actually present given a positive result has occurred (indicating that the disease is present) is 0.582. Table 4.5 summarizes the computation of the probabilities and Figure 4.6 presents the decision tree.

TABLE 4.5 Bayes' Theorem Calculations for the Medical Diagnosis Problem

Event D_i	Prior Probability $P(D_i)$	Conditional Probability $P(T \mid D_i)$	Joint Probability $P(T \mid D_i)P(D_i)$	Revised Probability $P(D_i \mid T)$
D = has disease	0.03	0.90	0.0270	$0.0270/0.0464 = 0.582 = P(D \mid T)$
D' = does not have disease	0.97	0.02	0.0194	$0.0194/0.0464 = 0.418 = P(D' \mid T)$
			0.0464	

FIGURE 4.6

Decision Tree for the Medical Diagnosis Problem

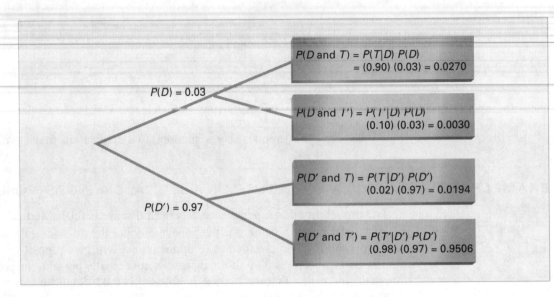

The denominator in Bayes' theorem represents $P(T)$, the probability of a positive test result, which in this case is 0.0464 or 4.64%.

PROBLEMS FOR SECTION 4.3

Learning the Basics

 4.30 If $P(B) = 0.05$, $P(A \mid B) = 0.80$, $P(B') = 0.95$, and $P(A \mid B') = 0.40$, find $P(B \mid A)$.

 4.31 If $P(B) = 0.30$, $P(A \mid B) = 0.60$, $P(B') = 0.70$, and $P(A \mid B') = 0.50$, find $P(B \mid A)$.

Applying the Concepts

4.32 In Example 4.10, suppose that the probability that a medical diagnostic test will give a positive result if the disease is not present is reduced from 0.02 to 0.01. Given this information,

a. If the medical diagnostic test has given a positive result (indicating the disease is present), what is the probability that the disease is actually present?

b. If the medical diagnostic test has given a negative result (indicating that the disease is not present), what is the probability that the disease is not present?

  4.33 An advertising executive is studying television viewing habits of married men and women during prime-time hours. On the basis of past viewing records, the executive has determined that during prime time, husbands are watching television 60% of the time. When the husband is watching television, 40% of the time the wife is also watching. When the husband is not watching television, 30% of the time the wife is watching television. Find the probability that

a. if the wife is watching television, the husband is also watching television.

b. the wife is watching television in prime time.

4.34 Olive Construction Company is determining whether it should submit a bid for a new shopping center. In the past, Olive's main competitor, Base Construction Company, has submitted bids

70% of the time. If Base Construction Company does not bid on a job, the probability that Olive Construction Company will get the job is 0.50. If Base Construction Company bids on a job, the probability that Olive Construction Company will get the job is 0.25.

a. If Olive Construction Company gets the job, what is the probability that Base Construction Company did not bid?

b. What is the probability that Olive Construction Company will get the job?

4.35 Laid-off workers who become entrepreneurs because they cannot find meaningful employment with another company are known as *entrepreneurs by necessity*. The Wall Street Journal reports that these entrepreneurs by necessity are less likely to grow into large businesses than are *entrepreneurs by choice* (Jeff Bailey, "Desire—More Than Need—Builds a Business," *The Wall Street Journal*, May 21, 2001, B4). This article states that 89% of the entrepreneurs in the United States are entrepreneurs by choice and 11% are entrepreneurs by necessity. Only 2% of entrepreneurs by necessity expect their new business to employ 20 or more people within five years, while 14% of entrepreneurs by choice expect to employ at least 20 people within five years.

a. If an entrepreneur is selected at random and that individual expects that their new business will employ 20 or more people within five years, what then is the probability that this individual is an entrepreneur by choice?

b. Discuss several possible reasons why entrepreneurs by choice are more likely to believe that they will grow their business.

4.36 The editor of a textbook publishing company is trying to decide whether to publish a proposed business statistics textbook. Information on previous textbooks published indicates that 10% are huge successes, 20% are modest successes, 40% break even, and 30% are losers. However, before a publishing decision is made, the book will be reviewed. In the past, 99% of the huge successes received favorable reviews, 70% of the moderate successes received favorable reviews, 40% of the break-even books received favorable reviews, and 20% of the losers received favorable reviews.

a. If the proposed text receives a favorable review, how should the editor revise the probabilities of the various outcomes to take this information into account?

b. What proportion of textbooks receives favorable reviews?

4.37 A municipal bond service has three rating categories (*A, B,* and *C*). Suppose that in the past year, of the municipal bonds issued throughout the United States, 70% were rated *A*, 20% were rated *B*, and 10% were rated *C*. Of the municipal bonds rated *A*, 50% were issued by cities, 40% by suburbs, and 10% by rural areas. Of the municipal bonds rated *B*, 60% were issued by cities, 20% by suburbs, and 20% by rural areas. Of the municipal bonds rated *C*, 90% were issued by cities, 5% by suburbs, and 5% by rural areas.

a. If a new municipal bond is to be issued by a city, what is the probability that it will receive an A rating?

b. What proportion of municipal bonds is issued by cities?

c. What proportion of municipal bonds is issued by suburbs?

4.4   COUNTING RULES

In Equation (4.1), the probability of occurrence of an outcome was defined as the number of ways the outcome occurs, divided by the total number of possible outcomes. In many instances, there are a large number of possible outcomes and it is difficult to determine the exact number. In these circumstances, rules for counting the number of possible outcomes have been developed. In this section five different counting rules are presented.

COUNTING RULE 1

If any one of k different mutually exclusive and collectively exhaustive events can occur on each of n trials, the number of possible outcomes is equal to

$$k^n \tag{4.10}$$

EXAMPLE 4.11   COUNTING RULE 1

Suppose you toss a coin five times. What is the number of different possible outcomes (the sequences of heads and tails)?

SOLUTION If you toss a coin (having two sides) five times, using Equation (4.10), the number of outcomes is $2^5 = 2 \times 2 \times 2 \times 2 \times 2 = 32$.

EXAMPLE 4.12   ROLLING A DIE TWICE

Suppose you roll a die twice. How many different possible outcomes can occur?

SOLUTION If a die (having six sides) is rolled twice, using Equation (4.10) the number of different outcomes is $6^2 = 36$.

The second counting rule is a more general version of the first, and allows for the number of possible events to differ from trial to trial.

COUNTING RULE 2

If there are k_1 events on the first trial, k_2 events on the second trial, . . . , and k_n events on the nth trial, then the number of possible outcomes is

$$(k_1)(k_2) \ldots (k_n) \qquad (4.11)$$

EXAMPLE 4.13   COUNTING RULE 2

A state motor vehicle department would like to know how many license plate numbers are available if the license plates consist of three letters followed by three numbers.

SOLUTION Using Equation (4.11), if a license plate consists of three letters followed by three numbers (0 through 9), the total number of possible outcomes is $(26)(26)(26)(10)(10)(10) =$ 17,576,000.

EXAMPLE 4.14   DETERMINING THE NUMBER OF DIFFERENT DINNERS

A restaurant menu has a price-fixed complete dinner that consists of an appetizer, entrée, beverage, and dessert. You have a choice of five appetizers, ten entrées, three beverages, and six desserts. Determine the total number of possible dinners.

SOLUTION Using Equation (4.11), the total number of possible dinners is $(5)(10)(3)(6) = 900$.

The third counting rule involves the computation of the number of ways that a set of items can be arranged in order.

COUNTING RULE 3

The number of ways that all n items can be arranged in order is

$$n! = (n)(n - 1) \ldots (1)$$

where $n!$ is called n *factorial* and 0! is defined as 1.

EXAMPLE 4.15   COUNTING RULE 3

If a set of six textbooks is to be placed on a shelf, in how many ways can the six books be arranged?

SOLUTION To begin, you must realize that any of the six books could occupy the first position on the shelf. Once the first position is filled, there are five books to choose from in filling the second. You continue this assignment procedure until all the positions are occupied. The number of ways that you can arrange six books is

$$n! = 6! = (6)(5)(4)(3)(2)(1) = 720$$

In many instances you need to know the number of ways in which a subset of the entire group of items can be arranged in *order*. Each possible arrangement is called a **permutation**.

COUNTING RULE 4

Permutations: The number of ways of arranging X objects selected from n objects in order is

$$_nP_X = \frac{n!}{(n-X)!} \tag{4.13}$$

EXAMPLE 4.16   COUNTING RULE 4

Modifying Example 4.15, if you have six textbooks, but there is room for only four books on the shelf, in how many ways can you arrange these books on the shelf?

SOLUTION Using Equation (4.13), the number of ordered arrangements of four books selected from six books is equal to

$$_nP_X = \frac{n!}{(n-X)!} = \frac{6!}{(6-4)!} = \frac{(6)(5)(4)(3)(2)(1)}{(2)(1)} = 360$$

In many situations you are not interested in the *order* of the outcomes, but only in the number of ways that X items can be selected from n items, *irrespective of order*. This rule is called the rule of **combinations**.

COUNTING RULE 5

Combinations: The number of ways of selecting X objects from n objects, irrespective of order, is equal to

$$_nC_X = \frac{n!}{X!(n-X)!} \tag{4.14}$$

Comparing this rule to the previous one, you see that it differs only in the inclusion of a term $X!$ in the denominator. When permutations were used, all of the arrangements of the X objects are distinguishable. With combinations, the $X!$ possible arrangements of objects are irrelevant.

EXAMPLE 4.17   COUNTING RULE 5

Modifying Example 4.16, if the order of the books on the shelf is irrelevant, in how many ways can you arrange these books on the shelf?

SOLUTION Using Equation (4.14), the number of combinations of four books selected from six books is equal to

$$_nC_X = \frac{n!}{X!(n-X)!} = \frac{6!}{4!(6-4)!} = \frac{(6)(5)(4)(3)(2)(1)}{(4)(3)(2)(1)(2)(1)} = 15$$

PROBLEMS FOR SECTION 4.4

Applying the Concepts

 4.38 If there are ten multiple-choice questions on an exam, each having three possible answers, how many different sequences of answers are there?

4.39 A lock on a bank vault consists of three dials, each with 30 positions. In order for the vault to open, each of the three dials must be in the correct position.
a. How many different possible "dial combinations" are there for this lock?
b. What is the probability that if you randomly select a position on each dial, you will be able to open the bank vault?
c. Explain why "dial combinations" are not mathematical combinations expressed by Equation (4.14).

4.40 a. If a coin is tossed seven times, how many different outcomes are possible?
b. If a die is tossed seven times, how many different outcomes are possible?
c. Discuss the differences in your answers to (a) and (b).

 4.41 A particular brand of women's jeans is available in seven different sizes, three different colors, and three different styles. How many different jeans does the store manager need to order to have one pair of each type?

4.42 You would like to make a salad that consists of lettuce, tomato, cucumber, and sprouts. You go to the supermarket intending to purchase one type of each of these ingredients. You discover that there are eight types of lettuce, four types of tomatoes, three types of cucumbers, and three types of sprouts for sale at the supermarket. How many different salads do you have to choose from?

 4.43 If each letter is used once, how many different four-letter "words" can be made from the letters E, L, O, and V?

4.44 In Major League Baseball, there are five teams in the Western Division of the National League: Arizona, Los Angeles, San Francisco, San Diego, and Colorado. How many different orders of finish are there for these five teams? Do you believe that all these orders are equally likely? Discuss.

4.45 Referring to problem 4.44, how many different orders of finish are possible for the first four positions?

4.46 A gardener has six rows available in his vegetable garden to place tomatoes, eggplant, peppers, cucumbers, beans, and lettuce. Each vegetable will be allowed one and only one row. How many ways are there to position these vegetables in his garden?

 4.47 The Big Triple at the local racetrack consists of picking the correct order of finish of the first three horses in the ninth race. If there are 12 horses entered in today's ninth race, how many Big Triple outcomes are there?

4.48 The Quinella at the local racetrack consists of picking the horses that will place first and second in a race *irrespective* of order. If eight horses are entered in a race, how many Quinella combinations are there?

 4.49 A student has seven books that she would like to place in an attaché case. However, only four books can fit into the attaché case. Regardless of the arrangement, how many ways are there of placing four books into the attaché case?

4.50 A daily lottery is conducted in which two winning numbers are selected out of 100 numbers. How many different combinations of winning numbers are possible?

4.51 A reading list for a course contains 20 articles. How many ways are there to choose three articles from this list?

4.5   ETHICAL ISSUES AND PROBABILITY

Ethical issues can arise when any statements relating to probability are presented to the public, particularly when these statements are part of an advertising campaign for a product or service. Unfortunately, many people are not comfortable with numerical concepts (see reference 3) and tend to misinterpret the meaning of the probability. In some instances, the misinterpretation is not intentional, but in other cases, advertisements may unethically try to mislead potential customers.

One example of a potentially unethical application of probability relates to advertisements for state lotteries. When purchasing a lottery ticket, the customer selects a set of numbers (such as 6) from a larger list of numbers (such as 54). Although virtually all participants know that they are unlikely to win the lottery, they also have very little idea of how unlikely it is for them to select all 6 winning numbers from the list of 54 numbers. They have even less of an idea of the probability of winning a consolation prize by selecting either 4 or 5 winning numbers.

Given this background, you might consider a recent commercial for a state lottery that stated, "We won't stop until we have made everyone a millionaire," to be deceptive and possibly unethical. Given the fact that the lottery brings millions of dollars into the state treasury, the state is never going to stop running it, although in our lifetime no one can be sure of becoming a millionaire by winning the lottery.

Another example of a potentially unethical application of probability relates to an investment newsletter promising a 90% probability of a 20% annual return on investment. To make the claim in the newsletter an ethical one, the investment service needs to (a) explain the basis on which this probability estimate rests, (b) provide the probability statement in another format such as 9 chances in 10, and (c) explain what happens to the investment in the 10% of the cases in which a 20% return is not achieved (e.g., Is the entire investment lost?).

PROBLEMS FOR SECTION 4.5

Applying the Concepts

4.52 Write an advertisement for the state lottery that ethically describes the probability of winning.

4.53 Write an advertisement for the investment newsletter that ethically states the probability of a 20% return.

CHAPTER REVIEW PROBLEMS

Checking Your Understanding

4.54 What are the differences between *a priori* classical probability, empirical classical probability, and subjective probability?

4.55 What is the difference between a simple event and a joint event?

4.56 How can you use the addition rule to find the probability of occurrence of event *A or B*?

4.57 What is the difference between mutually exclusive events and collectively exhaustive events?

4.58 How does conditional probability relate to the concept of statistical independence?

4.59 How does the multiplication rule differ for events that are and are not independent?

4.60 How can you use Bayes' theorem to revise probabilities in light of new information?

4.61 What is the difference between a permutation and a combination?

Applying the Concepts

4.62 A soft-drink bottling company maintains records concerning the number of unacceptable bottles of soft drink from the filling and capping machines. Based on past data, the probability that a bottle came from machine I and was nonconforming is 0.01 and the probability that a bottle came from machine II and was nonconforming is 0.025. Half the bottles are filled on machine I and the other half are filled on machine II. If a filled bottle of soft drink is selected at random, what is the probability that

a. it is a nonconforming bottle?
b. it was filled on machine I *and* is a conforming bottle?
c. it was filled on machine I *or* is a conforming bottle?
d. Suppose you know that the bottle was produced on machine I. What is the probability that it is nonconforming?
e. Suppose you know that the bottle is nonconforming. What is the probability that it was produced on machine I?
f. Explain the difference in the answers to (d) and (e).
(*Hint:* Construct a 2 × 2 contingency table or a Venn diagram to evaluate the probabilities.)

4.63 A survey asked workers which aspects of his or her job are extremely important. The results in percentages are as follows:

Is Aspect Extremely Important?		
Aspect of Job	**Men**	**Women**
Good relationship with boss	63%	77%
Up-to-date equipment	59	69
Resources to do the job	55	74
Easy commute	48	60
Flexible hours at work	40	53
Able to work at home	21	34

Source: Extracted from "Snapshot," USA Today, May 15, 2000.

Suppose the survey was based on the responses of 500 men and 500 women. Construct a contingency table for the different responses concerning each aspect of the job. If a respondent is chosen at random, what is the probability that

a. he or she feels that a good relationship with the boss is an important aspect of the job?
b. he or she feels that an easy commute is an important aspect of the job?
c. the person is a male and feels that a good relationship with the boss is an important aspect of the job?
d. the person is a female and feels that having flexible hours is an important aspect of the job?
e. Given that the person feels that having a good relationship with the boss is an important aspect of the job, what is the probability that the person is a male?
f. Are any of the things that workers say are extremely important aspects of a job statistically independent of the gender of the respondent? Explain.

4.64 Many companies use Web sites to conduct business transactions such as taking orders or performing financial exchanges. These sites are referred to as transactional public Web sites. An analysis of 490 firms listed in the Fortune 500 identified firms by their level of sales and whether or not the firm had a transactional public Web site (D. Young, and J. Benamati, "A Cross-Industry Analysis of Large Firm Transactional Public Web Sites," *Mid-American Journal of Business*, 19(2004), 37–46). The results of this analysis are given in the following table.

SALES (IN BILLIONS OF DOLLARS)	TRANSACTIONAL PUBLIC WEB SITE	
	Yes	No
Greater than $10 billion	71	88
Up to $10 billion	99	232

a. Give an example of a simple event and a joint event.
b. What is the probability that a firm in the Fortune 500 has a transactional public Web site?
c. What is the probability that a firm in the Fortune 500 has sales in excess of ten billion dollars and a transactional Web site?
d. Are the events sales in excess of ten billion dollars and has a transactional public Web site independent? Explain.

4.65 The owner of a restaurant serving Continental-style entrées was interested in studying ordering patterns of patrons for the Friday to Sunday weekend time period. Records were maintained that indicated the demand for dessert during the same time period. The owner decided to study two other variables along with whether a dessert was ordered: the gender of the individual and whether a beef entrée was ordered. The results are as follows:

DESSERT ORDERED	GENDER		
	Male	Female	Total
Yes	96	40	136
No	224	240	464
Total	320	280	600

DESSERT ORDERED	BEEF ENTRÉE		
	Yes	No	Total
Yes	71	65	136
No	116	348	464
Total	187	413	600

A waiter approaches a table to take an order. What is the probability that the first customer to order at the table

a. orders a dessert?
b. orders a dessert *or* a beef entrée?
c. is a female *and* does not order a dessert?
d. is a female *or* does not order a dessert?
e. Suppose the first person that the waiter takes the dessert order from is a female. What is the probability that she does not order dessert?
f. Are gender and ordering dessert statistically independent?
g. Is ordering a beef entrée statistically independent of whether the person orders dessert?

4.66 Unsolicited commercial e-mail messages containing product advertisements, commonly referred to as spam, are routinely deleted before being read by more than 80% of all e-mail users. Furthermore, a small percentage of those reading the spam actually follow through and purchase items. Yet, many companies use these unsolicited e-mail advertisements because of the extremely low cost involved. Movies Unlimited, a mail-order video and DVD business in Philadelphia, is one of the more successful companies in terms of generating sales through this form of e-marketing. Ed Weiss, general manager of Movies Unlimited, estimates that somewhere from 15% to 20% of their e-mail recipients read the advertisements. Moreover, approximately 15% of those who read the advertisements place an order (Stacy Forster, "E-Marketers Look to Polish Spam's Rusty Image," *The Wall Street Journal*, May 22, 2002, D2).

a. Using Mr. Weiss's lower estimate that the probability a recipient will read the advertisement is 0.15, what is the probability that a recipient will read the advertisement and place an order?
b. Movies Unlimited uses a 175,000-customer database to send e-mail advertisements. If an e-mail advertisement is sent to everyone in its customer database, how many customers do you expect will read the advertisement and place an order?
c. If the probability a recipient will read the advertisement is 0.20, what is the probability that a recipient will read the advertisement and place an order?

d. What is your answer to (b) assuming the probability that a recipient will read the advertisement is 0.20?

 4.67 In February 2002, the Argentine peso lost 70% of its value compared to the United States dollar. This devaluation drastically raised the price of imported products. According to a survey conducted by AC Nielsen in April 2002, 68% of the consumers in Argentina were buying fewer products than before the devaluation, 24% were buying the same number of products, and 8% were buying more products. Furthermore, in a trend toward purchasing less-expensive brands, 88% indicated that they had changed the brands they purchased (Michelle Wallin, "Argentines Hone Art of Shopping in a Crisis," *The Wall Street Journal*, May 28, 2002, A15). Suppose the following complete set of results were reported.

	NUMBER OF PRODUCTS PURCHASED			
BRANDS PURCHASED	**Fewer**	**Same**	**More**	**Total**
Same	10	14	24	48
Changed	262	82	8	352
Total	272	96	32	400

What is the probability that a consumer selected at random:
a. purchased fewer products than before?
b. purchased the same number or more products than before?
c. purchased fewer products and changed brands?
d. Given that a consumer changed the brands they purchased, what then is the probability that the consumer purchased fewer products than before?
e. Compare the results from (a) with (d).

 4.68 Sport utility vehicles (SUVs), vans, and pickups are generally considered to be more prone to roll over than cars. In 1997, 24.0% of all highway fatalities involved a rollover; 15.8% of all fatalities in 1997 involved SUVs, vans, and pickups, given that the fatality involved a rollover. Given that a rollover was not involved, 5.6% of all fatalities involved SUVs, vans, and pickups (Anna Wilde Mathews, "Ford Ranger, Chevy Tracker Tilt in Test," *The Wall Street Journal*, July 14, 1999, A2). Consider the following definitions:

A = fatality involved an SUV, van, or pickup

B = fatality involved a rollover

a. Use Bayes' theorem to find the probability that the fatality involved a rollover, given that the fatality involved an SUV, van, or pickup.
b. Compare the result in (a) to the probability that the fatality involved a rollover, and comment on whether SUVs, vans, and pickups are generally more prone to rollover accidents.

4.69 Enzyme-linked immunosorbent assays (ELISA) is the most common type of screening test for detecting the HIV virus. A positive result from an ELISA indicates that the HIV virus is present. For most populations, ELISA has a high degree of sensitivity (to detect infection) and specificity (to detect noninfection). (See HIVInsite, at **HIVInsite.ucsf.edu/**.) Suppose that the probability a person is infected with the HIV virus for a certain population is 0.015. If the HIV virus is actually present, the probability that the ELISA test will give a positive result is 0.995. If the HIV virus is not actually present, the probability of a positive result from an ELISA is 0.01. If the ELISA has given a positive result, use Bayes' theorem to find the probability that the HIV virus is actually present.

WEB CASE

Apply your knowledge about contingency tables and the proper application of simple and joint probabilities in this continuing Web Case from Chapter 3.

Visit the StockTout Guaranteed Investment Package Web page **www.prenhall.com/Springville/ST_Guaranteed.htm**. Read the claims and examine the supporting data. Then answer the following:
1. How accurate is the claim of the probability of success for StockTout's Guaranteed Investment Package? In what ways is the claim misleading? How would you

calculate and state the probability of having an annual rate of return not less than 15%?
2. What mistake was made in reporting the 7% probability claim? Using the table found on the "Winning Probabilities'" Web page **ST_Guaranteed3.htm**, compute the proper probabilities for the group of investors.
3. Are there any probability calculations that would be appropriate for rating an investment service? Why, or why not?

REFERENCES

1. Kirk, R. L., ed., *Statistical Issues: A Reader for the Behavioral Sciences* (Belmont, CA: Wadsworth, 1972).
2. *Microsoft Excel 2003* (Redmond, WA: Microsoft Corp., 2002).
3. Paulos, J. A., *Innumeracy* (New York: Hill and Wang, 1988).

CHAPTER 5

Some Important Discrete Probability Distributions

USING STATISTICS: The Accounting Information System of the Saxon Home Improvement Company

LEARNING OBJECTIVES

In this chapter, you learn:

- The properties of a probability distribution

- To compute the expected value, variance, and standard deviation of a probability distribution

- To compute probabilities from binomial and Poisson distributions

- How to use the binomial and Poisson distributions to solve business problems

USING STATISTICS

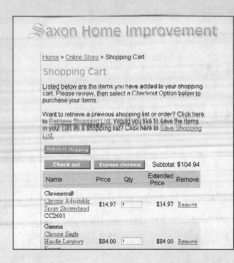

The Accounting Information System of the Saxon Home Improvement Company

Accounting information systems collect, process, store, transform, and distribute financial information to decision-makers both internal and external to a business organization (see reference 5). These systems continuously audit accounting information, looking for errors or incomplete or improbable information. For example, when customers of the Saxon Home Improvement Company submit an online order, the order forms are reviewed by the company's accounting information system for possible mistakes. Any questionable invoices are *tagged* and included in a daily *exceptions report*. Recent data collected by the company show that the likelihood is 0.10 that an order form will be tagged. Saxon would like to determine the likelihood of finding a certain number of tagged forms in a sample of a specific size. For example, what would be the likelihood that none of the order forms are tagged in a sample of four forms? One of the order forms is tagged?

How could the Saxon Home Improvement Company determine the solution to this type of probability problem? One way is to use a model, or small-scale representation, that approximates the process. By using such an approximation, Saxon managers could make inferences about the actual order process. Although model-building is a difficult task for some endeavors, in this case the Saxon managers can use *probability distributions*, mathematical models suited for solving the type of probability problems the managers are facing. Reading this chapter will help you learn about characteristics of a probability distribution and how to specifically apply the binomial and Poisson distributions to business problems.

5.1 DISCRETE PROBABILITY DISTRIBUTIONS: INTRODUCTORY CONCEPTS

Definitions

Random Variable: A variable whose value is determined by the outcome of a random experiment. Symbol is very often 'X'.

Discrete Random Variable: A random variable whose possible values are discrete, i.e. clearly separated individual values.

Discrete Probability Distribution: A table or formula that shows the probability associated with each possible value of a discrete random variable.

EXAMPLE 5.1

A study of the number of cars sold on Sunday at a particular dealership shows that the following probability distribution exists:

let X = # cars sold on Sunday

Probability distribution of X is:

TABLE 5.1

X	P(X)
0	0.1
1	0.1
2	0.4
3	0.3
4	0.1
Total	1.0

EXAMPLE 5.2

A company is in the process of trying to decide whether or not to market a particular new product that it is considering. A market analysis has determined that the probabilities of various acceptance levels are as follows: high with a probability of 0.2, medium with a probability of 0.5, and low with a probability of 0.3. If the company decides to build a local manufacturing facility, the estimated profits over the life of the product if there is high acceptance is $10 million, if there is medium acceptance the profit should be around $3 million and if there is low acceptance there will be a loss of $2 million.

let X = estimated profit over life of product ($ million)

Probability distribution of X is:

TABLE 5.2

Product Acceptance	X	P(X)
High	10	0.2
Medium	3	0.5
Low	-2	0.3
Total		1.0

EXAMPLE 5.3

Toss a fair coin three times. The sample space is composed of eight equally likely outcomes, namely:

S = {HHH HHT HTH THH TTH THT HTT TTT}

let X = # tails

Probability distribution of X is:

TABLE 5.3

X	P(X)
0	1/8 = 0.125
1	3/8 = 0.375
2	3/8 = 0.375
3	1/8 = 0.125
Total	1.000

EXAMPLE 5.4   Roll a fair die. The sample space is composed of 6 equally likely outcomes, namely:

S = {1 2 3 4 5 6}

let X = # rolled

The probability distribution of X is:

TABLE 5.4

X	P(X)
1	1/6 = 0.167
2	1/6 = 0.167
3	1/6 = 0.167
4	1/6 = 0.167
5	1/6 = 0.167
6	1/6 = 0.167
Total	6/6 = 1

EXAMPLE 5.5   Roll two fair dice. The sample space, as seen previously, is composed of 36 equally likely outcomes.

let X = total of the two dice

Probability distribution of X is:

TABLE 5.5

X	P(X)
2	1/36 = 0.028
3	2/36 = 0.056
4	3/36 = 0.083
5	4/36 = 0.111
6	5/36 = 0.139
7	6/36 = 0.167
8	5/36 = 0.139
9	4/36 = 0.111
10	3/36 = 0.083
11	2/36 = 0.056
12	1/36 = 0.028
Total	36/36 = 1

Mean, Variance and Standard Deviation

A discrete probability distribution is equivalent to a *population* of data. We can calculate any parameters that can be calculated for a population. However, the formulas will look a little different.

I. Mean or Expected Value:

Formula: $\mu = E(X) = \sum XP(X)$

EXAMPLE 5.1
(Revisit)

A study of the number of cars sold on Sunday at a particular dealership shows that the following probability distribution exists:

let X = # cars sold on Sunday

The mean or expected number of cars that will be sold on Sunday can be calculated as follows:

TABLE 5.6

X	P(X)	XP(X)
0	0.1	0.0
1	0.1	0.1
2	0.4	0.8
3	0.3	0.9
4	0.1	0.4
Total	1.0	2.2

Therefore, the *average* number of cars sold on *infinite* Sunday's is 2.2. Also, we can say that the number of cars the dealer *expects* to sell on Sunday is 2.2 .

Notes: 1. Calculating a mean for a discrete probability distribution is essentially the same as calculating a *weighted mean*, where the probabilities are the weights.

$$\bar{x}_w = \frac{\sum xw}{\sum w} = \frac{\sum xP(x)}{\sum P(x)} = \sum xP(x) \text{ since } \sum P(x) = 1$$

2. To calculate the mean on the Casio calculator, enter the data as follows and set-up as if calculating a weighted mean of the X data.

Example 5.1:

List 1	List 2
0	.1
1	.1
2	.4
3	.3
4	.1

Example 5.4:

List 1	List 2
1	1÷6
2	1÷6
3	1÷6
4	1÷6
5	1÷6
6	1÷6

Xlist: L1
Freq: L2   yields $\bar{x} = 2.2$

Xlist: L1
Freq: L2   yields $\bar{x} = 3.5$

EXAMPLE 5.2
(Revisit)

Referring to the product marketing decision example 5.2:

let X = estimated profit over the life of product ($ million)

TABLE 5.7

Product Acceptance	X	P(X)	XP(X)
High	10	0.2	2.0
Medium	3	0.5	1.5
Low	−2	0.3	−0.6
Total		1.0	2.9

Therefore, the expected profit $2.9 million.

EXAMPLE 5.6

Toss a fair coin three times.

let X = # tails

TABLE 5.8

X	P(X)	XP(X)
0	0.125	0.000
1	0.375	0.375
2	0.375	0.750
3	0.125	0.375
Total	1.000	1.5

The average number of tails when a coin is tossed three times, an *infinite* number of times, is 1.5 . Also, the expected number of tails if you toss a coin three times is 1.5 .

EXAMPLE 5.4
(Revisit)

Roll a fair die.   Let X = # rolled

TABLE 5.9

X	P(X)	XP(X)
1	1/6 = 0.167	1/6
2	1/6 = 0.167	2/6
3	1/6 = 0.167	3/6
4	1/6 = 0.167	4/6
5	1/6 = 0.167	5/6
6	1/6 = 0.167	6/6
Total	6/6 = 1	21/6 = 3.5

If you roll one die infinite times, the average number rolled will be 3.5 . Therefore, if you roll a die once, the expected value is 3.5 .

EXAMPLE 5.5
(Revisit)

Roll two fair dice.

let X = total of the two dice

TABLE 5.10

X	P(X)	XP(X)
2	1/36 = 0.028	2/36
3	2/36 = 0.056	6/36
4	3/36 = 0.083	12/36
5	4/36 = 0.111	20/36
6	5/36 = 0.139	30/36
7	6/36 = 0.167	42/36
8	5/36 = 0.139	40/36
9	4/36 = 0.111	36/36
10	3/36 = 0.083	30/36
11	2/36 = 0.056	22/36
12	1/36 = 0.028	12/36
Total	36/36 = 1	252/36 = 7

Therefore, if we roll two dice we can expect to get a total of 7.

II. Variance

Formula:
$$\sigma^2 = \sum (X - \mu)^2 P(X) \qquad (5.1)$$

III. Standard Deviation

Formula:
$$\sigma = \sqrt{\left(\sum (X - \mu)^2 P(X) \right)} \qquad (5.2)$$

Note: We are not interested in showing the use of this formula manually, since if you need to calculate the standard deviation of a random variable you will use your calculator as illustrated above.

Expected Value Decision Making

EXAMPLE 5.7

A fast food company plans to install a new ice-cream dispensing unit in one of two store locations. The company figures that the probability of a unit being successful in location A is 3/4 and the annual profit in this case is $150,000. If it is not successful there will be losses of $80,000. At location B the probability of succeeding is 1/2 but the potential profit and loss are $240,000 and $48,000 respectively.

a) Where should the company locate to maximize expected profit?

Solution:

Location A		Location B	
Profit	Prob.	Profit	Prob.
$150,000	0.75	$240,000	0.5
–$80,000	0.25	–$48,000	0.5
Location A: E(X) = $92,500		Location B: E(X) = $96,000	

b) Which location is less risky, i.e. has the lowest relative variability?

$$\text{Location A: } CV = \frac{\sigma}{\mu} \times 100 = \frac{\$99{,}593}{\$92{,}500} \times 100 = 108\%$$

$$\text{Location B: } CV = \frac{\sigma}{\mu} \times 100 = \frac{\$144{,}000}{\$96{,}000} \times 100 = 150\%$$

EXAMPLE 5.8

An investment advisor sends information to various clients via express delivery companies. In all cases it is important that the client receive the information on the day it is sent. Three companies are capable of providing the delivery service. The following information is available:

TABLE 5.11

Company	Cost	Probability of same day arrival
Can-Express	$22.00	0.99
Can-Parcel	14.00	0.97
Canada Mail	6.00	0.89

The average payoff is $200 when the information arrives on time, but there is no payoff if the delivery is late. Based on maximizing expected profit, which delivery service should be used?

Solution:

Let X = profit

TABLE 5.12

Can-Express		Can-Parcel		Canada Mail	
X	P(X)	X	P(X)	X	P(X)
178	0.99	186	0.97	194	0.89
-22	0.01	-14	0.03	-6	0.11

The expected values are:

Can-Express: E(X) = $176
Can-Parcel: E(X) = $180
Canada Mail: E(X) = $172

Therefore the company should choose **Can-Parcel**.

PROBLEMS FOR SECTION 5.1

Learning the Basics

PH Grade ASSIST **5.1** Given the following probability distributions:

Distribution A		Distribution B	
X	P(X)	X	P(X)
0	0.50	0	0.05
1	0.20	1	0.10
2	0.15	2	0.15
3	0.10	3	0.20
4	0.05	4	0.50

a. Compute the expected value for each distribution.
b. Compute the standard deviation for each distribution.
c. Compare and contrast the results of distributions A and B.

PH Grade ASSIST **5.2** Given the following probability distributions:

Distribution C		Distribution D	
X	P(X)	X	P(X)
0	0.20	0	0.10
1	0.20	1	0.20
2	0.20	2	0.40
3	0.20	3	0.20
4	0.20	4	0.10

a. Compute the expected value for each distribution.
b. Compute the standard deviation for each distribution.
c. Compare and contrast the results of distributions C and D.

Applying the Concepts

PH Grade ASSIST **5.3** Using the company records for the past 500 working days, the manager of Konig Motors, a suburban automobile dealership, has summarized the number of cars sold per day into the following table:

Number of Cars Sold per Day	Frequency of Occurrence
0	40
1	100
2	142
3	66
4	36
5	30
6	26
7	20
8	16
9	14
10	8
11	2
Total	500

a. Form the probability distribution for the number of cars sold per day.
b. Compute the mean or expected number of cars sold per day.
c. Compute the standard deviation.

5.4 The following table contains the probability distribution for the number of traffic accidents daily in a small city.

Number of Accidents Daily (X)	P(X)
0	0.10
1	0.20
2	0.45
3	0.15
4	0.05
5	0.05

a. Compute the mean or expected number of accidents per day.
b. Compute the standard deviation.

 SELF Test **5.5** The manager of a large computer network has developed the following probability distribution of the number of interruptions per day:

Interruptions (X)	P(X)
0	0.32
1	0.35
2	0.18
3	0.08
4	0.04
5	0.02
6	0.01

a. Compute the mean or expected number of interruptions per day.
b. Compute the standard deviation.

5.6 In the carnival game Under-or-Over-Seven, a pair of fair dice is rolled once, and the resulting sum determines whether the player wins or loses his or her bet. For example, the player can bet $1.00 that the sum will be under 7—that is, 2, 3, 4, 5, or 6. For this bet the player will lose $1.00 if the outcome equals or exceeds 7 or will win $1.00 if the result is under 7. Similarly, the player can bet $1.00 that the sum will be over 7—that is, 8, 9, 10, 11, or 12. Here the player wins $1.00 if the result is over 7 but loses $1.00 if the result is 7 or under. A third method of play is to bet $1.00 on the outcome 7. For this bet the player will win $4.00 if the result of the roll is 7 and lose $1.00 otherwise.

a. Construct the probability distribution representing the different outcomes that are possible for a $1.00 bet on being under 7.
b. Construct the probability distribution representing the different outcomes that are possible for a $1.00 bet on being over 7.
c. Construct the probability distribution representing the different outcomes that are possible for a $1.00 bet on 7.
d. Show that the expected long-run profit (or loss) to the player is the same, no matter which method of play is used.

Discrete Probability Distribution

5.7 At the 2nd Cup coffee shop they offer free refills. The following information has been gathered by studying many customers.

# refills	Prob.
0	0.3
1	0.4
2	0.2
3	0.1

Calculate the mean and standard deviation of the number of refills.

5.8 The director of admissions at Expected University has predicted the probability distribution of applications for the coming year based on past experience.

# applicants	Prob.
1000	0.6
1200	0.3
1500	0.1

a. What is the expected number of applicants for the coming year?
b. What is the standard deviation?

5.9 After consulting the sales reps, a marketing manager has decided that the following table represents the potential profits they might make next year for one of the company's products.

Profit	Prob.
$50,000	0.02
35,000	0.12
20,000	0.50
10,000	0.25
0	0.08
−10,000	0.03

What is the expected profit?

5.10 The Chancit Marketing Company is considering the distribution of a new item. They think there is a 20% chance that the item will be successful, in which case they will make $1,000,000 revenue. There is a 40% chance that they will break-even and the other possibility is that there will be virtually no revenues. The distribution expenses in all cases will be $200,000. What is the expected net profit from the distribution of this item?

5.11 A mail order magazine service has the exclusive subscription rights to a certain magazine. Subscriptions can be reserved for one, two, three or five years. A study of the subscriber list for other similar magazines reveals that the following information regarding the probabilities of subscription length would be appropriate: there are five time as many one year subscriptions as five year subscriptions and that the number of two year and three year subscriptions are each one fifth of the total.

The mail order service company receives a fee of $2.00 for a one year subscription, $3.50 for each two year subscription and an additional dollar for every year over two years.

a. What is the probability distribution of subscription fees?
b. What is the expected total fee revenue from 125 new subscriptions?

5.12 A financial analyst for Petrified Paper Products has submitted the following probability distributions of profit for three investment proposals. The company has sufficient funds to consider only one of the proposals.

Project 1		Project 2		Project 3	
Profit	Prob.	Profit	Prob.	Profit	Prob.
−5,000	0.1	−2,000	0.10	−3,000	0.10
0	0.1	0	0.15	2,000	0.20
2,000	0.2	2,000	0.30	4,000	0.40
4,000	0.3	4,000	0.30	6,000	0.25
6,000	0.3	7,000	0.15	8,000	0.05

a. Based on expected profit, which proposal should be selected?
b. Which proposal has the lowest relative variability, i.e. risk?

5.13 An export company may ship goods to country A at a cost of $2,000, country B at a cost of $3,000 or country C at a cost of $5,000. The revenues earned by selling the goods in these countries are $5,000, $7,000 and $10,000, respectively. Currently the countries are all involved in wars and only 70% of shipments have been arriving at the destination country. The remainder are being lost at sea.

Based on expected values, to which country would you ship the next shipment of goods?

5.14 B. F. Retread, a tire manufacturer, wants to select one of the feasible designs for a new longer-wearing radial tire. The manufacturing cost of each type of tire is shown below.

Tire Design	Fixed Cost/year	Variable Cost per Tire
A	$60,000	$30
B	90,000	20
C	120,000	15

There are 3 possible levels of annual demand: 4,000 tires, 7,000 tires and 10,000 tires. The respective probabilities are 0.3, 0.5 and 0.2. The selling price will be $80 for A, $75 for B and $75 for C. Based on expected profit, which design should be produced?

5.15 The normal weekly demand of a certain perishable product sold by QMS Inc. is given by the following distribution:

Demand	Probability
8	0.1
9	0.2
10	0.3
11	0.3
12	0.1

The product costs QMS $3 each. The product sells for $10 each. If not sold by the end of the week, the leftover units must be scrapped.

The supplier only has 10 or 11 units available for QMS to purchase. How many would you recommend QMS purchase based on expected profit?

5.2   BINOMIAL PROBABILITY DISTRIBUTION

Characteristics of a Binomial Experiment

1. The experiment consists of 'n' repetitions (trials) of some action.
   or
   A sample of 'n' items are selected from a large population.
2. Each trial will result in one of 2 possible outcomes called *success* or *failure*, where success is when the outcome of interest occurs.
   or
   Each item in the sample will either possess a certain characteristic (success) or it will not (failure).
3. The probability of success on each trial or selection is the *same* and is given the symbol 'π'. The probability of failure is therefore $(1 - \pi)$. Note that this condition implies that the trials are *independent*.

The **random variable** associated with a binomial experiment is:

$$X = \text{\# of successes}$$

To calculate the probability that X takes on a specific value we use the

Binomial Probability Distribution Function:

$$P(X = x) = \frac{n!}{x!(n-x)!} \pi^x (1-\pi)^{n-x}$$

where   n = # of trials or sample size
π = probability of success on each trial
n! = n factorial
= n(n-1)(n-2)(n-3) ... 3•2•1

Example: 6! = 6•5•4•3•2•1 = 720

EXAMPLE 5.9

Toss a coin 6 times. Find the probability of getting 2 tails?

Solution: $X = $ # of tails

$n = 6$

$\pi = 0.5$

$$P(X = 2) = \frac{6!}{2!(6-2)!}(0.5)^2(1-0.5)^{6-2} = 0.2344$$

Note: The part of the binomial formula $\dfrac{n!}{x!(n-x)!}$ calculates the number of outcomes where there are x successes in n trials. For example, if a coin is tossed 6 times, there will be $\dfrac{6!}{2!(6-2)!} = 15$ possible outcomes that have exactly 2 tails. These outcomes are:

TTHHHH	THTHHH	THHTHH	THHHTH	THHHHT
HTTHHH	HTHTHH	HTHHTH	HTHHHT	
HHTTHH	HHTHTH	HHTHHT		
HHHTTH	HHHTHT			
HHHHTT				

The factor $\dfrac{n!}{x!(n-x)!}$ is often given the shorthand symbol $_nC_r$.

EXAMPLE 5.10

Roll a die 10 times. Find the probability of getting three 5's ?

Solution: $X = $ # of 5's

$n = 10$

$\pi = 1/6$

$$P(X = 3) = \frac{10!}{3!(10-3)!}\left(\frac{1}{6}\right)^3\left(1-\frac{1}{6}\right)^{10-3} = 0.1550$$

EXAMPLE 5.11

A survey of people in the 30 and under 40 age bracket shows that 43 percent of them have investments in mutual funds. In a particular condominium there are 18 adults in this age bracket. What is the probability that:

a. 5 of them will have investments in mutual funds?

Solution: $X = $ # of people in their 30's with investments in mutual funds

$n = 18$

$\pi = 0.43$

$$P(X = 5) = \frac{18!}{5!(18-5)!}(0.43)^5(1-0.43)^{18-5} = 0.0845$$

b. at most 2 of these people will have investments in mutual funds?

Solution: $P(X \leq 2) = P(X = 0) + P(X = 1) + P(X = 2)$

$= 0.00004 + 0.00055 + 0.00351 \doteq 0.0041$

c. more that 10 of these people will have investments in mutual funds?

Solution: $P(X > 10) = 1 - P(X \leq 10)$
$$= 1 - 0.9049 = 0.0951$$

Explanation:

X	P(X)
0	0.00004
1	0.00055
2	0.00351
3	0.0141
4	0.0400
5	0.0844
6	0.1380
7	0.1785
8	0.1852
9	0.1552
10	0.1054
11	0.0578
12	0.0254
13	0.0089
14	0.0024
15	0.00048
16	0.00007
17	0.00001
18	0.00000
Total	1

d. from 3 to 9 of these people will have investments in mutual funds?

Solution: $P(3 \leq X \leq 9) = P(3) + P(4) + \ldots + P(9)$
$$= P(X \leq 9) - P(X \leq 2)$$
$$= 0.7996 - 0.0041 = 0.7955$$

Binomial Template

You will notice that a similar style is used to present all the answers to the sample examples above. You are *not* to follow this style exactly however, since you will be using a calculator or computer to determine the probability value. Your answers should look like the following template:

X = # of _____
         (successes)

n = _____

π = _____
    (dec.)

P(_____) = P(X symbol #) = _____ = 0._ _ _ _
   (words*)   (calculator or SPSS input)   (4 dec.)

* If the question does not directly say what the number is.

The Mean or Expected Value of a Binomial random variable

The mean of a binomial random variable can be calculated using the formula shown previously for calculating the mean of a discrete random variable, namely:

$$\mu = E(X) = \sum XP(X)$$

EXAMPLE 5.12   Refer to the mutual funds example 5.15. We will get the following:

TABLE 5.13

X	P(X)	XP(X)
0	0.00004	0
1	0.00055	0.00055
2	0.00351	0.00702
3	0.0141	0.0423
4	0.0400	0.1600
5	0.0844	0.4220
6	0.1380	0.8280
7	0.1785	1.2495
8	0.1852	1.4816
9	0.1552	1.3968
10	0.1054	1.0540
11	0.0578	0.6358
12	0.0254	0.3048
13	0.0089	0.1157
14	0.0024	0.0336
15	0.00048	0.0072
16	0.00007	0.00112
17	0.00001	0.00017
18	0.00000	0.00000
Total	1	7.74016

From these calculations, we see that: $\mu = E(X) = 7.74$ people

i.e. If infinite groups of 18 people were selected, and the number who had investments in mutual funds was determined for each group, and then the average number of people who had investments in mutual funds was calculated: the average would be 7.74 people.

You will note that it was quite tedious calculating the mean in this fashion. Even if we were to input the data in 2 lists in the calculator and calculate the mean using the weighted method of calculating, it would still take some time. However, it can be shown that for any binomial distribution, the following formula applies:

$$\mu = E(X) = n\pi \qquad\qquad 5.3$$

Now referring back to the example:

$$\mu = E(X) = n\pi = 18(0.43) = 7.74 \ people$$

The Standard Deviation of a Binomial random variable

The standard deviation can also be calculated using the methods shown in the discrete random variable section 5.1, however, there is a simple formula that can be used for all binomial distributions. The formula is:

$$\sigma = \sqrt{n\pi(1-\pi)} \qquad\qquad 5.4$$

Now referring back to Example 5.16:

$$\sigma = \sqrt{n\pi(1-\pi)} = \sqrt{18 \times 0.43(1-0.43)} = 2.10 \; people$$

CALCULATOR LESSON 3

CASIO FX-9750G OR CFX-9850GB CALCULATOR

Lesson 3—Binomial Probabilities

Note: The following instructions refer to examples in the notes on the Binomial Probability Distribution.

The Casio calculator has *two* Binomial probability functions programmed into its memory. These are:

i. **Bpd** which stands for **B**inomial **p**robability **d**istribution. This function calculates a Binomial probability of the form:

$$P(X = \#)$$

ii. **Bcd** which stands for **B**inomial **c**umulative **d**istribution. This function calculates a Binomial probability of the form:

$$P(X \le \#)$$

A. Individual values of X—using the built-in **Bpd** distribution function

EXAMPLE 5.9
(Revisit)

$P(X = 2)$ where n = 6 and π = 0.5

STAT F5(DIST)   **F5**(BINM)   **F1**(Bpd)   then select the following options

Data	: **F2**(Var) ▼ (Note: Do not key EXE now)
x	: **2 EXE**
Numtrial	: **6 EXE**
p	: **.5 EXE**

Now key **EXE** or **F1**(Calc)

The calculator will now show the result 0.23437

To calculate another Binomial probability key **EXE** and enter new values where necessary.

B. Cumulative values of X—using the built-in **Bcd** distribution function

EXAMPLE 5.11a
(Revisit)

$P(X \le 2)$ where n = 18 and π = 0.43

STAT F5(DIST)   **F5**(BINM)   **F2**(Bcd)   then select the following options

Data   : F2(Var) ▼ (Note: Do not key EXE now)
x   : 2 EXE
Numtrial   : 18 EXE
p   : .43 EXE

Now key **EXE** or **F1**(Calc)

The calculator will now show the result 4.1007 E –03 which is scientific notation for the value 0.0041 . E –03 means that you should move the decimal point 3 places to the left.

EXAMPLE 5.11c
(Revisit)

$P(X>10) = 1 - P(X \le 10)$ where n = 18 and π = 0.43

You must *first* calculate $P(X \le 10)$

STAT F5(DIST) **F5**(BINM) **F2**(Bcd)   then select the following options

Data   : F2(Var) ▼ (Note: Do not key EXE now)
x   : 10 EXE
Numtrial   : 18 EXE
p   : .43 EXE

Now key **EXE** or **F1**(Calc)

The calculator will now show the result 0.90494.

Therefore, $P(X>10) = 1 - P(X \le 10) = 1 - 0.9049 = 0.0951$

EXAMPLE 5.11d
(Revisit)

$P(3 \le X \le 9) = P(X \le 9) - P(X \le 2)$ where n = 18 and π = 0.43

You will have to calculate the two cumulative probabilities separately and then record the results and subtract the appropriate values to get the final result 0.7955 .

PROBLEMS FOR SECTION 5.2

Problems 5.16–5.23 can be solved manually or by using Microsoft Excel or Minitab. We recommend that you solve problems 5.24–5.26 using Microsoft Excel or Minitab.

Learning the Basics

5.16 If $n = 5$ and $p = 0.40$, what is the probability that
a. $X = 4$
b. $X \le 3$
c. $X < 2$
d. $X > 1$

PH Grade ASSIST **5.17** Determine the following:
a. For $n = 4$ and $p = 0.12$, what is $P(X = 0)$?
b. For $n = 10$ and $p = 0.40$, what is $P(X = 9)$?
c. For $n = 10$ and $p = 0.50$, what is $P(X = 8)$?
d. For $n = 6$ and $p = 0.83$, what is $P(X = 5)$?

Applying the Concepts

5.18 The increase or decrease in the price of a stock between the beginning and the end of a trading day is assumed to be an equally likely random event. What is the probability that a stock will show an increase in its closing price on five consecutive days?

5.19 Sixty percent of Americans read their employment contract, including the fine print ("Snapshots," **usatoday.com**, January 20, 2004). Assume that the number of employees who read every word of their contract can be modeled using the binomial distribution. For a group of five employees, what is the probability that
a. all five will have read every word of their contract?
b. at least three will have read every word of their contract?
c. less than two will have read every word of their contract?
d. What are your answers in (a) through (c) if the probability is 0.80 that an employee reads every word of their contract?

5.20 A student is taking a multiple-choice exam in which each question has four choices. Assuming that she has no knowledge of the correct answers to any of the questions, she has decided on a strategy in which she will place four balls (marked *A, B, C,* and *D*) into a box. She randomly selects one ball for each question and replaces the ball in the box. The marking on the ball will determine her answer to the question. There are five multiple-choice questions on the exam. What is the probability that she will get

a. five questions correct?
b. at least four questions correct?
c. no questions correct?
d. no more than two questions correct?

 5.21 In Example 5.4, you and two friends decided to go to Burger King. Instead, suppose that you went to McDonald's, which last month filled 90% of the orders accurately. What is the probability that

a. all three orders will be filled accurately?
b. none of the three will be filled accurately?
c. at least two of the three will be filled accurately?
d. What is the mean and standard deviation of the number of orders filled accurately?

5.22 The commission rate commercial airlines pay travel agents has been declining for several years. In an attempt by travel agencies to raise revenue, many agencies are now charging their customers a ticket fee, typically between $10 and $25. According to the American Society of Ticket Agents, about 90% of travel agents charge customers fees when purchasing an airline ticket (Kortney Stringer, "American Air Fees for Travel Agents to Be Cut Again," *The Wall Street Journal*, August 20, 2001, B2).

a. Is the 90% figure quoted by the American Society of Ticket Agents best classified as *a priori* classical probability, empirical classical probability, or subjective probability?
b. You select a random sample of 10 travel agencies. Assume that the number of the 10 travel agencies charging a ticket fee is distributed as a binomial random variable. What are the mean and standard deviation of this distribution?
c. What assumptions are necessary in (b)?

5.23 Referring to problem 5.22, compute the probability that of the 10 travel agencies:
a. zero charge ticket fees?
b. exactly one charges ticket fees?
c. two or fewer charge ticket fees?
d. three or more charge ticket fees?

 5.24 When a customer places an order with Rudy's On-Line Office Supplies, a computerized accounting information system (AIS) automatically checks to see if the customer has exceeded his or her credit limit. Past records indicate that the probability of customers exceeding their credit limit is 0.05. Suppose that, on a given day, 20 customers place orders. Assume that the number of customers that the AIS detects as having exceeded their credit limit is distributed as a binomial random variable.

a. What are the mean and standard deviation of the number of customers exceeding their credit limits?
b. What is the probability that zero customers will exceed their limit?
c. What is the probability that one customer will exceed his or her limit?
d. What is the probability that two or more customers will exceed their limits?

5.25 The broadcast networks introduce new television shows each fall. In an attempt to get viewers interested in the new shows, television commercials are aired during the summer as part of a promotional campaign conducted prior to the fall debuts. The networks then conduct surveys to see what percentage of the viewing public is *aware* of the shows. According to network sources, in the fall of 2001, 68% of viewers aged 18–49 were aware of the new series *Criminal Intent*, whereas only 24% of viewers aged 18–49 were aware of *Inside Schwartz* (Joe Flint, "Viewers Awareness of New Shows Rises," *The Wall Street Journal*, August 20, 2001, B7).

a. Are the 68% and 24% figures quoted by networks best classified as a priori classical probability, empirical classical probability, or subjective probability?
Suppose that a random sample of 20 viewers aged 18–49 is selected. What is the probability that:
b. less than five of the viewers are aware of *Criminal Intent*?
c. 10 or more are aware of *Criminal Intent*?
d. all 20 are aware of *Criminal Intent*?

5.26 Referring to problem 5.25, consider another sample of 20 viewers aged 18–49. For the new show *Inside Schwartz*, what is the probability that:
a. less than five of the viewers are aware of *Inside Schwartz*?
b. 10 or more are aware of *Inside Schwartz*?
c. all 20 are aware of *Inside Schwartz*?
d. Compare the results of (a) through (c) to those for *Criminal Intent* in problem 5.25 (b) through (d).

Binomial Probability Distribution

Binomial Template:

X = # of _____
                    (successes)

n = _____

π = _____
        (dec.)

P(_____) = P(X symbol #) =
    (words*)

_____ = 0. _____
    (calculator or SPSS input)   (4 dec.)

* If the question does not directly say what the number is.

5.27 A new public school is presently being built in your community. The classrooms will include chairs that have a small table attached on the right or left side. The school is trying to determine how many left-handed tables should be included in each classroom. If only 7% of the population is left-handed, what is the probability that in a class of 25 students:

a. two will be left-handed?
b. more than three will be left-handed?
c. What is the expected number of left-handed children in a class of 25?

5.28 The quality inspector for a company that produces heptium computer chips has determined that 3% of the production is defective. The company does not perform final product inspection, but instead agrees to replace any defective chip found by any customer and will give the customer a $5 discount on their next order.

a. If a customer orders 30 heptium chips, what is the probability that 3 or more defective chips will be included in the order?

b. What is the expected number of defective chips in the above order?

c. Another customer assembles computer motherboards, each with 7 heptium chips. If any chip fails, then the motherboard fails. What is the probability that a motherboard will fail?

5.29 According to a well-known accounting firm, the chances of your tax return being audited by Revenue Canada are about 9 in 1000 if your income is less than $50,000. The chances increase to 22 in 1000 if your income is more than $50,000. You are presently employed by an accounting firm and have prepared tax returns for 58 clients with income under $50,000 and for 42 clients with income over $50,000.

a. What is the probability that at most 3 of the clients with incomes under $50,000 will be audited?

b. What is the probability that at least 4 of your clients that have incomes over $50,000 will be audited?

5.30 A salesperson has to sell a minimum of 50 cars in a month in order to get a bonus. One particular salesperson has sold 43 cars so far this month. Today he has appointments with 9 prospective customers. Based on past experience he has a 55% chance of selling a car to any customer. What is the probability that he will earn his bonus today?

5.31 A certain soft drink manufacturer believes that 40% of the people that drink cola prefer their brand. A random sample of 60 cola drinkers was surveyed. If the manufacturer is correct:

a. What is the probability that less than half of those surveyed will prefer the manufacturer's product?

b. What is the probability that at least the expected number of people will prefer the manufacturer's product?

5.3   POISSON PROBABILITY DISTRIBUTION

Characteristics of a Poisson Experiment

1. The experiment consists of observing some situation for a period of *time*.
   or
   An *amount of space* is inspected or analyzed. SPACE may be length, area, volume or weight.
2. In each infinitesimally small amount of time or space there will either be one success or no successes, where success is when the outcome of interest occurs. The successes must occur *randomly*. Note that this condition implies that the successes are *independent* of each other.
3. The average rate of success for the amount of time or space we are interested in is given the symbol λ (lambda).

The **random variable** associated with a Poisson experiment is:

X = # of successes IN a certain amount of time or space.

To calculate the probability that X takes on a specific value we use the

Poisson Probability Distribution Function:

$$P(X = x) = \frac{e^{-\lambda}\lambda^x}{x!}$$ (5.5)

where $e = 2.718281828459\ldots$ (a mathematical constant)

Note: On your calculator there is an 'e^x' key. Try calculating 'e^1'.

EXAMPLE 5.13

Records have been kept for the past several months and they show that customers arrive to use a certain banking machine at an average rate of 15 per hour.

a. What is the probability that 12 customers will use the machine in the next hour?

Solution: X = # of customers at the bank machine IN 1 hour
λ = 15 / hour

$$P(X = 12) = \frac{e^{-\lambda}\lambda^x}{x!} = \frac{e^{-15}15^{12}}{12!} = 0.0829$$

b.   What is the probability that there will be less than 3 customers in the next 10 minutes?

Solution: X = # of customers at the bank machine IN 10 minutes
λ = 15 / hour = 2.5 / 10 minutes
$$P(X < 3) = P(X = 0) + P(X = 1) + P(X = 2)$$
$$= \frac{e^{-2.5}2.5^0}{0!} + \frac{e^{-2.5}2.5^1}{1!} + \frac{e^{-2.5}2.5^2}{2!} = 0.0821 + 0.2052 + 0.2565 = 0.5438$$

c. What is the probability that there will be more than 40 customers in the next 2 hours?

Solution: X = # of customers at the bank machine IN 2 hours
λ = 15 / hour = 30 / 2 hours
$$P(X > 40) = 1 - P(X \le 40) = 1 - 0.9677 = 0.0323$$

EXAMPLE 5.14

It has been noted that potholes on the 401 highway occur randomly. An inspection of a 200 km stretch of the 401 indicated that there were 450 potholes. Today the pothole repair work crew will repair 3 km. of the highway. What is the probability that they will repair at least 6 potholes?

Solution: X = # of potholes IN 3 km.
λ = 450 / 200 km = 2.25 / km = 6.75 / 3 km.
$$P(X \ge 6) = 1 - P(X \le 5) = 1 - 0.3338 = 0.6662$$

CALCULATOR LESSON 4

CASIO FX-9750G OR CFX-9850GB CALCULATOR

Lesson 4—Poisson Probabilities

Note: The following instructions refer to examples in the notes on the Poisson Probability Distribution.

The Casio calculator has *two* Poisson probability functions programmed into its memory. These are:

i. **Ppd** which stands for **P**oisson **p**robability **d**istribution. This function calculates a Poisson probability of the form:

$$P(X = \#)$$

ii. **Pcd** which stands for **P**oisson **c**umulative **d**istribution. This function calculates a Poisson probability of the form:

$$P(X \leq \#)$$

A. Individual values of X—using the built-in **Ppd** distribution function

EXAMPLE 5.13a (Revisit)

$P(X = 12)$ where $\lambda = 15$

STAT F5(DIST)   **F6**(▷)   **F1**(POISN)   **F1**(Ppd)   then select the following options

Data   : **F2**(Var) ▼ (Note: Do not key EXE now)
x   : **12 EXE**
μ   : **15 EXE**   (Note: the calc. Uses the 'μ' symbol instead of 'λ')

Now key **EXE** or **F1**(Calc)

The calculator will now show the result 0.082859

To calculate another Poisson probability key **EXE** and enter new values where necessary.

B. Cumulative values of X—using the built-in **Pcd** distribution function

EXAMPLE 5.13b (Revisit)

$P(X < 3) = P(X \leq 2)$ where $\lambda = 2.5$

STAT F5(DIST)   **F6**(▷)   **F1**(POISN)   **F2**(Pcd)   then select the following options

Data   : **F2**(Var) ▼ (Note: Do not key EXE now)
x   : **2 EXE**
μ   : **2.5 EXE**

Now key **EXE** or **F1**(Calc)

The calculator will now show the result 0.54381

EXAMPLE 5.13c (Revisit)

$P(X > 40) = 1 - P(X \leq 40)$ where $\lambda = 30$

You must *first* calculate $P(X \leq 40)$

STAT F5(DIST)   **F5**(BINM)   **F2**(Bcd)   then select the following options

Data   : **F2**(Var) ▼ (Note: Do not key EXE now)
x   : **40 EXE**
μ   : **30 EXE**

Now key **EXE** or **F1**(Calc)

The calculator will now show the result 0.96769

Therefore, $P(X>40) = 1 - P(X \leq 40) = 1 - 0.9677 = 0.0323$

PROBLEMS FOR SECTION 5.3

Learning the Basics

PH Grade ASSIST **5.32** Assume a Poisson distribution.
  a. If $\lambda = 2.5$, find $P(X = 2)$.
  b. If $\lambda = 8.0$, find $P(X = 8)$.
c. If $\lambda = 0.5$, find $P(X = 1)$.
d. If $\lambda = 3.7$, find $P(X = 0)$.

PH Grade ASSIST **5.33** Assume a Poisson distribution.
  a. If $\lambda = 2.0$, find $P(X \geq 2)$.
  b. If $\lambda = 8.0$, find $P(X \geq 3)$.
c. If $\lambda = 0.5$, find $P(X \leq 1)$.
d. If $\lambda = 4.0$, find $P(X \geq 1)$.
e. If $\lambda = 5.0$, find $P(X \leq 3)$.

5.34 Assume a Poisson distribution with $\lambda = 5.0$. What is the probability that
a. $X = 1$.
b. $X < 1$.
c. $X > 1$.
d. $X \leq 1$.

Applying the Concepts

Problems 5.35–5.45 can be solved manually or by using Microsoft Excel or Minitab.

5.35 Assume that the number of network errors experienced in a day on a local area network (LAN) is distributed as a Poisson random variable. The mean number of network errors experienced in a day is 2.4. What is the probability that in any given day
a. zero network errors will occur?
b. exactly one network error will occur?
c. two or more network errors will occur?
d. fewer than three network errors will occur?

✓SELF Test **5.36** The quality control manager of Marilyn's Cookies is inspecting a batch of chocolate-chip cookies that has just been baked. If the production process is in control, the mean number of chip parts per cookie is 6.0. What is the probability that in any particular cookie being inspected
a. fewer than five chip parts will be found?
b. exactly five chip parts will be found?
c. five or more chip parts will be found?
d. either four or five chip parts will be found?

5.37 Refer to problem 5.22. How many cookies in a batch of 100 should the manager expect to discard if company policy requires that all chocolate-chip cookies sold must have at least four chocolate-chip parts?

5.38 The U.S. Department of Transportation maintains statistics for mishandled bags per 1,000 passengers. In 2003 Jet Blue had 3.21 mishandled bags per 1,000 passengers. What is the probability that in the next 1,000 passengers Jet Blue will have
a. no mishandled bags?
b. at least one mishandled bag?
c. at least two mishandled bags?
d. Compare the results in (a) through (c) to those of Delta in problem 5.25 (a) through (c).

5.39 The U.S. Department of Transportation maintains statistics for mishandled bags per 1,000 passengers. In 2003 Delta had 3.84 mishandled bags per 1,000 passengers. What is the probability that in the next 1,000 passengers Delta will have
a. no mishandled bags?
b. at least one mishandled bag?
c. at least two mishandled bags?
d. Compare the results in (a) through (c) to those of Jet Blue in problem 5.38 (a) through (c).

PH Grade ASSIST **5.40** Based on past experience, it is assumed that the number of flaws per foot in rolls of grade 2 paper follows a Poisson distribution with a mean of 1 flaw per 5 feet of paper (0.2 flaw per foot). What is the probability that in a
a. 1-foot roll there will be at least 2 flaws?
b. 12-foot roll there will be at least 1 flaw?
c. 50-foot roll there will be between 5 and 15 (inclusive) flaws?

5.41 J.D. Power & Associates calculates and publishes various statistics concerning car quality. The Initial Quality score measures the number of problems per new car sold. For 2003 model cars, the Lexus was the top brand with 1.63 problems per car. Korea's Kia came in last with 5.09 problems per car (L. Hawkins, "Finding a Car That's Built to Last?" *The Wall Street Journal*, July 9, 2003, D1, D5). Let the random variable X be equal to the number of problems with a newly purchased Lexus.
a. What assumptions must be made in order for X to be distributed as a Poisson random variable? Are these assumptions reasonable?
Making the assumptions as in (a), if you purchased a 2003 Lexus, what is the probability that the new car will have:
b. zero problems?
c. two or fewer problems?
d. Give an operational definition for "problem." Why is the operational definition important in interpreting the Initial Quality score?

5.42 Refer to problem 5.41. If you purchased a 2003 Kia, what is the probability that the new car will have:
a. zero problems?
b. two or fewer problems?
c. Compare your answers in (a) and (b) to those for the Lexus in problem 5.27 (b) and (c).

5.43 In 2004, both Lexus and Kia improved their performance (D. Hakim, "Hyundai Near Top of a Quality Ranking," *The New York Times*, April 29, 2004, C.8). Lexus had 0.87 problems per car and Korea's Kia had 1.53 problems per car. If you purchased a 2004 Lexus, what is the probability that the new car will have:
a. zero problems?
b. two or fewer problems?
c. compare your answers in (a) and (b) to those of the 2003 Lexus in problem 5.41 (b) and (c).

5.44 Refer to problem 5.43. If you purchased a 2004 Kia, what is the probability that the new car will have:
a. zero problems?
b. two or fewer problems?
c. Compare your answers in (a) and (b) to those for the 2003 Kia in problem 5.42 (a) and (b).

5.45 A toll-free phone number is available from 9 A.M. to 9 P.M. for your customers to register a complaint with a product purchased from your company. Past history indicates that an average of 0.4 calls are received per minute.
a. What properties must be true about the situation described above in order to use the Poisson distribution to calculate probabilities concerning the number of phone calls received in a 1-minute period?
Assuming that this situation matches the properties you discussed in (a), what then is the probability that during a 1-minute period:
b. zero phone calls will be received?
c. three or more phone calls will be received?
d. What is the maximum number of phone calls that will be received in a 1-minute period 99.99% of the time?

Poisson Probability Distribution

Poisson Template:

Your answers should look like the following template:

X = # of _____ IN _____
                (successes)   (time or space)

$\lambda =$ _____ = _____
        (given)   (new—if needed)

P(_____) = P(X symbol #) =
    (words*)

_____ = 0._ _ _ _
    (calculator or SPSS input)   (4 dec.)

* If the question does not directly say what the number is.

5.46 A taxicab company has found that, on the average, two accidents occur in a month. The accidents appear to occur randomly. Find the probability of there being 5 or more accidents during a given month.

5.47 Customers arrive randomly at a service desk at an average rate of 2 every five minutes. Find the probability that:
a. None arrive in a five minute period.
b. More than four arrive in a ten minute period.

5.48 Bankruptcies of convenience stores in Toronto occur randomly at an average rate of 4.5 per year. Find the probability that:
a. there will be no corner store bankruptcies in the next four months.
b. there will be at most 3 corner store bankruptcies this year.

5.49 Flaws in plate glass used for large office buildings occur randomly at an average of 1 per 10 square feet. What is the probability that a 6 ft. by 10 ft. sheet of this type of glass will contain:
a. less than 2 flaws?
b. at least 1 flaw?

5.50 A data entry typist makes an average of 2 errors per page. If the errors occur randomly, what is the probability that:
a. there will be one error on the next page?
b. there will be more than 5 errors on the next 2 pages?

5.51 Two students have started a business to seal driveways during the summer months. They rent a pickup truck and a power sprayer. With this they will use a tar based spray to seal asphalt driveways. Past experience has shown that the best time to sign up customers is to ring their doorbells between 5:00 and 8:00 p.m. on any weekday evening. Any jobs that they obtain will be completed the next day. In the months of June, July and August they find that they get an average 2 customers per hour ringing doorbells.
a. What is the probability that they will get from 5 to 9 jobs in an evening of soliciting?
b. They charge $25 per driveway. If the truck costs $50 per day, and the spraying equipment costs $20 per day and the material to seal one driveway costs $5, what is the probability that they will make a profit on any given day.

CHAPTER REVIEW PROBLEMS

Checking Your Understanding

5.52 What is the meaning of the expected value of a probability distribution?

5.53 What are the four properties of a situation that must be present in order to use the binomial distribution?

5.54 What are the four properties of a situation that must be present in order to use the Poisson distribution?

Applying the Concepts

Problems 5.55–5.71 can be solved manually or by using Microsoft Excel or Minitab.

5.55 Event insurance allows promoters of sporting and entertainment events to protect themselves from financial losses due to uncontrollable circumstances such as rainouts. For example, each spring Cincinnati's Downtown Council puts on the Taste of Cincinnati. This is a rainy time of year in Cincinnati, and the chance of receiving an inch or more of rain during a spring weekend is about one out of four. An article in the *Cincinnati Enquirer*, by Jim Knippenberg ("Chicken Pox Means 3 Dog Night Remedy," *Cincinnati Enquirer*, May 28, 1997, E1), gave the details for an insurance policy purchased by the Downtown Council. The policy would pay $100,000 if it rained more than an inch during the weekend festival. The cost of the policy was reported to be $6,500.
a. Determine whether or not you believe that these dollar amounts are correct. (*Hint:* Calculate the expected value of the profit to be made by the insurance company.)
b. Assume that the dollar amounts are correct. Is this policy a good deal for Cincinnati's Downtown Council?

5.56 From 1872 to 2000, stock prices have risen in 74% of the years (Mark Hulbert, "The Stock Market Must Rise in 2002? Think Again," *The New York Times*, December 6, 2001, Business, 6). Based on this information, and assuming a binomial distribution, what do you think the probability is that the stock market will rise
a. next year?
b. the year after next?
c. in four of the next five years?
d. in none of the next five years?
e. For this situation, what assumption of the binomial distribution might not be valid?

5.57 The mean cost of a phone call handled by an automated customer-service system is $0.45. The mean cost of a phone call passed on to a "live" operator is $5.50. However, as more and more companies have implemented automated systems, customer annoyance with such systems has grown. Many customers are quick to leave the automated system when given an option such as "Press zero to talk to a customer-service representative." According to the Center for Client Retention, 40% of all callers to automated customer-service systems will automatically opt to go to a live operator when given the chance (Jane Spencer, "In Search of the Operator," *The Wall Street Journal*, May 8, 2002, D1).

If 10 independent callers contact an automated customer-service system, what is the probability
a. zero will automatically opt to talk to a live operator?
b. exactly one will automatically opt to talk to a live operator?
c. two or fewer will automatically opt to talk to a live operator?
d. all ten will automatically opt to talk to a live operator?
e. If all ten automatically opt to talk to a live operator, do you think that the 40% figure given in the article applies to this particular system? Explain.

5.58 One theory concerning the Dow Jones Industrial Average is that it is likely to increase during U.S. presidential election years. From 1964 through 2000, the Dow Jones Industrial Average has increased in eight of the ten U.S. presidential election years. Assuming that this indicator is a random event with no predictive value, you would expect that the indicator would be correct 50% of the time. What is the probability of the Dow Jones Industrial Average increasing in eight or more of the ten U.S. presidential election years if the true probability of an increase in the Dow Jones Industrial Average is
a. 0.50?
b. 0.70?
c. 0.90?
d. Based on the results of (a) through (c), what do you think is the probability that the Dow Jones Industrial Average will increase in a U.S. presidential election year?

5.59 Priority Mail is the United States Postal Service's alternative to commercial express mail companies like Federal Express. An article in the *Wall Street Journal* presents some interesting conclusions comparing Priority Mail shipments with the much cheaper first-class shipments (Rick Brooks, "New Data Reveal 'Priority Mail' Is Slower Than a Stamp," *The Wall Street Journal*, May 29, 2002, D1). When comparing shipments intended for delivery in 3 days, first-class deliveries failed to deliver on-time 19% of the time, while Priority Mail failed 33% of the time. Note that at the time of the article, first-class deliveries started as low as $0.34 and Priority Mail started at $3.50.

If 10 items are to be shipped first-class to 10 different destinations claimed to be in a 3-day delivery location, what is the probability that
a. zero items will take more than 3 days?

b. exactly one will take more than 3 days?

c. two or more will take more than 3 days?

d. What are the mean and the standard deviation of the probability distribution?

5.60 Refer to problem 5.59. If the shipments are made using Priority Mail, what is the probability that

a. zero items will take more than 3 days?

b. exactly one will take more than 3 days?

c. two or more will take more than 3 days?

d. What are the mean and the standard deviation of the probability distribution?

e. Compare the results of (a) through (c) to those of problem 5.59 (a) through (c).

5.61 Cinema advertising is increasing. Normally 60 to 90 seconds long, these advertisements are longer and more extravagant, and tend to have more captive audiences than television advertisements. Thus, it is not surprising that the recall rates for viewers of cinema advertisements are higher than for television advertisements. According to survey research conducted by the ComQUEST division of BBM Bureau of Measurement in Toronto, the probability a viewer will remember a cinema advertisement is 0.74, whereas the probability a viewer will remember a 30-second television advertisement is 0.37 (Nate Hendley, "Cinema Advertising Comes of Age," *Marketing Magazine*, May 6, 2002, 16).

a. Is the 0.74 probability reported by the BBM Bureau of Measurement best classified as *a priori* classical probability, empirical classical probability, or subjective probability?

b. Suppose that 10 viewers of a cinema advertisement are randomly sampled. Consider the random variable defined by the number of viewers that recall the advertisement. What assumptions must be made in order to assume that this random variable is distributed as a binomial random variable?

c. Assuming that the number of viewers that recall the cinema advertisement is a binomial random variable, what are the mean and standard deviation of this distribution?

d. Based on your answer to (c), if none of the viewers can recall the ad, what can be inferred about the 0.74 probability given in the article?

5.62 Refer to problem 5.61. Compute the probability that of the 10 viewers:

a. exactly zero can recall the advertisement.

b. all 10 can recall the advertisement.

c. more than half can recall the advertisement.

d. eight or more can recall the advertisement.

5.63 Refer to problem 5.62. For a television advertisement using the given probability of recall, 0.37, compute the probability that of the 10 viewers:

a. exactly zero can recall the advertisement.

b. all 10 can recall the advertisement.

c. more than half can recall the advertisement.

d. eight or more can recall the advertisement.

e. Compare the results of (a) through (d) to those of problem 5.62 (a) through (d).

5.64 In a survey conducted by the Council for Marketing and Opinion Research (CMOR), a national nonprofit research industry trade group based in Cincinnati, 1,628 of 3,700 adults contacted in the United States refuse to participate in phone surveys (Steve Jarvis, "CMOR Finds Survey Refusal Rate Still Rising," *Marketing News*, February 4, 2002, 4). Suppose that you are to randomly call 10 adults in the United States and ask them to participate in a phone survey. Using the results of the CMOR study, what is the probability:

a. all 10 will refuse?

b. exactly 5 will refuse?

c. at least 5 will refuse?

d. less than 5 will refuse?

e. less than 5 will agree to be surveyed?

f. What is the expected number of people that will refuse to participate? Explain the practical meaning of this number.

5.65 Credit card companies are increasing their revenues by raising the late fees charged to their customers. According to a study by **cardweb.com**, late fees represent the third largest revenue source for card companies after interest charges and payments from the merchants who accept their cards. In a recent year, 58% of all credit card customers had to pay a late fee (Ron Lieber, "Credit-Card Firms Collect Record Levels of Late Fees," *The Wall Street Journal*, May 21, 2002, D1).

If a random sample of 20 credit card holders is selected, what is the probability that

a. zero had to pay a late fee?

b. no more than 5 had to pay a late fee?

c. more than 10 had to pay a late fee?

d. What assumptions did you have to make to answer (a) through (c)?

5.66 For e-commerce merchants, getting a customer to visit a Web site isn't enough. Merchants must also persuade online shoppers to spend money by completing a purchase. Experts at Andersen Consulting estimated that 88% of Web shoppers abandon their virtual shopping carts before completing their transaction (Rebecca Quick, "The Lessons Learned," *The Wall Street Journal*, April 17, 2000, R6). Consider a sample of 20 customers who visit an e-commerce Web site, and assume that the probability a customer will leave the site before completing a transaction is 0.88. Use the binomial model to answer the following questions:

a. What is the expected value, or mean, of the binomial distribution?

b. What is the standard deviation of the binomial distribution?

c. What is the probability that all 20 of the customers will leave the site without completing a transaction?

d. What is the probability that 18 or more of the customers will leave the site without completing a transaction?

e. What is the probability that 15 or more of the customers will leave the site without completing a transaction?

5.67 Refer to problem 5.66. If the Web site is enhanced so that only 70% of the customers will leave the site without completing their transaction,

a. what is the expected value, or mean, of the binomial distribution?

b. what is the standard deviation of the binomial distribution?

c. what is the probability that all 20 of the customers will leave the site without completing a transaction?

d. what is the probability that 18 or more of the customers will leave the site without completing a transaction?

e. what is the probability that 15 or more of the customers will leave the site without completing a transaction?

f. Compare the results of (a) through (e) to those of problem 5.66 (a) through (e).

5.68 One theory concerning the Standard & Poor's 500 index is that if it increases during the first five trading days of the year, it is likely to increase during the entire year. From 1950 through 2003, the Standard & Poor's 500 index had these early gains in 34 years. In 29 of these 34 years, the Standard & Poor's 500 index increased. Assuming that this indicator is a random event with no predictive value, you would expect that the indicator would be correct 50% of the time. What is the probability of the Standard & Poor's 500 index increasing in 29 or more years if the true probability of an increase in the Standard & Poor's 500 index is

a. 0.50?

b. 0.70?

c. 0.90?

d. Based on the results of (a) through (c), what do you think is the probability that the Standard & Poor's 500 index will increase if there is an early gain in the first five trading days of the year? Explain.

5.69 Spurious correlation refers to the apparent relationship between variables that either have no true relationship or are related to other variables that have not been measured. One widely publicized stock market indicator in the United States that is an example of spurious correlation is the relationship between the winner of the National Football League Superbowl and the performance of the Dow Jones Industrial Average in that year. The indicator states that when a team representing the National Football Conference wins the Superbowl, the Dow Jones Industrial Average will increase in that year. When a team representing the American Football Conference wins the Superbowl, the Dow Jones Industrial Average will decline in that year. During the time period 1967 to 2003, a 37-year period, the indicator has been correct 31 out of 37 times. Assuming that this indicator is a random event with no predictive value, you would expect that the indicator would be correct 50% of the time.

a. What is the probability that the indicator would be correct 31 or more times in 37 years?

b. What does this tell you about the usefulness of this indicator?

5.71 Worldwide golf ball sales total more than $1 billion annually. One reason for such a large number of golf ball purchases is that golfers lose them at a rate of 4.5 per 18-hole round ("Snapshots," **usatoday.com**, January 29, 2004). Assume that the number of golf balls lost in an 18-hole round is distributed as a Poisson random variable.

a. What assumptions need to be made so that the number of golf balls lost in an 18-hole round is distributed as a Poisson random variable?

Making the assumptions given in (a), what is the probability that

b. 0 balls will be lost in an 18-hole round?

c. 5 or fewer balls will be lost in an 18-hole round?

d. 6 or more balls will be lost in an 18-hole round?

5.71 A study of the homepages for Fortune 500 companies reports that the mean number of bad links per homepage is 0.4 and the mean number of spelling errors per homepage is 0.16 (Nabil Tamimi, Murii Rajan, and Rose Sebastianella, "Benchmarking the Home Pages of 'Fortune' 500 Companies," *Quality Progress*, July 2000). Use the Poisson distribution to find the probability that a randomly selected homepage will contain

a. exactly 0 bad links.

b. 5 or more bad links.

c. exactly 0 spelling errors.

d. 10 or more spelling errors.

RUNNING CASE
MANAGING THE *SPRINGVILLE HERALD*

The *Herald* marketing department is seeking to increase home-delivery sales through an aggressive direct-marketing campaign that includes mailings, discount coupons, and telephone solicitations. Feedback from these efforts indicates that getting their newspapers delivered early in the morning is a very important factor for both prospective as well as existing subscribers.

After several brainstorming sessions, a team consisting of members from the marketing and circulation departments decided that guaranteeing newspaper delivery by a specific time could be an important selling point in retaining and getting new subscribers. The team concluded that the *Herald* should offer a guarantee that customers will receive their newspapers by a certain time or else that day's issue is free.

To assist the team in setting a guaranteed delivery time, Al Leslie, the research director, noted that the circulation department had the data that would show the percentage of newspapers yet undelivered every quarter-hour from 6 A.M. to 8 A.M. Jan Shapiro remembered that customers were asked on their subscription forms at what time would they be looking for their copy of the *Herald* to be delivered. These data were subsequently combined and posted on an internal *Herald* Web page (see **Circulation_Data.htm** in the HeraldCase folder on the CD-ROM that accompanies this text or link to **www.prenhall.com/HeraldCase/Circulation_Data.htm**).

EXERCISES

Review the internal data and propose a reasonable time (to the nearest quarter-hour) to guarantee delivery. To help explore the effects of your choice, calculate the following probabilities:

SH5.1 If a sample of 50 customers is selected on a given day, what is the probability, given your selected delivery time, that:

  a. fewer than 3 customers would receive a free newspaper?

  b. 2, 3, or 4 customers would receive a free newspaper?

  c. more than 5 customers would receive a free newspaper?

SH5.2 Consider the effects of improving the newspaper delivery process so that the percentage of newspapers that go undelivered by your guaranteed delivery time decreases by 2%. If a sample of 50 customers is selected on a given day, what is the probability, given your selected delivery time (and the delivery improvement), that:

  a. fewer than 3 customers would receive a free newspaper?

  b. 2, 3, or 4 customers would receive a free newspaper?

  c. more than 5 customers would receive a free newspaper?

REFERENCES

1. Bernstein, P. L., *Against the Gods: The Remarkable Story of Risk* (New York: Wiley, 1996).
2. Emery, D. R., and J. D. Finnerty, *Corporate Financial Management*, 2nd ed. (Upper Saddle River, NJ: Prentice Hall, 2000).
3. Kirk, R. L., ed., *Statistical Issues: A Reader for the Behavioral Sciences* (Belmont, CA: Wadsworth, 1972).
4. Levine, D. M., P. Ramsey, and R. Smidt, *Applied Statistics for Engineers and Scientists Using Microsoft Excel and Minitab* (Upper Saddle River, NJ: Prentice Hall, 2001).
5. Mescove, S. A., M. G. Simkin, and A. Barganoff, *Core Concepts of Accounting Information Systems*, 7th ed. (New York: John Wiley, 2001).
6. *Microsoft Excel 2003* (Redmond, WA: Microsoft Corp., 2002).
7. *Minitab for Windows Version 14* (State College, PA: Minitab Inc., 2004).

CHAPTER 6

The Normal Distribution

USING STATISTICS: Download Time for a Web Site Homepage

6.1 CONTINUOUS PROBABILITY DISTRIBUTIONS

6.2 THE NORMAL DISTRIBUTION
Calculator Lesson 5

LEARNING OBJECTIVES

In this chapter, you learn:

- To compute probabilities from the normal distribution
- To use the normal probability plot to determine whether a set of data is approximately normally distributed

USING STATISTICS

Download Time for a Web Site Homepage

You are a designer for the OnCampus! Web site that targets college students. To attract and retain users, you need to make sure that the homepage downloads quickly. Both the design of the homepage and the load on the company's Web server affect the download time. To check how fast the homepage loads, you open a Web browser on a PC at the corporate offices of OnCampus! and measure the download time, the number of seconds that passes from first linking to the Web site until the homepage is fully displayed.

Past data indicate that the mean download time is 7 seconds and that the standard deviation is 2 seconds. Approximately two-thirds of the download times are between 5 and 9 seconds, and about 95% of the download times are between 3 and 11 seconds. In other words, the download times are distributed as a bell-shaped curve with a clustering around the mean of 7 seconds. How could you use this information to answer questions about the download times of the current homepage?

In the last chapter, Saxon Home Improvement Company managers wanted to be able to solve problems about the number of occurrences of a certain type of outcome in a given sample size. As an OnCampus! Web designer, you face a different task, one that involves a continuous measurement because a download time could be any value and not just a whole number. How then can you answer questions about this *continuous numerical variable* such as:

- What proportion of the homepage downloads take more than 10 seconds?
- How many seconds elapse before 10% of the downloads are complete?
- How many seconds elapse before 99% of the downloads are complete?
- How would redesigning the homepage to download faster affect the answers to the above questions?

As in the previous chapter, you can use a probability distribution as a model. Reading this chapter will help you learn about characteristics of a continuous probability distribution and how to use the normal distribution to solve business problems.

6.1 CONTINUOUS PROBABILITY DISTRIBUTIONS

A **continuous probability density function** is the mathematical expression that defines the distribution of the values for a continuous random variable. Figure 6.1 graphically displays three continuous probability density functions. Panel A depicts a normal distribution. The normal distribution is symmetric and bell-shaped, implying that most values tend to cluster around the mean, which, due to its symmetric shape, is equal to the median. Although theoretically the values in a normal distribution can range from negative infinity to positive infinity, the shape of the distribution makes it very unlikely that extremely large or extremely small values will occur. Panel B depicts a uniform distribution where the probability of occurrence of a value is equally likely to occur anywhere in the range between the smallest value *a* and the largest value *b*. Sometimes referred to as the rectangular distribution, the uniform distribution is symmetric and therefore the mean equals the median. An exponential distribution is illustrated in panel C. This distribution is skewed to the right, making the mean larger than the median. The range for an exponential distribution is zero to positive infinity but its shape makes the occurrence of extremely large values unlikely.

FIGURE 6.1

Three Continuous
Distributions

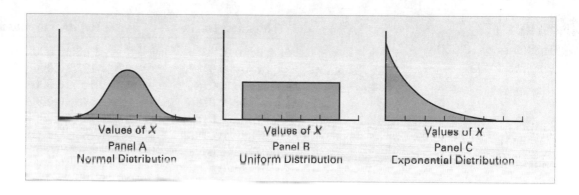

6.2 THE NORMAL DISTRIBUTION

The **normal distribution** (sometimes referred to as the *Gaussian* distribution) is the most common continuous distribution used in statistics. The normal distribution is vitally important in statistics for three main reasons:

- Numerous continuous variables common in the business world have distributions that closely resemble the normal distribution.
- The normal distribution can be used to approximate various discrete probability distributions such as the binomial and Poisson distributions.
- The normal distribution provides the basis for *classical statistical inference* because of its relationship to the *central limit theorem* (which is discussed in section 7.2).

The normal distribution is represented by the classic bell-shape depicted in panel A of Figure 6.1. In the normal distribution, you can calculate the probability that various values occur within certain ranges or intervals. However, the *exact* probability of a *particular value* from a continuous distribution such as the normal distribution is zero. This property distinguishes continuous variables, which are measured, from discrete variables, which are counted. As an example, time (in seconds) is measured and not counted. Therefore you can determine the probability that the download time for a home page on a Web browser is between 7 and 10 seconds or the probability that the download time is between 8 and 9 seconds or the probability that the download time is between 7.99 and 8.01 seconds. However, the probability that the download time is *exactly* 8 seconds is zero.

The normal distribution has several important theoretical properties:

- It is bell-shaped (and thus symmetrical) in its appearance.
- Its measures of central tendency (mean, median, and mode) are all identical.
- Its "middle fifty" is equal to 1.33 standard deviations. This means that the interquartile range is contained within an interval of two-thirds of a standard deviation below the mean to two-thirds of a standard deviation above the mean.
- Its associated random variable has an infinite range ($-\infty < X < \infty$).

In practice, many variables have distributions that closely resemble the theoretical properties of the normal distribution. The data in Table 6.1 represent the thickness (in inches) of 10,000 brass washers manufactured by a large company. The continuous variable of interest, thickness, can be approximated by the normal distribution. The measurements of the thickness of the 10,000 brass washers cluster in the interval 0.0190 to 0.0192 inch and distribute symmetrically around that grouping, forming a "bell-shaped" pattern. As demonstrated in Table 6.1, if the nonoverlapping (*mutually exclusive*) listing contains all possible class intervals (is *collectively exhaustive*), the probabilities will sum to 1. Such a probability distribution is a relative frequency distribution, as described in section 2.3, where, except for the two open-ended classes, the midpoint of every other class interval represents the data in that interval.

TABLE 6.1

Thickness of 10,000
Brass Washers

Thickness (inches)	Relative Frequency
Under 0.0180	48/10,000 = 0.0048
0.0180 < 0.0182	122/10,000 = 0.0122
0.0182 < 0.0184	325/10,000 = 0.0325
0.0184 < 0.0186	695/10,000 = 0.0695
0.0186 < 0.0188	1,198/10,000 − 0.1198
0.0188 < 0.0190	1,664/10,000 = 0.1664
0.0190 < 0.0192	1,896/10,000 = 0.1896
0.0192 < 0.0194	1,664/10,000 = 0.1664
0.0194 < 0.0196	1,198/10,000 = 0.1198
0.0196 < 0.0198	695/10,000 = 0.0695
0.0198 < 0.0200	325/10,000 = 0.0325
0.0200 < 0.0202	122/10,000 = 0.0122
0.0202 or above	48/10,000 = 0.0048
Total	1.0000

Figure 6.2 depicts the relative frequency histogram and polygon for the distribution of the thickness of 10,000 brass washers. For these data, the first three theoretical properties of the normal distribution are approximately satisfied; however, the fourth does not hold. The random variable of interest, thickness, cannot possibly be zero or below, and a washer cannot be so thick that it becomes unusable. From Table 6.1 above you see that only 48 out of every 10,000 brass washers manufactured are expected to have a thickness of 0.0202 inch or more, whereas an equal number are expected to have a thickness under 0.0180 inch. Thus, the chance of randomly getting a washer so thin or so thick is 0.0048 + 0.0048 = 0.0096—or less than 1 in 100.

FIGURE 6.2

Relative Frequency
Histogram and Polygon
of the Thickness of
10,000 Brass Washers

Source: *Data are taken from
Table 6.1.*

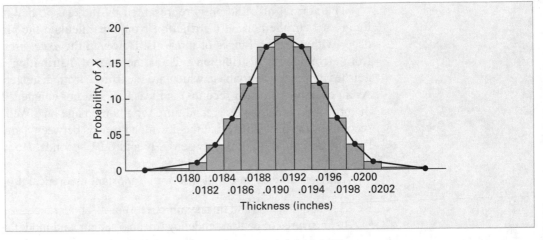

The mathematical expression representing a continuous probability density function is denoted by the symbol $f(X)$. For the normal distribution, the **normal probability density function** is given in Equation (6.1).

THE NORMAL PROBABILITY DENSITY FUNCTION

$$f(X) = \frac{1}{\sqrt{2\pi}\sigma} e^{-(1/2)[(X-\mu)/\sigma]^2} \qquad (6.1)$$

where

e is the mathematical constant approximated by 2.71828

π is the mathematical constant approximated by 3.14159

μ is the mean

σ is the standard deviation

X is any value of the continuous variable, where $(-\infty < X < \infty)$

Because e and π are mathematical constants, the probabilities of the random variable X are dependent only on the two parameters of the normal distribution—the mean μ and the standard deviation σ. Every time you specify a *particular combination* of μ and σ, a *different* normal probability distribution is generated. Figure 6.3 illustrates three different normal distributions. Distributions A and B have the same mean (μ) but have different standard deviations. Distributions A and C have the same standard deviation (σ) but have different means. Distributions B and C depict two normal probability density functions that differ with respect to both μ and σ.

FIGURE 6.3
Three Normal
Distributions

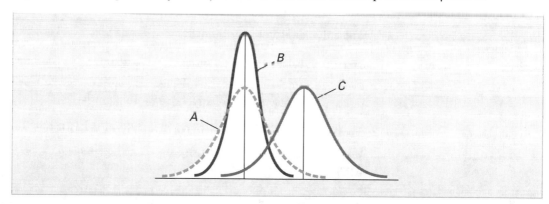

CALCULATOR LESSON 5

CASIO FX-9750G OR CFX-9850GB CALCULATOR

Lesson 5—Normal Distribution

The Casio calculator has *two* Normal probability functions programmed into its memory. These are:

i. **Ncd** which stands for **N**ormal **c**umulative **d**istribution. This function calculates a Normal probability of the form:

$$P(X \leq \#)$$

ii. **InvN** which stands for **I**nverse **N**ormal. This function calculates an 'x' value, i.e.?, for a known Normal probability of the form:

$$P(X \leq ?) = \text{given probability}$$

EXAMPLE 6.1

Suppose that the weights of adults are normally distributed with a mean of 170.0 lbs. and a standard deviation of 25.0 lbs.

a. What is the probability that a person weighs from 150 to 190 lbs.?

Solution: X = a person's weight
μ = 170.0 lbs.
σ = 25.0 lbs.

STAT F5(DIST) **F1**(NORM) **F2**(Ncd)   then select the following options

Lower   : **150 EXE**
Upper   : **190 EXE**
σ : **25 EXE**
μ : **170 EXE**

Now key **EXE** or **F1**(Calc)

The calculator will now show the result 0.57628

i.e. $P(150 \leq X \leq 190) = 0.5763$

b. What is the probability that a person weighs less than 140 lbs.?

Lower	: −100 EXE
Upper	: 140 EXE
σ	: 25 EXE
μ	: 170 EXE

Now key **EXE** or **F1**(Calc)

The calculator will now show the result 0.11506

i.e. $P(X \leqslant 140) = 0.1151$

Note: To represent −∞ use any value less than: $\mu - 6\sigma$
To represent ∞ use any value more than: $\mu + 6\sigma$

c. What is the probability that a person weighs at least 160 lbs.?

Lower	: 160 EXE
Upper	: 1000 EXE
σ	: 25 EXE
μ	: 170 EXE

$P(X \geq 160) = 0.6554$

d. What is the maximum weight of the lightest 15% of the adult population?

$P(X \leq ?) = 0.15$

STAT F5(DIST) **F1**(NORM) **F3**(InvN)   then select the following options

Area	: .15 EXE
σ	: 25 EXE
μ	: 170 EXE

Now key **EXE** or **F1**(Calc)   The calculator will now show the result 144.09

i.e. The lightest 15% of adults weigh at most 144.1 lbs.

e. What is the minimum weight to be in the heaviest 30% of the adult population?

$P(X \geq ?) = 0.3$

STAT F5(DIST) **F1**(NORM) **F3**(InvN)   then select the following options

Area	: .7 EXE
σ	: 25 EXE
μ	: 170 EXE

Now key **EXE** or **F1**(Calc)   The calculator will now show the result 183.11

i.e. The heaviest 30% weigh at least 183.1 lbs.

Note: When using the InvN function, the *Area* value that is required is the area to the *LEFT* of the desired X value.

PROBLEMS FOR CALCULATOR LESSON 5: NORMAL PROBABILITY

Normal Probability

Normal Template:

X = _____

μ =
            } Normal
σ =

P(_____) – P(X symbol #) –
  (words*)

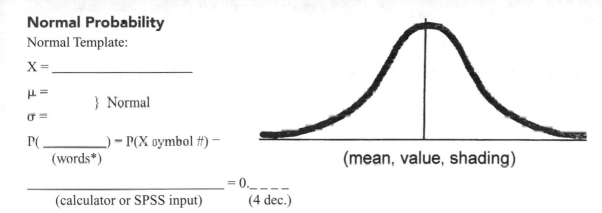

(mean, value, shading)

————————————————————— = 0._ _ _ _
(calculator or SPSS input)   (4 dec.)

Inverse Normal Template:

X = _____

μ =
            } Normal
σ =

P(_____) = P(X symbol ?) = 0._____
  (words*)   (given)

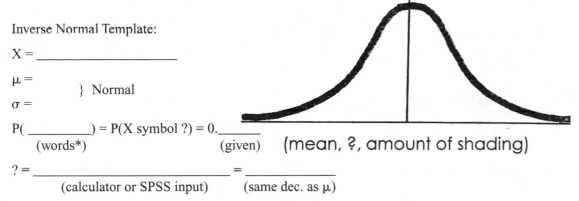

(mean, ?, amount of shading)

? = _____ = _____
     (calculator or SPSS input)   (same dec. as μ)

Concluding statement.

6.1 The lifetime of a certain brand of tire is normally distributed with a mean of 90,000 km. and standard deviation of 8,000 km. The tire carries a warranty for 80,000 km.
a. What is the probability that the tire you recently purchased will last more than 100,000 km.?
b. What percent of this brand of tire will fail before the warranty expires?
c. What should the mileage warranty be so that only 4% of the tires need to be replaced under warranty?

6.2 A firm's marketing manager believes that total sales for next year can be represented by a normal distribution, with a mean of $2.5 million and a standard deviation of $300,000. The firm has fixed costs of $1.8 million.
a. What is the probability that the firm's sales will be less than $3.0 million?
b. What is the probability that the firm will have sufficient sales to cover fixed costs?
c. What is the probability that the firm's sales will be within $150,000 of the expected, i.e. mean, sales?
d. Determine the sales level that has only a 9% chance of being exceeded.

6.3 The owner of a convenience store has copies of the local newspaper delivered early each morning. The demand for papers is normally distributed with a mean of 75 and a standard deviation of 16.
a. What is the probability that the newspapers will be sold out if the owner orders 65 copies?
b. How many copies should be ordered so that the probability of selling out is at most 15%?

6.4 In the movie *Forest Gump,* the public school required an IQ of at least 80 to be admitted.
a. If IQ test scores are normally distributed with a mean of 100 and a standard deviation of 16, what percent of children would qualify for admittance to the school?
b. If the public school wished to have 95% of all children qualify for admittance, what minimum IQ test score should be required for admittance?

6.5 An investment broker reports that the annual returns on common stock and municipal bonds are both normally distributed. The stocks have a mean return of 12.4% with a standard deviation of 20.6%. On the other hand the bonds have a mean return of 5.2% with a standard deviation of 8.6%.

a. If you are a conservative investor and just don't like to lose money, which type of investment should you choose?

b. If you are more ambitious an investor and would like to have the best chance of making more than 15%, which investment should you choose?

c. What minimum return would a stock have to earn to be rated in top 20% of stocks in term of return?

6.6 At a certain university the cumulative grade point average (CGPA) of first year students usually averages 2.73 with a standard deviation 0.37. It has been found that the marks are usually approximately normally distributed.

a. What is the probability that a student will have a CGPA that is between 2.00 and 3.00?

b. What percent of students will be on probation, i.e. their CGPA is less than 2.00 ?

c. Academic scholarships are awarded to the top 1 % of first year students. What minimum CGPA is needed to receive a scholarship?

6.2   THE NORMAL DISTRIBUTION (continued)

The mathematical expression in Equation (6.1) is computationally tedious and requires integral calculus. Fortunately, normal probability tables are available and you can avoid these complicated computations. The first step in finding normal probabilities is to use the **transformation formula**, given in Equation (6.2), to convert any normal random variable X to a **standardized normal random variable** Z.

THE TRANSFORMATION FORMULA

The Z value is equal to the difference between X and the mean μ, divided by the standard deviation σ.

$$Z = \frac{X - \mu}{\sigma} \qquad \textbf{(6.2)}$$

Although the original data for the random variable X had mean μ and standard deviation σ, the standardized random variable Z will always have mean $\mu = 0$ and standard deviation $\sigma = 1$.

By substituting $\mu = 0$ and $\sigma = 1$ in Equation (6.1), the probability density function of a standardized normal variable Z is given in Equation (6.3).

THE STANDARDIZED NORMAL PROBABILITY DENSITY FUNCTION

$$f(Z) = \frac{1}{\sqrt{2\pi}} e^{-(1/2)Z^2} \qquad \textbf{(6.3)}$$

Any set of normally distributed values can be converted to its standardized form. Then you can determine the desired probabilities using Table E.2, the **cumulative standardized normal distribution**.

To see how the transformation formula is applied and the results used to find probabilities from Table E.2[1], recall from the "Using Statistics" scenario on page 170 that past data indicate that the time to download the Web page is normally distributed with a mean $\mu = 7$ seconds and a standard deviation $\sigma = 2$ seconds. From Figure 6.4, you see that every measurement X has a corresponding standardized measurement Z computed from the transformation formula [Equation (6.2)]. Therefore, a download time of 9 seconds is equivalent to 1 standardized unit (i.e., 1 standard deviation above the mean) because

$$Z = \frac{9 - 7}{2} = +1$$

A download time of 1 second is equivalent to 3 standardized units (3 standard deviations) below the mean because

$$Z = \frac{1-7}{2} = -3$$

Thus, the standard deviation is the unit of measurement. In other words, a time of 9 seconds is 2 seconds (i.e., 1 standard deviation) higher, or *slower*, than the mean time of 7 seconds. Similarly, a time of 1 second is 6 seconds (i.e., 3 standard deviations) lower, or *faster*, than the mean time.

FIGURE 6.4

Transformation
of Scales

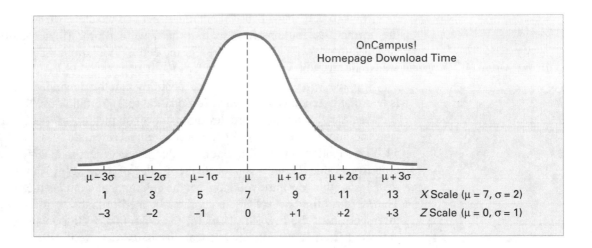

To further illustrate the transformation formula, suppose that the homepage of another Web site has a download time that is normally distributed with a mean $\mu = 4$ seconds and a standard deviation $\sigma = 1$ second. This distribution is illustrated in Figure 6.5.

FIGURE 6.5

A Different
Transformation
of Scales

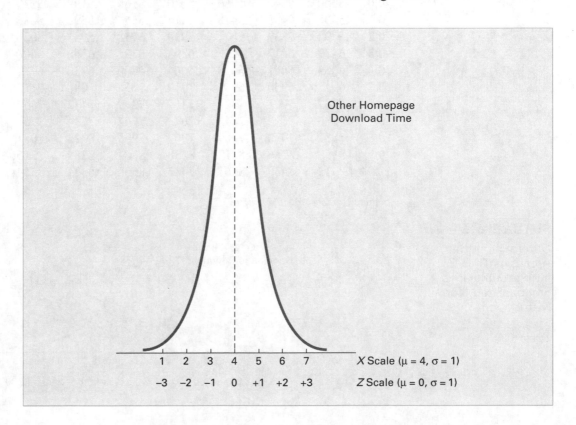

Comparing these results with those of the OnCampus! Web site, you see that a download time of 5 seconds is 1 standard deviation above the mean download time because

$$Z = \frac{5-4}{1} = +1$$

A time of 1 second is 3 standard deviations below the mean download time because

$$Z = \frac{1-4}{1} = -3$$

The two bell-shaped curves in Figures 6.4 and 6.5 show the relative frequency polygons of the normal distributions representing the download time (in seconds) for the two Web sites. Because the download times represent the entire population, the *probabilities* or proportion of area under the entire curve must add to 1.

Suppose you wanted to find the probability that the download time for the OnCampus! site is less than 9 seconds. First, you use Equation (6.2) to transform $X = 9$ to standardized Z units. Because $X = 9$ is one standard deviation above the mean, $Z = +1.00$. Next you use Table E.2 to find the cumulative area under the normal curve calculated less than (i.e., to the left of) $Z = +1.00$. To read the probability or area under the curve less than $Z = +1.00$, scan down the Z column from Table E.2 until you locate the Z value of interest (in 10ths) in the Z row for 1.0. Next read across this row until you intersect the column that contains the 100ths place of the Z value. Therefore, in the body of the table, the tabulated probability for $Z = 1.00$ corresponds to the intersection of the row $Z = 1.0$ with the column $Z = .00$, as shown in Table 6.2, which is extracted from Table E.2. This probability is 0.8413. As illustrated in Figure 6.6, there is an 84.13% chance that the download time will be less than 9 seconds.

TABLE 6.2

Finding a Cumulative Area under the Normal Curve

Z	.00	.01	.02	.03	.04	.05	.06	.07	.08	.09
0.0	.5000	.5040	.5080	.5120	.5160	.5199	.5239	.5279	.5319	.5359
0.1	.5398	.5438	.5478	.5517	.5557	.5596	.5636	.5675	.5714	.5753
0.2	.5793	.5832	.5871	.5910	.5948	.5987	.6026	.6064	.6103	.6141
0.3	.6179	.6217	.6255	.6293	.6331	.6368	.6406	.6443	.6480	.6517
0.4	.6554	.6591	.6628	.6664	.6700	.6736	.6772	.6808	.6844	.6879
0.5	.6915	.6950	.6985	.7019	.7054	.7088	.7123	.7157	.7190	.7224
0.6	.7257	.7291	.7324	.7357	.7389	.7422	.7454	.7486	.7518	.7549
0.7	.7580	.7612	.7642	.7673	.7704	.7734	.7764	.7794	.7823	.7852
0.8	.7881	.7910	.7939	.7967	.7995	.8023	.8051	.8078	.8106	.8133
0.9	.8159	.8186	.8212	.8238	.8264	.8289	.8315	.8340	.8365	.8389
1.0	.8413	.8438	.8461	.8485	.8508	.8531	.8554	.8577	.8599	.8621

Source: Extracted from Table E.2.

FIGURE 6.6

Determining the Area Less Than Z from a Cumulative Standardized Normal Distribution

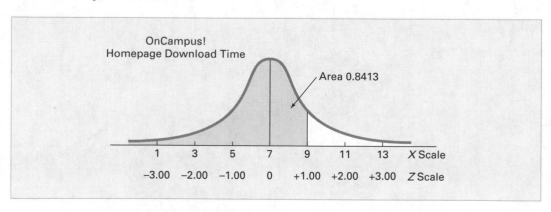

OnCampus! Homepage Download Time

Area 0.8413

X Scale	1	3	5	7	9	11	13
Z Scale	−3.00	−2.00	−1.00	0	+1.00	+2.00	+3.00

However, for the other homepage, from Figure 6.5 on page 182, you see that a time of 5 seconds is 1 standardized unit above the mean time of 4 seconds. Thus, the probability that the download time will be less than 5 seconds is also 0.8413. Figure 6.7 shows that regardless of the value of the mean μ and standard deviation σ of a normally distributed variable, Equation (6.2) can transform the problem to Z values.

FIGURE 6.7

Demonstrating a Transformation of Scales for Corresponding Cumulative Portions under Two Normal Curves

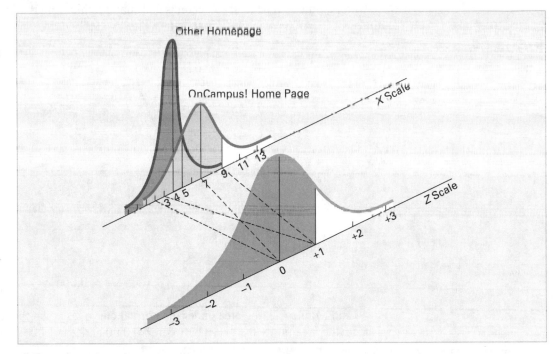

Now that you have learned to use Table E.2 with Equation (6.2), you can answer many questions related to the OnCampus! homepage using the normal distribution.

EXAMPLE 6.2

FINDING $P(X > 9)$

What is the probability that the download time will be more than 9 seconds?

SOLUTION The probability that the download time will be less than 9 seconds is 0.8413 (see Figure 6.6). Thus, the probability that the download time will be more than 9 seconds is the *complement* of less than 9 seconds, $1 - 0.8413 = 0.1587$. Figure 6.8 illustrates this result.

FIGURE 6.8

Finding P(X > 9)

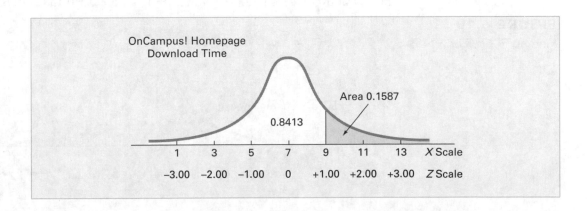

EXAMPLE 6.3

FINDING $P(7 < X < 9)$

What is the probability that the download time will be between 7 and 9 seconds?

SOLUTION From Figure 6.6, you already determined that the probability that a download time will be less than 9 seconds is 0.8413. Now you must determine the probability that the download time will be under 7 seconds and subtract this from the probability that the download time is under 9 seconds. This is shown in Figure 6.9.

FIGURE 6.9

Finding $P(7 < X < 9)$

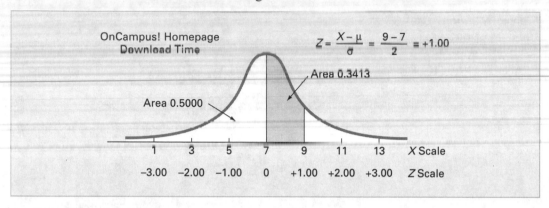

Using Equation (6.2)

$$Z = \frac{7-7}{2} = 0.00$$

Using Table E.2, the area under the normal curve less than the mean of $Z = 0.00$ is 0.5000. Hence, the area under the curve between $Z = 0.00$ and $Z = 1.00$ is $0.8413 - 0.5000 = 0.3413$.

EXAMPLE 6.4

FINDING $P(X < 7$ OR $X > 9)$

What is the probability that the download time is under 7 seconds or over 9 seconds?

SOLUTION From Figure 6.9, the probability that the download time is between 7 and 9 seconds is 0.3413. The probability that the download time is under 7 seconds or over 9 seconds is its complement, $1 - 0.3413 = 0.6587$.

Another way to view this problem, however, is to separately calculate both the probability of a download time of less than 7 seconds and the probability of a download time of over 9 seconds and to then add these two probabilities together to compute the desired result. This result is depicted in Figure 6.10. Because the mean and median are the same for normally distributed data, 50% of download times are under 7 seconds. From Example 6.1, the probability of a download time of over 9 seconds is 0.1587. Hence, the probability that a download time is under 7 or over 9 seconds, $P(X < 7$ or $X > 9)$, is $0.5000 + 0.1587 = 0.6587$.

FIGURE 6.10

Finding $P(X < 7$ or $X > 9)$

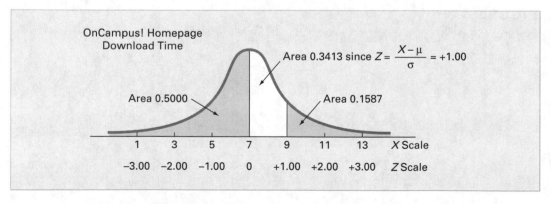

EXAMPLE 6.5

FINDING $P(5 < X < 9)$

What is the probability that the download time will be between 5 and 9 seconds, that is, $P(5 < X < 9)$?

SOLUTION In Figure 6.11, you can see that the area of interest is located between two values, 5 and 9. Because Table E.2 permits you only to find probabilities less than a particular value of interest, use the following three steps to find the desired probability:

1. Determine the probability of less than 9 seconds.
2. Determine the probability of less than 5 seconds.
3. Subtract the smaller result from the larger.

FIGURE 6.11

Finding $P(5 < X < 9)$

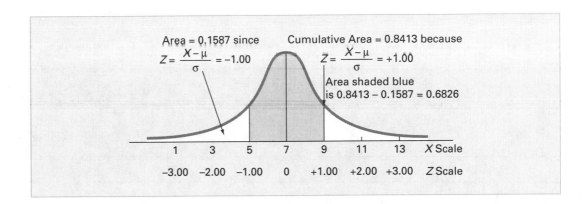

For this example, you have already completed step 1. The area under the normal curve less than 9 seconds is 0.8413. To find the area under the normal curve less than 5 seconds (step 2),

$$Z = \frac{5 - 7}{2} = -1.00$$

Using Table E.2, you look up $Z = -1.00$ and find 0.1587. From step 3, the probability that the download time will be between 5 and 9 seconds is $0.8413 - 0.1587 = 0.6826$, as displayed in Figure 6.11.

The result of Example 6.5 is important and allows you to generalize the findings. For any normal distribution there is a 0.6826 chance that a randomly selected item will fall within ± 1 standard deviation of the mean. From Figure 6.12, slightly more than 95% of the items will fall within ± 2 standard deviations of the mean. Thus, 95.44% of the download times are between 3 and 11 seconds. From Figure 6.13, 99.73% of the items will fall within ± 3 standard deviations above or below the mean. Thus, 99.73% of the download times are between 1 and 13 seconds. Therefore, it is unlikely (0.0027, or only 27 in 10,000) that a download time will be so fast or so slow that it will take under 1 second or more than 13 seconds. This is why 6σ (i.e., 3 standard deviations above the mean to 3 standard deviations below the mean) is often used as a *practical approximation of the range* for normally distributed data.

Therefore, for any normal distribution:

- Approximately 68.26% of the items will fall within ± 1 standard deviations of the mean.
- Approximately 95.44% of the items will fall within ± 2 standard deviations of the mean.
- Approximately 99.73% of the items will fall within ± 3 standard deviations of the mean.

The above result is the justification for the empirical rule presented on page 96. The closer a data set follows the normal distribution, the more accurate the empirical rule is.

FIGURE 6.12

Finding $P(3 < X < 11)$

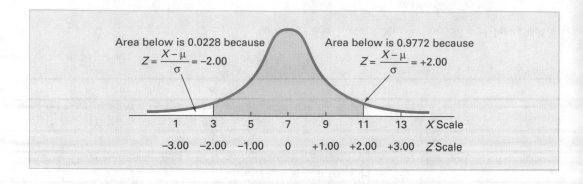

FIGURE 6.13

Finding $P(1 < X < 13)$

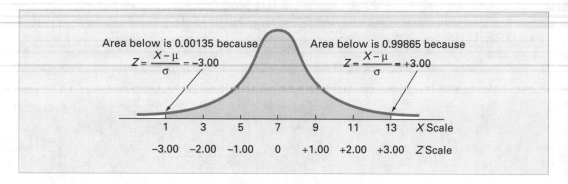

EXAMPLE 6.6

FINDING $P(X < 3.5)$

What is the probability that a download time will be under 3.5 seconds?

SOLUTION To calculate the probability that a download time will be under 3.5 seconds, you need to examine the shaded lower left-tail region of Figure 6.14.

FIGURE 6.14

Finding $P(X < 3.5)$

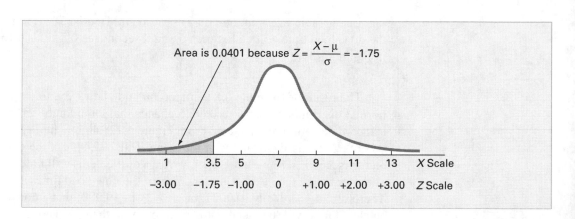

To determine the area under the curve below 3.5 seconds, first calculate

$$Z = \frac{X - \mu}{\sigma} = \frac{3.5 - 7}{2} = -1.75$$

Look up the Z value of -1.75 in Table E.2 by matching the appropriate Z row (-1.7) with the appropriate Z column (.05) as shown in Table 6.3 (which is extracted from Table E.2). The resulting probability or area under the curve less than -1.75 standard deviations below the mean is 0.0401.

TABLE 6.3

Finding a Cumulative Area under the Normal Curve

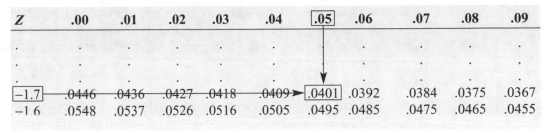

Z	.00	.01	.02	.03	.04	.05	.06	.07	.08	.09
.	.	.	.	.	.	.	.	.	.	.
.	.	.	.	.	.	.	.	.	.	.
−1.7	.0446	.0436	.0427	.0418	.0409	.0401	.0392	.0384	.0375	.0367
−1.6	.0548	.0537	.0526	.0516	.0505	.0495	.0485	.0475	.0465	.0455

Source: Extracted from Table E.2.

VISUAL EXPLORATIONS Exploring the Normal Distribution

Use the Visual Explorations Normal Distribution command to see the effects of changes in the mean and standard deviation on the area under a normal distribution curve.

Open the **Visual Explorations.xla** file and select **VisualExplorations → Normal Distribution** from the Microsoft Excel menu bar. You will see a normal curve for the "Using Statistics" homepage download example and a floating control panel that allows you to adjust the shape of the curve and the shaded area under the curve (see illustration below).

Use the control panel spinner buttons to change the values for the mean, standard deviation, and X value, while noting their effects on the probability of X <= value and the corresponding shaded area under the curve (see illustration below). If you prefer, you can select the Z Values option button to see the normal curve labeled with Z Values.

Click the Reset button to reset the control panel values or click Help for additional information about the problem. Click Finish when you are done exploring.

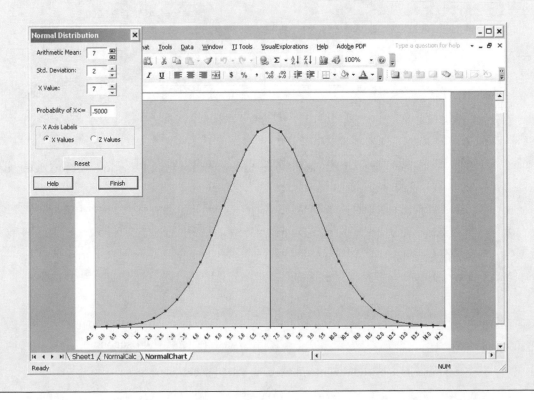

Examples 6.1 through 6.6 require you to use the normal tables to find an area under the normal curve that corresponds to a specific X value. There are many circumstances when you want to do the opposite. Examples 6.7 and 6.8 illustrate how to find the X value that corresponds to a specific area.

EXAMPLE 6.7

FINDING THE X VALUE FOR A CUMULATIVE PROBABILITY OF 0.10

How much time (in seconds) will elapse before 10% of the downloads are complete?

SOLUTION Because 10% of the homepages are expected to download in under X seconds, the area under the normal curve less than this Z value is 0.1000. Using the body of Table E.2, you search for the area or probability of 0.1000. The closest result is 0.1003, as shown in Table 6.4 (which is extracted from Table E.2).

TABLE 6.4

Finding a Z Value Corresponding to a Particular Cumulative Area (0.10) under the Normal Curve

Z	.00	.01	.02	.03	.04	.05	.06	.07	.08	.09
.	.	.	.	.	.	.	.	.	.	.
.	.	.	.	.	.	.	.	.	.	.
−1.5	.0668	.0655	.0643	.0630	.0618	.0606	.0594	.0582	.0571	.0559
−1.4	.0808	.0793	.0778	.0764	.0749	.0735	.0721	.0708	.0694	.0681
−1.3	.0968	.0951	.0934	.0918	.0901	.0885	.0869	.0853	.0838	.0823
−1.2	.1151	.1131	.1112	.1093	.1075	.1056	.1038	.1020	.1003	.0985

Source: Extracted from Table E.2.

Working from this area to the margins of the table, the Z value corresponding to the particular Z row (−1.2) and Z column (.08) is −1.28 (see Figure 6.15).

FIGURE 6.15

Finding Z to Determine X

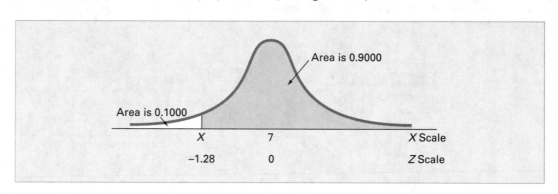

Once you find Z, use the transformation formula Equation (6.2) to determine the X value as follows. Let

$$Z = \frac{X - \mu}{\sigma}$$

then

$$X = \mu + Z\sigma$$

Substituting $\mu = 7$, $\sigma = 2$, and $Z = -1.28$,

$$X = 7 + (-1.28)(2) = 4.44 \text{ seconds}$$

Thus, 10% of the download times are 4.44 seconds or less.

Equation (6.4) is used for finding an X value.

FINDING AN X VALUE ASSOCIATED WITH KNOWN PROBABILITY

The X value is equal to the mean μ plus the product of the Z value and the standard deviation σ.

$$X = \mu + Z\sigma \qquad (6.4)$$

To find a *particular* value associated with a known probability, follow these steps.

1. Sketch the normal curve, and then place the values for the means on the respective X and Z scales.
2. Find the cumulative area less than X.
3. Shade the area of interest.
4. Using Table E.2, determine the Z value corresponding to the area under the normal curve less than X.
5. Using Equation (6.4), solve for X:

$$X = \mu + Z\sigma$$

EXAMPLE 6.8

FINDING THE X VALUES THAT INCLUDE 95% OF THE DOWNLOAD TIMES

What are the lower and upper values of X, located symmetrically around the mean, that include 95% of the download times?

SOLUTION First, you need to find the lower value of X (called X_L). Then you find the upper value of X (called X_U). Since 95% of the values are between X_L and X_U, and X_L and X_U are equal distance from the mean, 2.5% of the values are below X_L (see Figure 6.16).

FIGURE 6.16

Finding Z to Determine X_L

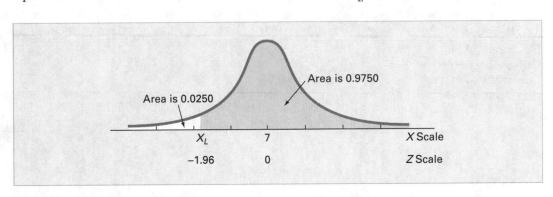

Although X_L is not known, you can find the corresponding Z because the area under the normal curve less than this Z is 0.0250. Using the body of Table 6.5, you search for the probability 0.0250.

TABLE 6.5

Finding a Z Value Corresponding to a Cumulative Area of 0.025 under the Normal Curve

Z	.00	.01	.02	.03	.04	.05	.06	.07	.08	.09
.	.	.	.	.	.	.	.	.	.	.
.	.	.	.	.	.	.	.	.	.	.
.	.	.	.	.	.	.	.	.	.	.
−2.0	.0228	.0222	.0217	.0212	.0207	.0202	.0197	.0192	.0188	.0183
−1.9	.0287	.0281	.0274	.0268	.0262	.0256	.0250	.0244	.0239	.0233
−1.8	.0359	.0351	.0344	.0336	.0329	.0232	.0314	.0307	.0301	.0294

Source: Extracted from Table E.2.

Working from the body of the table to the margins of the table, you see that the Z value corresponding to the particular Z row (-1.9) and Z column ($.06$) is -1.96.

Once you find Z, the final step is to use Equation (6.4) as follows,

$$X = \mu + Z\sigma$$
$$= 7 + (-1.96)(2)$$
$$= 7 - 3.92$$
$$= 3.08 \text{ seconds}$$

You use a similar process to find X_U. Since only 2.5% of the homepage downloads take longer than X_U seconds, 97.5% of the homepage downloads take less than X_U seconds. From the symmetry of the normal distribution, the desired Z value as shown in Figure 6.17 is $+1.96$ (because Z lies to the right of the standardized mean of 0). You can also extract this Z value from Table 6.6. Note that 0.975 is the area under the normal curve less than the Z value of $+1.96$.

FIGURE 6.17
Finding Z to Determine X_U

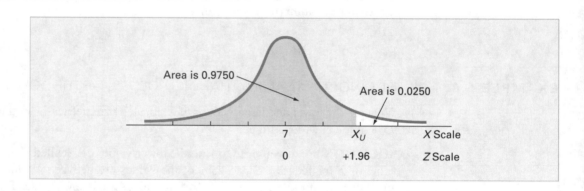

TABLE 6.6
Finding a Z Value Corresponding to a Cumulative Area of 0.975 under the Normal Curve

Z	.00	.01	.02	.03	.04	.05	.06	.07	.08	.09
.	.	.	.	.	.	.		.	.	.
.	.	.	.	.	.	.		.	.	.
.	.	.	.	.	.	.		.	.	.
+1.8	.9641	.9649	.9656	.9664	.9671	.9678	.9686	.9693	.9699	.9706
+1.9	.9713	.9719	.9726	.9732	.9738	.9744	.9750	.9756	.9761	.9767
+2.0	.9772	.9778	.9783	.9788	.9793	.9798	.9803	.9808	.9812	.9817

Source: Extracted from Table E.2.

Therefore, using Equation (6.4),

$$X = \mu + Z\sigma$$
$$= 7 + (+1.96)(2)$$
$$= 7 + 3.92$$
$$= 10.92 \text{ seconds}$$

Therefore, 95% of the download times are between 3.08 and 10.92 seconds.

You can also use Microsoft Excel or Minitab to compute normal probabilities. Figure 6.18 illustrates a Microsoft Excel worksheet for Examples 6.6 and 6.7, and Figure 6.19 illustrates Minitab output for Examples 6.1 and 6.7.

FIGURE 6.18

Microsoft Excel
Worksheet for
Computing Normal
Probabilities

	A	B	
1	**Normal Probabilities**		
2			
3	**Common Data**		
4	**Mean**	7	
5	**Standard Deviation**	2	
6			
7	**Probability for X <=**		
8	**X Value**	3.5	
9	**Z Value**	-1.75	=STANDARDIZE(B8, B4, B5)
10	**P(X<=3.5)**	0.0401	=NORMDIST(B8, B4, B5, TRUE)
11			
12	**Find X and Z Given Cum. Pctage.**		
13	**Cumulative Percentage**	10.00%	
14	**Z Value**	-1.2816	=NORMSINV(B13)
15	**X Value**	4.4369	=NORMINV(B13, B4, B5)

FIGURE 6.19

Minitab Normal
Probabilities

```
Cumulative Distribution Function

Normal with mean = 7 and standard deviation = 2

x   P( X <= x )
9      0.841345


Inverse Cumulative Distribution Function

Normal with mean = 7 and standard deviation = 2

P( X <= x )          x
        0.1   4.43690
```

PROBLEMS FOR SECTION 6.2

Learning the Basics

PH Grade ASSIST 6.7 Given a standardized normal distribution (with a mean of 0 and a standard deviation of 1, as in Table E.2), what is the probability that
a. Z is less than 1.57?
b. Z is greater than 1.84?
c. Z is between 1.57 and 1.84?
d. Z is less than 1.57 or greater than 1.84?

6.8 Given a standardized normal distribution (with a mean of 0 and a standard deviation of 1, as in Table E.2), what is the probability that
a. Z is between −1.57 and 1.84?
b. Z is less than −1.57 or greater than 1.84?
c. What is the value of Z if only 2.5% of all possible Z values are larger?
d. Between what two values of Z (symmetrically distributed around the mean) will 68.26% of all possible Z values be contained?

PH Grade ASSIST 6.9 Given a standardized normal distribution (with a mean of 0 and a standard deviation of 1 as in Table E.2), what is the probability that
a. Z is less than 1.08?
b. Z is greater than −0.21?
c. Z is less than −0.21 or greater than the mean?
d. Z is less than −0.21 or greater than 1.08?

6.10 Given a standardized normal distribution (with a mean of 0 and a standard deviation of 1 as in Table E.2), determine the following probabilities:
a. $P(Z > 1.08)$
b. $P(Z < −0.21)$
c. $P(−1.96 < Z < −0.21)$
d. What is the value of Z if only 15.87% of all possible Z values are larger?

PH Grade ASSIST 6.11 Given a normal distribution with $\mu = 100$ and $\sigma = 10$, what is the probability that

a. $X > 75$?

b. $X < 70$?

c. $X < 80$ or $X > 110$?

d. 80% of the values are between what two X values (symmetrically distributed around the mean)?

 6.12 Given a normal distribution with $\mu = 50$ and $\sigma = 4$, what is the probability that

a. $X > 43$?

b. $X < 42$?

c. 5% of the values are less than what X value?

d. 60% of the values are between what two X values (symmetrically distributed around the mean)?

Applying the Concepts

6.13 During 2001, 61.3% of U.S. households purchased ground coffee and spent an average of $36.16 on ground coffee during the year ("Annual Product Preference Study," *Progressive Grocer*, May 1, 2002, 31). Consider the annual ground coffee expenditures for households purchasing ground coffee, assuming that these expenditures are approximately distributed as a normal random variable with a mean of $36.16 and a standard deviation of $10.00.

a. Find the probability that a household spent less than $25.00.

b. Find the probability that a household spent more than $50.00.

c. What proportion of the households spent between $30.00 and $40.00?

d. 99% of the households spent less than what amount?

  6.14 Toby's Trucking Company determined that on an annual basis the distance traveled per truck is normally distributed with a mean of 50.0 thousand miles and a standard deviation of 12.0 thousand miles.

a. What proportion of trucks can be expected to travel between 34.0 and 50.0 thousand miles in the year?

b. What percentage of trucks can be expected to travel either below 30.0 or above 60.0 thousand miles in the year?

c. How many miles will be traveled by at least 80% of the trucks?

d. What are your answers to (a) through (c) if the standard deviation is 10.0 thousand miles?

 6.15 The breaking strength of plastic bags used for packaging produce is normally distributed with a mean of 5 pounds per square inch and a standard deviation of 1.5 pounds per square inch. What proportion of the bags have a breaking strength of

a. less than 3.17 pounds per square inch?

b. at least 3.6 pounds per square inch?

c. between 5 and 5.5 pounds per square inch?

d. Between what two values symmetrically distributed around the mean will 95% of the breaking strengths fall?

6.16 A set of final examination grades in an introductory statistics course is normally distributed with a mean of 73 and a standard deviation of 8.

a. What is the probability of getting a grade of 91 or less on this exam?

b. What is the probability that a student scored between 65 and 89?

c. The probability is 5% that a student taking the test scores higher than what grade?

d. If the professor grades on a curve (gives A's to the top 10% of the class regardless of the score), are you better off with a grade of 81 on this exam or a grade of 68 on a different exam where the mean is 62 and the standard deviation is 3? Show your answer statistically and explain.

6.17 A statistical analysis of 1,000 long distance telephone calls made from the headquarters of the Bricks and Clicks Computer Corporation indicates that the length of these calls is normally distributed with $\mu = 240$ seconds and $\sigma = 40$ seconds.

a. What is the probability that a call lasted less than 180 seconds?

b. What is the probability that a particular call lasted between 180 and 300 seconds?

c. What is the probability that a call lasted between 110 and 180 seconds?

d. What is the length of a particular call if only 1% of all calls are shorter?

6.18 The number of shares traded daily on the New York Stock Exchange (NYSE) is referred to as the *volume* of trading. On April 23, 2004, 1.395 billion shares of stock were traded ("NYSE Volume," *The Wall Street Journal*, April 26, 2004, C2). This volume of trading is near the mean volume for the NYSE. Assume that the number of shares traded on the NYSE is a normal random variable with a mean of 1.4 billion and a standard deviation of 0.15 billion. For a randomly selected day, what is the probability that the volume of trading on the NYSE is:

a. below 1.7 billion?

b. below 1.25 billion?

c. below 1.0 billion?

d. above 1.0 billion?

6.19 Many manufacturing problems involve the accurate matching of machine parts such as shafts that fit into a valve hole. A particular design requires a shaft with a diameter of 22.000 mm., but shafts with diameters between 21.900 mm. and 22.010 mm. are acceptable. Suppose that the manufacturing process yields shafts with diameters normally distributed with a mean of 22.002 mm. and a standard deviation of 0.005 mm. For this process, what is

a. the proportion of shafts with a diameter between 21.90 mm. and 22.00 mm.?

b. the probability a shaft is acceptable?

c. the diameter that will be exceeded by only 2% of the shafts?

d. What would be your answers in (a) through (c) if the standard deviation of the shaft diameters were 0.004 mm.?

CHAPTER REVIEW PROBLEMS

Checking Your Understanding

6.20 Why is it that only one normal distribution table such as Table E.2 is needed to find any probability under the normal curve?

6.21 How do you find the area between two values under the normal curve?

6.22 How do you find the X value that corresponds to a given percentile of the normal distribution?

6.23 How can you use the normal probability plot to evaluate whether a set of data is normally distributed?

Applying the Concepts

6.24 An industrial sewing machine uses ball bearings that are targeted to have a diameter of 0.75 inch. The lower and upper specification limits under which the ball bearing can operate are 0.74 inch and 0.76 inch, respectively. Past experience has indicated that the actual diameter of the ball bearings is approximately normally distributed with a mean of 0.753 inch and a standard deviation of 0.004 inch. What is the probability that a ball bearing is

a. between the target and the actual mean?
b. between the lower specification limit and the target?
c. above the upper specification limit?
d. below the lower specification limit?
e. 93% of the diameters are greater than what value?

6.25 The fill amount of soft drink bottles is normally distributed with a mean of 2.0 liters and a standard deviation of 0.05 liter. Bottles that contain less than 95% of the listed net content (1.90 liters in this case) can make the manufacturer subject to penalty by the state office of consumer affairs. Bottles that have a net content above 2.10 liters may cause excess spillage upon opening. What proportion of the bottles will contain

a. between 1.90 and 2.0 liters?
b. between 1.90 and 2.10 liters?
c. below 1.90 liters or above 2.10 liters?
d. 99% of the bottles contain at least how much soft drink?
e. 99% of the bottles contain an amount that is between which two values (symmetrically distributed) around the mean?

6.26 In an effort to reduce the number of bottles that contain less than 1.90 liters, the bottler in problem 6.28 sets the filling machine so that the mean is 2.02 liters. Under these circumstances, what are your answers in (a) through (e)?

6.27 An orange juice producer buys all his oranges from a large orange grove. The amount of juice squeezed from each of these oranges is approximately normally distributed with a mean of 4.70 ounces and a standard deviation of 0.40 ounce.

a. What is the probability that a randomly selected orange will contain between 4.70 and 5.00 ounces?

b. What is the probability that a randomly selected orange will contain between 5.00 and 5.50 ounces?
c. 77% of the oranges will contain at least how many ounces of juice?
d. 80% of the oranges are between what two values (in ounces) symmetrically distributed around the population mean?

6.28 According to *Investment Digest* ("Diversification and the Risk/Reward Relationship," Winter 1994, 1–3), the mean of the annual return for common stocks from 1926 to 1992 was 12.4%, and the standard deviation of the annual return was 20.6%. The article claims that the distribution of annual returns for common stocks is approximately bell-shaped and symmetric. Assume that the distribution is normally distributed with the mean and standard deviation given above. Find the probability that the return for common stocks will be

a. greater than 0%.
b. greater than 10%.
c. greater than 20%.
d. less than −10%.

6.29 During the same 67-year time span mentioned in problem 6.31, the mean of the annual return for long-term government bonds was 5.2%, and the standard deviation was 8.6%. The article claims that the distribution of annual returns for long-term government bonds is approximately bell-shaped and symmetric. Assume that the distribution is normally distributed with the mean and standard deviation given above. Find the probability that the return for long-term government bonds will be

a. greater than 0%.
b. greater than 10%.
c. greater than 20%.
d. less than −10%.
e. Discuss the differences in the annual return between common stocks and long-term government bonds.

6.30 *The Wall Street Journal* reported that almost all the major stock market indexes had posted strong gains in the last 12 months ("What's Hot . . . and Not," *The Wall Street Journal*, April 26, 2004, C3). The one-year return for the S&P 500, a group of 500 very large companies, was approximately +27%. The one-year return in the Russell 2000, a group of 2000 small companies, was approximately +52%. Historically, the one-year returns are approximately normal. The standard deviation in the S&P 500 returns is approximately 20%, and in the Russell 2000 the standard deviation is approximately 35%.

a. What is the probability that a stock in the S&P 500 gained 30% or more in the last year? Gained 60% or more in the last year?

b. What is the probability that a stock in the S&P 500 lost money in the last year? Lost 30% or more?

c. Repeat (a) and (b) for a stock in the Russell 2000.

d. Write a short summary on your findings. Be sure to include a discussion of the risks associated with a large standard deviation.

6.31 The *New York Times* reported (Laurie J. Flynn, "Tax Surfing," *The New York Times*, March 25, 2002, C10) that the mean time to download the homepage from the Internal Revenue Service Web site **www.irs.gov** is 0.8 seconds. Suppose that the download time is normally distributed with a standard deviation of 0.2 seconds. What is the probability that a download time is

a. less than 1 second?

b. between 0.5 and 1.5 seconds?

c. above 0.5 second?

d. 99% of the download times are above how many seconds?

e. 95% of the download times are between what two values symmetrically distributed around the mean?

6.32 The same article mentioned in problem 6.34 also reported that the mean download time for the H&R Block Web site **www.hrblock.com** is 2.5 seconds. Suppose that the download time is normally distributed with a standard deviation of 0.5 seconds. What is the probability that a download time is

a. less than 1 second?

b. between 0.5 and 1.5 seconds?

c. above 0.5 second?

d. 99% of the download times are above how many seconds?

e. Compare the results for the IRS site computed in problem 6.34 to those of the H&R Block site.

6.33 (**Class Project**) According to Burton G. Malkiel, the daily changes in the closing price of stock follow a *random walk*—that is, these daily events are independent of each other and move upward or downward in a random manner—and can be approximated by a normal distribution. To test this theory, use either a newspaper or the Internet to select one company traded on the New York Stock Exchange, one company traded on the American Stock Exchange, and one company traded "over the counter" (i.e., on the NASDAQ national market) and then do the following:

1. Record the daily closing stock price of each of these companies for 6 consecutive weeks (so that you have 30 values per company).

2. Record the daily changes in the closing stock price of each of these companies for 6 consecutive weeks (so that you have 30 values per company).

For each of your six data sets, decide whether the data are approximately normally distributed by

a. examining the stem-and-leaf display, histogram or polygon and the box-and-whisker plot.

b. evaluating the actual versus theoretical properties.

c. constructing a normal probability plot.

d. Discuss the results of (a), (b), and (c). What can you now say about your three stocks with respect to daily closing prices and daily changes in closing prices? Which, if any, of the data sets are approximately normally distributed?

Note: The random-walk theory pertains to the daily *changes* in the closing stock price, not the daily closing stock price.

TEAM PROJECT

The data file **MUTUALFUNDS2004** contains information regarding 12 variables from a sample of 121 mutual funds. The variables are:

Fund—The name of the mutual fund.

Category—Type of stocks comprising the mutual fund—small cap, mid cap, large cap

Objective—Objective of stocks comprising the mutual fund—growth or value

Assets—In millions of dollars

Fees—Sales charges (no or yes)

Expense ratio—Ratio of expenses to net assets in percentage

2003 Return—Twelve-month return in 2003

Three-year return—Annualized return 2001–2003

Five-year return—Annualized return 1999–2003

Risk—Risk-of-loss factor of the mutual fund classified as low, average, or high

Best quarter—Best quarterly performance 1999–2003

Worst quarter—Worst quarterly performance 1999–2003

6.34 Consider the variables expense ratio, three-year annualized return, and five-year annualized return. For each of these variables decide whether the data are approximately normally distributed by

a. evaluating the actual versus theoretical properties.

b. constructing a normal probability plot.

RUNNING CASE
MANAGING THE *SPRINGVILLE HERALD*

The production department of the newspaper has embarked on a quality improvement effort. Its first project relates to the blackness of the newspaper print. Each day a determination needs to be made concerning how "black" the newspaper is printed. Blackness is measured on a standard scale in which the target value is 1.0. Data collected over the past year indicate that the blackness is normally distributed with a mean of 1.005 and a standard deviation of 0.10.

Each day, one spot on the first newspaper printed is chosen and the blackness of the spot is measured. The blackness of the newspaper is considered acceptable if the blackness of the spot is between 0.95 and 1.05.

EXERCISE

SH6.1 Assuming that the distribution has not changed from what it was in the past year, what is the probability that the blackness of the spot is:

a. less than 1.0?
b. between 0.95 and 1.0?
c. between 1.0 and 1.05?
d. less than 0.95 or greater than 1.05?

SH6.2 The objective of the production team is to reduce the probability that the blackness is below 0.95 or above 1.05. Would it be better off focusing on process improvement that lowered the mean to the target value of 1.0 or on process improvement that reduced the standard deviation to 0.075? Explain.

WEB CASE

Apply your knowledge about the normal distribution in this Web Case that extends the "Using Statistics" scenario from this chapter.

To satisfy concerns of potential advertisers, the management of OnCampus! has undertaken a research project to learn the amount of time viewers linger at their Web sites (known as the "stickiness" of viewers). The marketing department has collected data and has made some claims based on the assertion that the data follow a normal distribution. These data and conclusions can be found in a report located on the internal Web page **www.prenhall. com/Springville/OC_MarketingSurvey.htm**.

Read this marketing report and then answer the following:

1. Can the collected data be approximated by the normal distribution?
2. Review and evaluate the conclusions made by the OnCampus! marketing department. Which conclusions are correct? Which ones are incorrect?
3. If OnCampus! can improve the mean time by five minutes, how would the probabilities change?

REFERENCES

1. Gunter, B., "Q-Q Plots," *Quality Progress* (February 1994), 81–86.
2. Marascuilo, L. A., and M. McSweeney, *Nonparametric and Distribution-Free Methods for the Social Sciences* (Monterey, CA: Brooks/Cole, 1977).
3. *Microsoft Excel 2003* (Redmond, WA: Microsoft Corp., 2003).
4. *Minitab for Windows Version 14* (State College, PA: Minitab Inc., 2004).

CHAPTER 7

Sampling Distributions

USING STATISTICS: Cereal-Fill Packaging Process

LEARNING OBJECTIVES

In this chapter, you learn:

- The concept of the sampling distribution
- To compute probabilities related to the sample mean and the sample proportion
- The importance of the Central Limit Theorem
- To distinguish between different survey sampling methods

USING STATISTICS

Cereal-Fill Packaging Process

At Oxford Cereal Company plants, thousands of boxes of cereal are filled during each eight-hour shift. As the operations manager of a plant, you are in charge of monitoring the amount of cereal contained in the boxes. Boxes are supposed to contain a mean of 368 grams of cereal as indicated on the package label. Because of the speed of the process, the cereal weight varies from box to box, causing some boxes to be underfilled and some overfilled. If the process is not working properly, the mean weight in the boxes could vary too much from the label weight of 368 grams to be acceptable. Because weighing every single box is too time-consuming, costly, and inefficient, you must take a sample of boxes and make a decision regarding the probability that the cereal-filling process is working properly. Each time you select a sample of boxes and weigh the individual boxes, you calculate a sample mean $\overline{X}$. You need to determine the probability that such an $\overline{X}$ could have been randomly drawn from a population whose population mean is 368 grams. Based on this assessment, you will have to decide whether to maintain, alter, or shut down the process.

In the last chapter, you used the normal distribution to study the distribution of download times for the OnCampus! Web site. In this chapter, you need to make a decision about the cereal-filling process based on a *sample* of cereal boxes. You will learn about *sampling distributions* and how to use them to solve business problems. As in the previous chapter, the normal distribution is used to calculate probabilities.

7.1   SAMPLING DISTRIBUTIONS

In many applications you want to make statistical inferences, that is, to use statistics calculated from samples to estimate the values of population parameters. In this chapter you will learn about the sample mean, a statistic used to estimate a population mean (a parameter). You will also learn about the sample proportion, a statistic used to estimate the population proportion (a parameter). Your main concern when making a statistical inference is drawing conclusions about a population, *not* about a sample. For example, a political pollster is interested in the sample results only as a way of estimating the actual proportion of the votes that each candidate will receive from the population of voters. Likewise, as an operations manager for the Oxford Cereal Company, you are only interested in using the sample mean calculated from a sample of cereal boxes for estimating the mean weight contained in a population of boxes.

In practice, you select a single random sample of a predetermined size from the population. The items included in the sample are determined through the use of a random number generator, such as a table of random numbers (see section 7.4 and Table E.1).

Hypothetically, to use the sample statistic to estimate the population parameter, you should examine *every* possible sample that could occur. A **sampling distribution** is the distribution of the results if you actually selected all possible samples.

7.2 SAMPLING DISTRIBUTION OF THE MEAN

In Chapter 3, several measures of central tendency were discussed. Undoubtedly, the mean is the most widely used measure of central tendency. The sample mean is often used to estimate the population mean. The **sampling distribution of the mean** is the distribution of all possible sample means if you select all possible samples of a certain size.

The Unbiased Property of the Sample Mean

The sample mean is **unbiased** because the mean of all the possible sample means (of a given sample size *n*) is equal to the population mean μ. A simple example concerning a population of four administrative assistants demonstrates this property. Each assistant is asked to type the same page of a manuscript. Table 7.1 presents the number of errors.

TABLE 7.1

Number of Errors Made by Each of Four Administrative Assistants

Administrative Assistant	Number of Errors
Ann	$X_1 = 3$
Bob	$X_2 = 2$
Carla	$X_3 = 1$
Dave	$X_4 = 4$

This population distribution is shown in Figure 7.1.

FIGURE 7.1

Number of Errors Made by a Population of Four Administrative Assistants

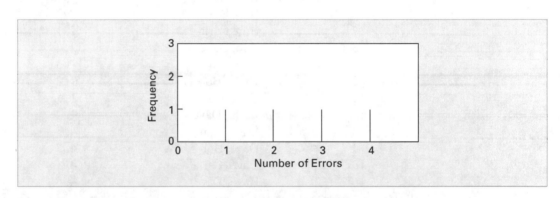

When you have the data from a population, you compute the mean using Equation (7.1):

POPULATION MEAN

The population mean is the sum of the values in the population divided by the population size N.

$$\mu = \frac{\sum_{i=1}^{N} X_i}{N} \tag{7.1}$$

You compute the population standard deviation σ using Equation (7.2):

POPULATION STANDARD DEVIATION

$$\sigma = \sqrt{\frac{\sum_{i=1}^{N} (X_i - \mu)^2}{N}} \tag{7.2}$$

Thus, for the data of Table 7.1,

$$\mu = \frac{3 + 2 + 1 + 4}{4} = 2.5 \text{ errors}$$

and

$$\sigma = \sqrt{\frac{(3 - 2.5)^2 + (2 - 2.5)^2 + (1 - 2.5)^2 + (4 - 2.5)^2}{4}} = 1.12 \text{ errors}$$

If you select samples of two administrative assistants *with* replacement from this population, there are 16 possible samples ($N^n = 4^2 = 16$). Table 7.2 lists the 16 possible sample outcomes. If you average all 16 of these sample means, the mean of these values, $\mu_{\bar{X}}$, is equal to 2.5, which is also the mean of the population μ.

TABLE 7.2

All 16 Samples of $n = 2$ Administrative Assistants from a Population of $N = 4$ Administrative Assistants When Sampling *with* Replacement

Sample	Administrative Assistants	Sample Outcomes	Sample Mean
1	Ann, Ann	3, 3	$\bar{X}_1 = 3$
2	Ann, Bob	3, 2	$\bar{X}_2 = 2.5$
3	Ann, Carla	3, 1	$\bar{X}_3 = 2$
4	Ann, Dave	3, 4	$\bar{X}_4 = 3.5$
5	Bob, Ann	2, 3	$\bar{X}_5 = 2.5$
6	Bob, Bob	2, 2	$\bar{X}_6 = 2$
7	Bob, Carla	2, 1	$\bar{X}_7 = 1.5$
8	Bob, Dave	2, 4	$\bar{X}_8 = 3$
9	Carla, Ann	1, 3	$\bar{X}_9 = 2$
10	Carla, Bob	1, 2	$\bar{X}_{10} = 1.5$
11	Carla, Carla	1, 1	$\bar{X}_{11} = 1$
12	Carla, Dave	1, 4	$\bar{X}_{12} = 2.5$
13	Dave, Ann	4, 3	$\bar{X}_{13} = 3.5$
14	Dave, Bob	4, 2	$\bar{X}_{14} = 3$
15	Dave, Carla	4, 1	$\bar{X}_{15} = 2.5$
16	Dave, Dave	4, 4	$\bar{X}_{16} = 4$
			$\mu_{\bar{X}} = 2.5$

Since the mean of the 16 sample means is equal to the population mean, the sample mean is an unbiased estimator of the population mean. Therefore, although you do not know how close the sample mean of any particular sample selected comes to the population mean, you are at least assured that the mean of all the possible sample means that could have been selected is equal to the population mean.

Standard Error of the Mean

Figure 7.2 illustrates the variation in the sample mean when selecting all 16 possible samples. In this small example, although the sample mean varies from sample to sample depending on which administrative assistants are selected, the sample mean does not vary as much as the individual values in the population. That the sample means are less variable than the individual values in the population follows directly from the fact that each sample mean averages together all the values in the sample. A population consists of individual outcomes that can take on a wide range of values from extremely small to extremely large. However, if a sample contains an extreme value, although this value will have an effect on the sample mean, the effect is reduced because the value is averaged with all the other values in the sample. As the sample size increases, the effect of a single extreme value becomes smaller because it is averaged with more values.

FIGURE 7.2

Sampling Distribution of the Mean Based on All Possible Samples Containing Two Administrative Assistants

Source: Data are from Table 7.2

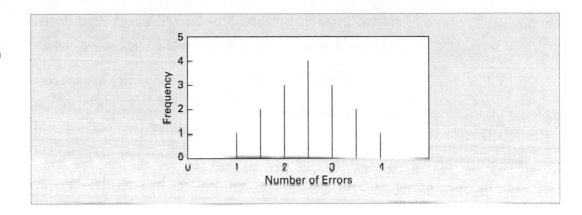

The value of the standard deviation of all possible sample means, called the **standard error of the mean**, expresses how the sample mean varies from sample to sample. Equation (7.3) defines the standard error of the mean when sampling *with* replacement, or *without* replacement (see page 213) from large or infinite populations.

STANDARD ERROR OF THE MEAN

The standard error of the mean $\sigma_{\bar{X}}$ is equal to the standard deviation in the population σ divided by the square root of the sample size n.

$$\sigma_{\bar{X}} = \frac{\sigma}{\sqrt{n}} \qquad (7.3)$$

Therefore, as the sample size increases, the standard error of the mean decreases by a factor equal to the square root of the sample size.

You can also use Equation (7.3) as an approximation to the standard error of the mean when the sample is selected without replacement if the sample contains less than 5% of the entire population. Example 7.1 computes the standard error of the mean for such a situation.

EXAMPLE 7.1

COMPUTING THE STANDARD ERROR OF THE MEAN

Return to the cereal-filling process described in the "Using Statistics" scenario on page 194. If you randomly select a sample of 25 boxes without replacement from the thousands of boxes filled during a shift, the sample contains far less than 5% of the population. Given that the standard deviation of the cereal-filling process is 15 grams, compute the standard error of the mean.

SOLUTION Using Equation (7.3) above with $n = 25$ and $\sigma = 15$, the standard error of the mean is

$$\sigma_{\bar{X}} = \frac{\sigma}{\sqrt{n}} = \frac{15}{\sqrt{25}} = \frac{15}{5} = 3$$

The variation in the sample means for samples of $n = 25$ is much less than the variation in the individual boxes of cereal (i.e., $\sigma_{\bar{X}} = 3$ while $\sigma = 15$).

Sampling from Normally Distributed Populations

Now that the concept of a sampling distribution has been introduced and the standard error of the mean has been defined, what distribution will the sample mean $\overline{X}$ follow? If you are sampling from a population that is normally distributed with mean μ and standard deviation σ, regardless of the sample size n, the sampling distribution of the mean is normally distributed with mean $\mu_{\overline{X}} = \mu$ and standard error of the mean $\sigma_{\overline{X}}$.

In the simplest case, if you take samples of size $n = 1$, each possible sample mean is a single value from the population because

$$\overline{X} = \frac{\sum_{i=1}^{n} X_i}{n} = \frac{X_i}{1} = X_i$$

Therefore, if the population is normally distributed with mean μ and standard deviation σ, then the sampling distribution of $\overline{X}$ for samples of $n = 1$ must also follow the normal distribution with mean $\mu_{\overline{X}} = \mu$ and standard error of the mean $\sigma_{\overline{X}} = \sigma/\sqrt{1} = \sigma$. In addition, as the sample size increases, the sampling distribution of the mean still follows a normal distribution with mean $\mu_{\overline{X}} = \mu$, but the standard error of the mean decreases, so that a larger proportion of sample means are closer to the population mean. Figure 7.3 illustrates this reduction in variability in which 500 samples of sizes 1, 2, 4, 8, 16, and 32 were randomly selected from a

FIGURE 7.3

Sampling Distribution of the Mean from 500 Samples of Sizes $n = 1$, 2, 4, 8, 16, and 32 Selected from a Normal Population

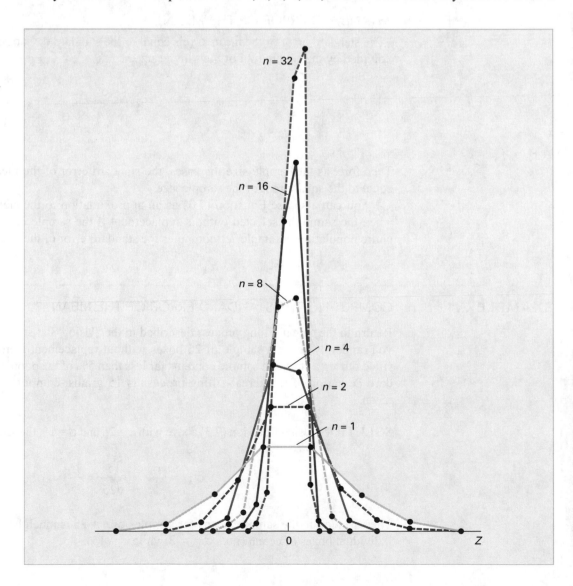

normally distributed population. From the polygons in Figure 7.3 you can see that, although the sampling distribution of the mean is approximately[1] normal for each sample size, the sample means are distributed more tightly around the population mean as the sample size is increased.

To examine the concept of the sampling distribution of the mean further, consider the "Using Statistics" scenario described on page 194. The packaging equipment that is filling 368-gram boxes of cereal is set so that the amount of cereal in a box is normally distributed with a mean of 368 grams. From past experience, the population standard deviation for this filling process is 15 grams.

If you randomly select a sample of 25 boxes from the many thousands that are filled in a day and the mean weight is computed for this sample, what type of result could you expect? For example, do you think that the sample mean could be 368 grams? 200 grams? 365 grams?

The sample acts as a miniature representation of the population, so if the values in the population are normally distributed, the values in the sample should be approximately normally distributed. Thus, if the population mean is 368 grams, the sample mean has a good chance of being close to 368 grams.

How can you determine the probability that the sample of 25 boxes will have a mean below 365 grams? From the normal distribution (section 6.2) you know that you can find the area below any value X by converting to standardized Z units.

$$Z = \frac{X - \mu}{\sigma}$$

In the examples in section 6.2, you studied how any single value X differs from the mean. Now, in the cereal-fill example, the value involved is a sample mean $\bar{X}$ and you wish to determine the likelihood that a sample mean is below 365. Thus, by substituting $\bar{X}$ for X, $\mu_{\bar{X}}$ for μ, and $\sigma_{\bar{X}}$ for σ, the appropriate Z value is defined in Equation (7.4):

FINDING Z FOR THE SAMPLING DISTRIBUTION OF THE MEAN

The Z value is equal to the difference between the sample mean $\bar{X}$ and the population mean μ, divided by the standard error of the mean $\sigma_{\bar{X}}$.

$$Z = \frac{\bar{X} - \mu_{\bar{X}}}{\sigma_{\bar{X}}} = \frac{\bar{X} - \mu}{\frac{\sigma}{\sqrt{n}}} \qquad (7.4)$$

To find the area below 365 grams, from Equation (7.4),

$$Z = \frac{\bar{X} - \mu_{\bar{X}}}{\sigma_{\bar{X}}} = \frac{365 - 368}{\frac{15}{\sqrt{25}}} = \frac{-3}{3} = -1.00$$

The area corresponding to $Z = -1.00$ in Table E.2 is 0.1587. Therefore, 15.87% of all the possible samples of size 25 have a sample mean below 365 grams.

The above statement is not the same as saying that a certain percentage of *individual* boxes will have less than 365 grams of cereal. You compute that percentage as follows:

$$Z = \frac{X - \mu}{\sigma} = \frac{365 - 368}{15} = \frac{-3}{15} = -0.20$$

The area corresponding to $Z = -0.20$ in Table E.2 is 0.4207. Therefore, 42.07% of the *individual* boxes are expected to contain less than 365 grams. Comparing these results, you see that many more *individual boxes* than *sample means* are below 365 grams. This result is explained by the fact that each sample consists of 25 different values, some small and some large. The averaging process dilutes the importance of any individual value, particularly when the sample size is large. Thus, the chance that the sample mean of 25 boxes is far away from the population mean is less than the chance that a *single* box is far away.

Examples 7.2 and 7.3 show how these results are affected by using a different sample size.

EXAMPLE 7.2

THE EFFECT OF SAMPLE SIZE n ON THE COMPUTATION OF $\sigma_{\overline{X}}$

How is the standard error of the mean affected by increasing the sample size, from 25 to 100 boxes?

SOLUTION If $n = 100$ boxes, then using Equation (7.3):

$$\sigma_{\overline{X}} = \frac{\sigma}{\sqrt{n}} = \frac{15}{\sqrt{100}} = \frac{15}{10} = 1.5$$

The fourfold increase in the sample size from 25 to 100 reduces the standard error of the mean by half—from 3 grams to 1.5 grams. This demonstrates that taking a larger sample results in less variability in the sample means from sample to sample.

EXAMPLE 7.3

THE EFFECT OF SAMPLE SIZE n ON THE CLUSTERING OF MEANS IN THE SAMPLING DISTRIBUTION

In the cereal-fill example, if you select a sample of 100 boxes, what is the probability that the sample mean is below 365 grams?

SOLUTION Using Equation (7.4),

$$Z = \frac{\overline{X} - \mu_{\overline{X}}}{\sigma_{\overline{X}}} = \frac{365 - 368}{\dfrac{15}{\sqrt{100}}} = \frac{-3}{1.5} = -2.00$$

From Table E.2, the area less than $Z = -2.00$ is 0.0228. Therefore, 2.28% of the samples of 100 have means below 365 grams, as compared with 15.87% for samples of 25.

Sometimes you need to find the interval that contains a fixed proportion of the sample means. You need to determine a distance below and above the population mean containing a specific area of the normal curve. From Equation (7.4),

$$Z = \frac{\overline{X} - \mu}{\dfrac{\sigma}{\sqrt{n}}}$$

Solving for $\overline{X}$ results in Equation (7.5).

FINDING $\overline{X}$ FOR THE SAMPLING DISTRIBUTION OF THE MEAN

$$\overline{X} = \mu + Z\frac{\sigma}{\sqrt{n}} \tag{7.5}$$

Example 7.4 illustrates the use of Equation (7.5).

EXAMPLE 7.4   DETERMINING THE INTERVAL THAT INCLUDES A FIXED PROPORTION
OF THE SAMPLE MEANS

In the cereal-fill example, find an interval around the population mean that will include 95% of the sample means based on samples of 25 boxes.

SOLUTION If 95% of the sample means are in the interval, then 5% are outside the interval. Divide the 5% into two equal parts of 2.5%. The value of Z in Table E.2 corresponding to an area of 0.0250 in the lower tail of the normal curve is −1.96, and the value of Z corresponding to a cumulative area of 0.975 (i.e., 0.025 in the upper tail of the normal curve) is +1.96. The lower value of $\bar{X}$ (called $\bar{X}_L$) and the upper value of $\bar{X}$ (called $\bar{X}_U$) are found by using Equation (7.5):

$$\bar{X}_L = 368 + (-1.96)\frac{15}{\sqrt{25}} = 368 - 5.88 = 362.12$$

$$\bar{X}_U = 368 + (1.96)\frac{15}{\sqrt{25}} = 368 - 5.88 = 373.88$$

Therefore, 95% of all sample means based on samples of 25 boxes are between 362.12 and 373.88 grams.

Sampling from Nonnormally Distributed Populations—The Central Limit Theorem

So far in this section, the sampling distribution of the mean for a normally distributed population has been discussed. However, in many instances, either you know that the population is not normally distributed or it is unrealistic to assume a normal distribution. An important theorem in statistics, the Central Limit Theorem, deals with this situation.

THE CENTRAL LIMIT THEOREM

The **Central Limit Theorem** states that as the sample size (i.e., the number of values in each sample) gets *large enough*, the sampling distribution of the mean is approximately normally distributed. This is true regardless of the shape of the distribution of the individual values in the population.

What sample size is large enough? A great deal of statistical research has gone into this issue. As a general rule, statisticians have found that for many population distributions, when the sample size is at least 30, the sampling distribution of the mean is approximately normal. However, you can apply the Central Limit Theorem for even smaller sample sizes if the population distribution is approximately bell-shaped. In the uncommon case where the distribution is extremely skewed or has more than one mode, you may need sample sizes larger than 30 to ensure normality.

Figure 7.4 illustrates the application of the Central Limit Theorem to different populations. The sampling distributions from three different continuous distributions (normal, uniform, and exponential) for varying sample sizes ($n = 2, 5, 30$) are displayed.

Panel A of Figure 7.4 shows the sampling distribution of the mean selected from a normal population. As mentioned earlier, when the population is normally distributed, the sampling distribution of the mean is normally distributed for any sample size. (You can measure the variability using the standard error of the mean, Equation 7.3 on page 197.) Because of the unbiasedness property, the mean of any sampling distribution is always equal to the mean of the population.

FIGURE 7.4

Sampling Distribution of the Mean for Different Populations for Samples of $n = 2$, 5, and 30

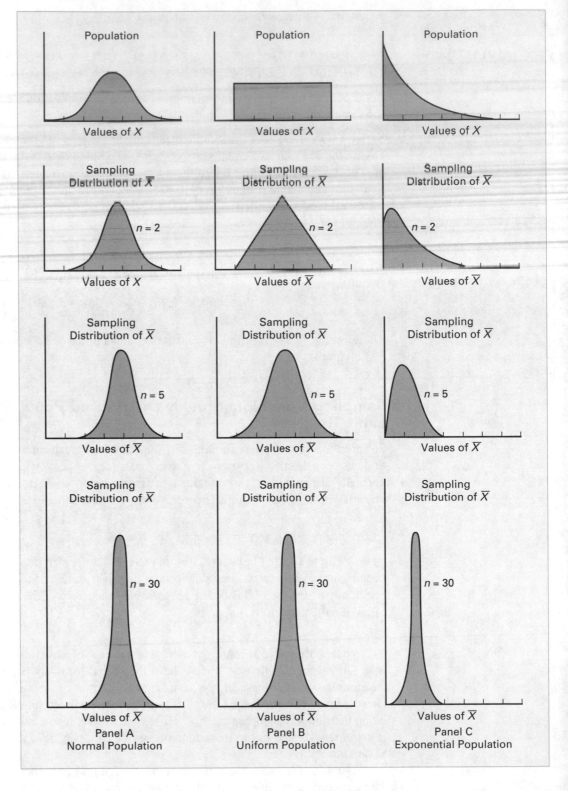

Panel A
Normal Population

Panel B
Uniform Population

Panel C
Exponential Population

Panel B of Figure 7.4 depicts the sampling distribution from a population with a uniform (or rectangular) distribution. When samples of size $n = 2$ are selected, there is a peaking or *central limiting* effect already working. For $n = 5$, the sampling distribution is bell-shaped and approximately normal. When $n = 30$, the sampling distribution looks very similar to a normal distribution. In general, the larger the sample size, the more closely the sampling distribution will follow a normal distribution. As with all cases, the mean of each sampling distribution is equal to the mean of the population, and the variability decreases as the sample size increases.

Panel C of Figure 7.4 presents an exponential distribution. This population is heavily skewed to the right. When $n = 2$, the sampling distribution is still highly skewed to the right but less so than the distribution of the population. For $n = 5$, the sampling distribution is more symmetric with only a slight skew to the right. When $n = 30$, the sampling distribution looks approximately normal. Again, the mean of each sampling distribution is equal to the mean of the population, and the variability decreases as the sample size increases.

Using the results from these well-known statistical distributions (normal, uniform, and exponential), you can make the following conclusions regarding the Central Limit Theorem.

- For most population distributions, regardless of shape, the sampling distribution of the mean is approximately normally distributed if samples of at least 30 are selected.
- If the population distribution is fairly symmetrical, the sampling distribution of the mean is approximately normal for samples as small as 5.
- If the population is normally distributed, the sampling distribution of the mean is normally distributed regardless of the sample size.

The Central Limit Theorem is of crucial importance in using statistical inference to draw conclusions about a population. It allows you to make inferences about the population mean without having to know the specific shape of the population distribution.

VISUAL EXPLORATIONS: Exploring Sampling Distributions

Use the Visual Explorations **Two Dice Probability** procedure to observe the effects of simulated throws on the frequency distribution of the sum of the two dice. Open the Visual Explorations.xla macro workbook (**Visual Explorations.xla**) and select **VisualExplorations → Two Dice Probability** from the Microsoft Excel menu bar. The procedure produces a worksheet that contains an empty frequency distribution table and his-

togram and a floating control panel (see illustration below).

Click the **Tally** button to tally a set of throws in the frequency distribution table and histogram. Optionally, use the spinner buttons to adjust the number of throws per tally (round).

Click the **Help** button for more information about this simulation. Click **Finish** when you are done with this exploration.

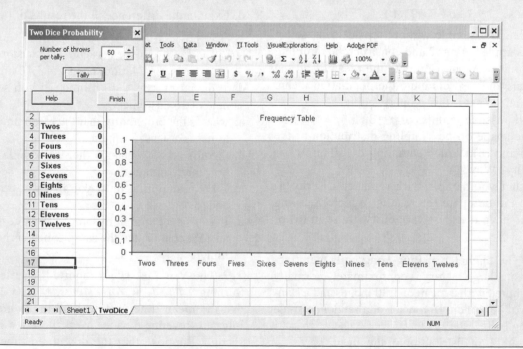

PROBLEMS FOR SECTION 7.2

Learning the Basics

 7.1 Given a normal distribution with $\mu = 100$ and $\sigma = 10$, if you select a sample of $n = 25$, what is the probability that $\bar{X}$ is
a. less than 95?
b. between 95 and 97.5?
c. above 102.2?
d. There is a 65% chance that $\bar{X}$ is above what value?

 7.2 Given a normal distribution with $\mu = 50$ and $\sigma = 5$, if you select a sample of $n = 100$, what is the probability that $\bar{X}$ is
a. less than 47?
b. between 47 and 49.5?
c. above 51.1?
d. There is a 35% chance that $\bar{X}$ is above what value?

Applying the Concepts

7.3 For each of the following three populations, indicate what the sampling distribution for samples of 25 would consist of.
a. Travel expense vouchers for a university in an academic year
b. Absentee records (days absent per year) in 2004 for employees of a large manufacturing company
c. Yearly sales (in gallons) of unleaded gasoline at service stations located in a particular county

7.4 The following data represent the number of days absent per year in a population of six employees of a small company:

$$1 \quad 3 \quad 6 \quad 7 \quad 9 \quad 10$$

a. Assuming that you sample without replacement, select all possible samples of $n = 2$ and construct the sampling distribution of the mean. Compute the mean of all the sample means and also compute the population mean. Are they equal? What is this property called?
b. Do (a) for all possible samples of $n = 3$.
c. Compare the shape of the sampling distribution of the mean in (a) and (b). Which sampling distribution has less variability? Why?
d. Assuming that you sample with replacement, do (a) through (c) and compare the results. Which sampling distributions have the least variability, those in (a) or (b)? Why?

 7.5 The diameter of Ping-Pong balls manufactured at a large factory is approximately normally distributed with a mean of 1.30 inches and a standard deviation of 0.04 inch. If you select a random sample of 16 Ping-Pong balls,
a. what is the sampling distribution of the mean?

b. what is the probability that the sample mean is less than 1.28 inches?
c. what is the probability that the sample mean is between 1.31 and 1.33 inches?
d. The probability is 60% that the sample mean will be between what two values symmetrically distributed around the population mean?

7.6 The U.S. Commerce Department reported that the median price of a new house sold in March 2004 was $201,400, and the mean price $260,000 (Michael Schroeder, "New-Home Sales Increase 8.9%, the Biggest Rise in Nine Months," *The Wall Street Journal*, April 27, 2004, A15). Assume that the standard deviation of the prices is $90,000.
a. If you take samples of $n = 2$, describe the shape of the sampling distribution of $\bar{X}$.
b. If you take samples of $n = 100$, describe the shape of the sampling distribution of $\bar{X}$.
c. If you take a random sample of $n = 100$, what is the probability that the sample mean will be less than $250,000?

 7.7 Time spent using e-mail per session is normally distributed with $\mu = 8$ minutes and $\sigma = 2$ minutes. If you select a random sample of 25 sessions,
a. what is the probability that the sample mean is between 7.8 and 8.2 minutes?
b. what is the probability that the sample mean is between 7.5 and 8 minutes?
c. If you select a random sample of 100 sessions, what is the probability that the sample mean is between 7.8 and 8.2 minutes?
d. Explain the difference in the results of (a) and (c).

  7.8 The amount of time a bank teller spends with each customer has a population mean $\mu = 3.10$ minutes and standard deviation $\sigma = 0.40$ minute. If you select a random sample of 16 customers,
a. what is the probability that the mean time spent per customer is at least 3 minutes?
b. there is an 85% chance that the sample mean is below how many minutes?
c. What assumption must you make in order to solve (a) and (b)?
d. If you select a random sample of 64 customers, there is an 85% chance that the sample mean is below how many minutes?

7.9 The *New York Times* reported (Laurie J. Flynn, "Tax Surfing," *The New York Times*, March 25, 2002, C10) that the mean time to download the homepage from the Internal Revenue Service Web site **www.irs.gov** was 0.8 second. Suppose that the download time was normally distributed with a standard deviation of 0.2 second. If you select a random sample of 30 download times,

a. what is the probability that the sample mean is less than 0.75 second?

b. what is the probability that the sample mean is between 0.70 and 0.90 second?

c. the probability is 80% that the sample mean is between what two values symmetrically distributed around the population mean?

d. the probability is 90% that the sample mean is less than what value?

7.10 The article discussed in problem 7.9 also reported that the mean download time for the H&R Block Web site www.hrblock.com was 2.5 seconds. Suppose that the download time for the H&R Block Web site was normally distributed with a standard deviation of 0.5 second. If you select a random sample of 30 download times,

a. what is the probability that the sample mean is less than 2.75 seconds?

b. what is the probability that the sample mean is between 2.70 and 2.90 seconds?

c. the probability is 80% that the sample mean is between what two values symmetrically distributed around the population mean?

d. the probability is 90% that the sample mean is less than what value?

Central Limit Theorem

Central Limit Theorem Template:

X = _____

μ =
      } Normal or blank
σ =

n =

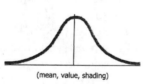

(mean, value, shading)

Info about $\overline{X}$

1. $\mu_{\overline{x}} = \mu =$

2. $\sigma_{\overline{x}} = \dfrac{\sigma}{\sqrt{n}} =$

3. a) Original population is normal, therefore $\overline{X}$ is normal.

   OR

   b) Original population is not normal, but $\overline{X}$ is normal because n ≥ 30.

P(_____) = P($\overline{X}$ symbol #) = _____ = 0._ _ _ _
  (words*)   (calc. or SPSS input) (4 dec.)

7.11 The weight of mini-boxes of raisins has a mean of 14.1 grams and a standard deviation of 1.4 grams.

What is the probability that a case of 50 boxes will weigh more than 725 grams?

7.12 A large company has its annual sales convention in Whistler each year for its top sellers. The Toronto office of the firm has kept records of the trip cost over the past years. The mean cost per person has been $2200 with a standard deviation of $150. The distribution of the cost per person has been normally distributed.

a. If only one person from the Toronto office is eligible to attend this years convention, what is the probability that the cost will be between $2000 and $2500?

b. If five people from the Toronto office are eligible, what is the probability that the total cost will exceed $12,000?

7.13 The Long-Life Tire Co. claims that their Super-All-Season tire lasts an average of 110,000 km. It is known that the tire life is normally distributed with a standard deviation of 2800 km. Your company has just purchased all new tires for its fleet of 10 cars. Assuming that the manufacturer's claim is true:

a. What is the probability that a tire will last longer than 112,000 km.?

b. What is the probability that the tires for your company car will last an average of at least 112000 km.?

c. What is the probability that the average life of all the tires purchased by your company will be at least 112,000 km?

d. What is the probability that all the tires for your car will last more than 112,000 km?

Probability Distributions—Review Exercises

(Note: The answers shown were obtained using the SPSS computer program. The answers given by the Casio calculator may be slightly different on some questions.)

7.14 A manufacturing company anticipates that its daily demand for electric power during the next few months will fluctuate around a mean of 100.0 kilowatts. Based on past results, the daily power usage distribution should be normally distributed with a standard deviation of 10.0 kilowatts.

a.   What is the probability that the demand for electric power on a given day will range from 90.0 to 125.0 kilowatts?

b.   What is the level of usage that will be exceeded only 20 percent of the time?

7.15 The defects in an automatic weaving process occur randomly at an average rate of 0.0025 per square metre and a standard deviation of 0.05 per square metre. The process has just been set up to run 1000 square meters of fabric. What is the probability that there will be at least 4 defects in this fabric?

7.16 The occurrence of the first breakdown of an automatic washing machine is normally distributed with a mean of 5.9 years and a standard deviation of 1.5 years. How long (full years) should these washing machines be guaranteed so that no more than 10% would require repairs during the warrantee period?

7.17 A large company is currently evaluating 14 cost-reducing proposals submitted by employees. Past experience has shown that 30 percent of such proposals are implemented by the company.
a. What is the probability that more than 5 proposals will be implemented?
b. What is the probability that at least half of the proposals will be implemented?
c. What is the expected number of proposals implemented?

7.18 The manufacturer of a quartz travel clock claims that, on average, its clocks deviate from perfect time by an average of 30 seconds in a month, with a standard deviation of 10 seconds. The test group that works for a consumer magazine purchased 40 of these clocks and found that the average deviation from perfect time was 35 seconds after one month.
a. If the manufacturer's claim is correct, what is the probability that the average deviation from perfect time for the 40 clocks would be 35 seconds or more?
b. If the average clock deviates by 33 seconds from perfect in one month, what is the probability that the average deviation from perfect time for the 40 clocks would be 35 seconds or more?

7.19 The Executours Corp. offers tours of the city to visiting businesspersons and uses a 12-passenger luxury bus. From past experience 10% of the people who make advance reservations will cancel at the last minute, therefore, Executours usually takes 13 reservations. For what percent of tours will they have enough seats for the passengers who show up for the tour?

7.20 The number of man-hours required by the Victory Construction Co. to assemble its prefabricated 2-bedroom house is normally distributed with a mean of 400 man-hours and a standard deviation of 40 man-hours.
a. The probability is 0.9 that the assembly of a house will take less than how many hours?
b. What is the probability that assembly of a house will take more than 420 man-hours?

7.21 There are two major steps in the production of solar covers for swimming pools. First, a 1 metre wide continuous strip of plastic air bubble material is produced. Then the material is cut to the required length (in this case 10 metres) and an appropriate number of these strips are sewn together to produce a solar cover.

Records kept by the quality control department indicate that on average:
i. there is 1 puncture in every 1,000 m² of plastic material.
ii. there is 1 sewing defect for every 1,500 m. of sewing.

For a 4m. by 10 m. solar cover:
a. What is the probability that the cover will not have a puncture?
b. What is the probability that the cover will not have a sewing defect?

7.22 In an attempt to improve sales, the management of a large chain of fast food restaurants has decided to implement a Reward/Reprimand system based on monthly sales figures. The initial standards have been set up as follows:
i. Reward the mangers of restaurants that have placed in the top 15% of sales for the month.
ii. Reprimand managers with sales less than $180,000 for the month.

For the month just past, the sales figures for the 4,350 restaurants were normally distributed with a mean of $230,000 and a standard deviation of $22,000.
a. How many managers will be reprimanded?
b. What will be the minimum sales that will qualify for a reward?

7.23 A checkout counter is considered 'over-occupied' if more than 8 customers arrive within a five-minute period. The average number of customers per hour is 78.
a. What is the probability that in one minute at most two customers arrive?
b. What is the probability that the counter is 'over-occupied' in a five-minute period?

7.24 From past experience, an airline has found that the luggage weight for individual air travelers on their trans-Atlantic route averages 40 kilograms with a standard deviation of 10 kg. The plane consistently is booked with 100 passengers. The pilot insists on loading an extra 500 litres of fuel whenever the total luggage weight exceeds 4200 kg. On what percent of the flights will the extra fuel be required?

7.25 A sand and gravel dealer has received an order for five hundred 10.0 kg. bags of sand. Presently the company has 5150 kg. of sand available.

A specialized sand-bag filling machine will be used to fill the bags. The machine can fill 100 bags per hour. The weight of sand in each bag will be normally distributed with a standard deviation of 0.3 kg. The sand bag's mean weight can be adjusted by the filling machine operator.

If the mean weight is set at 10.25 kg., how many of the 500 bags are expected to meet the customer's expectations?

7.26 An automobile battery has a mean life of 1200 days with a standard deviation of 100 days. If the battery lifetimes are normally distributed, how long should the manufacturer make the guarantee in order to replace at most 10% of the batteries under warrantee?

7.27 A hardware store chain has just received a truckload of 5000 electric drills. Before accepting the shipment, the purchasing manager will test a random selection of 10 drills. The drills will be tested for maximum power consumption and the shipment will be rejected if the mean consumption is more than the 300 watts indicated on the product label. Suppose that the maximum power consumption of the drills in the shipment is normally distributed and averages only 295 watts with a standard deviation of 12 watts.

a. What is the probability that the shipment will be rejected?

b. How many of the drills in the shipment are expected to exceed the maximum power consumption indicated on the label?

7.28 The quality control manager of Marilyn's Cookies is inspecting a batch of chocolate-chip cookies that has just been baked. If the production process is operating properly, the average number of chocolate chips per cookie is 6.76 with a standard deviation of 2.6 chocolate chips. What percent of the cookies will have less than 4 chocolate chips?

7.29 A student is about to write his marketing final exam that consists of 30 multiple-choice questions, each of which has 5 possible answers. If he has done no studying and has no common sense regarding marketing, and thus has to guess the answer to each question, what is the probability that he will pass the exam?

7.30 The time to get an oil change at a certain car dealership averages 42.3 minutes with a standard deviation of 8.6 minutes.

a. There are 45 cars booked for oil changes today. What is the probability that the jobs can be done in an average of 38 minutes or less?

b. Suppose 90 oil changes were done in one particular week. There is a 95% chance that the mean time was more than _____ minutes.

7.31 The following table appeared in the Nov. 2000 issue of Quality Progress magazine. Assume that the salary distributions for all categories of analysts are normal.

a. What is the probability that an analyst with 3.1 to 6 years experience in the quality field will earn more than $60,000?

b. What is the 3rd quartile salary of analysts with 10.1 to 20 years experience in the quality field?

7.32 The following table appeared in the Autumn 2003 issue of Canadian Social Trends.

CST — One in four rotating shift employees worry about the risk of accident or injury

	Total '000	Too many demands/ hours	Risk of accident/ injury	Poor interpersonal relations	Threat of layoff/ job loss	Having to learn computer skills	Other
				%			
Work arrangements							
Class of worker							
All workers	16,800	34	13	15	13	11	6
Self-employed	2,800	37	12	10	8	11	10
Employees	14,000	34	13	16	14	11	6
Employees only							
Hours of work							
All employees[1]	14,000	34	13	16	14	11	6
Full-time	11,500	37	14	17	15	12	8
30-35 hours/week	1,900	29	11	15	15	11	6
36-40 hours/week	6,100	33	14	17	16	12	6
41 or more hours/week	3,600	47	16	18	13	13	6
Part-time	2,300	20	9	11	10	7	5
1-15 hours/week	900	16	6	10	8	4E	4E
16-29 hours/week	1,400	22	11	12	11	9	5
Work schedules							
Regular daytime	9,500	35	11	15	14	12	6
Rotating shift	1,800	35	24	20	16	11	5
Regular evening or night	1,400	27	16	16	12	5	4
Irregular/split shift	900	35	17	16	13	11	5E
Other/on call	300	21	11E	15E	13E	F	9E

1. Full-time and part-time employees.
E High sampling variability.
F Sample too small to provide reliable estimate.
Source: Statistics Canada, General Social Survey, 2000.

Living in one particular neighbourhood are 183 full-time workers that work 36-40 hours per week.

a. What is the probability that more than 15% of them worry about the risk of accident or injury?

b. In a sample of 120 rotating shift workers, what is the relative variability of the number who worry about the threat of layoff or job loss?

Probability Distributions—Combination Questions

7.33 There are 12 agents in one office of a certain real estate firm. Much of the business in this office is conducted by taking a prospective customer out to view a particular property. The time to drive to and view a property is normally distributed and averages 47.3 minutes with a standard deviation of 11.7 minutes. Past studies have shown that twenty-six (26) percent of customers that visit properties with an agent will eventually buy a property being shown by that agent. On average each agent visits 3.6 properties a day, with a standard deviation of 1.9 visits. All of the above activities are independent of each other.

Table A. Salary by Job Title and Number of Years' Experience in the Quality Field for Respondents Who Work in the United States

	Minimum	Maximum	Standard deviation	Count	Mean	Median
Analyst						
Less than 1 year	$50,000	$64,000	$ 7,095	3	$56,333	$55,000
1 to 3 years	22,000	70,000	13,414	29	43,835	42,300
3.1 to 6 years	28,500	85,000	14,148	34	48,351	45,000
6.1 to 10 years	30,000	98,000	16,221	26	50,438	44,000
10.1 to 20 years	26,800	85,000	14,780	36	50,733	53,000
More than 20 years	21,000	83,000	18,851	9	54,111	55,000
No experience	42,000	77,000	11,404	6	58,731	58,000

a. What is the probability that an agent will visit at least 7 properties over the next three days?

b. What is the probability that the average time of the next 50 property viewings will be less than 45 minutes?

c. A particular agent currently has 17 prospective customers that are being shown properties for sale. What is the probability that less than 4 of these customers will eventually buy a property being shown by the agent?

d. Eighty-two (82) percent of property visits will take what range of time, centred at the mean?

7.34 For the Seashell gas station in your neighbourhood, records indicate that the number of customers arriving in any 5-minute interval averages 0.94 customers, with a standard deviation of 0.97 customers. Sixty-five (65) percent of the customers use a credit card to pay for their purchase. There are 8 pumps at this service station. The time that a car is parked at a pump is normally distributed with a mean of 6.35 minutes and a standard deviation of 2.10 minutes. All the above activities are independent of each other.

a. Ninety-four (94) percent of the customers will be parked for what maximum amount of time?

b. For 12 randomly selected customers, what is the probability that at least 10 of them will pay using a credit card?

c. What is the probability that more than 5 customers will arrive in a 15-minute period?

d. What is the probability that the average parked time for the next 40 customers is less than 6 minutes?

7.35 There are 12 brokers in one office of a certain brokerage firm. Much of the business in this office is conducted by telephone. The duration of a telephone call is normally distributed and averages 7.45 minutes with a standard deviation of 1.7 minutes. Past studies have shown that fifty-seven (57) percent of telephone calls result in a buy or sell order. On average each broker receives 1.6 calls every 20 minutes, with a standard deviation of 1.3 calls. All of the above activities are independent of each other.

a. What is the probability that a broker will receive at least 4 calls in the next hour?

b. What is the probability that the average duration of the next 40 calls will be less than 7 minutes?

c. For 9 randomly selected calls, what is the probability that at least 7 of them result in a buy or sell order?

d. Ninety-two (92) percent of the calls will last for what minimum amount of time?

7.36 During the month of December at Reader's Bookstore, the average number of customers entering the store is 7.84 every 20 minutes with a standard deviation of 2.8 customers. The time to get through the check-out counter is approximately normally distributed with a mean of 5.6 minutes and a standard deviation of 1.9 minutes. Fifteen percent of customers are first-time shoppers and 25% of all customers use their debit card to pay for their books.

a. Presently there are 40 customers in the store. What is the probability that more than three quarters of them will have shopped at Reader's before?

b. What is the probability that a customer will take less than 4 minutes to check-out?

c. What is the probability that more than 10 customers will enter the store in the next half-hour?

d. Ten percent of the customers will take longer than _____ to check-out.

7.37 New houses are being built and sold at record paces in the GTA this year. It was reported on the radio last week that on the average one new home was sold every six minutes. In February 3,215 new houses were sold in the GTA region, of which 80% were located in the '905' area code municipalities.

The prices of new homes being built and sold this year are also at record high levels. The average price of a 2-bedroom home was $212,000 with a standard deviation of $5,300. The mean and standard deviation of the prices of 3-bedroom homes were $276,000 and $10,700, respectively. For 4-bedroom homes the corresponding figures were $328,000 and $24,800. All the price data sets were normally distributed.

The figures also showed that 32% of homes being built this year had 2 bedrooms, 45% had 3 bedrooms, 15% had 4 bedrooms, and the remainder were equal amounts of 5 and 6 bedroom homes. The time to build a 3-bedroom home averaged 205 days, with a standard deviation of 12 days. The sizes of 3-bedroom homes were normally distributed with a mean of 2,540 ft^2 and a standard deviation of 175 ft^2.

In Mississauga, just west of Winston Churchill Blvd., a large new community of 2400 houses is being built on a 3 square kilometer (3,000,000 m^2) area. Only 10% of the houses will be bungalows, i.e. one storey. All others will be 2-storey houses. The bungalows are to be randomly distributed throughout the community.

(Note: All figures above, except those in the 1st paragraph, also apply to the Mississauga community.)

a. What is the probability that a 2-bedroom home will cost more than $225,000 ?

b. On one street in the Mississauga development there are 23 houses. What is the probability that at most five of them have 4-bedrooms?

c. One developer is building fifty-three 3-bedroom homes in the new Mississauga community. What is the probability that the mean time to construct these homes will be less than 200 days?

d. What is the probability that 12 new homes will be sold in an hour?

e. One developer in the new Mississauga community has a special deal this weekend on 3-bedroom houses. There will be a $20,000 price discount on the largest 15% of houses. How big a 3-bedroom house do you have to buy to get this discount?

f. What is the expected number of bedrooms in new homes being built this year?

g. What is the probability that there would be at least 3 bungalows in a 10,000 m² area in the new development in Mississauga?

7.38 The production process used to produce 500 ft. spools of electrical cable operates continuously, 24 hours a day, and is capable of producing approximately 6 spools per day. The time required to produce one spool is normally distributed with a mean of 4.23 hours and a standard deviation of 0.45 hours. Defects occur in the wire at an average rate of 1 per 1000 feet. As a result, 61% of all spools have no defects. The machine used to produce the wire, needs to

be adjusted an average of 4 times per day with a standard deviation of 2 times per day.

a. What is the probability that in a week's production, i.e. 42 spools, there will be at least 35 spools without defects?

b. What is the probability that a spool can be produced in less than 4 hours?

c. What is the probability that the wire producing machine will need to be adjusted at most once in an 8 hour shift?

d. What is the probability that the average time to produce the next 15 spools will be more than 4.1 hours?

e. Seventy-eight (78) percent of spools will be produced within what range of time, centred at the mean?

7.3 SAMPLING DISTRIBUTION OF THE PROPORTION

Consider a categorical variable that has only two categories, such as the customer prefers your brand or the customer prefers the competitor's brand. Of interest is the proportion of items belonging to one of the categories, for example, the proportion of customers that prefers your brand. The population proportion, represented by π, is the proportion of items in the entire population with the characteristic of interest. The sample proportion, represented by p, is the proportion of items in the sample with the characteristic of interest. The sample proportion, a statistic, is used to estimate the population proportion, a parameter. To calculate the sample proportion you assign the two possible outcomes scores of 1 or 0 to represent the presence or absence of the characteristic. You then sum all the 1 and 0 scores and divide by n, the sample size. For example, if, in a sample of five customers, three preferred your brand and two did not, you have three 1's and two 0's. Summing the three 1's and two 0's and dividing by the sample size of 5 gives you a sample proportion of 0.60.

THE SAMPLE PROPORTION

$$p = \frac{X}{n} = \frac{\text{number of items having the characteristic of interest}}{\text{sample size}} \quad \textbf{(7.6)}$$

The sample proportion p takes on values between 0 and 1. If all individuals possess the characteristic, you assign each a score of 1 and p is equal to 1. If half the individuals possess the characteristic, you assign half a score of 1, and assign the other half a score of 0, and p is equal to 0.5. If none of the individuals possesses the characteristic, you assign each a score of 0 and p is equal to 0.

While the sample mean $\overline{X}$ is an unbiased estimator of the population mean μ, the statistic p is an unbiased estimator of the population proportion π. By analogy to the sampling distribution of the mean, the **standard error of the proportion** σ_p is given in Equation (7.7).

STANDARD ERROR OF THE PROPORTION

$$\sigma_p = \sqrt{\frac{\pi(1 - \pi)}{n}} \quad \textbf{(7.7)}$$

If you select all possible samples of a certain size, the distribution of all possible sample proportions is referred to as the **sampling distribution of the proportion**. When sampling with replacement from a finite population, the sampling distribution of the proportion follows the binomial distribution as discussed in section 5.2. However, you can use the normal distribution to approximate the binomial distribution when $n\pi$ and $n(1-\pi)$ are each at least 5. In most cases in which inferences are made about the proportion, the sample size is substantial enough to meet the conditions for using the normal approximation (see reference 1). Therefore, in many instances, you can use the normal distribution to estimate the sampling distribution of the proportion. Substituting p for $\bar{X}$, π for μ, and $\sqrt{\dfrac{\pi(1-\pi)}{n}}$ for $\dfrac{\sigma}{\sqrt{n}}$ in Equation (7.4), results in Equation (7.8).

DIFFERENCE BETWEEN THE SAMPLE PROPORTION AND THE POPULATION PROPORTION IN STANDARDIZED NORMAL UNITS

$$Z = \frac{p - \pi}{\sqrt{\dfrac{\pi(1-\pi)}{n}}} \qquad (7.8)$$

To illustrate the sampling distribution of the proportion, suppose that the manager of the local branch of a savings bank determines that 40% of all depositors have multiple accounts at the bank. If you select a random sample of 200 depositors, the probability that the sample proportion of depositors with multiple accounts is less than 0.30 is calculated as follows.

Because $n\pi = 200(0.40) = 80 \geq 5$ and $n(1-\pi) = 200(0.60) = 120 \geq 5$, the sample size is large enough to assume that the sampling distribution of the proportion is approximately normally distributed. Using Equation (7.8),

$$Z = \frac{p - \pi}{\sqrt{\dfrac{\pi(1-\pi)}{n}}}$$

$$= \frac{0.30 - 0.40}{\sqrt{\dfrac{(0.40)(0.60)}{200}}} = \frac{-0.10}{\sqrt{\dfrac{0.24}{200}}} = \frac{-0.10}{0.0346}$$

$$= -2.89$$

Using Table E.2, the area under the normal curve less than $Z = -2.89$ is 0.0019. Therefore, the probability that the sample proportion is less than 0.30 is 0.0019—a highly unlikely event. This means that if the true proportion of successes in the population is 0.40, less than one-fifth of 1% of the samples of $n = 200$ are expected to have sample proportions of less than 0.30.

PROBLEMS FOR SECTION 7.3

Learning the Basics

 7.39 In a random sample of 64 people, 48 are classified as "successful." If the population proportion is 0.70,

a. determine the sample proportion p of "successful" people.

b. determine the standard error of the proportion.

 7.40 A random sample of 50 households was selected for a telephone survey. The key question asked was, "Do you or any member of your household own a cellular telephone with text messaging?" Of the 50 respondents, 15 said yes and 35 said no. If the population proportion is 0.40,

a. determine the sample proportion p of households with cellular telephones.

b. determine the standard error of the proportion.

7.41 The following data represent the responses (Y for yes and N for no) from a sample of 40 college students to the question, "Do you currently own shares in any stocks?"

N N Y N N Y N Y N Y N N Y N Y Y N N N Y

N Y N N N N Y N N Y Y N N N N Y N N Y N N

If the population proportion is 0.30,

a. determine the sample proportion p of college students who own shares of stock.

b. determine the standard error of the proportion.

Applying the Concepts

  7.42 A political pollster is conducting an analysis of sample results in order to make predictions on election night. Assuming a two-candidate election, if a specific candidate receives at least 55% of the vote in the sample, then that candidate will be forecast as the winner of the election. If you select a random sample of 100 voters, what is the probability that a candidate will be forecast as the winner when

a. the true percentage of her vote is 50.1%?

b. the true percentage of her vote is 60%?

c. the true percentage of her vote is 49% (and she will actually lose the election)?

d. If the sample size is increased to 400, what are your answers to (a), (b), and (c)? Discuss.

 7.43 You plan to conduct a marketing experiment in which students are to taste one of two different brands of soft drink. Their task is to correctly identify the brand he or she tasted. You select a random sample of 200 students and assume that the students have no ability to distinguish between the two brands. (*Hint:* If an individual has no ability to distinguish between the two soft drinks, then each brand is equally likely to be selected.)

a. What is the probability that the sample will have between 50% and 60% of the identifications correct?

b. The probability is 90% that the sample percentage is contained within what symmetrical limits of the population percentage?

c. What is the probability that the sample percentage of correct identifications is greater than 65%?

d. Which is more likely to occur—more than 60% correct identifications in the sample of 200 or more than 55% correct identifications in a sample of 1,000? Explain.

7.44 A study of women in corporate leadership was conducted by Catalyst, a New York research organization. The study concluded that slightly more than 15% of corporate officers at Fortune 500 companies are women (Carol Hymowitz, "Women Put Noses to the Grindstone, and Miss Opportunities," *The Wall Street Journal*, February 3, 2004, B1). Suppose that you select a random sample of 200 corporate officers and the true proportion held by women is 0.15.

a. What is the probability that in the sample less than 15% of the corporate officers will be women?

b. What is the probability that in the sample between 13% and 17% of the corporate officers will be women?

c. What is the probability that in the sample between 10% and 20% of the corporate officers will be women?

d. If a sample of 100 is taken, how does this change your answers to (a) through (c)?

7.45 The NBC hit comedy *Friends* was TiVo's most popular show during the week of April 18–24, 2004. According to the Nielsen ratings, 29.7% of TiVo owners in the United States either recorded *Friends* or watched it live ("Prime-time Nielsen Ratings," *USA Today*, April 28, 2004, 3D). Suppose you select a random sample of 50 TiVo owners.

a. What is the probability that more than half the people in the sample watched or recorded *Friends*?

b. What is the probability that less than 25% of the people in the sample watched or recorded *Friends*?

c. If a random sample of size 500 is taken, how does this change your answers to (a) and (b)?

7.46 Millions of Americans arrange their travel plans on the Web. According to an article in *USA Today*, 77% of travelers purchase plane tickets on the Web ("Travelers Head Online," *USA Today Snapshots*, July 22, 2003, A1). If you select a random sample of 200 travelers,

a. what is the probability that the sample will have between 75% and 80% purchase plane tickets on the Web?

b. The probability is 90% that the sample percentage will be contained within what symmetrical limits of the population percentage?

c. The probability is 95% that the sample percentage will be contained within what symmetrical limits of the population percentage?

 7.47 According to the National Restaurant Association, 20% of fine-dining restaurants have instituted policies restricting the use of cell phones ("Business Bulletin," *The Wall Street Journal*, June 1, 2000, A1). If you select a random sample of 100 fine-dining restaurants,

a. what is the probability that the sample has between 15% and 25% that have established policies restricting cell phone use?

b. the probability is 90% that the sample percentage will be contained within what symmetrical limits of the population percentage?

c. the probability is 95% that the sample percentage will be contained within what symmetrical limits of the population percentage?

7.48 An article (P. Kitchen, "Retirement Plan: To Keep Working," *Newsday*, September 24, 2003) discussed the retirement plans of Americans ages 50 to 70 who were employed full-time or part-time. Twenty-nine percent of the respondents said that they did not intend to work for pay at all. If you select a random sample of 400 Americans ages 50 to 70 who were employed full-time or part-time,

a. what is the probability that the sample has between 25% and 30% who do not intend to work for pay at all?

b. If a current sample of 400 Americans ages 50 to 70 who were employed full-time or part-time has 35% who do not intend to work for pay at all, what can you infer about the population estimate of 29%? Explain.

c. If a current sample of 100 Americans ages 50 to 70 who were employed full-time or part-time has 35% who do not intend to work for pay at all, what can you infer about the population estimate of 29%? Explain.

d. Explain the difference in the results in (b) and (c).

7.49 The Internal Revenue Service (IRS) discontinued random audits in 1988. Instead, the IRS conducts audits on returns deemed as questionable by their Discriminant Function System (DFS), a complicated and highly secretive computerized analysis system. In an attempt to reduce the proportion of "no-change" audits (i.e., audits that uncover that no additional taxes are due) the IRS only audits returns the DFS scores as highly questionable. The proportion of "no-change" audits has risen over the years and is currently approximately 0.25 (Tom Herman,

"Unhappy Returns: IRS Moves to Bring Back Random Audits," *The Wall Street Journal*, June 20, 2002, A1). Suppose that you select a random sample of 100 audits. What is the probability that the sample will have

a. between 24% and 26% no-change audits?

b. between 20% and 30% no-change audits?

c. more than 30% no-change audits?

7.50 The IRS announced that it planned to resume totally random audits in 2002. Suppose that you select a random sample of 200 totally random audits, and that only 10% of all the returns filed would result in audits requiring additional taxes. What is the probability that the sample has

a. between 89% and 91% no-change audits?

b. between 85% and 95% no-change audits?

c. more than 95% no-change audits?

7.4   TYPES OF SURVEY SAMPLING METHODS

In section 1.1, a sample was defined as the portion of the population that has been selected for analysis. Rather than taking a complete census of the whole population, statistical sampling procedures focus on collecting a small representative group of the larger population. The sample results are used to estimate characteristics of the entire population. The three main reasons for drawing a sample are:

- A sample is less time-consuming than a census.
- A sample is less costly to administer than a census.
- A sample is less cumbersome and more practical to administer than a census.

The sampling process begins by defining the frame. The **frame** is a listing of items that make up the population. Frames are data sources such as population lists, directories, or maps. Samples are drawn from these frames. Inaccurate or biased results can result if the frame excludes certain groups of the population. Using different frames to generate data can lead to opposite conclusions.

Once you select a frame, you draw a sample from the frame. As illustrated in Figure 7.5, there are two kinds of samples: the nonprobability sample and the probability sample.

FIGURE 7.5

Types of Samples

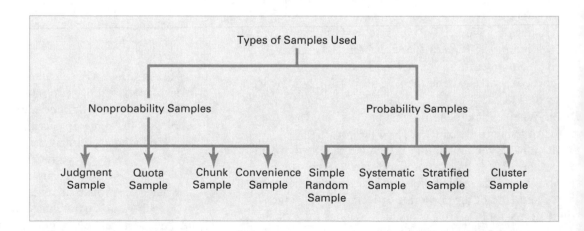

In a **nonprobability sample** you select the items or individuals without knowing their probabilities of selection. Thus, the theory that has been developed for probability sampling cannot be applied to nonprobability samples. A common type of nonprobability sampling is convenience sampling. In **convenience sampling**, items are selected based only on the fact that they are easy, inexpensive, or convenient to sample. In some cases participants are self-selected. For example, many companies conduct surveys by giving visitors to their World Wide Web site the opportunity to complete survey forms and submit them electronically. The response to these surveys can provide large amounts of data quickly, but the sample consists of self-selected Web users. For many studies, only a nonprobability sample such as a judgment sample is available. In a **judgment sample**, you get the opinions of preselected experts in the subject matter. Some other common procedures of nonprobability sampling are quota sampling and chunk sampling. These are discussed in detail in specialized books on sampling methods (see reference 1).

Nonprobability samples can have certain advantages such as convenience, speed, and lower cost. However, their lack of accuracy due to selection bias and lack of generalizability of the results more than offset these advantages. Therefore, you should restrict the use of non-probability sampling methods to situations in which you want to get rough approximations at low cost in order to satisfy your curiosity about a particular subject or to small-scale studies that precede more rigorous investigations.

In a **probability sample** you select the items based on known probabilities. Whenever possible, you should use probability sampling methods. The samples based on these methods allow you to make unbiased inferences about the population of interest. In practice, it is often difficult to take a probability sample. However, you should work toward achieving a probability sample and acknowledge any potential biases that might exist. The four types of probability samples most commonly used are simple random, systematic, stratified, and cluster. These sampling methods vary from one another in their cost, accuracy, and complexity.

Simple Random Sample

In a **simple random sample** every item from a frame has the same chance of selection as every other item. In addition, every sample of a fixed size has the same chance of selection as every other sample of that size. Simple random sampling is the most elementary random sampling technique. It forms the basis for the other random sampling techniques.

With simple random sampling, you use n to represent the sample size and N to represent the frame size. You number every item in the frame from 1 to N. The chance that you will select any particular member of the frame on the first draw is $1/N$.

You select samples with replacement or without replacement. **Sampling with replacement** means that after you select an item, you return it to the frame, where it has the same probability of being selected again. Imagine you have a fishbowl with N business cards. On the first selection, you select the card for Judy Craven. You record pertinent information and replace the business card in the bowl. You then shuffle the cards in the bowl and select the second card. On the second selection, Judy Craven has the same probability of being selected again, $1/N$. You repeat this process until you have selected the desired sample size n. However, it is usually more desirable to have a sample of different items than to permit a repetition of measurements on the same item.

Sampling without replacement means that once you select an item it cannot be selected again. The chance you will select any particular item in the frame, say the business card for Judy Craven, on the first draw is $1/N$. The chance you will select any card not previously selected on the second draw is now 1 out of $N - 1$. This process continues until you have selected the desired sample of size n.

Regardless of whether you have sampled with or without replacement, "fishbowl" methods for sample selection have a major drawback—the ability to thoroughly mix the cards and randomly pull the sample. As a result, fishbowl methods are not very useful. You need to use less cumbersome and more scientific methods of selection.

One such method uses a **table of random numbers** (see Table E.1) for selecting the sample. A table of random numbers consists of a series of digits listed in a randomly generated sequence (see reference 8). Because the numeric system uses 10 digits (0, 1, 2, . . . , 9), the chance you will randomly generate any particular digit is equal to the probability of generating any other digit. This probability is 1 out of 10. Hence, if a sequence of 800 digits were generated, you would expect about 80 of them to be the digit 0, 80 to be the digit 1, and so on. In fact, those who use tables of random numbers usually test the generated digits for randomness prior to using them. Table E.1 has met all such criteria for randomness. Because every digit or sequence of digits in the table is random, the table can be read either horizontally or vertically. The margins of the table designate row numbers and column numbers. The digits themselves are grouped into sequences of five in order to make reading the table easier.

To use such a table instead of a fishbowl for selecting the sample, you first need to assign code numbers to the individual members of the frame. Then you get the random sample by reading the table of random numbers and selecting those individuals from the frame whose assigned code numbers match the digits found in the table. You can better understand the process of sample selection by examining Example 7.5.

EXAMPLE 7.5

SELECTING A SIMPLE RANDOM SAMPLE USING A TABLE OF RANDOM NUMBERS

A company wants to select a sample of 32 full-time workers from a population of 800 full-time employees in order to collect information on expenditures concerning a company-sponsored dental plan. How do you select a simple random sample?

SOLUTION The company assumes that not everyone will respond to the survey, so you need to mail more than 32 surveys to get the desired 32 responses. Assuming that 8 out of 10 full-time workers will respond to such a survey (i.e., a response rate of 80%), you decide to mail 40 surveys.

The frame consists of a listing of the names and company mailbox numbers of all $N = 800$ full-time employees taken from the company personnel files. Thus, the frame is an accurate and complete listing of the population. To select the random sample of 40 employees from this frame, you use a table of random numbers. Because the population size (800) is a three-digit number, each assigned code number must also be three digits so that every full-time worker has an equal chance for selection. You give a code of 001 to the first full-time employee in the population listing, a code of 002 to the second full-time employee in the population listing, and so on, until a code of 800 is given to the Nth full-time worker in the listing. Because $N = 800$ is the largest possible coded value, you discard all three-digit code sequences greater than N (i.e., 801 through 999 and 000).

To select the simple random sample, you choose an arbitrary starting point from the table of random numbers. One method you can use is to close your eyes and strike the table of random numbers with a pencil. Suppose you used this procedure and you selected row 06, column 05, of Table 7.3 (which is extracted from Table E.1), as the starting point. Although you can go in any direction, in this example, you will read the table from left to right in sequences of three digits without skipping.

The individual with code number 003 is the first full-time employee in the sample (row 06 and columns 05–07), the second individual has code number 364 (row 06 and columns 08–10), and the third individual has code number 884. Because the highest code for any employee is 800, you discard this number. Individuals with code numbers 720, 433, 463, 363, 109, 592, 470, and 705 are selected third through tenth, respectively.

You continue the selection process until you get the needed sample size of 40 full-time employees. During the selection process, if any three-digit coded sequence repeats, you include the employee corresponding to that coded sequence again as part of the sample if sampling with replacement. You discard the repeating coded sequence if sampling without replacement.

TABLE 7.3

Using a Table of
Random Numbers

		Column							
Row	**00000** **12345**	**00001** **67890**	**11111** **12345**	**11112** **67890**	**22222** **12345**	**22223** **67890**	**33333** **12345**	**33334** **67890**
01	49280	88924	35779	00283	81163	07275	89863	02348
02	61870	41657	07468	08612	98083	97349	20775	45091
03	43898	65923	25078	86129	78496	97653	91550	08078
04	62993	93912	30454	84598	56095	20664	12872	64647
05	33850	58555	51438	85507	71865	79488	76783	31708
06	97340	03364	88472	04334	63919	36394	11095	92470
07	70543	29776	10087	10072	55980	64688	68239	20461
08	89382	93809	00796	95945	34101	81277	66090	88872
09	37818	72142	67140	50785	22380	16703	53362	44940
10	60430	22834	14130	96593	23298	56203	92671	15925
11	82975	66158	84731	19436	55790	69229	28661	13675
12	39087	71938	40355	54324	08401	26299	49420	59208
13	55700	24586	93247	32596	11865	63397	44251	43189
14	14756	23997	78643	75912	83832	32768	18928	57070
15	32166	53251	70654	92827	63491	04233	33825	69662
16	23236	73751	31888	81718	06546	83246	47651	04877
17	45794	26926	15130	82455	78305	55058	52551	47182
18	09893	20505	14225	68514	46427	56788	96297	78822
19	54382	74598	91499	14523	68479	27686	46162	83554
20	94750	89923	37089	20048	80336	94598	26940	36858
21	70297	34135	53140	33340	42050	82341	44104	82949
22	85157	47954	32979	26575	57600	40881	12250	73742
23	11100	02340	12860	74697	96644	89439	28707	25815
24	36871	50775	30592	57143	17381	68856	25853	35041
25	23913	48357	63308	16090	51690	54607	72407	55538

Begin selection (row 06, column 05) — marks rows 06–09

Source: Partially extracted from The Rand Corporation, A Million Random Digits with 100,000 Normal Deviates *(Glencoe, IL: The Free Press, 1955) and displayed in Table E.1 in Appendix E of this book.*

Systematic Sample

In a **systematic sample**, you partition the N items in the frame into n groups of k items where,

$$k = \frac{N}{n}$$

You round k to the nearest integer. To select a systematic sample, you choose the first item to be selected at random from the first k items in the frame. Then you select the remaining $n - 1$ items by taking every k th item thereafter from the entire frame.

If the frame consists of a listing of prenumbered checks, sales receipts, or invoices, a systematic sample is faster and easier to take than a simple random sample. A systematic sample is also a convenient mechanism for collecting data from telephone books, class rosters, and consecutive items coming off an assembly line.

To take a systematic sample of $n = 40$ from the population of $N = 800$ employees, you partition the frame of 800 into 40 groups, each of which contains 20 employees. You then select a random number from the first 20 individuals, and include every twentieth individual after the first selection in the sample. For example, if the first number you select is 008, your subsequent selections are 028, 048, 068, 088, 108, . . . , 768, and 788.

Although they are simpler to use, simple random sampling and systematic sampling are generally less efficient than other, more sophisticated, probability sampling methods. Even greater possibilities for selection bias and lack of representation of the population characteristics occur from systematic samples than from simple random samples. If there is a pattern in the frame, you could have severe selection biases. To overcome the potential problem of disproportionate representation of specific groups in a sample, you can use either stratified sampling methods or cluster sampling methods.

Stratified Sample

In a **stratified sample**, you first subdivide the N items in the frame into separate subpopulations, or **strata**. A strata is defined by some common characteristic. You select a simple random sample within each of the strata, and combine the results from the separate simple random samples. This method is more efficient than either simple random sampling or systematic sampling because you are ensured of the representation of items across the entire population. The homogeneity of items within each stratum provides greater precision in the estimates of underlying population parameters.

EXAMPLE 7.6

SELECTING A STRATIFIED SAMPLE

A company wants to select a sample of 32 full-time workers from a population of 800 full-time employees in order to estimate expenditures from a company-sponsored dental plan. Of the full-time employees, 25% are managerial and 75% are nonmanagerial workers. How do you select the stratified sample in order for the sample to represent the correct proportion of managerial workers?

SOLUTION If you assume an 80% response rate, you need to distribute 40 surveys to get the desired 32 responses. The frame consists of a listing of the names and company mailbox numbers of all $N = 800$ full-time employees included in the company personnel files. Since 25% of the full-time employees are managerial, you first separate the population frame into two strata: a subpopulation listing of all 200 managerial-level personnel and a separate subpopulation listing of all 600 full-time nonmanagerial workers. Since the first stratum consists of a listing of 200 managers, you assign three-digit code numbers from 001 to 200. Since the second stratum contains a listing of 600 nonmanagerial-level workers, you assign three-digit code numbers from 001 to 600.

To collect a stratified sample proportional to the sizes of the strata, you select 25% of the overall sample from the first stratum and 75% of the overall sample from the second stratum. You take two separate simple random samples, each of which is based on a distinct random starting point from a table of random numbers (Table E.1). In the first sample you select 10 managers from the listing of 200 in the first stratum, and in the second sample you select 30 nonmanagerial workers from the listing of 600 in the second stratum. You then combine the results to reflect the composition of the entire company.

Cluster Sample

In a **cluster sample**, you divide the N items in the frame into several clusters so that each cluster is representative of the entire population. You then take a random sample of clusters, and study all items in each selected cluster. **Clusters** are naturally occurring designations, such as counties, election districts, city blocks, households, or sales territories.

Cluster sampling is often more cost-effective than simple random sampling, particularly if the population is spread over a wide geographic region. However, cluster sampling often requires a larger sample size to produce results as precise as those from simple random sampling or stratified sampling. A detailed discussion of systematic sampling, stratified sampling, and cluster sampling procedures can be found in reference 1.

PROBLEMS FOR SECTION 7.4

Learning the Basics

 7.51 For a population containing $N = 902$ individuals, what code number would you assign for
a. the first person on the list?
b. the fortieth person on the list?
c. the last person on the list?

7.52 For a population of $N = 902$, verify that by starting in row 05 of the table of random numbers (Table E.1), you need only six rows to select a sample of $n = 60$ *without* replacement.

 7.53 Given a population of $N = 93$, starting in row 29 of the table of random numbers (Table E.1), and reading across the row, select a sample of $n = 15$
a. *without* replacement.
b. *with* replacement.

Applying the Concepts

7.54 For a study that consists of personal interviews with participants (rather than mail or phone surveys), explain why a simple random sample might be less practical than some other methods.

 7.55 You want to select a random sample of $n = 1$ from a population of three items (which are called A, B, and C). The rule for selecting the sample is: Flip a coin; if it is heads, pick item A; if it is tails, flip the coin again; this time, if it is heads, choose B; if it is tails, choose C. Explain why this is a random sample but not a simple random sample.

7.56 A population has four members (call them A, B, C, and D). You would like to draw a random sample of $n = 2$, which you decide to do in the following way: Flip a coin; if it is heads, the sample will be items A and B; if it is tails, the sample will be items C and D. Although this is a random sample, it is not a simple random sample. Explain why. (If you did problem 7.55, compare the procedure described there with the procedure described in this problem.)

✓ SELF Test **7.57** The registrar of a college with a population of $N = 4,000$ full-time students is asked by the president to conduct a survey to measure satisfaction with the quality of life on campus. The following table contains a breakdown of the 4,000 registered full-time students by gender and class designation:

| | Class Designation | | | | |
Gender	Fr.	So.	Jr.	Sr.	Total
Female	700	520	500	480	2,200
Male	560	460	400	380	1,800
Total	1,260	980	900	860	4,000

The registrar intends to take a probability sample of $n = 200$ students and project the results from the sample to the entire population of full-time students.
a. If the frame available from the registrar's files is an alphabetical listing of the names of all $N = 4,000$ registered full-time students, what type of sample could you take? Discuss.
b. What is the advantage of selecting a simple random sample in (a)?
c. What is the advantage of selecting a systematic sample in (a)?
d. If the frame available from the registrar's files is a listing of the names of all $N = 4,000$ registered full-time students compiled from eight separate alphabetical lists based on the gender and class designation breakdowns shown in the class designation table, what type of sample should you take? Discuss.
e. Suppose that each of the $N = 4,000$ registered full-time students lived in one of the 20 campus dormitories. Each dormitory contains four floors with 50 beds per floor, and therefore accommodates 200 students. It is college policy to fully integrate students by gender and class designation on each floor of each dormitory. If the registrar is able to compile a frame through a listing of all student occupants on each floor within each dormitory, what type of sample should you take? Discuss.

7.58 Prenumbered sales invoices are kept in a sales journal. The invoices are numbered from 0001 to 5,000.
a. Beginning in row 16, column 1, and proceeding horizontally in Table E.1, select a simple random sample of 50 invoice numbers.
b. Select a systematic sample of 50 invoice numbers. Use the random numbers in row 20, columns 5–7, as the starting point for your selection.
c. Are the invoices selected in (a) the same as those selected in (b)? Why or why not?

 7.59 Suppose that 5,000 sales invoices are separated into four strata. Stratum 1 contains 50 invoices, stratum 2 contains 500 invoices, stratum 3 contains 1,000 invoices, and stratum 4 contains 3,450 invoices. A sample of 500 sales invoices is needed.
a. What type of sampling should you do? Why?
b. Explain how you would carry out the sampling according to the method stated in (a).
c. Why is the sampling in (a) not simple random sampling?

7.5   EVALUATING SURVEY WORTHINESS

Nearly every day, you read or hear about survey or opinion poll results in newspapers, on the Internet, or on radio or television. To identify surveys that lack objectivity or credibility, you must critically evaluate what you read and hear by examining the worthiness of the survey. First, you must evaluate the purpose of the survey, why it was conducted, and for whom it was conducted. An opinion poll or survey conducted to satisfy curiosity is mainly for entertainment. Its result is an end in itself rather than a means to an end. You should be skeptical of such a survey because the result should not be put to further use.

The second step in evaluating the worthiness of a survey is for you to determine whether it was based on a probability or a nonprobability sample (as discussed in section 7.4). You need to remember that the only way to make correct statistical inferences from a sample to a population is through the use of a probability sample. Surveys that use nonprobability sampling methods are subject to serious, perhaps unintentional, biases that may render the results meaningless, as illustrated in the following example from the 1948 U.S. presidential election.

In 1948, major pollsters predicted the outcome of the U.S. presidential election between Harry S. Truman, the incumbent president, and Thomas E. Dewey, then governor of New York, as going to Dewey. The *Chicago Tribune* was so confident of the polls' predictions that it printed its early edition based on the predictions rather than waiting for the ballots to be counted.

An embarrassed newspaper and the pollsters it had relied on had a lot of explaining to do. How had the pollsters been so wrong? Intent on discovering the source of the error, the pollsters found that their use of a nonprobability sampling method was the culprit (see reference 7). As a result, polling organizations adopted probability sampling methods for future elections.

Survey Errors

Even when surveys use random probability sampling methods, they are subject to potential errors. Four types of survey errors are:

- Coverage error
- Nonresponse error
- Sampling error
- Measurement error

Good survey research design attempts to reduce or minimize these various survey errors, often at considerable cost.

Coverage Error   The key to proper sample selection is an adequate frame. Remember, a frame is an up-to-date list of all the items from which you will select the sample. **Coverage error** occurs if certain groups of items are excluded from this frame so that they have no chance of being selected in the sample. Coverage error results in a **selection bias**. If the frame is inadequate because certain groups of items in the population were not properly included, any random probability sample selected will provide an estimate of the characteristics of the frame, not the *actual* population.

Nonresponse Error   Not everyone is willing to respond to a survey. In fact, research has shown that individuals in the upper and lower economic classes tend to respond less frequently to surveys than do people in the middle class. **Nonresponse error** arises from the failure to collect data on all items in the sample and results in a **nonresponse bias**. Because you cannot generally assume that persons who do not respond to surveys are similar to those who do, you need to follow up on the nonresponses after a specified period of time. You should make several attempts to convince such individuals to complete the survey. The follow-up responses are then compared to the initial responses in order to make valid inferences from the survey (reference 1).

The mode of response you use affects the rate of response. The personal interview and the telephone interview usually produce a higher response rate than does the mail survey—but at a higher cost. The following is a famous example of coverage error and nonresponse bias.

In 1936, the magazine *Literary Digest* predicted that Governor Alf Landon of Kansas would receive 57% of the votes in the U.S. presidential election and overwhelmingly defeat President Franklin D. Roosevelt's bid for a second term. However, Landon was soundly defeated when he received only 38% of the vote. Such an unprecedented error by a magazine with respect to a major poll had never occurred before. As a result, the prediction devastated the magazine's credibility with the public, eventually causing it to go bankrupt. *Literary Digest* thought it had done everything right. It had based its prediction on a huge sample size, 2.4 million respondents, out of a survey sent to 10 million registered voters. What went wrong? There are two answers: selection bias and nonresponse bias.

To understand the role of selection bias, some historical background must be provided. In 1936 the United States was still suffering from the Great Depression. Not accounting for this, the *Literary Digest* compiled its frame from such sources as telephone books, club membership lists, magazine subscriptions, and automobile registrations (reference 7). Inadvertently, it chose a frame primarily composed of the rich and excluded the majority of the voting population who, during the Great Depression, could not afford telephones, club memberships, magazine subscriptions, and automobiles. Thus, the 57% estimate for the Landon vote may have been very close to the frame but certainly not the total U.S. population.

Nonresponse error produced a possible bias when the huge sample of 10 million registered voters produced only 2.4 million responses. A response rate of only 24% is far too low to yield accurate estimates of the population parameters without some mechanism to ensure that the 7.6 million individual nonrespondents have similar opinions. However, the problem of nonresponse bias was secondary to the problem of selection bias. Even if all 10 million registered voters in the sample had responded, this would not have compensated for the fact that the frame differed substantially in composition from the actual voting population.

Sampling Error   There are three main reasons for you to select a sample rather than taking a complete census: It is more expedient, less costly, and more efficient. However, chance dictates which individuals or items will or will not be included in the sample. **Sampling error** reflects the heterogeneity, or "chance differences," from sample to sample based on the probability of particular individuals or items being selected in the particular samples.

When you read about the results of surveys or polls in newspapers or magazines, there is often a statement regarding margin of error or precision. For example, "the results of this poll are expected to be within ±4 percentage points of the actual value." This margin of error is the sampling error. You can reduce sampling error by taking larger sample sizes, although this also increases the cost of conducting the survey.

Measurement Error   In the practice of good survey research, you design a questionnaire with the intention of gathering meaningful information. But you have a dilemma here—getting meaningful measurements is often easier said than done. Consider the following proverb:

A man with one watch always knows what time it is;
A man with two watches always searches to identify the correct one;
A man with ten watches is always reminded of the difficulty in measuring time.

Unfortunately, the process of getting a measurement is often governed by what is convenient, not what is needed. The measurements are often only a proxy for the ones you really desire. Much attention has been given to measurement error that occurs because of a weakness in question wording (reference 3). A question should be clear, not ambiguous. Furthermore, in order to avoid *leading questions*, you need to present them in a neutral manner.

There are three sources of **measurement error**: ambiguous wording of questions, the halo effect, and respondent error. As an example of ambiguous wording, in November 1993 the Labor Department reported that the unemployment rate in the United States had been underestimated for more than a decade because of poor questionnaire wording in the Current Population Survey. In particular, the wording led to a significant undercount of women in the labor force. Because unemployment rates are tied to benefit programs such as state unemployment compensation systems, it was imperative that government survey researchers rectify the situation by adjusting the questionnaire wording.

The "halo effect" occurs when the respondent feels obligated to please the interviewer. Proper interviewer training can minimize the halo effect.

Respondent error occurs as a result of overzealous or underzealous effort by the respondent. You can minimize this error in two ways: (1) by carefully scrutinizing the data and calling back those individuals whose responses seem unusual and (2) by establishing a program of random callbacks in order to determine the reliability of the responses.

Ethical Issues

Ethical considerations arise with respect to the four types of potential errors that can occur when designing surveys that use probability samples: coverage error, nonresponse error, sampling error, and measurement error. Coverage error can result in selection bias and becomes an ethical issue if particular groups or individuals are *purposely* excluded from the frame so that the survey results are skewed, indicating a position more favorable to the survey's sponsor. Nonresponse error can lead to nonresponse bias and becomes an ethical issue if the sponsor knowingly designs the survey in such a manner that particular groups or individuals are less likely to respond. Sampling error becomes an ethical issue if the findings are purposely presented without reference to sample size and margin of error so that the sponsor can promote a viewpoint that might otherwise be truly insignificant. Measurement error becomes an ethical issue in one of three ways: (1) a survey sponsor chooses leading questions that guide the responses in a particular direction; (2) an interviewer, through mannerisms and tone, purposely creates a halo effect or otherwise guides the responses in a particular direction; (3) a respondent, having a disdain for the survey process, willfully provides false information.

Ethical issues also arise when the results of nonprobability samples are used to form conclusions about the entire population. When you use a nonprobability sampling method, you need to explain the sampling procedures and state that the results cannot be generalized beyond the sample.

PROBLEMS FOR SECTION 7.5

Applying the Concepts

7.60 "A survey indicates that the vast majority of college students own their own personal computers." What information would you want to know before you accepted the results of this survey?

7.61 A simple random sample of $n = 300$ full-time employees is selected from a company list containing the names of all $N = 5,000$ full-time employees in order to evaluate job satisfaction.
a. Give an example of possible coverage error.
b. Give an example of possible nonresponse error.
c. Give an example of possible sampling error.
d. Give an example of possible measurement error.

7.62 According to a survey of 1,000 AOL subscribers (Harry Berkowitz, "Screen Name Loyalty," *Newsday*, December 1, 2002, A42), 92% of the AOL subscribers gave "don't want to change e-mail address" as a reason for sticking with the online service. What information would you want to know before you accepted the results of the survey?

7.63 A survey of online shoppers was conducted by Forrester Research Inc. (Michael Totty, "The Masses Have Arrived," *The Wall Street Journal*, January 27, 2003, R8).

For those shoppers who have been buying online for less than one year, 39% have a college degree, 57% are women, and the mean annual income of these shoppers is $52,300. What information would you want to know before you accepted the results of the survey?

7.64 According to a Maritz poll of 1,004 adult drivers ("Snapshots," *USA Today*, October 23, 2002), 45% admit to often or sometimes eating or drinking while driving and 36% admit to talking on a cellphone. What information would you want to know before you accepted the results of the survey?

7.65 According to a survey conducted by MessageOne, among people who have e-mail at work, almost four in 10 indicate that they cannot live without it (Anne R. Carey and Chad Palmer, "Snapshots," *USA Today*, January 14, 2004, A1). More specifically, 37% said they "Can't live without it," 26% said e-mail was "Important," 19% said "Not essential," 13% said "Don't use," and 5% said "Not important." What information would you want to know before you accepted the results of this survey?

7.66 What do restaurant diners want? In a survey conducted by Caravan for IHOP, 56% responded that they want "Great food." Other responses were "Reasonable prices" 22%, "Atmosphere" 11%, "Quick service" 8%, and "Don't know" 3% "(Darryl Haralson and Jeff Dionise, "Snapshots," *USA Today*, January 16, 2004, A1). What information would you want to know before you accepted the results of this survey?

KEY FORMULAS

Population Mean

$$\mu = \frac{\sum_{i=1}^{N} X_i}{N} \quad (7.1)$$

Population Standard Deviation

$$\sigma = \sqrt{\frac{\sum_{i=1}^{N}(X_i - \mu)^2}{N}} \quad (7.2)$$

Standard Error of the Mean

$$\sigma_{\bar{X}} = \frac{\sigma}{\sqrt{n}} \quad (7.3)$$

Finding Z for the Sampling Distribution of the Mean

$$Z = \frac{\bar{X} - \mu_{\bar{X}}}{\sigma_{\bar{X}}} = \frac{\bar{X} - \mu}{\frac{\sigma}{\sqrt{n}}} \quad (7.4)$$

Finding $\bar{X}$ for the Sampling Distribution of the Mean

$$\bar{X} = \mu + Z\frac{\sigma}{\sqrt{n}} \quad (7.5)$$

Sample Proportion

$$p = \frac{X}{n} \quad (7.6)$$

Standard Error of the Sample Proportion

$$\sigma_p = \sqrt{\frac{\pi(1 - \pi)}{n}} \quad (7.7)$$

Finding Z for the Sampling Distribution of the Proportion

$$Z = \frac{p - \pi}{\sqrt{\frac{\pi(1 - \pi)}{n}}} \quad (7.8)$$

CHAPTER REVIEW PROBLEMS

Checking Your Understanding

7.67 Why is the sample mean an unbiased estimator of the population mean?

7.68 Why does the standard error of the mean decrease as the sample size *n* increases?

7.69 Why does the sampling distribution of the mean follow a normal distribution for a large enough sample size even though the population may not be normally distributed?

7.70 What is the difference between a probability distribution and a sampling distribution?

7.71 Under what circumstances does the sampling distribution of the proportion approximately follow the normal distribution?

7.72 What is the difference between probability and nonprobability sampling?

7.73 What are some potential problems with using "fishbowl" methods to select a simple random sample?

7.74 What is the difference between sampling *with* replacement versus *without* replacement?

7.75 What is the difference between a simple random sample and a systematic sample?

7.76 What is the difference between a simple random sample and a stratified sample?

7.77 What is the difference between a stratified sample and a cluster sample?

Applying the Concepts

7.78 An industrial sewing machine uses ball bearings that are targeted to have a diameter of 0.75 inch. The lower and upper specification limits under which the ball bearing can operate are 0.74 inch (lower) and 0.76 inch (upper). Past experience has indicated that the actual diameter of the ball bearings is approximately normally distributed with a mean of 0.753 inch and a standard deviation of 0.004 inch. If you select a random sample of 25 ball bearings, what is the probability that the sample mean is

a. between the target and the population mean of 0.753?
b. between the lower specification limit and the target?
c. above the upper specification limit?
d. below the lower specification limit?
e. The probability is 93% that the sample mean diameter will be above what value?

7.79 The fill amount of bottles of soft drink is normally distributed with a mean of 2.0 liters and a standard deviation of 0.05 liter. If you select a random sample of 25 bottles, what is the probability that the sample mean will be

a. between 1.99 and 2.0 liters?
b. below 1.98 liters?
c. above 2.01 liters?
d. The probability is 99% that the sample mean will contain at least how much soft drink?
e. The probability is 99% that the sample mean will contain an amount that is between which two values (symmetrically distributed around the mean)?

7.80 An orange juice producer buys all his oranges from a large orange grove that has one variety of orange. The amount of juice squeezed from each of these oranges is approximately normally distributed with a mean of 4.70 ounces and a standard deviation of 0.40 ounce. Suppose that you select a sample of 25 oranges:

a. What is the probability that the sample mean will be at least 4.60 ounces?
b. The probability is 70% that the sample mean will be contained between what two values symmetrically distributed around the population mean?
c. The probability is 77% that the sample mean will be above what value?

7.81 DiGiorno's frozen pizza has some of the most creative and likeable advertisements on television. *USA Today's* Ad Track claims that 20% of viewers like the ads "a lot" (Theresa Howard, "DiGiorno Campaign Delivers Major Sales," **www.usatoday.com**, April 1, 2002). Suppose that a sample of 400 television viewers is shown the advertisements. What is the probability that the sample will have between

a. 18% and 22% who like the ads "a lot"?
b. 16% and 24% who like the ads "a lot"?
c. 14% and 26% who like the ads "a lot"?
d. 12% and 28% who like the ads "a lot"?

7.82 Mutual funds reported modest earnings in the first quarter of 2004. U.S. diversified equity funds, large baskets of stocks from a wide variety of companies, had a 2.98% return (Michael J. Martinez, "Mutual-fund Returns Minimal in First Quarter," **Cincinnati.com**, April 3, 2004). Assume that the returns for U.S. funds were distributed as a normal random variable with a mean of 2.98 and a standard deviation of 4. If you selected a random sample of 10 funds from this population, what is the probability that the sample would have a mean return

a. less than 0, that is, a loss?
b. between 0 and 6?
c. greater than 10?

7.83 Mutual funds reported modest earnings in the first quarter of 2004. International funds, which are historically slightly more volatile than U.S. funds, had a mean return of 5.13% (Michael J. Martinez, "Mutual-fund Returns Minimal in First Quarter," **Cincinnati.com**, April 3, 2004). Assume that the returns for international funds were distributed as a normal random variable with a mean of 5.13 and a standard deviation of 6. If you select an individual fund from this population, what is the probability that it would have a return

a. less than 0, that is, a loss?
b. between 0 and 6?
c. greater than 10?

If you selected a random sample of 10 funds from this population, what is the probability that the sample would have a mean return

d. less than 0, that is, a loss?
e. between 0 and 6?
f. greater than 10?
g. Compare your results in parts (d) through (f) to (a) through (c).
h. Compare your results in parts (d) through (f) to problem 7.82 (a) through (c).

7.84 Political polling has traditionally used telephone interviews. Researchers at Harris Black International Ltd. argue that Internet polling is less expensive, faster, and offers higher response rates than telephone surveys. Critics are concerned about the scientific reliability of this approach (*The Wall Street Journal*, April 13, 1999). Even amid this strong criticism, Internet polling is becoming more and more common. What concerns, if any, do you have about Internet polling?

7.85 A study by Rajesh Mirani and Albert Lederer ("An Instrument for Accessing the Organizational Benefits of IS Projects," *Decision Sciences*, vol. 29, 1998, 803–838) discusses the organizational benefits of information systems (IS) projects. The researchers mailed 936 questionnaires to randomly selected members of a large nationwide information systems organization. Two hundred valid responses were received, for a response rate of 21%. Of the 200 respondents, 190 answered questions concerning a recently completed IS project. The average budget for these projects was $3.8 million with a range of $4,000 to $100 million. Of these 190 responses, 45% indicated that the CEO was required to give approval before starting the projects.

a. What was the source of the data used in this study?

b. Discuss the sampling method used in this study.

c. What types of survey errors do you think the researchers are most likely to encounter?

7.86 As part of a mediation process overseen by a federal judge to end a lawsuit that accuses Cincinnati, Ohio, of decades of discrimination against African Americans, surveys on how to improve Cincinnati police–community relations were taken. One survey was sent to the 1,020 members of the Cincinnati police force. The survey included a cover letter encouraging participation by the chief of police and president of the Fraternal Order of Police. Respondents could either return a hard copy of the survey or complete the survey online. To the researchers' dismay, only 158 surveys were completed ("Few Cops Fill Out Survey," *The Cincinnati Enquirer*, August 22, 2001, B3).

a. What type of errors or biases should the researchers be especially concerned with?

b. What step(s) should the researchers take to try to overcome the problems noted in (a)?

c. What could have been done differently to improve the survey's worthiness?

7.87 According to a survey conducted by International Communications Research for Capital One Financial, 24% of teens ages 13 to 19 own a cell phone and 10% own a beeper ("USA Snapshots," *USA Today*, August 16, 2001, A1).

a. What other information would you want to know before you accepted the results of this survey?

b. Suppose that you wished to conduct a similar survey for the geographic region you live in. Describe the population for your survey.

c. Explain how you could minimize the chance of a coverage error in this type of survey.

d. Explain how you could minimize the chance of a nonresponse error in this type of survey.

e. Explain how you could minimize the chance of a sampling error in this type of survey.

f. Explain how you could minimize the chance of a measurement error in this type of survey.

7.88 According to Dr. Sarah Beth Estes, sociology professor at the University of Cincinnati, and Dr. Jennifer Glass, sociology professor at the University of Iowa, working women who take advantage of family-friendly schedules can fall behind in wages. More specifically, the sociologists report that in a study of 300 working women who had children and returned to work and opted for flextime, telecommuting, and so on, these women had pay raises that averaged between 16% and 26% less than other workers ("Study: 'Face Time' Can Affect Moms' Raises," *The Cincinnati Enquirer*, August 28, 2001, A1).

a. What other information would you want to know before you accepted the results of this survey?

b. If you were to perform a similar study in the geographic area where you live, define a population, frame, and sampling method you could use.

7.89 (**Class Project**) The table of random numbers is an example of a uniform distribution because each digit is equally likely to occur. Starting in the row corresponding to the day of the month in which you were born, use the table of random numbers (Table E.1) to take one digit at a time.

Select five different samples of $n = 2$, $n = 5$, and $n = 10$. Compute the sample mean of each sample. Develop a frequency distribution of the sample means for the results of the entire class based on samples of sizes $n = 2$, $n = 5$, and $n = 10$.

What can be said about the shape of the sampling distribution for each of these sample sizes?

7.90 (**Class Project**) Toss a coin 10 times and record the number of heads. If each student performs this experiment five times, a frequency distribution of the number of heads can be developed from the results of the entire class. Does this distribution seem to approximate the normal distribution?

7.91 (**Class Project**) The number of cars waiting in line at a car wash is distributed as follows:

Number of Cars	Probability
0	0.25
1	0.40
2	0.20
3	0.10
4	0.04
5	0.01

You can use the table of random numbers (Table E.1) to select samples from this distribution by assigning numbers for the waiting line length as follows:

1. Start in the row corresponding to the day of the month in which you were born.
2. Select a two-digit random number.
3. If you select a random number from 00 to 24, record a length of 0; if from 25 to 64, record a length of 1; if from 65 to 84, record a length of 2; if from 85 to 94, record a length of 3; if from 95 to 98, record a length of 4; if it is 99, record a length of 5.

Select samples of $n = 2$, $n = 5$, and $n = 10$. Compute the mean for each sample. For example, if a sample of size 2 results in random numbers 18 and 46, these would correspond to waiting line lengths of 0 and 1, respectively, producing a sample mean of 0.5. If each student selects five different samples for each sample size, a frequency distribution of the sample means (for each sample size) can be developed from the results of the entire class. What con-clusions can you reach concerning the sampling distribution of the mean as the sample size is increased?

7.92 (Class Project) The table of random numbers can simulate the selection of different colored balls from a bowl as follows:

1. Start in the row corresponding to the day of the month in which you were born.
2. Select one-digit numbers.
3. If a random digit between 0 and 6 is selected, consider the ball white; if a random digit is a 7, 8, or 9, consider the ball red.

Select samples of $n = 10$, $n = 25$, and $n = 50$ digits. In each sample, count the number of white balls and compute the proportion of white balls in the sample. If each student in the class selects five different samples for each sample size, a frequency distribution of the proportion of white balls (for each sample size) can be developed from the results of the entire class. What conclusions can you reach about the sampling distribution of the proportion as the sample size is increased?

7.93 (Class Project) Suppose that step 3 of problem 7.92 uses the following rule: "If a random digit between 0 and 8 is selected, consider the ball to be white; if a random digit of 9 is selected, consider the ball to be red." Compare and contrast the results in this problem and in problem 7.92.

RUNNING CASE
MANAGING THE *SPRINGVILLE HERALD*

Continuing its quality improvement effort first described in the Chapter 6 "Managing the Springville Herald" case, the production department of the newspaper has been monitoring the blackness of the newspaper print. As before, blackness is measured on a standard scale in which the target value is 1.0. Data collected over the past year indicate that the blackness is normally distributed with a mean of 1.005 and a standard deviation of 0.10.

SH7.1 Each day, 25 spots on the first newspaper printed are chosen and the blackness of the spots is measured. Assuming that the distribution has not changed from what it was in the past year, what is the probability that the mean blackness of the spots is:

a. less than 1.0?
b. between 0.95 and 1.0?
c. between 1.0 and 1.05?
d. less than 0.95 or greater than 1.05?
e. Suppose that the mean blackness of today's sample of 25 spots is 0.952. What conclusion can you make about the blackness of the newspaper based on this result? Explain.

WEB CASE

Apply your knowledge about sampling distributions in this Web case that reconsiders the Oxford Cereals "Using Statistics" scenario.

The TriCities Consumers Concerned About Cereal Companies That Cheat organization (TCCACCTC) suspects that cereal companies, including Oxford Cereals, are cheating consumers by packaging cereals at less than labeled weights. Visit the organization's Web site **www.prenhall.com/Springville/CerealCheaters.htm**, examine their claims and supporting data and then answer the following:

1. Are the data collection procedures used by the TCCACCTC to form its conclusions flawed? What procedures could the group follow to make their analysis more rigorous?
2. Assume that the two samples of five cereal boxes (one sample for each of two cereal varieties) listed on the TCCACCTC Web site were collected randomly by organization members. For each sample, do the following:

a. Calculate the sample mean.
b. Assume the standard deviation of the process is 15 grams. Calculate the percentage of all samples for each process that would have a sample mean less than the value you calculated in step (a).
c. Again, assuming the standard deviation is 15 grams, calculate the percentage of individual boxes of cereal that would have a weight less than the value you calculated in step (a).

3. What, if any, conclusions can you form using your calculations about the filling processes of the two different cereals?
4. A representative from Oxford Cereals has asked that the TCCACCTC take down its page discussing shortages in boxes of Oxford Cereals. Is that request reasonable? Why, or why not?
5. Can the techniques of this chapter be used to prove cheating in the manner alleged by the TCCACCTC? Why, or why not?

REFERENCES

1. Cochran, W. G., *Sampling Techniques*, 3rd ed. (New York: Wiley, 1977).
2. Gallup, G. H., *The Sophisticated Poll-Watcher's Guide* (Princeton, NJ: Princeton Opinion Press, 1972).
3. Goleman, D., "Pollsters Enlist Psychologists in Quest for Unbiased Results," *The New York Times*, September 7, 1993, C1 and C11.
4. Levine, D. M., P. Ramsey, and R. Smidt, *Applied Statistics for Engineers and Scientists Using Microsoft Excel and Minitab* (Upper Saddle River, NJ: Prentice Hall, 2001).
5. *Microsoft Excel 2003* (Redmond, WA: Microsoft Corp., 2003).
6. *Minitab for Windows Version 14* (State College, PA: Minitab Inc., 2004).
7. Mosteller, F., et al., *The Pre-Election Polls of 1948* (New York: Social Science Research Council, 1949).
8. Rand Corporation, *A Million Random Digits with 100,000 Normal Deviates* (New York: The Free Press, 1955).

CHAPTER 8

Confidence Interval Estimation

USING STATISTICS: Auditing Sales Invoices at the Saxon Home Improvement Company

LEARNING OBJECTIVES

In this chapter, you learn:

- To construct and interpret confidence interval estimates for the mean and the proportion

- How to determine the sample size necessary to develop a confidence interval for the mean or proportion

USING STATISTICS

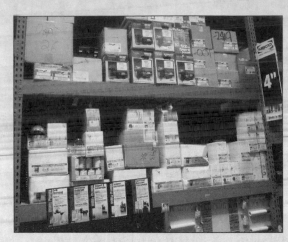

Auditing Sales Invoices at the Saxon Home Improvement Company

Saxon Home Improvement Company distributes home improvement supplies in the northeastern United States. As a company accountant, you are responsible for the accuracy of the integrated inventory management and sales information system. You could review the contents of each and every record to check the accuracy of this system, but such a detailed review would be time-consuming and costly. A better approach is to use statistical inference techniques to draw conclusions about the population of all records from a relatively small sample collected during an audit. At the end of each month, you can select a sample of the sales invoices to determine the following:

- The mean dollar amount listed on the sales invoices for the month.
- The proportion of sales invoices that contain errors.

How accurate are the results from the samples and how do you use this information? Are the sample sizes large enough to give you the information you need?

Statistical inference is the process of using sample results to draw conclusions about the characteristics of a population. Inferential statistics enables you to *estimate* unknown population characteristics such as a population mean or a population proportion. There are two types of estimates used to estimate population parameters: point estimates and interval estimates. A **point estimate** is the value of a single sample statistic. A **confidence interval estimate** is a range of numbers, called an interval, constructed around the point estimate. The confidence interval is constructed such that the probability the population parameter is located somewhere within the interval is known.

Suppose that you would like to estimate the mean GPA of all the students in your university. The mean GPA for all the students is an unknown population mean, denoted by μ. You select a sample of students and find that the sample mean is 2.80. The sample mean $\bar{X} = 2.80$ is a point estimate of the population mean μ. How accurate is 2.80? To answer this question you must construct a confidence interval estimate.

In this chapter you will learn how to construct and interpret confidence interval estimates. Recall that the sample mean $\bar{X}$ is a point estimate of the population mean μ. However, the sample mean will vary from sample to sample because it depends on the items selected in the sample. By taking into account the known variability from sample to sample (see section 7.2 on the sampling distribution of the mean), you will learn how to develop the interval estimate for the population mean. The interval constructed will have a specified confidence of correctly estimating the value of the population parameter μ. In other words, there is a specified confidence that μ is somewhere in the range of numbers defined by the interval.

Suppose that after studying this chapter, you find that a 95% confidence interval for the mean GPA at your university is $(2.75 \leq \mu \leq 2.85)$. You can interpret this interval estimate by stating that you are 95% confident that the mean GPA at your university is between 2.75 and 2.85. There is a 5% chance that the mean GPA is below 2.75 or above 2.85.

After learning about the confidence interval for the mean, you will learn how to develop an interval estimate for the population proportion. Then you will learn how large a sample to select when constructing confidence intervals.

8.1 CONFIDENCE INTERVAL ESTIMATION FOR THE MEAN (σ KNOWN)

In section 7.2 you used the Central Limit Theorem and knowledge of the population distribution to determine the percentage of sample means that fall within certain distances of the population mean. For instance, in the cereal-filling example used throughout Chapter 7, 95% of all sample means are between 362.12 and 373.88 grams. This statement is based on *deductive reasoning*. However, *inductive reasoning* is what you need here.

You need inductive reasoning because, in statistical inference, you use the results of a single sample to draw conclusions about the population, not vice versa. Suppose that in the cereal-fill example, you wish to estimate the unknown population mean using the information from only a sample. Thus, rather than take $\mu \pm (1.96)(\sigma/\sqrt{n})$ to find the upper and lower limits around μ as in section 7.2, you substitute the sample mean $\overline{X}$ for the unknown μ and use $\overline{X} \pm (1.96)(\sigma/\sqrt{n})$ as an interval to estimate the unknown μ. Although in practice you select a single sample of size n and compute the mean $\overline{X}$, in order to understand the full meaning of the interval estimate, you need to examine a hypothetical set of all possible samples of n values.

Suppose that a sample of $n = 25$ boxes has a mean of 362.3 grams. The interval developed to estimate μ is $362.3 \pm (1.96)(15)/(\sqrt{25})$ or 362.3 ± 5.88. The estimate of μ is

$$356.42 \leq \mu \leq 368.18$$

Because the population mean μ (equal to 368) is included within the interval, this sample has led to a correct statement about μ (see Figure 8.1 below).

FIGURE 8.1

Confidence Interval Estimates for Five Different Samples of $n = 25$ Taken from a Population Where $\mu = 368$ and $\sigma = 15$

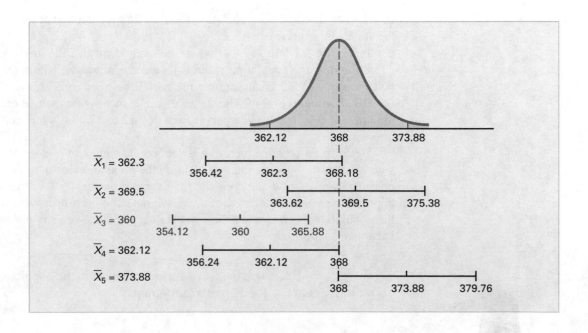

To continue this hypothetical example, suppose that for a different sample of $n = 25$ boxes, the mean is 369.5. The interval developed from this sample is

$$369.5 \pm (1.96)(15)/(\sqrt{25})$$

or 369.5 ± 5.88. The estimate is

$$363.62 \leq \mu \leq 375.38$$

Because the population mean μ (equal to 368) is also included within this interval, this statement about μ is correct.

Now, before you begin to think that correct statements about μ are always made by developing a confidence interval estimate, suppose a third hypothetical sample of $n = 25$ boxes is selected and the sample mean is equal to 360 grams. The interval developed here is $360 \pm (1.96)(15)/(\sqrt{25})$ or 360 ± 5.88. In this case, the estimate of μ is

$$354.12 < \mu < 365.88$$

This estimate is *not* a correct statement, because the population mean μ is not included in the interval developed from this sample (see Figure 8.1). Thus, for some samples the interval estimate of μ is correct, but for others it is incorrect. In practice, only one sample is selected, and because the population mean is unknown, you cannot determine whether the interval estimate is correct.

To resolve this dilemma of sometimes having an interval that provides a correct estimate and sometimes having an interval that provides an incorrect estimate, you need to determine the proportion of samples producing intervals that result in correct statements about the population mean μ. To do this, consider two other hypothetical samples: the case in which $\overline{X} = 362.12$ grams and the case in which $\overline{X} = 373.88$ grams. If $\overline{X} = 362.12$, the interval is $362.12 \pm (1.96)(15)/(\sqrt{25})$ or 362.12 ± 5.88. This leads to the following interval

$$356.24 \leq \mu \leq 368.00$$

Because the population mean of 368 is at the upper limit of the interval, the statement is a correct one (see Figure 8.1).

When $\overline{X} = 373.88$, the interval is $373.88 \pm (1.96)(15)/(\sqrt{25})$ or 373.88 ± 5.88. The interval for the sample mean is

$$368.00 \leq \mu \leq 379.76$$

In this case, because the population mean of 368 is included at the lower limit of the interval, the statement is correct.

In Figure 8.1 you see that when the sample mean falls anywhere between 362.12 and 373.88 grams, the population mean is included *somewhere* within the interval. In section 7.2, you found that 95% of the sample means fall between 362.12 and 373.88 grams. Therefore, 95% of all samples of $n = 25$ boxes have sample means that include the population mean within the interval developed. The interval from 362.12 to 373.88 is referred to as a 95% confidence interval.

Because, in practice, you only select one sample and μ is unknown, you never know for sure whether the specific interval includes the population mean or not. However, if you take all possible samples of n and compute their sample means, 95% of the intervals will include the population mean and only 5% of them will not. In other words, you have 95% confidence that the population mean is somewhere in the interval. Thus, you can interpret the confidence interval above as follows:

"I am 95% confident that the mean amount of cereal in the population of boxes is somewhere between 362.12 and 373.88 grams."

In some situations, you might want a higher degree of confidence (such as 99%) of including the population mean within the interval. In other cases, you might accept less confidence (such as 90%) of correctly estimating the population mean.

In general, the **level of confidence** is symbolized by $(1 - \alpha) \times 100\%$, where α is the proportion in the tails of the distribution that is outside the confidence interval. The proportion in the upper tail of the distribution is $\alpha/2$, and the proportion in the lower tail of the distribution is $\alpha/2$. You use Equation (8.1) to construct a $(1 - \alpha) \times 100\%$ confidence interval estimate of the mean with σ known.

CONFIDENCE INTERVAL FOR A MEAN (σ KNOWN)

$$X \pm Z \frac{\sigma}{\sqrt{n}}$$

or

$$\bar{X} - Z \frac{\sigma}{\sqrt{n}} \leq \mu \leq \bar{X} + Z \frac{\sigma}{\sqrt{n}} \tag{8.1}$$

where Z = the value corresponding to a cumulative area of $1 - \alpha/2$ from the standardized normal distribution, that is, an upper-tail probability of $\alpha/2$.

The value of Z needed for constructing a confidence interval is called the **critical value** for the distribution. 95% confidence corresponds to an α value of 0.05. The critical Z value corresponding to a cumulative area of 0.9750 is 1.96 because there is 0.025 in the upper tail of the distribution and the cumulative area less than $Z = 1.96$ is 0.975.

There is a different critical value for each level of confidence $1 - \alpha$. A level of confidence of 95% leads to a Z value of 1.96 (see Figure 8.2). 99% confidence corresponds to an α value of 0.01. The Z value is approximately 2.58 because the upper-tail area is 0.005 and the cumulative area less than $Z = 2.58$ is 0.995 (see Figure 8.3).

FIGURE 8.2

Normal Curve for Determining the Z Value Needed for 95% Confidence

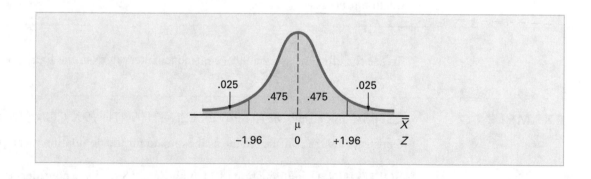

FIGURE 8.3

Normal Curve for Determining the Z Value Needed for 99% Confidence

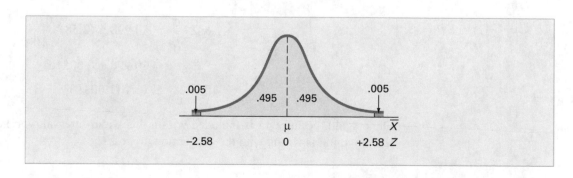

Now that various levels of confidence have been considered, why not make the confidence level as close to 100% as possible? Before doing so, you need to realize that any increase in the level of confidence is achieved only by widening (and making less precise) the confidence interval. There is no "free lunch" here. You would have more confidence that the population mean is within a broader range of values. However, this might make the interpretation of the confidence interval less useful. The trade-off between the width of the confidence interval and the level of confidence is discussed in greater depth in the context of determining the sample size in section 8.4.

Example 8.1 illustrates the application of the confidence interval estimate.

EXAMPLE 8.1

ESTIMATING THE MEAN PAPER LENGTH WITH 95% CONFIDENCE

A manufacturer of computer paper has a production process that operates continuously throughout an entire production shift. The paper is expected to have a mean length of 11 inches and the standard deviation of the length is 0.02 inch. At periodic intervals, a sample is selected to determine whether the mean paper length is still equal to 11 inches or whether something has gone wrong in the production process to change the length of the paper produced. You select a random sample of 100 sheets, and the mean paper length is 10.998 inches. Construct a 95% confidence interval estimate for the population mean paper length.

SOLUTION Using Equation (8.1), with $Z = 1.96$ for 95% confidence,

$$\bar{X} \pm Z \frac{\sigma}{\sqrt{n}} = 10.998 \pm (1.96) \frac{0.02}{\sqrt{100}}$$

$$= 10.998 \pm 0.00392$$

$$10.99408 \le \mu \le 11.00192$$

Thus, with 95% confidence, you conclude that the population mean is between 10.99408 and 11.00192 inches. Because the interval includes 11, the value indicating that the production process is working properly, you have no reason to believe that anything is wrong with the production process.

To see the effect of using a 99% confidence interval, examine Example 8.2

EXAMPLE 8.2

ESTIMATING THE MEAN PAPER LENGTH WITH 99% CONFIDENCE

Construct a 99% confidence interval estimate for the population mean paper length.

SOLUTION Using Equation (8.1), with $Z = 2.58$ for 99% confidence,

$$\bar{X} \pm Z \frac{\sigma}{\sqrt{n}} = 10.998 \pm (2.58) \frac{0.02}{\sqrt{100}}$$

$$= 10.998 \pm 0.00516$$

$$10.99284 \le \mu \le 11.00316$$

Once again, because 11 is included within this wider interval, you have no reason to believe that anything is wrong with the production process.

PROBLEMS FOR SECTION 8.1

Learning the Basics

 8.1 If $\bar{X} = 85$, $\sigma = 8$, and $n = 64$, construct a 95% confidence interval estimate of the population mean μ.

 8.2 If $\bar{X} - 125$, $\sigma = 24$, and $n = 36$, construct a 99% confidence interval estimate of the population mean μ.

8.3 A market researcher states that she has 95% confidence that the mean monthly sales of a product are between $170,000 and $200,000. Explain the meaning of this statement.

8.4 Why is it not possible in Example 8.1 to have 100% confidence? Explain.

8.5 From the results of Example 8.1 regarding paper production, is it true that 95% of the sample means will fall between 10.99408 and 11.00192 inches? Explain.

8.6 Is it true in Example 8.1 that you do not know for sure whether the population mean is between 10.99408 and 11.00192 inches? Explain.

Applying the Concepts

 8.7 The manager of a paint supply store wants to estimate the actual amount of paint contained in 1-gallon cans purchased from a nationally known manufacturer. It is known from the manufacturer's specifications that the standard deviation of the amount of paint is equal to 0.02 gallon. A random sample of 50 cans is selected, and the sample mean amount of paint per 1-gallon can is 0.995 gallon.
a. Construct a 99% confidence interval estimate of the population mean amount of paint included in a 1-gallon can.
b. On the basis of your results, do you think that the manager has a right to complain to the manufacturer? Why?

c. Must you assume that the population amount of paint per can is normally distributed here? Explain.
d. Construct a 95% confidence interval estimate. How does this change your answer to (b)?

  8.8 The quality control manager at a lightbulb factory needs to estimate the mean life of a large shipment of light bulbs. The standard deviation is 100 hours. A random sample of 64 lightbulbs indicated a sample mean life of 350 hours.
a. Construct a 95% confidence interval estimate of the population mean life of lightbulbs in this shipment.
b. Do you think that the manufacturer has the right to state that the lightbulbs last an average of 400 hours? Explain.
c. Must you assume that the population of lightbulb life is normally distributed? Explain.
d. Suppose that the standard deviation changed to 80 hours. What are your answers in (a) and (b)?

 8.9 The inspection division of the Lee County Weights and Measures Department wants to estimate the actual amount of soft drink in 2-liter bottles at the local bottling plant of a large nationally known soft-drink company. The bottling plant has informed the inspection division that the population standard deviation for 2-liter bottles is 0.05 liter. A random sample of 100 2-liter bottles at this bottling plant indicates a sample mean of 1.99 liters.
a. Construct a 95% confidence interval estimate of the population mean amount of soft drink in each bottle.
b. Must you assume that the population of soft-drink fill is normally distributed? Explain.
c. Explain why a value of 2.02 liters for a single bottle is not unusual, even though it is outside the confidence interval you calculated.
d. Suppose that the sample mean had been 1.97 liters. What is your answer to (a)?

8.2 CONFIDENCE INTERVAL ESTIMATION FOR THE MEAN (σ UNKNOWN)

Just as the mean of the population μ is usually unknown, you rarely know the actual standard deviation of the population σ. Therefore, you need to develop a confidence interval estimate of μ using only the sample statistics $\bar{X}$ and S.

Student's t Distribution

At the beginning of the twentieth century, a statistician for Guinness Breweries in Ireland (see reference 3) named William S. Gosset wanted to make inferences about the mean when σ was unknown. Because Guinness employees were not permitted to publish research work under their own names, Gosset adopted the pseudonym "Student." The distribution that he developed is known as **Student's t distribution**.

If the random variable X is normally distributed, then the following statistic has a t distribution with $n - 1$ **degrees of freedom**:

$$t = \frac{\overline{X} - \mu}{\frac{S}{\sqrt{n}}}$$

This expression has the same form as the Z statistic in Equation (7.4), except that S is used to estimate the unknown σ. The concept of *degrees of freedom* is discussed further on page 235.

Properties of the t Distribution

In appearance, the t distribution is very similar to the standardized normal distribution. Both distributions are bell-shaped. However, the t distribution has more area in the tails and less in the center than does the standardized normal distribution (see Figure 8.4). Because the value of σ is unknown and S is used to estimate it, the values of t are more variable than for Z.

FIGURE 8.4

Standardized Normal Distribution and t Distribution for 5 Degrees of Freedom

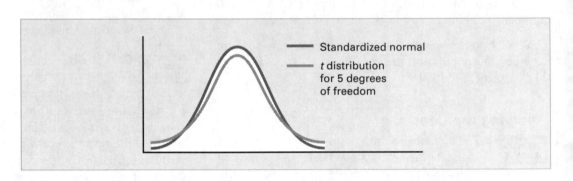

The degrees of freedom $n - 1$ are directly related to the sample size n. As the sample size and degrees of freedom increase, S becomes a better estimate of σ and the t distribution gradually approaches the standardized normal distribution until the two are virtually identical. With a sample size of about 120 or more, S estimates σ precisely enough that there is little difference between the t and Z distributions. For this reason, most statisticians use Z instead of t when the sample size is greater than 120.

As stated earlier, the t distribution assumes that the random variable X is normally distributed. In practice, however, as long as the sample size is large enough and the population is not very skewed, you can use the t distribution to estimate the population mean when σ is unknown. When dealing with a small sample size and a skewed population distribution, the validity of the confidence interval is a concern. To assess the assumption of normality, you can evaluate the shape of the sample data by using a histogram, stem-and-leaf display, box-and-whisker plot, or normal probability plot.

You find the critical values of t for the appropriate degrees of freedom from the table of the t distribution (see Table E.3). The columns of the table represent the area in the upper tail of the t distribution. Each row represents the particular t value for each specific degree of freedom. For example, with 99 degrees of freedom, if you want 95% confidence, you find the appropriate value of t as shown in Table 8.1. The 95% confidence level means that 2.5% of the values (an area of .025) are in each tail of the distribution. Looking in the column for an upper-tail area of .025 and in the row corresponding to 99 degrees of freedom, gives you a critical value for t of 1.9842. Because t is a symmetrical distribution with a mean of 0, if the upper-tail value is +1.9842, the value for the lower-tail area (lower .025) is −1.9842. A t value of −1.9842 means that the probability that t is less than −1.9842 is 0.025, or 2.5% (see Figure 8.5).

TABLE 8.1

Determining the Critical Value from the *t* Table for an Area of 0.025 in Each Tail with 99 Degrees of Freedom

Degrees of Freedom	Upper-Tail Areas					
	.25	.10	.05	.025	.01	.005
1	1.0000	3.0777	6.3138	12.7062	31.8207	63.6574
2	0.8165	1.8856	2.9200	4.3027	6.9646	9.9248
3	0.7649	1.6377	2.3534	3.1824	4.5407	5.8409
4	0.7407	1.5332	2.1318	2.7764	3.7469	4.6041
5	0.7267	1.4759	2.0150	2.5706	3.3649	4.0322
.	.	.	.	.	.	.
.	.	.	.	.	.	.
.	.	.	.	.	.	.
96	0.6771	1.2904	1.6609	1.9850	2.3658	2.6280
97	0.6770	1.2903	1.6607	1.9847	2.3654	2.6275
98	0.6770	1.2902	1.6606	1.9845	2.3650	2.6269
99	0.6770	1.2902	1.6604	1.9842	2.3646	2.6264
100	0.6770	1.2901	1.6602	1.9840	2.3642	2.6259

Source: Extracted from Table E.3.

FIGURE 8.5

t Distribution with 99 Degrees of Freedom

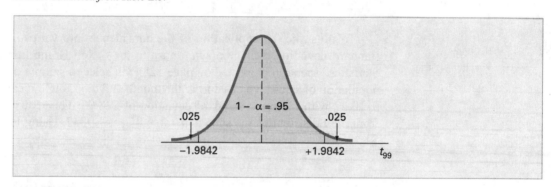

The Concept of Degrees of Freedom

In Chapter 3 you learned that the numerator of the sample variance S^2 requires the computation of

$$\sum_{i=1}^{n}(X_i - \overline{X})^2$$

In order to compute S^2, you first need to know $\overline{X}$. Therefore, only $n-1$ of the sample values are free to vary. This means that you have $n-1$ degrees of freedom. For example, suppose a sample of five values has a mean of 20. How many values do you need to know before you can determine the remainder of the values? The fact that $n = 5$ and $\overline{X} = 20$ also tells you that

$$\sum_{i=1}^{n} X_i = 100$$

because

$$\frac{\sum_{i=1}^{n} X_i}{n} = \overline{X}$$

Thus, when you know four of the values, the fifth one will *not* be free to vary because the sum must add to 100. For example, if four of the values are 18, 24, 19, and 16, the fifth value must be 23 so that the sum equals 100.

The Confidence Interval Statement

Equation (8.2) defines the $(1 - \alpha) \times 100\%$ confidence interval estimate for the mean with σ unknown.

CONFIDENCE INTERVAL FOR THE MEAN (σ UNKNOWN)

$$\bar{X} \pm t_{n-1} \frac{S}{\sqrt{n}}$$

or

$$\bar{X} - t_{n-1} \frac{S}{\sqrt{n}} \leq \mu \leq \bar{X} + t_{n-1} \frac{S}{\sqrt{n}} \tag{8.2}$$

where t_{n-1} is the critical value of the t distribution with $n - 1$ degrees of freedom for an area of $\alpha/2$ in the upper tail.

To illustrate the application of the confidence interval estimate for the mean when the standard deviation σ is unknown, return to the Saxon Home Improvement Company "Using Statistics" scenario presented on page 228. You select a sample of 100 sales invoices from the population of sales invoices during the month and the sample mean of the 100 sales invoices is $110.27 with a sample standard deviation of $28.95. For 95% confidence, the critical value from the t distribution (as shown in Table 8.1) is 1.9842. Using Equation (8.2),

$$\bar{X} \pm t_{n-1} \frac{S}{\sqrt{n}}$$

$$= 110.27 \pm (1.9842) \frac{28.95}{\sqrt{100}}$$

$$= 110.27 \pm 5.74$$

$$\$104.53 \leq \mu \leq \$116.01$$

A Microsoft Excel worksheet for these data is presented in Figure 8.6.

FIGURE 8.6

Microsoft Excel Worksheet to Compute a Confidence Interval Estimate for the Mean Sales Invoice Amount for the Saxon Home Improvement Company

	A	B	
1	Estimate for the Mean Sales Invoice Amount		
2			
3	Data		
4	Sample Standard Deviation	28.95	
5	Sample Mean	110.27	
6	Sample Size	100	
7	Confidence Level	95%	
8			
9	Intermediate Calculations		
10	Standard Error of the Mean	2.8950	=B4/SQRT(B6)
11	Degrees of Freedom	99	=B6 - 1
12	t Value	1.9842	=TINV(1-B7,B11)
13	Interval Half Width	5.7443	=B12 * B10
14			
15	Confidence Interval		
16	Interval Lower Limit	104.53	=B5 - B13
17	Interval Upper Limit	116.01	=B5 + B13

Thus, with 95% confidence, you conclude that the mean amount of all the sales invoices is between $104.53 and $116.01. The 95% confidence level indicates that if you selected all possible samples of 100 (something that is never done in practice), 95% of the intervals developed would include the population mean somewhere within the interval. The validity of this confidence interval estimate depends on the assumption of normality for the distribution of the amount of the sales invoices. With a sample of 100, the normality assumption is not overly restrictive and the use of the *t* distribution is likely appropriate. Example 8.3 further illustrates how you construct the confidence interval for a mean when the population standard deviation is unknown.

EXAMPLE 8.3

ESTIMATING THE MEAN FORCE REQUIRED TO BREAK ELECTRIC INSULATORS

A manufacturing company produces electric insulators. If the insulators break when in use, you are likely to have a short circuit. To test the strength of the insulators, you carry out destructive testing to determine how much *force* is required to break the insulators. You measure force by observing how many pounds are applied to the insulator before it breaks. Table 8.2 lists thirty values from this experiment. FORCE Construct a 95% confidence interval estimate for the population mean force required to break the insulator.

TABLE 8.2

Force (in Pounds) Required to Break the Insulator

1,870	1,728	1,656	1,610	1,634	1,784	1,522	1,696	1,592	1,662
1,866	1,764	1,734	1,662	1,734	1,774	1,550	1,756	1,762	1,866
1,820	1,744	1,788	1,688	1,810	1,752	1,680	1,810	1,652	1,736

SOLUTION

Figure 8.7 shows that the sample mean is $\bar{X} = 1,723.4$ pounds and the sample standard deviation is $S = 89.55$ pounds. Using Equation (8.2) to construct the confidence interval, you need to determine the critical value from the *t* table for an area of 0.025 in each tail with 29 degrees of freedom. From Table E.3, you see that $t_{29} = 2.0452$. Thus, using $\bar{X} = 1,723.4$, $S = 89.55$, $n = 30$, and $t_{29} = 2.0452$,

$$\bar{X} \pm t_{n-1}\frac{S}{\sqrt{n}}$$

$$= 1,723.4 \pm (2.0452)\frac{89.55}{\sqrt{30}}$$

$$= 1,723.4 \pm 33.44$$

$$1,689.96 \leq \mu \leq 1,756.84$$

FIGURE 8.7

Minitab Confidence Interval Estimate for the Mean Amount of Force Required to Break Electric Insulators

One-Sample T: Force

Variable	N	Mean	StDev	SE Mean	95% CI
Force	30	1723.40	89.55	16.35	(1689.96, 1756.84)

You conclude with 95% confidence that the mean force required for the population of insulators is between 1,689.96 and 1,756.84 pounds. The validity of this confidence interval estimate depends on the assumption that the force required is normally distributed. Remember, however, that you can slightly relax this assumption for large sample sizes. Thus, with a sample of 30, you can use the *t* distribution even if the amount of force required is slightly skewed. From the normal probability plot displayed in Figure 8.8 or the box-and-whisker plot displayed in Figure 8.9, the amount of force required appears slightly skewed. Thus, the *t* distribution is appropriate for these data.

FIGURE 8.8

Minitab Normal Probability Plot for the Amount of Force Required to Break Electric Insulators

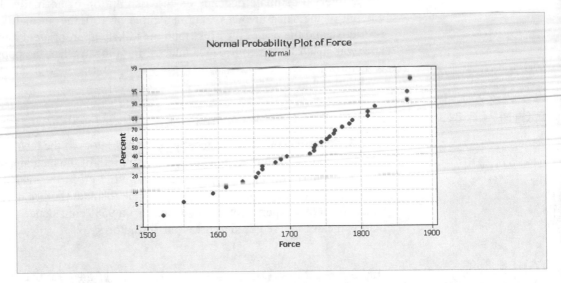

FIGURE 8.9

Minitab Box-and-Whisker Plot for the Amount of Force Required to Break Electric Insulators

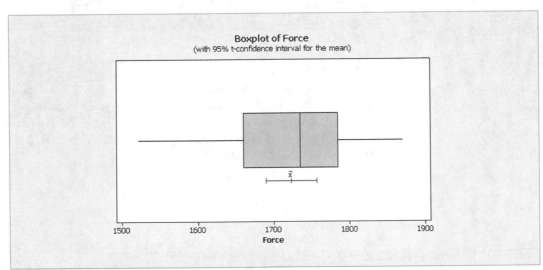

PROBLEMS FOR SECTION 8.2

Learning the Basics

8.10 Determine the critical value of *t* in each of the following circumstances:

a. $1 - \alpha = 0.95$, $n = 10$.
b. $1 - \alpha = 0.99$, $n = 10$.
c. $1 - \alpha = 0.95$, $n = 32$.
d. $1 - \alpha = 0.95$, $n = 65$.
e. $1 - \alpha = 0.90$, $n = 16$.

8.11 If $\overline{X} = 75$, $S = 24$, $n = 36$, and assuming that the population is normally distributed, construct a 95% confidence interval estimate of the population mean μ.

8.12 If $\overline{X} = 50$, $S = 15$, $n = 16$, and assuming that the population is normally distributed, construct a 99% confidence interval estimate of the population mean μ.

8.13 Construct a 95% confidence interval estimate for the population mean, based on each of the following sets of data, assuming that the population is normally distributed:

Set 1: 1, 1, 1, 1, 8, 8, 8, 8
Set 2: 1, 2, 3, 4, 5, 6, 7, 8

Explain why these data sets have different confidence intervals even though they have the same mean and range.

8.14 Construct a 95% confidence interval for the population mean, based on the numbers 1, 2, 3, 4, 5, 6, and 20. Change the number 20 to 7 and recalculate the confidence interval. Using these results, describe the effect of an outlier (i.e., extreme value) on the confidence interval.

Applying the Concepts

You can solve Problems 8.15–8.22 with or without Microsoft Excel, Minitab, or SPSS. You should use Microsoft Excel, Minitab, or SPSS to solve problem 8. 23.

  8.15 The owner of a stationery store wants to estimate the mean retail value of greeting cards that the store has in its inventory. A random sample of 20 greeting cards indicates a mean value of $1.67 and a standard deviation of $0.32.
a. Assuming a normal distribution, construct a 95% confidence interval estimate of the mean value of all greeting cards in the store's inventory.
b. How are the results in (a) useful in assisting the store owner to estimate the total value of her inventory?

8.16 Southside hospital in Bay Shore, New York, commonly conducts stress tests to study the heart muscle after a person has a heart attack. Members of the diagnostic imaging department conducted a quality improvement project to try to reduce the turnaround time for stress tests. Turnaround time is defined as the time from when the test is ordered to when the radiologist signs off on the test results. Initially the mean turnaround time for a stress test was 68 hours. After incorporating changes into the stress-test process, the quality improvement team collected a sample of 50 turnaround times. In this sample, the mean turnaround time was 32 hours with a standard deviation of 9 hours (Eric Godin, Dennis Raven, Carolyn Sweetapple, and Frank R. Del Guidice, "Faster Test Results," *Quality Progress*, January 2004, 37(1):33–39).
a. Construct a 95% confidence interval for the population mean turnaround time.
b. Interpret the interval constructed in (a)
c. Do you think the quality improvement project was a success? Explain.

 8.17 The U.S. Department of Transportation requires tire manufacturers to provide tire performance information on the sidewall of the tire to better inform prospective customers when making a purchasing decision. One very important measure of tire performance is the tread wear index, which indicates the tire's resistance to tread wear compared with a tire graded with a base of 100. This means that a tire with a grade of 200 should last twice as long, on average, as a tire graded with a base of 100. A consumer organization wants to estimate the actual tread wear index of a brand name of tires graded 200 that are produced by a certain manufacturer. A random sample of $n = 18$ indicates a sample mean tread wear index of 195.3 and a sample standard deviation of 21.4.

a. Assuming that the population of tread wear indices is normally distributed, construct a 95% confidence interval estimate of the population mean tread wear index for tires produced by this manufacturer under this brand name.
b. Do you think that the consumer organization should accuse the manufacturer of producing tires that do not meet the performance information provided on the sidewall of the tire? Explain.
c. Explain why an observed tread wear index of 210 for a particular tire is not unusual, even though it is outside the confidence interval developed in (a).

8.18 The following data represent the bounced check fee in dollars for a sample of 23 banks for direct-deposit customers who maintain a $100 balance. BANKCOST1

26	28	20	20	21	22	25	25	18	25	15	20
18	20	25	25	22	30	30	30	15	20	29	

Source: Extracted from "The New Face of Banking," Copyright © 2000 by Consumers Union of U.S. Inc., Yonkers, NY 10703–1057. Adapted with permission from Consumer Reports, June 2000.

a. Construct a 95% confidence interval for the population mean bounced check fee.
b. Interpret the interval constructed in (a)

8.19 The following data represent the monthly service fee in dollars if a customer's account falls below the minimum required $1,500 balance for a sample of 26 banks for direct-deposit customers. BANKCOST2

12	8	5	5	6	6	10	10	9	7	10	7	7
5	0	10	6	9	12	0	5	10	8	5	5	9

Source: Extracted from "The New Face of Banking," Copyright © 2000 by Consumers Union of U.S. Inc., Yonkers, NY 10703–1057. Adapted with permission from Consumer Reports, June 2000.

a. Construct a 95% confidence interval for the population mean monthly service fee in dollars if a customer's account falls below the minimum required balance.
b. Interpret the interval constructed in (a).

8.20 One of the major measures of the quality of service provided by any organization is the speed with which it responds to customer complaints. A large family-held department store selling furniture and flooring including carpeting had undergone a major expansion in the past several years. In particular, the flooring department had expanded from 2 installation crews to an installation supervisor, a measurer, and 15 installation crews. Last year there were 50 complaints concerning carpeting installation. The following data FURNITURE represent the number of days between the receipt of the complaint and the resolution of the complaint.

54	5	35	137	31	27	152	2	123	81	74	27
11	19	126	110	110	29	61	35	94	31	26	5
12	4	165	32	29	28	29	26	25	1	14	13
13	10	5	27	4	52	30	22	36	26	20	23
33	68										

a. Construct a 95% confidence interval estimate of the mean number of days between the receipt of the complaint and the resolution of the complaint.
b. What assumption must you make about the population distribution in (a)?
c. Do you think that the assumption made in (b) is seriously violated? Explain.
d. What effect might your conclusion in (c) have on the validity of the results in (a)?

8.21 In New York state, savings banks are permitted to sell a form of life insurance called Savings Bank Life Insurance (SBLI). The approval process consists of underwriting, which includes a review of the application, a medical information bureau check, possible requests for additional medical information and medical exams, and a policy compilation stage where the policy pages are generated and sent to the bank for delivery. The ability to deliver approved policies to customers in a timely manner is critical to the profitability of this service to the bank. During a period of 1 month, a random sample of 27 approved policies was selected INSURANCE and the total processing time in days recorded:

  73 19 16 64 28 28 31 90 60 56 31 56 22 18
  45 48 17 17 17 91 92 63 50 51 69 16 17

a. Construct a 95% confidence interval estimate of the mean processing time.
b. What assumption must you make about the population distribution in (a)?
c. Do you think that the assumption made in (b) is seriously violated? Explain.

8.22 The following data represent the daily hotel cost and rental car cost for 20 U.S. cities during a week in October 2003. HOTEL-CAR

City	Hotel	Cars
San Francisco	205	47
Los Angeles	179	41
Seattle	185	49
Phoenix	210	38
Denver	128	32
Dallas	145	48
Houston	177	49
Minneapolis	117	41
Chicago	221	56

City	Hotel	Cars
St. Louis	159	41
New Orleans	205	50
Detroit	128	32
Cleveland	165	34
Atlanta	180	46
Orlando	198	41
Miami	158	40
Pittsburgh	132	39
Boston	283	67
New York	269	69
Washington D.C.	204	40

Source: Extracted from the Wall Street Journal, *October 10, 2003, W4.*

a. Construct a 95% confidence interval for the population mean hotel rate.
b. Construct a 95% confidence interval for the population mean car rental rate.
c. What assumption do you need to make about the populations of interest to construct the intervals in (a) and (b)?
d. Given the data presented, do you think the assumption needed in (a) and (b) is valid? Explain.

8.23 One operation of a mill is to cut pieces of steel into parts that are used later in the frame for front seats in an automobile. The steel is cut with a diamond saw and requires the resulting parts to be within plus or minus 0.005 inch of the length specified by the automobile company. The measurement reported from a sample of 100 steel parts STEEL is the difference in inches between the actual length of the steel part as measured by a laser measurement device, and the specified length of the steel part. For example, the first observation, −0.002, represents a steel part that is 0.002 inch shorter than the specified length.
a. Construct a 95% confidence interval estimate of the mean difference between the actual length of the steel part, and the specified length of the steel part.
b. What assumption must you make about the population distribution in (a)?
c. Do you think that the assumption made in (b) is seriously violated? Explain.
d. Compare the conclusions reached in (a) with those of problem 2.26.

8.3 CONFIDENCE INTERVAL ESTIMATION FOR THE PROPORTION

This section extends the concept of the confidence interval to categorical data. Here you are concerned with estimating the proportion of items in a population having a certain characteristic of interest. The unknown population proportion is represented by the Greek letter π. The point estimate for π is the sample proportion, $p = X/n$, where n is the sample size and X is the number of items in the sample having the characteristic of interest. Equation (8.3) defines the confidence interval estimate for the population proportion.

CONFIDENCE INTERVAL ESTIMATE FOR THE PROPORTION

$$p \pm Z \sqrt{\frac{p(1-p)}{n}}$$

or

$$p - Z\sqrt{\frac{p(1-p)}{n}} \leq \pi \leq p + Z\sqrt{\frac{p(1-p)}{n}} \qquad (8.3)$$

where p = sample proportion $= \dfrac{X}{n} = \dfrac{\text{number of items having the characteristic}}{\text{sample size}}$

π = population proportion

Z = critical value from the standardized normal distribution

n = sample size

assuming both X and $n - X$ are greater than 5

You can use the confidence interval estimate of the proportion defined in Equation (8.3) to estimate the proportion of sales invoices that contain errors (see the "Using Statistics" scenario on page 228). Suppose that in a sample of 100 sales invoices, 10 contain errors. Thus, for these data, $p = X/n = 10/100 = 0.10$. Using Equation (8.3) and $Z = 1.96$ for 95% confidence,

$$p \pm Z\sqrt{\frac{p(1-p)}{n}}$$

$$= 0.10 \pm (1.96)\sqrt{\frac{(0.10)(0.90)}{100}}$$

$$= 0.10 \pm (1.96)(0.03)$$

$$= 0.10 \pm 0.0588$$

$$0.0412 \leq \pi \leq 0.1588$$

Therefore, you have 95% confidence that between 4.12% and 15.88% of all the sales invoices contain errors. Figure 8.10 shows a Microsoft Excel worksheet for these data, while Figure 8.11 illustrates Minitab output.

FIGURE 8.10

Microsoft Excel Worksheet to Form a Confidence Interval Estimate for the Proportion of Sales Invoices that Contain Errors

	A	B	
1	Proportion of In-Error Sales Invoices		
2			
3	Data		
4	Sample Size	100	
5	Number of Successes	10	
6	Confidence Level	95%	
7			
8	Intermediate Calculations		
9	Sample Proportion	0.1	=B5/B4
10	Z Value	-1.9600	=NORMSINV((1 - B6)/2)
11	Standard Error of the Proportion	0.03	=SQRT(B9 * (1 - B9)/B4)
12	Interval Half Width	0.0588	=ABS(B10 * B11)
13			
14	Confidence Interval		
15	Interval Lower Limit	0.0412	=B9 - B12
16	Interval Upper Limit	0.1588	=B9 + B12

```
Sample   X    N  Sample p         95% CI
1       10  100  0.100000  (0.041201, 0.158799)
```

FIGURE 8.11 Minitab Confidence Interval Estimate for the Proportion of Sales Invoices that Contain Errors

Example 8.4 illustrates another application of a confidence interval estimate for the proportion.

EXAMPLE 8.4

ESTIMATING THE PROPORTION OF NONCONFORMING NEWSPAPERS PRINTED

A newspaper publisher wants to estimate the proportion of newspapers printed that have a nonconforming attribute, such as excessive ruboff, improper page setup, missing pages, or duplicate pages. A random sample of 200 newspapers is selected from all the newspapers printed during a single day. For this sample of 200, 35 contain some type of nonconformance. Construct and interpret a 90% confidence interval for the proportion of newspapers printed during the day that have a nonconforming attribute.

SOLUTION Using Equation (8.3):

$$p = \frac{35}{200} = 0.175, \text{ and with a 90\% level of confidence } Z = 1.645$$

$$p \pm Z\sqrt{\frac{p(1-p)}{n}}$$

$$= 0.175 \pm (1.645)\sqrt{\frac{(0.175)(0.825)}{200}}$$

$$= 0.175 \pm (1.645)(0.0269)$$

$$= 0.175 \pm 0.0442$$

$$0.1308 \le \pi \le 0.2192$$

You conclude with 90% confidence that between 13.08% and 21.92% of the newspapers printed on that day have some type of nonconformance.

Equation (8.3) contains a Z statistic since you can use the normal distribution to approximate the binomial distribution when the sample size is sufficiently large. In Example 8.4, the confidence interval using Z provides an excellent approximation for the population proportion since both X and $n - X$ are greater than 5. However, if you do not have a sufficiently large sample size, then you should use the binomial distribution rather than Equation (8.3) (see references 1, 2, and 7). The exact confidence intervals for various sample sizes and proportions of successes have been tabulated by Fisher and Yates (reference 2) and can be computed using Minitab.

PROBLEMS FOR SECTION 8.3

Learning the Basics

 8.24 If $n = 200$ and $X = 50$, construct a 95% confidence interval estimate of the population proportion.

8.25 If $n = 400$ and $X = 25$, construct a 99% confidence interval estimate of the population proportion.

Applying the Concepts

  8.26 The telephone company wants to estimate the proportion of households that would purchase an additional telephone line if it were made available at a substantially reduced installation cost. A random sample of 500 households is selected. The results indicate that 135 of the households would purchase the additional telephone line at a reduced installation cost.

a. Construct a 99% confidence interval estimate of the population proportion of households that would purchase the additional telephone line.

b. How would the manager in charge of promotional programs concerning residential customers use the results in (a)?

8.27 According to the Center for Work-Life Policy, a survey of 500 highly educated women who left careers for family reasons found 66% wanted to return to work (Anne Marie Chaker and Hilary Stout, "After Years Off, Women Struggle to Revive Careers," *The Wall Street Journal*, May 6, 2004, A1).

a. Construct a 95% confidence interval for the population proportion of highly educated women who left careers for family reasons who want to return to work.

b. Interpret the interval in (a).

8.28 Millions of Americans arrange travel plans on the Web ("Travelers Head Online," *USA Today Snapshots*, July 22, 2003). A recent survey reported that 77% purchase plane tickets on the Web. Suppose the survey was based on 1,000 respondents.

a. Construct a 95% confidence interval estimate for the population proportion of Americans who purchase plane tickets on the Web.

b. Construct a 90% confidence interval estimate for the population proportion of Americans who purchase plane tickets on the Web.

c. Which interval is wider? Explain why this is true.

8.29 The number of older consumers in the United States is growing and they are becoming an even bigger economic force. Many feel overwhelmed when confronted with the task of selecting investments, banking services, health care providers, or phone service providers. A telephone survey of 1,900 older consumers found that 27% said they didn't have enough time to be good money managers ("Seniors Confused by Financial Choices—Study," **msnbc.com**, May 6, 2004).

a. Construct a 95% confidence interval for the population proportion of older consumers that don't think they have enough time to be good money managers.

b. Interpret the interval in (a).

8.30 To study the problem of using cellphones while driving ("Drivers Using Cell Phones Have Problems," *USA Today*, May 16, 2001, 1A), a survey of drivers who use cellphones was conducted. In the survey, 46% of the respondents reported having to swerve and 10% knew someone who had a crash while talking on a cellphone. Suppose the survey was based on 500 respondents.

a. Construct a 95% confidence interval for the proportion of all drivers who have had to swerve.

b. Construct a 95% confidence interval for the proportion of all drivers who know someone who had a crash while talking on a cellphone.

8.31 As health-insurance costs and the number of disabled employees increase, more companies are firing these employees. A survey of 723 employers found that 195 dismiss employees as soon as they go on long-term disability (J. Pereira, "To Save on Health-care Costs, Firms Fire Disabled Workers," *The Wall Street Journal*, July, 14, 2003, A1–A7).

a. Construct a 95% confidence interval for the proportion of employers who dismiss employees as soon as they go on long-term disability.

b. Construct a 99% confidence interval for the proportion of employers who dismiss employees as soon as they go on long-term disability.

c. Which interval is wider? Explain why this is true.

8.32 A survey of working women in North America was conducted by the Clinique unit of Estee Lauder Cosmetics. Of the 1,000 women surveyed, 55% believed that companies should hold positions for those on maternity leave for six months or less, and 45% felt that they should hold those positions for more than six months ("Work Week," *The Wall Street Journal*, September 11, 2001, A1).

a. Construct a 95% confidence interval for the proportion of all working women in North America who believe that companies should hold positions for those on maternity leave for more than six months.

b. Interpret the interval constructed in (a).

8.33 A large number of companies are trying to reduce the cost of prescription drug benefits by requiring employees to purchase drugs through a mandatory mail-order program. In a survey of 600 employers, 126 indicated that they either have a mandatory mail-order program in place or are adopting one by the end of 2004 (Barbara Martinez, "Forcing Employees to Buy Drugs Via Mail," *The Wall Street Journal*, February 18, 2004, D1).

a. Construct a 95% confidence interval for the population proportion of employers who have a mandatory mail-order program in place or are adopting one by the end of 2004.

b. Construct a 99% confidence interval for the population proportion of employers who have a mandatory mail-order program in place or are adopting one by the end of 2004.

c. Interpret the intervals in (a) and (b).

d. Discuss the effect on the confidence interval estimate when you change the level of confidence.

8.4 DETERMINING SAMPLE SIZE

In each example of confidence interval estimation, you selected the sample size without regard to the width of the resulting confidence interval. In the business world, determining the proper sample size is a complicated procedure, subject to the constraints of budget, time, and the amount of acceptable sampling error. If, in the Saxon Home Improvement Company example, you want to estimate the mean dollar amount of the sales invoices or the proportion of sales invoices that contain errors, you must determine in advance how large a sampling error to allow in estimating each of the parameters. You must also determine in advance the level of confidence to use in estimating the population parameter.

Sample Size Determination for the Mean

To develop a formula for determining the appropriate sample size needed when constructing a confidence interval estimate of the mean, recall Equation (8.1):

$$\bar{X} \pm Z \frac{\sigma}{\sqrt{n}}$$

The amount added to or subtracted from $\bar{X}$ is equal to half the width of the interval. This quantity represents the amount of imprecision in the estimate that results from sampling error. The **sampling error**[1] e is defined as

[1]In this context, some statisticians refer to e as the "margin of error."

$$e = Z \frac{\sigma}{\sqrt{n}}$$

Solving for n gives the sample size needed to construct the appropriate confidence interval estimate for the mean. "Appropriate" means that the resulting interval will have an acceptable amount of sampling error.

SAMPLE SIZE DETERMINATION FOR THE MEAN

The sample size n is equal to the product of the Z value squared and the variance σ^2, divided by the sampling error e squared.

$$n = \frac{Z^2 \sigma^2}{e^2} \tag{8.4}$$

To determine the sample size, you must know three factors:

[2]You use Z instead of t because, to determine the critical value of t, you need to know the sample size, but you do not know it yet. For most studies, the sample size needed is large enough that the standardized normal distribution is a good approximation of the t distribution.

1. The desired confidence level, which determines the value of Z, the critical value from the standardized normal distribution[2]
2. The acceptable sampling error e
3. The standard deviation σ

In some business-to-business relationships requiring estimation of important parameters, legal contracts specify acceptable levels of sampling error and the confidence level required. For companies in the food or drug sectors, government regulations often specify sampling errors and confidence levels. In general, however, it is usually not easy to specify the two factors needed to determine the sample size. How can you determine the level of confidence and sampling error? Typically, these questions are answered only by the subject matter expert (i.e., the individual most familiar with the variables under study). Although 95% is the most common confidence level used, if more confidence is desired, then 99% might be more appropriate; if less confidence is deemed acceptable, then 90% might be used. For the sampling error, you should think not of how much sampling error you would like to have (you really do not want any error), but of how much you can tolerate when drawing conclusions from the data.

In addition to specifying the confidence level and the sampling error, you need an estimate of the standard deviation. Unfortunately, you rarely know the population standard deviation σ. In some instances, you can estimate the standard deviation from past data. In other situations, you can make an educated guess by taking into account the range and distribution of the variable. For example, if you assume a normal distribution, the range is approximately equal to 6 σ (i.e., $\pm 3\sigma$ around the mean) so that you estimate σ as the range divided by 6. If you cannot estimate σ in this way, you can conduct a small scale study and estimate the standard deviation from the resulting data.

To explore how to determine the sample size needed for estimating the population mean, consider again the audit at Saxon Home Improvement Company. In section 8.2, you selected a sample of 100 sales invoices and developed a 95% confidence interval estimate of the population mean sales invoice amount. How was this sample size determined? Should you have selected a different sample size?

Suppose that, after consultation with company officials, you determine that a sampling error of no more than $\pm\$5$ is desired along with 95% confidence. Past data indicate that the standard deviation of the sales amount is approximately $25. Thus, $e = \$5$, $\sigma = \$25$, and $Z = 1.96$ (for 95% confidence). Using Equation (8.4),

$$n = \frac{Z^2\sigma^2}{e^2} = \frac{(1.96)^2(25)^2}{(5)^2}$$

$$= 96.04$$

Because the general rule is to slightly oversatisfy the criteria by rounding the sample size up to the next whole integer, you should select a sample of size 97. Thus, the sample of size 100 used on page 236 is close to what is necessary to satisfy the needs of the company based on the estimated standard deviation, desired confidence level, and sampling error. Because the calculated sample standard deviation is slightly higher than expected, $28.95 compared to $25.00, the confidence interval is slightly wider than desired. Figure 8.12 illustrates the Microsoft Excel worksheet to determine the sample size.

FIGURE 8.12

Microsoft Excel Worksheet for Determining Sample Size for Estimating the Mean Sales Invoice Amount for the Saxon Home Improvement Company

	A	B	
1	For the Mean Sales Invoice Amount		
2			
3	Data		
4	Population Standard Deviation	25	
5	Sampling Error	5	
6	Confidence Level	95%	
7			
8	Intemediate Calculations		
9	Z Value	-1.9600	=NORMSINV((1 - B6)/2)
10	Calculated Sample Size	96.0365	=((B9 * B4)/B5)^2
11			
12	Result		
13	Sample Size Needed	97	=ROUNDUP(B10, 0)

Example 8.5 illustrates another application of determining the sample size needed to develop a confidence interval estimate for the mean.

EXAMPLE 8.5   DETERMINING THE SAMPLE SIZE FOR THE MEAN

Returning to Example 8.3, suppose you want to estimate the population mean force required to break the insulator to within ± 25 pounds with 95% confidence. On the basis of a study taken the previous year, you believe that the standard deviation is 100 pounds. Find the sample size needed.

SOLUTION Using Equation (8.4) and $e = 25$, $\sigma = 100$, and $Z = 1.96$ for 95% confidence,

$$n = \frac{Z^2\sigma^2}{e^2} = \frac{(1.96)^2(100)^2}{(25)^2}$$

$$= 61.47$$

Therefore, you should select a sample size of 62 insulators because the general rule for determining sample size is to always round up to the next integer value in order to slightly oversatisfy the criteria desired.

An actual sampling error slightly larger than 25 will result if the sample standard deviation calculated in this sample of 62 is greater than 100, and slightly smaller if the sample standard deviation is less than 100.

Sample Size Determination for the Proportion

So far in this section, you learned how to determine the sample size needed for estimating the population mean. Now suppose that you want to determine the sample size necessary for estimating the proportion of sales invoices at the Saxon Home Improvement Company that contain errors.

To determine the sample size needed to estimate a population proportion (π), you use a method similar to the method for a population mean. Recall that in developing the sample size for a confidence interval for the mean, the sampling error is defined by

$$e = Z\frac{\sigma}{\sqrt{n}}$$

When estimating a proportion, you replace σ by $\sqrt{\pi(1-\pi)}$. Thus, the sampling error is

$$e = Z\sqrt{\frac{\pi(1-\pi)}{n}}$$

Solving for n, you have the sample size necessary to develop a confidence interval estimate for a proportion.

SAMPLE SIZE DETERMINATION FOR THE PROPORTION

The sample size n is equal to the Z value squared times the population proportion π, times 1 minus the population proportion π, divided by the sampling error e squared.

$$n = \frac{Z^2\pi(1-\pi)}{e^2} \tag{8.5}$$

To determine the sample size, you must know three factors:

1. The desired confidence level, which determines the value of Z, the critical value from the standardized normal distribution
2. The acceptable sampling error e
3. The population proportion π

In practice, selecting these quantities requires some planning. Once you determine the desired level of confidence, you can find the appropriate Z value from the standardized normal distribution. The sampling error e indicates the amount of error that you are willing to tolerate in estimating the population proportion. The third quantity π is actually the population parameter that you want to estimate! Thus, how do you state a value for the very thing that you are taking a sample in order to determine?

Here you have two alternatives. In many situations, you may have past information or relevant experiences that provide an educated estimate of π. Or, if you do not have past information or relevant experiences, you can try to provide a value for π that would never *underestimate* the sample size needed. Referring to Equation (8.5), you can see that the quantity $\pi(1 - \pi)$ appears in the numerator. Thus, you need to determine the value of π that will make the quantity $\pi(1 - \pi)$ as large as possible. When $\pi = 0.5$, the product $\pi(1 - \pi)$ achieves its maximum result. To show this, several values of π along with the accompanying products of $\pi(1 - \pi)$ are as follows:

When $\pi = 0.9$, then $\pi(1 - \pi) = (0.9)(0.1) = 0.09$
When $\pi = 0.7$, then $\pi(1 - \pi) = (0.7)(0.3) = 0.21$
When $\pi = 0.5$, then $\pi(1 - \pi) = (0.5)(0.5) = 0.25$
When $\pi = 0.3$, then $\pi(1 - \pi) = (0.3)(0.7) = 0.21$
When $\pi = 0.1$, then $\pi(1 - \pi) = (0.1)(0.9) = 0.09$

Therefore, when you have no prior knowledge or estimate of the population proportion π, you should use $\pi = 0.5$ for determining the sample size. This produces the largest possible sample size, and results in the highest possible cost of sampling. Using $\pi = 0.5$ may overestimate the sample size needed because you use the actual sample proportion in developing the confidence interval. You will get a confidence interval narrower than originally intended if the actual sample proportion is different from 0.5. The increased precision comes at the cost of spending more time and money for an increased sample size.

Returning to the Saxon Home Improvement Company "Using Statistics" scenario, suppose that the auditing procedures require you to have 95% confidence in estimating the population proportion of sales invoices with errors to within ± 0.07. The results from past months indicate that the largest proportion has been no more than 0.15. Thus, using Equation (8.5) and $e = 0.07$, $\pi = 0.15$, and $Z = 1.96$ for 95% confidence,

$$n = \frac{Z^2\pi(1 - \pi)}{e^2}$$

$$= \frac{(1.96)^2(0.15)(0.85)}{(0.07)^2}$$

$$= 99.96$$

Because the general rule is to round the sample size up to the next whole integer to slightly oversatisfy the criteria, a sample size of 100 is needed. Thus, the sample size needed to satisfy the requirements of the company based on the estimated proportion, desired confidence level, and sampling error is equal to the sample size taken on page 241. The actual confidence interval is narrower than required since the sample proportion is 0.10 while 0.15 was used for π in Equation (8.5). Figure 8.13 below shows a Microsoft Excel worksheet.

FIGURE 8.13

Microsoft Excel Worksheet for Determining Sample Size for Estimating the Proportion of Sales Invoices with Errors for the Saxon Home Improvement Company

	A	B	
1	For the Proportion of In-Error Sales Invoices		
2			
3	Data		
4	Estimate of True Proportion	0.15	
5	Sampling Error	0.07	
6	Confidence Level	95%	
7			
8	Intermediate Calculations		
9	Z Value	-1.9600	=NORMSINV((1 - B6)/2)
10	Calculated Sample Size	99.9563	=(B9^2 * B4 * (1 - B4))/B5^2
11			
12	Result		
13	Sample Size Needed	100	=ROUNDUP(B10, 0)

Example 8.6 provides a second application of determining the sample size for estimating the population proportion.

EXAMPLE 8.6

DETERMINING THE SAMPLE SIZE FOR THE POPULATION PROPORTION

You want to have 90% confidence of estimating the proportion of office workers who respond to email within an hour to within ±0.05. Because you have not previously undertaken such a study, there is no information available from past data. Determine the sample size needed.

SOLUTION Because no information is available from past data, assume $\pi = 0.50$. Using Equation (8.5) and $e = 0.05$, $\pi = 0.50$, and $Z = 1.645$ for 90% confidence,

$$n = \frac{(1.645)^2(0.50)(0.50)}{(0.05)^2}$$

$$= 270.6$$

Therefore, you need a sample of 271 office workers to estimate the population proportion to within ±0.05 with 90% confidence.

PROBLEMS FOR SECTION 8.4

Learning the Basics

 8.34 If you want to be 95% confident of estimating the population mean to within a sampling error of ±5 and the standard deviation is assumed to be 15, what sample size is required?

 8.35 If you want to be 99% confident of estimating the population mean to within a sampling error of ±20 and the standard deviation is assumed to be 100, what sample size is required?

 8.36 If you want to be 99% confident of estimating the population proportion to within an error of ±0.04, what sample size is needed?

 8.37 If you want to be 95% confident of estimating the population proportion to within an error of ±0.02 and there is historical evidence that the population proportion is approximately 0.40, what sample size is needed?

Applying the Concepts

 8.38 A survey is planned to determine the mean annual family medical expenses of employees of a large company. The management of the company wishes to be 95% confident that the sample mean is correct to within ±$50 of the population mean annual family medical expenses. A previous study indicates that the standard deviation is approximately $400.

a. How large a sample size is necessary?

b. If management wants to be correct to within ±$25, what sample size is necessary?

8.39 If the manager of a paint supply store wants to estimate the mean amount of paint in a 1-gallon can to within ±0.004 gallon with 95% confidence and also assumes that the standard deviation is 0.02 gallon, what sample size is needed?

8.40 If a quality control manager wants to estimate the mean life of lightbulbs to within ±20 hours with 95% confidence and also assumes that the process standard deviation is 100 hours, what sample size is needed?

8.41 If the inspection division of a county weights and measures department wants to estimate the mean amount of soft-drink fill in 2-liter bottles to within ±0.01 liter with 95% confidence and also assumes that the standard deviation is 0.05 liter, what sample size is needed?

 8.42 A consumer group wants to estimate the mean electric bill for the month of July for single-family homes in a large city. Based on studies conducted in other cities, the standard deviation is assumed to be $25. The group wants to estimate the mean bill for July to within ±$5 with 99% confidence.

a. What sample size is needed?

b. If 95% confidence is desired, what sample size is necessary?

8.43 An advertising agency that serves a major radio station wants to estimate the mean amount of time that the station's audience spends listening to the radio daily. From past studies, the standard deviation is estimated as 45 minutes.
a. What sample size is needed if the agency wants to be 90% confident of being correct to within ±5 minutes?
b. If 99% confidence is desired, what sample size is necessary?

8.44 Suppose that a gas utility company wants to estimate its mean waiting time for installation of service to within ±5 days with 95% confidence. The company does not have access to previous data, but suspects that the standard deviation is approximately 20 days. What sample size is needed?

8.45 The U.S. Department of Transportation defines an airline flight as being "on-time" if it landed less than 15 minutes after the scheduled time shown in the carrier's Computerized Reservation System. Cancelled and diverted flights are counted as late. A study of the 10 largest U.S. domestic airlines found Southwest Airlines to have the lowest proportion of late arrivals, 0.1577 (Nikos Tsikriktsis and Janelle Heineke, "The Impact of Process Variation on Customer Dissatisfaction: Evidence from the U.S. Domestic Airline Industry," *Decision Sciences*, Winter 2004, 35(1):129–142). Suppose you were asked to perform a follow-up study for Southwest Airlines in order to update the estimated proportion of late arrivals. What sample size would you use in order to estimate the population proportion to within an error of
a. ±0.06 with 95% confidence?
b. ±0.04 with 95% confidence?
c. ±0.02 with 95% confidence?

8.46 In 2001 it was estimated that 45% of U.S. households purchased groceries at convenience stores and 29% purchased groceries at wholesale clubs ("68th Annual Report of the Grocery Industry," *Progressive Grocer*, April 2002, 29). Consider a follow-up study focusing on the last calendar year.
a. What sample size is needed to estimate the population proportion of U.S. households purchasing groceries at convenience stores to within ±0.02 with 95% confidence?
b. What sample size is needed to estimate the population proportion of U.S. households purchasing groceries at wholesale clubs to within ±0.02 with 95% confidence?
c. Compare the results of (a) and (b). Explain why these results differ.
d. If you were to design the follow-up study, would you use one sample and ask the respondents both questions, or would you select two separate samples? Explain the rationale behind your decision.

8.47 What proportion of people living in the United States use the Internet when planning their vacation? According to a poll conducted by American Express, 35% use the Internet (A. R. Carey, and K. Carter, "Snapshots," *USA Today*, January 14, 2003, 1A).
a. To conduct a follow-up study that would provide 95% confidence that the point estimate is correct to within ±0.04 of the population proportion, how large a sample size is required?
b. To conduct a follow-up study that would provide 99% confidence that the point estimate is correct to within ±0.04 of the population proportion, how large a sample size is required?
c. To conduct a follow-up study that would provide 95% confidence that the point estimate is correct to within ±0.02 of the population proportion, how large a sample size is required?
d. To conduct a follow-up study that would provide 99% confidence that the point estimate is correct to within ±0.02 of the population proportion, how large a sample size is required?
e. Discuss the effects of changing the desired confidence level and the acceptable sampling error on sample size requirements.

8.48 Have you had a business presentation disturbed by a ringing cellphone? In a poll of 326 business men and women, 303 answered this question "yes" and only 23 answered "no" ("You Say," *Presentations: Technology and Techniques for Effective Communication*, January 2003, 18).
a. Construct a 95% confidence interval for the population proportion of business men and women who have their presentations disturbed by cellphones.
b. Interpret the interval constructed in (a).
c. To conduct a follow-up study that would provide 95% confidence that the point estimate is correct to within ±0.04 of the population proportion, how large a sample size is required?
d. To conduct a follow-up study that would provide 99% confidence that the point estimate is correct to within ±0.04 of the population proportion, how large a sample size is required?

8.49 A study conducted by the Federal Reserve reported that 52% of 4,449 families interviewed in 2001 held stocks, either directly or through mutual funds (Barbara Hagenbaugh, "Nation's Wealth Disparity Widens," *USA Today*, January 22, 2003, 1A).
a. Construct a 95% confidence interval for the proportion of families that held stocks in 2001.
b. Interpret the interval constructed in (a).
c. To conduct a follow-up study to estimate the population proportion of families that currently hold stocks to within ±0.01 with 95% confidence, how many families would you interview?

8.5 CONFIDENCE INTERVAL ESTIMATION AND ETHICAL ISSUES

Ethical issues relating to the selection of samples and the inferences that accompany them can arise in several ways. The major ethical issue relates to whether or not confidence interval estimates are provided along with the sample statistics. To provide a sample statistic without also including the confidence interval limits (typically set at 95%), the sample size used, and an interpretation of the meaning of the confidence interval in terms that a layperson can understand, raises ethical issues because of their omission. Failure to include a confidence interval estimate might mislead the user of the results into thinking that the point estimate is all that is needed to predict the population characteristic with certainty. Thus, it is important that you indicate the interval estimate in a prominent place in any written communication, along with a simple explanation of the meaning of the confidence interval. In addition, you should highlight the size of the sample.

One of the most common areas where ethical issues concerning estimation occurs is in the publication of the results of political polls. Often, the results of the polls are highlighted on the front page of the newspaper and the sampling error involved along with the methodology used is printed on the page where the article is typically continued, often in the middle of the newspaper. To ensure an ethical presentation of statistical results, the confidence levels, sample size, and confidence limits should be made available for all surveys and other statistical studies.

KEY FORMULAS

Confidence Interval for the Mean (σ Known)

$$\bar{X} \pm Z \frac{\sigma}{\sqrt{n}} \quad (8.1)$$

or

$$\bar{X} - Z \frac{\sigma}{\sqrt{n}} \leq \mu \leq \bar{X} + Z \frac{\sigma}{\sqrt{n}}$$

Confidence Interval for the Mean (σ Unknown)

$$\bar{X} \pm t_{n-1} \frac{S}{\sqrt{n}} \quad (8.2)$$

or

$$\bar{X} - t_{n-1} \frac{S}{\sqrt{n}} \leq \mu \leq \bar{X} + t_{n-1} \frac{S}{\sqrt{n}}$$

Confidence Interval Estimate for the Proportion

$$p \pm Z \sqrt{\frac{p(1-p)}{n}} \quad (8.3)$$

or

$$p - Z \sqrt{\frac{p(1-p)}{n}} \leq \pi \leq p + Z \sqrt{\frac{p(1-p)}{n}}$$

Sample Size Determination for the Mean

$$n = \frac{Z^2 \sigma^2}{e^2} \quad (8.4)$$

Sample Size Determination for the Proportion

$$n = \frac{Z^2 \pi (1-\pi)}{e^2} \quad (8.5)$$

CHAPTER REVIEW PROBLEMS

Checking Your Understanding

8.50 Why is it that you can never really have 100% confidence of correctly estimating the population characteristic of interest?

8.51 When do you use the t distribution to construct the confidence interval estimate for the mean?

8.52 Why is it true that for a given sample size n, an increase in confidence is achieved by widening (and making less precise) the confidence interval?

8.53 When do you use the normal distribution to construct the confidence interval estimate for the mean?

8.54 For a given level of confidence, why is the critical value of t smaller for 80 degrees of freedom than for 20 degrees of freedom?

8.55 Why is the sample size needed to determine the proportion smaller when the population proportion is 0.20 than when the population proportion is 0.50?

Applying the Concepts

You can solve problems 8.56–8.70 with or without Microsoft Excel, Minitab, or SPSS. You should use Microsoft Excel, Minitab, or SPSS to solve problems 8.71–8.74.

8.56 *Redbook* magazine conducted a survey through its Internet Web site (Stacy Kravetz, "Work Week," *The Wall Street Journal*, April 13, 1999, A1). People visiting the Web site were given the opportunity to fill out an on-screen survey form. A total of 665 women responded to a question that asked whether they would prefer a four-day workweek or a 20% pay increase. A four-day workweek was the preference for 412 of the respondents.

a. Define the population from which this sample was drawn.
b. Is this a random sample from this population?
c. Is this a statistically valid study?
d. Describe how you would design a statistically valid study to investigate the proportion of *Redbook* subscribers who would prefer a four-day workweek rather than a 20% pay increase. Use the information above to determine the sample size needed to estimate this population proportion to within ±0.02 with 95% confidence.

8.57 Companies are spending more time screening applicants than in the past. A result of the more in-depth screening process is that companies are finding that many applicants are stretching the truth on their applications. A study conducted by Automatic Data Processing found inaccuracies between the applicant and past employers in 44% of the applications screened. Unfortunately the article did not disclose the sample size used in the study (Stephanie Armour, "Security Checks Worry Workers," *USA Today*, June 19, 2002, B1).

a. Suppose that 500 applications were screened. Construct a 95% confidence interval estimate of the population proportion of applications containing inaccuracies with past employers.
b. Based on (a), is it right to conclude that less than half of all applications contain inaccuracies with past employers?
c. Suppose that the study used a sample size of 200 applications. Construct a 95% confidence interval estimate of the population proportion of applications containing inaccuracies with the past employers.
d. Based on (c), is it right to conclude that less than half of all applications contain inaccuracies with their past employers?
e. Discuss the effect of sample size on your answers to (a) through (d).

8.58 A sales and marketing management magazine conducted a survey on salespeople cheating on their expense reports and other unethical conduct (D. Haralson and Q. Tian, "Cheating Hearts," *USA Today*, February 15, 2001,

1A). In the survey, managers have caught salespeople cheating on an expense report 58% of the time, working a second job on company time 50% of the time, listing a "strip bar" as a restaurant on an expense report 22% of the time, and giving a kickback to a customer 19% of the time. Suppose the survey was based on a sample of 200 managers. Construct a 95% confidence interval estimate of the population proportion of managers who have caught salespeople

a. cheating on an expense report.
b. working a second job on company time.
c. listing a "strip bar" as a restaurant on an expense report.
d. giving a kickback to a customer.
e. Use the information given in this problem to determine the sample size needed to estimate the proportion of managers who have caught salespeople working a second job on company time to within ±0.02 with 95% confidence.

8.59 Starwood Hotels conducted a survey of 401 top executives who play golf (Del Jones, "Many CEOs Bend the Rules (of Golf)," *USA Today*, June 26, 2002). Among the results were the following:

- 329 cheat at golf
- 329 hate others who cheat at golf
- 289 believe business and golf behavior parallel
- 80 would let a client win to get business
- 40 would call in sick to play golf

Construct 95% confidence interval estimates for each of these questions. What conclusions can you reach about CEO's attitudes toward golf from these results?

8.60 A market researcher for a consumer electronics company wants to study the television viewing habits of residents of a particular area. A random sample of 40 respondents is selected, and each respondent is instructed to keep a detailed record of all television viewing in a particular week. The results are as follows:

- Viewing time per week: $\overline{X} = 15.3$ hours, $S = 3.8$ hours.
- 27 respondents watch the evening news on at least 3 weeknights.

a. Construct a 95% confidence interval estimate for the mean amount of television watched per week in this city.
b. Construct a 95% confidence interval estimate for the population proportion who watch the evening news on at least 3 nights per week.

If the market researcher wants to take another survey in a different city, answer these questions:

c. What sample size is required to be 95% confident of estimating the population mean to within ±2 hours and assumes that the population standard deviation is equal to 5 hours?
d. What sample size is needed to be 95% confident of being within ±0.035 of the population proportion who watch the evening news on at least 3 weeknights if no previous estimate is available?

e. Based on (c) and (d), what sample size should the market researcher select if a single survey is being conducted?

8.61 The real estate assessor for a county government wants to study various characteristics of single-family houses in the county. A random sample of 70 houses reveals the following:
- Heated area of the house (in square feet): $\overline{X} = 1,759$, $S = 380$.
- 42 houses have central air-conditioning.

a. Construct a 99% confidence interval estimate of the population mean heated area of the house.

b. Construct a 95% confidence interval estimate of the population proportion of houses that have central air-conditioning.

8.62 The personnel director of a large corporation wishes to study absenteeism among clerical workers at the corporation's central office during the year. A random sample of 25 clerical workers reveals the following:
- Absenteeism: $\overline{X} = 9.7$ days, $S = 4.0$ days.
- 12 clerical workers were absent more than 10 days.

a. Construct a 95% confidence interval estimate of the mean number of absences for clerical workers last year.

b. Construct a 95% confidence interval estimate of the population proportion of clerical workers absent more than 10 days last year.

If the personnel director also wishes to take a survey in a branch office, answer these questions:

c. What sample size is needed to have 95% confidence in estimating the population mean to within ±1.5 days if the population standard deviation is 4.5 days?

d. What sample size is needed to have 90% confidence in estimating the population proportion to within ±0.075 if no previous estimate is available?

e. Based on (c) and (d), what sample size is needed if a single survey is being conducted?

8.63 The market research director for Dotty's department store wants to study women's spending on cosmetics. A survey is designed in order to estimate the proportion of women who purchase their cosmetics primarily from Dotty's department store, and the mean yearly amount that women spend on cosmetics. A previous survey found that the standard deviation of the amount women spend on cosmetics in a year is approximately $18.

a. What sample size is needed to have 99% confidence of estimating the population mean to within ±$5?

b. What sample size is needed to have 90% confidence of estimating the population proportion to within ±0.045?

c. Based on the results in (a) and (b), how many of the store's credit cardholders should be sampled? Explain.

8.64 The branch manager of a nationwide bookstore chain wants to study characteristics of her store's customers. She decides to focus on two variables: the amount of money spent by customers and whether the customers would con-

sider purchasing educational videotapes relating to graduate preparation exams such as GMAT, GRE, or LSAT. The results from a sample of 70 customers are as follows:
- Amount spent: $\overline{X} = \$28.52$, $S = \$11.39$.
- 28 customers stated that they would consider purchasing the educational videotapes.

a. Construct a 95% confidence interval estimate of the population mean amount spent in the bookstore.

b. Construct a 90% confidence interval estimate of the population proportion of customers who would consider purchasing educational videotapes.

Assume the branch manager of another store in the chain wants to conduct a similar survey in his store.

c. What sample size is needed to have 95% confidence of estimating the population mean amount spent in his store to within ±$2 if the standard deviation is assumed to be $10?

d. What sample size is needed to have 90% confidence of estimating the population proportion who would consider purchasing the educational videotapes to within ±0.04?

e. Based on your answers to (c) and (d), how large a sample should the manager take?

8.65 The branch manager of an outlet (store 1) of a nationwide chain of pet supply stores wants to study characteristics of her customers. In particular, she decides to focus on two variables: the amount of money spent by customers and whether the customers own only one dog, only one cat, or more than one dog and/or cat. The results from a sample of 70 customers are:
- Amount of money spent: $\overline{X} = \$21.34$, $S = \$9.22$.
- 37 customers own only a dog.
- 26 customers own only a cat.
- 7 customers own more than one dog and/or cat.

a. Construct a 95% confidence interval estimate of the population mean amount spent in the pet supply store.

b. Construct a 90% confidence interval estimate of the population proportion of customers who own only a cat.

The branch manager of another outlet (store 2) wishes to conduct a similar survey in his store. The manager does not have any access to the information generated by the manager of store 1.

c. What sample size is needed to have 95% confidence of estimating the population mean amount spent in his store to within ±$1.50 if the standard deviation is $10?

d. What sample size is needed to have 90% confidence of estimating the population proportion of customers who own only a cat to within ±0.045?

e. Based on your answers to (c) and (d), how large a sample should the manager take?

8.66 The owner of a restaurant that serves continental food wants to study characteristics of his customers. He decides to focus on two variables: the amount of money spent by customers and whether customers order dessert. The results from a sample of 60 customers are as follows:

- Amount spent: $\overline{X} = \$38.54$, $S = \$7.26$.
- 18 customers purchased dessert.

a. Construct a 95% confidence interval estimate of the population mean amount spent per customer in the restaurant.

b. Construct a 90% confidence interval estimate of the population proportion of customers who purchase dessert.

The owner of a competing restaurant wants to conduct a similar survey in her restaurant. This owner does not have access to the information of the owner of the first restaurant.

c. What sample size is needed to have 95% confidence of estimating the population mean amount spent in her restaurant to within ±$1.50 assuming the standard deviation is $8?

d. What sample size is needed to have 90% confidence of estimating the population proportion of customers who purchase dessert to within ±0.04?

e. Based on your answers to (c) and (d), how large a sample should the owner take?

8.67 The manufacturer of "Ice Melt" claims its product will melt snow and ice at temperatures as low as 0° Fahrenheit. A representative for a large chain of hardware stores is interested in testing this claim. The chain purchases a large shipment of five-pound bags for distribution. The representative wants to know with 95% confidence, within ±0.05, what proportion of bags of Ice Melt perform the job as claimed by the manufacturer.

a. How many bags does the representative need to test? What assumption should be made concerning the population proportion? (This is called *destructive testing*; that is, the product being tested is destroyed by the test and is then unavailable to be sold.) The representative tests 50 bags, and 42 do the job as claimed.

b. Construct a 95% confidence interval estimate for the population proportion that will do the job as claimed.

c. How can the representative use the results of (b) to determine whether to sell the Ice Melt product?

8.68 A manufacturing company produces steel housings for electrical equipment. The main component part of the housing is a steel trough that is made out of a 14-gauge steel coil. It is produced using a 250-ton progressive punch press with a wipe-down operation that puts two 90-degree forms in the flat steel to make the trough. The distance from one side of the form to the other is critical because of weatherproofing in outdoor applications. The data from a sample of 49 troughs follows: TROUGH

Width of Trough (in Inches)

8.312 8.343 8.317 8.383 8.348 8.410 8.351 8.373 8.481 8.422
8.476 8.382 8.484 8.403 8.414 8.419 8.385 8.465 8.498 8.447
8.436 8.413 8.489 8.414 8.481 8.415 8.479 8.429 8.458 8.462

8.460 8.444 8.429 8.460 8.412 8.420 8.410 8.405 8.323 8.420
8.396 8.447 8.405 8.439 8.411 8.427 8.420 8.498 8.409

a. Construct a 95% confidence interval estimate of the mean width of the troughs.

b. Interpret the interval developed in (a).

8.69 A quality characteristic of interest for a tea-bag-filling process is the weight of the tea in the individual bags. In this example, the label weight on the package indicates that the mean amount is 5.5 grams of tea in a bag. If the bags are underfilled, two problems arise. First, customers may not be able to brew the tea to be as strong as they wish. Second, the company may be in violation of the truth-in-labeling laws. On the other hand, if the mean amount of tea in a bag exceeds the label weight, the company is giving away product. Getting an exact amount of tea in a bag is problematic because of variation in the temperature and humidity inside the factory, differences in the density of the tea, and the extremely fast filling operation of the machine (approximately 170 bags a minute). The following table provides the weight in grams of a sample of 50 tea bags produced in one hour by a single machine. TEABAGS

Weight of Tea Bags in Grams

5.65 5.44 5.42 5.40 5.53 5.34 5.54 5.45 5.52 5.41
5.57 5.40 5.53 5.54 5.55 5.62 5.56 5.46 5.44 5.51
5.47 5.40 5.47 5.61 5.53 5.32 5.67 5.29 5.49 5.55
5.77 5.57 5.42 5.58 5.58 5.50 5.32 5.50 5.53 5.58
5.61 5.45 5.44 5.25 5.56 5.63 5.50 5.57 5.67 5.36

a. Construct a 99% confidence interval estimate of the population mean weight of the tea bags.

b. Is the company meeting the requirement set forth on the label that the mean amount of tea in a bag is 5.5 grams?

8.70 The manufacturer of "Boston" and "Vermont" asphalt shingles provide their customers with a 20-year warranty on most of their products. To determine whether a shingle will last as long as the warranty period, accelerated-life testing is conducted at the manufacturing plant. Accelerated-life testing exposes the shingle to the stresses it would be subject to in a lifetime of normal use via a laboratory experiment that takes only a few minutes to conduct. In this test, a shingle is repeatedly scraped with a brush for a short period of time and the amount of shingle granules that are removed by the brushing is weighed (in grams). Shingles that experience low amounts of granule loss are expected to last longer in normal use than shingles that experience high amounts of granule loss. In this situation, a shingle should experience no more than 0.8

grams of granule loss if it is expected to last the length of the warranty period. The data file **GRANULE** contains a sample of 170 measurements made on the company's Boston shingles, and 140 measurements made on Vermont shingles.

a. For the Boston shingles, construct a 95% confidence interval estimate of the mean granule loss.

b. For the Vermont shingles, construct a 95% confidence interval estimate of the mean granule loss.

c. Evaluate whether the assumption needed for (a) and (b) has been seriously violated.

d. Based on the results of (a) and (b), what conclusions can you reach concerning the mean granule loss of the Boston and Vermont shingles?

8.71 The manufacturer of "Boston" and "Vermont" asphalt shingles know that product weight is a major factor in the customer's perception of quality. The last stage of the assembly line packages the shingles before they are placed on wooden pallets. Once a pallet is full (a pallet for most brands holds 16 squares of shingles), it is weighed and the measurement is recorded. The data file **PALLET** contains the weight (in pounds) from a sample of 368 pallets of Boston shingles and 330 pallets of Vermont shingles.

a. For the Boston shingles, construct a 95% confidence interval estimate of the mean weight.

b. For the Vermont shingles, construct a 95% confidence interval estimate of the mean weight.

c. Evaluate whether the assumption needed for (a) and (b) has been seriously violated.

d. Based on the results of (a) and (b), what conclusions can you reach concerning the mean weight of the Boston and Vermont shingles?

8.72 Zagat's publishes restaurant ratings for various locations in the United States. The data file **RESTRATE** contains the Zagat rating for food, décor, and service, and the price per person for a sample of 50 restaurants located in New York City, and 50 restaurants located on Long Island, a suburb of New York City.

Source: Extracted from Zagat Survey 2002 New York City Restaurants *and* Zagat Survey 2001/2002 Long Island Restaurants.

For New York City and Long Island restaurants separately,

a. Construct 95% confidence interval estimates for the mean food rating, mean décor rating, mean service rating, and mean price per person.

b. What conclusions can you reach about the New York City and Long Island restaurants from the results in (a)?

Report Writing Exercises

8.73 Referring to the results in problem 8.68 on page 253 concerning the width of a steel trough, write a report that summarizes your conclusions.

TEAM PROJECT

8.74 Refer to the team project on page 62. Construct all appropriate confidence interval estimates of population characteristics of low-risk, average-risk, and high-risk mutual funds. Include these estimates in a report to the vice president for research at the financial investment service. **MUTUALFUNDS2004**

RUNNING CASE
MANAGING THE *SPRINGVILLE HERALD*

The marketing department has been considering ways to increase the number of new subscriptions and increase the rate of retention among those customers who agreed to a trial subscription. Following the suggestion of assistant manager Lauren Alfonso, the department staff designed a survey to help determine various characteristics of readers of the newspaper who were not home-delivery subscribers. The survey consists of the following ten questions:

1. Do you or a member of your household ever purchase the *Springville Herald*?

    (1) Yes (2) No

[If the respondent answers no, the interview is terminated.]

2. Do you receive the *Springville Herald* via home delivery?

    (1) Yes (2) No

[If no, skip to question 4.]]

3. Do you receive the *Springville Herald*:

    (1) Monday–Saturday (2) Sunday only (3) Every day

[If every day, skip to question 9.]

4. How often during the Monday–Saturday period do you purchase the *Springville Herald*?

    (1) Every day (2) Most days (3) Occasionally or never

5. How often do you purchase the *Springville Herald* on Sundays?

    (1) Every Sunday

    (2) 2–3 Sundays per month

    (3) No more than once a month

6. Where are you most likely to purchase the *Springville Herald*?
   (1) Convenience store
   (2) Newsstand/candy store
   (3) Vending machine (4) Supermarket (5) Other
7. Would you consider subscribing to the *Springville Herald* for a trial period if a discount was offered?
   (1) Yes (2) No
   [If no, skip to question 9.]
8. The *Springville Herald* currently costs 50 cents on Monday–Saturday and $1.50 on Sunday for a total of $4.50 per week. How much would you be willing to pay per week to get home delivery for a 90-day trial period?
9. Do you read a daily newspaper other than the *Springville Herald*?
   (1) Yes (2) No
10. As an incentive for long-term subscribers, the newspaper is considering the possibility of offering a card that would provide discounts at select restaurants in the Springville area to all subscribers who pay in advance for six months of home delivery. Would you want to get such a card under the terms of this offer?
    (1) Yes (2) No

The group agreed to use a random-digit dialing method to poll 500 local households by telephone. Using this approach, the last four digits of a telephone number are randomly selected to go with an area code and exchange (the first 6 digits of a ten-digit telephone number). Only those pairs of area codes and exchanges that were for the Springville city area were used for this survey.

Of the 500 households selected, 94 households either refused to participate, could not be contacted after repeated attempts, or represented telephone numbers that were not in service. The summary results are as follows:

Households that Purchase the Springville Herald	Frequency
Yes	352
No	54

Households with Home Delivery	Frequency
Yes	136
No	216

Type of Home Delivery Subscription	Frequency
Monday–Saturday	18
Sunday only	25
7 days a week	93

Purchase Behavior of Nonsubscribers for Monday–Saturday Editions	Frequency
Every day	78
Most days	95
Occasionally or never	43

Purchase Behavior of Nonsubscribers for Sunday editions	Frequency
Every Sunday	138
2–3 Sundays a month	54
No more than once a month	24

Nonsubscribers' Purchase Location	Frequency
Convenience store	74
Newsstand/candy store	95
Vending machine	21
Supermarket	13
Other locations	13

Would Consider Trial Subscription if Offered a Discount	Frequency
Yes	46
No	170

Rate Willing to Pay per Week (in Dollars) for a 90-Day Home-Delivery Trial Subscription SH8

$4.15 3.60 4.10 3.60 3.60 3.60 4.40 3.15 4.00 3.75 4.00 3.25 3.75 3.30 3.75 3.65 4.00 4.10 3.90 3.50 3.75 3.00 3.40 4.00 3.80 3.50 4.10 4.25 3.50 3.90 3.95 4.30 4.20 3.50 3.75 3.30 3.85 3.20 4.40 3.80 3.40 3.50 2.85 3.75 3.80 3.90

Read a Daily Newspaper Other than the Springville Herald	Frequency
Yes	138
No	214

Would Prepay 6 Months to Receive a Restaurant Discount Card	Frequency
Yes	66
No	286

EXERCISES

SH8.1 Some members of the marketing department are concerned about the random-digit dialing method used to collect survey responses. Prepare a memorandum that examines the following issues:
- The advantages and disadvantages of using the random-digit dialing method.
- Possible alternative approaches for conducting the survey and their advantages and disadvantages.

SH8.2 Analyze the results of the survey of Springville households. Write a report that discusses the marketing implications of the survey results for the *Springville Herald*.

WEB CASE

Apply your knowledge about confidence interval estimation in this Web Case that extends the OnCampus! Web Case from Chapter 6.

Among their other features, the *OnCampus!* Web site allows customers to purchase *OnCampus! LifeStyles* merchandise online. To handle payment processing, the management of *OnCampus!* has contracted with the following firms:

- PayAFriend (PAF): an online payments system in which customers and businesses such as *OnCampus!* register in order to exchange payments in a secure and convenient manner without the need for a credit card.
- Continental Banking Company (Conbanco): a processing services provider that allows *OnCampus!* customers to pay for merchandise using nationally recognized credit cards issued by a financial institution.

To reduce costs, the management is considering eliminating one of these two payment systems. However, Virginia Duffy of the sales department suspects that customers use the two forms of payment in unequal numbers and that customers display different buying behaviors when using the two forms of payment. Therefore, she would like to first determine:

a. The proportion of customers using PAF and the proportion of customers using a credit card to pay for their purchase.

b. The mean purchase amount when using PAF and the mean purchase amount when using a credit card.

Assist Ms. Duffy by preparing an appropriate analysis based on a random sample of 50 transactions that she has prepared and placed in an internal file on the *OnCampus!* Web site **www.prenhall.com/Springville/ OnCampus_PymtSample.htm**. Summarize your findings and determine if Ms. Duffy's conjectures of *OnCampus!* customer purchasing behaviors are correct. If you want the sampling error to be no more than $3, is Ms. Duffy's sample large enough to perform a valid analysis?

REFERENCES

1. Cochran, W. G., *Sampling Techniques*, 3rd ed. (New York: Wiley, 1977).
2. Fisher, R. A., and F. Yates, *Statistical Tables for Biological, Agricultural and Medical Research*, 5th ed. (Edinburgh: Oliver & Boyd, 1957).
3. Kirk, R. E., ed., *Statistical Issues: A Reader for the Behavioral Sciences* (Belmont, CA: Wadsworth, 1972).
4. Larsen, R. L., and M. L. Marx, *An Introduction to Mathematical Statistics and Its Applications*, 2nd ed. (Englewood Cliffs, NJ: Prentice Hall, 1986).
5. *Microsoft Excel 2003* (Redmond, WA: Microsoft Corporation, 2003).
6. *Minitab for Windows Version 14* (State College, PA: Minitab Inc., 2004).
7. Snedecor, G. W., and W. G. Cochran, *Statistical Methods*, 7th ed. (Ames, IA: Iowa State University Press, 1980).
8. *SPSS Base 12.0 Brief Guide* (Upper Saddle River, NJ: Prentice Hall, 2003).

CHAPTER 9

Fundamentals of Hypothesis Testing: One-Sample Tests

USING STATISTICS: The Oxford Cereal Company Revisited

LEARNING OBJECTIVES

In this chapter, you learn:

- The basic principles of hypothesis testing

- How to use hypothesis testing to test a mean or proportion

- The assumptions of each hypothesis-testing procedure, how to evaluate them, and the consequences if they are seriously violated

- How to avoid the pitfalls involved in hypothesis testing

- The ethical issues involved in hypothesis testing

USING STATISTICS

The Oxford Cereal Company Revisited

As in the Chapter 7 "Using Statistics" scenario, imagine that you are an operations manager for the Oxford Cereal Company and are responsible for monitoring the amount in each cereal box filled. You select and weigh a random sample of 25 boxes in order to calculate a sample mean and investigate how close the fill weights are to the company's specifications of a mean of 368 grams. This time you must make a decision and conclude whether (or not) the mean fill weight in the entire process is equal to 368 grams in order to know whether the fill process needs adjustment. How could you rationally make this decision?

Unlike Chapter 7 in which the problem facing the operations manager was to determine if the sample mean was consistent with a known population mean, this "Using Statistics" scenario asks how can the sample mean validate the claim that the population mean is 368 grams? To validate the claim, you need to first state the claim unambiguously. For example, the population mean is 368 grams. In the inferential method known as hypothesis testing you consider the evidence—the sample statistic—to see if the evidence better supports the statement, called the *null hypothesis*, or the mutually exclusive alternative that, in this case, states that the population mean is not 368 grams.

In this chapter the focus is on hypothesis testing, another aspect of statistical inference that, like confidence interval estimation, is based on sample information. A step-by-step methodology is developed that enables you to make inferences about a population parameter by *analyzing differences* between the results observed (the sample statistic) and the results you expect to get if some underlying hypothesis is actually true. For example, is the mean weight of the cereal boxes in the sample taken at Oxford Cereal Company a value consistent with what you would expect if the mean of the entire population of cereal boxes is 368 grams? Or, can you infer that the population mean is not equal to 368 grams because the sample mean is significantly different from 368 grams?

9.1   HYPOTHESIS-TESTING METHODOLOGY

The Null and Alternative Hypotheses

Hypothesis testing typically begins with some theory, claim, or assertion about a particular parameter of a population. For example, your initial hypothesis about the cereal example is that the process is working properly, meaning that the mean fill is 368 grams, and no corrective action is needed.

The hypothesis that the population parameter is equal to the company specification is referred to as the null hypothesis. A **null hypothesis** is always one of status quo, and is identified by the symbol H_0. Here the null hypothesis is that the filling process is working properly, and therefore the mean fill is the 368-gram specification. This is stated as

$$H_0: \mu = 368$$

Even though information is available only from the sample, the null hypothesis is written in terms of the population. Remember, your focus is on the population of all cereal boxes. The sample statistic is used to make inferences about the entire filling process. One inference may be that the results observed from the sample data indicate that the null hypothesis is false. If the null hypothesis is considered false, something else must be true.

Whenever a null hypothesis is specified, an alternative hypothesis is also specified, one that must be true if the null hypothesis is false. The **alternative hypothesis** H_1 is the opposite of the null hypothesis H_0. This is stated in the cereal example as

$$H_1: \mu \neq 368$$

The alternative hypothesis represents the conclusion reached by rejecting the null hypothesis. The null hypothesis is rejected when there is sufficient evidence from the sample information that the null hypothesis is false. In the cereal example, if the weights of the sampled boxes are sufficiently above or below the expected 368-gram mean specified by the company, you reject the null hypothesis in favor of the alternative hypothesis that the mean fill is different from 368 grams. You stop production and take whatever action is necessary to correct the problem. If the null hypothesis is not rejected, then you should continue to believe in the status quo that the process is working correctly and therefore no corrective action is necessary. In this second scenario, you have not proven that the process is working correctly. Rather, you have failed to prove that it is working incorrectly and therefore you continue your belief (although unproven) in the null hypothesis.

In the hypothesis-testing methodology, the null hypothesis is rejected when the sample evidence suggests that it is far more likely that the alternative hypothesis is true. However, failure to reject the null hypothesis is not proof that it is true. You can never prove that the null hypothesis is correct because the decision is based only on the sample information, not on the entire population. Therefore, if you fail to reject the null hypothesis, you can only conclude that there is insufficient evidence to warrant its rejection. The following key points summarize the null and alternative hypotheses:

- The null hypothesis H_0 represents the status quo or the current belief in a situation.
- The alternative hypothesis H_1 is the opposite of the null hypothesis and represents a research claim or specific inference you would like to prove.
- If you reject the null hypothesis, you have statistical proof that the alternative hypothesis is correct.
- If you do not reject the null hypothesis, then you have failed to prove the alternative hypothesis. The failure to prove the alternative hypothesis, however, does not mean that you have proven the null hypothesis.
- The null hypothesis H_0 always refers to a specified value of the population parameter (such as μ), not a sample statistic (such as $\overline{X}$).
- The statement of the null hypothesis always contains an equal sign regarding the specified value of the population parameter (e.g., $H_0: \mu = 368$ grams).
- The statement of the alternative hypothesis never contains an equal sign regarding the specified value of the population parameter (e.g., $H_1: \mu \neq 368$ grams).

EXAMPLE 9.1

THE NULL AND ALTERNATIVE HYPOTHESES

You are the manager of a fast-food restaurant. You want to determine whether the waiting time to place an order has changed in the last month from its previous population mean value of 4.5 minutes. State the null and alternative hypotheses.

SOLUTION The null hypothesis is that the population mean has not changed from its previous value of 4.5 minutes. This is stated as

$$H_0: \mu = 4.5$$

The alternative hypothesis is the opposite of the null hypothesis. Since the null hypothesis is that the population mean is 4.5 minutes, the alternative hypothesis is that the population mean is not 4.5 minutes. This is stated as

$$H_1: \mu \neq 4.5$$

The Critical Value of the Test Statistic

The logic behind the hypothesis-testing methodology is to determine how likely the null hypothesis is true by considering the information gathered in a sample. In the Oxford Cereal Company scenario, the null hypothesis is that the mean amount of cereal per box in the entire filling process is 368 grams (i.e., the population parameter specified by the company). You select a sample of boxes from the filling process, weigh each box, and compute the sample mean. This statistic is an estimate of the corresponding parameter (the population mean μ). Even if the null hypothesis is true, the statistic (the sample mean $\overline{X}$) is likely to differ from the value of the parameter (the population mean μ) because of variation due to sampling. However, you expect the sample statistic to be close to the population parameter if the null hypothesis is true. If the sample statistic is close to the population parameter, you have insufficient evidence to reject the null hypothesis. For example, if the sample mean is 367.9, you would conclude that the population mean has not changed (i.e., $\mu = 368$), because a sample mean of 367.9 is very close to the hypothesized value of 368. Intuitively, you think that it is likely that you could get a sample mean of 367.9 from a population whose mean is 368.

On the other hand, if there is a large difference between the value of the statistic and the hypothesized value of the population parameter, you will conclude that the null hypothesis is false. For example, if the sample mean is 320, you would conclude that the population mean is not 368 (i.e., $\mu \neq 368$), because the sample mean is very far from the hypothesized value of 368. In such a case you conclude that it is very unlikely to get a sample mean of 320 if the population mean is really 368. Therefore, it is more logical to conclude that the population mean is not equal to 368. Here you reject the null hypothesis.

Unfortunately, the decision-making process is not always so clear-cut. Determining what is "very close" and what is "very different" is arbitrary without clear definitions. Hypothesis-testing methodology provides clear definitions for evaluating differences. Furthermore, it enables you to quantify the decision-making process by computing the probability of getting a given sample result if the null hypothesis is true. You calculate this probability by determining the sampling distribution for the sample statistic of interest (e.g., the sample mean) and then computing the particular **test statistic** based on the given sample result. Because the sampling distribution for the test statistic often follows a well-known statistical distribution, such as the standardized normal distribution or *t* distribution, you can use these distributions to help determine whether the null hypothesis is true.

Regions of Rejection and Nonrejection

The sampling distribution of the test statistic is divided into two regions, a **region of rejection** (sometimes called the critical region) and a **region of nonrejection** (see Figure 9.1).

FIGURE 9.1

Regions of Rejection and Nonrejection in Hypothesis Testing

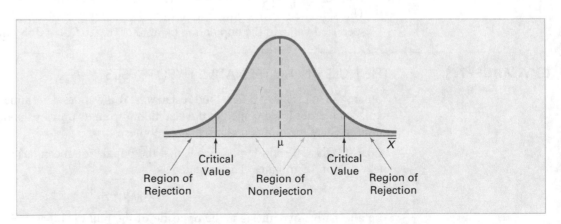

If the test statistic falls into the region of nonrejection, you do not reject the null hypothesis. In the Oxford Cereal Company scenario, you conclude that there is insufficient evidence that the population mean fill is different from 368 grams. If the test statistic falls into the rejection region, you reject the null hypothesis. In this case, you conclude that the population mean is not 368 grams.

The region of rejection consists of the values of the test statistic that are unlikely to occur if the null hypothesis is true. These values are more likely to occur if the null hypothesis is false. Therefore, if a value of the test statistic falls into this *rejection region*, you reject the null hypothesis because that value is unlikely if the null hypothesis is true.

To make a decision concerning the null hypothesis, you first determine the **critical value** of the test statistic. The critical value divides the nonrejection region from the rejection region. Determining this critical value depends on the size of the rejection region. The size of the rejection region is directly related to the risks involved in using only sample evidence to make decisions about a population parameter.

Risks in Decision Making Using Hypothesis-Testing Methodology

When using a sample statistic to make decisions about a population parameter, there is a risk that you will reach an incorrect conclusion. You can make two different types of errors when applying hypothesis-testing methodology, a Type I error and a Type II error.

> A **Type I error** occurs if you reject the null hypothesis H_0 when it is true and should not be rejected. The probability of a Type I error occurring is α.
> A **Type II error** occurs if you do not reject the null hypothesis H_0 when it is false and should be rejected. The probability of a Type II error occurring is β.

In the Oxford Cereal Company scenario, you make a Type I error if you conclude that the population mean fill is *not* 368 when it *is* 368. On the other hand, you make a Type II error if you conclude that the population mean fill *is* 368 when it is *not* 368.

The Level of Significance (α*)*   The probability of committing a Type I error, denoted by α (the lowercase Greek letter *alpha*), is referred to as the **level of significance** of the statistical test. Traditionally, you control the Type I error by deciding the risk level α that you are willing to have in rejecting the null hypothesis when it is true. Because you specify the level of significance before the hypothesis test is performed, the risk of committing a Type I error, α, is directly under your control. Traditionally, you select levels of 0.01, 0.05, or 0.10. The choice of a particular risk level for making a Type I error depends on the cost of making a Type I error. After you specify the value for α, you know the size of the rejection region because α is the probability of rejection under the null hypothesis. From this fact, you can then determine the critical value or values that divide the rejection and nonrejection regions.

The Confidence Coefficient   The complement of the probability of a Type I error $(1 - \alpha)$ is called the confidence coefficient. When multiplied by 100%, the confidence coefficient yields the confidence level that was studied when constructing confidence intervals (see section 8.1).

> The **confidence coefficient**, $1 - \alpha$, is the probability that you will not reject the null hypothesis H_0 when it is true and should not be rejected. The **confidence level** of a hypothesis test is $(1 - \alpha) \times 100\%$.

In terms of hypothesis-testing methodology, the confidence coefficient represents the probability of concluding that the value of the parameter as specified in the null hypothesis is plausible when it is true. In the Oxford Cereal Company scenario, the confidence coefficient measures the probability of concluding that the population mean fill is 368 grams when it actually is 368 grams.

The β Risk   The probability of committing a Type II error is denoted by β (the lowercase Greek letter *beta*). Unlike the Type I error, which you control by the selection of α, the probability of making a Type II error depends on the difference between the hypothesized and actual value of the population parameter. Because large differences are easier to find than small ones, if the difference between the hypothesized and actual value of the population parameter is large, β is small. For example, if the true population mean is 330 grams, there is a small chance (β) that you will conclude that the mean has not changed from 368. On the other hand, if the difference between the hypothesized and actual value of the parameter is small, the probability you will commit a Type II error is large. Thus, if the population mean is really 367 grams, you have a high probability of making a Type II error by concluding that the population mean fill amount is still 368 grams.

The Power of a Test   The complement of the probability of a Type II error (1 − β) is called the power of a statistical test.

> The **power of a statistical test**, 1 − β, is the probability that you will reject the null hypothesis when it is false and should be rejected.

In the Oxford Cereal Company scenario, the power of the test is the probability you will correctly conclude that the mean fill amount is not 368 grams when it actually is not 368 grams.

Risks in Decision Making: A Delicate Balance   Table 9.1 illustrates the results of the two possible decisions (do not reject H_0 or reject H_0) that you can make in any hypothesis test. Depending on the specific decision, you can make one of two types of errors or you can reach one of two types of correct conclusions.

TABLE 9.1

Hypothesis Testing and Decision Making

	Actual Situation	
Statistical Decision	H_0 True	H_0 False
Do not reject H_0	Correct decision Confidence = $1 - \alpha$	Type II error P(Type II error) = β
Reject H_0	Type I error P(Type I error) = α	Correct decision Power = $1 - \beta$

One way in which you can reduce the probability of making a Type II error is by increasing the size of the sample. Large samples generally permit you to detect even very small differences between the hypothesized values and the population parameters. For a given level of α, increasing the sample size will decrease β and therefore will increase the power of the test to detect that the null hypothesis H_0 is false. However, there is always a limit to your resources, and this will affect the decision as to how large a sample you can take. Thus, for a given sample size, you must consider the trade-offs between the two possible types of errors. Because you can directly control the risk of Type I error, you can reduce this risk by selecting a smaller value for α. For example, if the negative consequences associated with making a Type I error are substantial, you could select α = 0.01 instead of 0.05. However, when you decrease α, you increase β, so reducing the risk of a Type I error will result in an increased risk of Type II error. If, on the other hand, you wish to reduce β, you could select a larger value for α. Therefore, if it is important to try to avoid a Type II error, you can select α of 0.05 or 0.10 instead of 0.01.

In the Oxford Cereal Company scenario, the risk of a Type I error involves concluding that the mean fill amount has changed from the hypothesized 368 grams when it has not changed. The risk of a Type II error involves concluding that the mean fill amount has not changed from the hypothesized 368 grams when in truth it has changed. The choice of reasonable values for α and β depends on the costs inherent in each type of error. For example, if it is very costly to change the cereal-filling process, then you would want to be very confident that a change is needed before making any changes. In this case, the risk of a Type I error is most important and you would choose a small α. On the other hand, if you want to be very certain of detecting changes from a mean of 368 grams, the risk of a Type II error is most important, and you would choose a higher level of α.

PROBLEMS FOR SECTION 9.1

Learning the Basics

 9.1 You use the symbol H_0 for which hypothesis?

 9.2 You use the symbol H_1 for which hypothesis?

 9.3 What symbol do you use for the level of significance or chance of committing a Type I error?

9.4 What symbol do you use for the chance of committing a Type II error?

 9.5 What does $1 - \beta$ represent?

9.6 What is the relationship of α to the Type I error?

9.7 What is the relationship of β to the Type II error?

9.8 How is power related to the probability of making a Type II error?

 9.9 Why is it possible to reject the null hypothesis when it is true?

9.10 Why is it possible to not reject the null hypothesis when it is false?

9.11 For a given sample size, if α is reduced from 0.05 to 0.01, what will happen to β?

9.12 For H_0: $\mu = 100$, H_1: $\mu \neq 100$, and for a sample of size n, why is β larger if the actual value of μ is 90 than if the actual value of μ is 75?

Applying the Concepts

 9.13 In the U.S. legal system, a defendant is presumed innocent until proven guilty. Consider a null hypothesis H_0, that the defendant is innocent, and an alternative hypothesis H_1, that the defendant is guilty. A jury has two possible decisions: Convict the defendant (i.e., reject the null hypothesis) or do not convict the defendant (i.e., do not reject the null hypothesis). Explain the meaning of the risks of committing either a Type I or Type II error in this example.

9.14 Suppose the defendant in problem 9.13 is presumed guilty until proven innocent as in some other judicial systems. How do the null and alternative hypotheses differ from those in problem 9.13? What are the meanings of the risks of committing either a Type I or Type II error here?

9.15 The U.S. Food and Drug Administration (FDA) is responsible for approving new drugs. Many consumer groups feel that the approval process is too easy, and, therefore, too many drugs are approved that are later found to be unsafe. On the other hand, there are a number of industry lobbyists who are pushing for a more lenient approval process so that pharmaceutical companies can get new drugs approved more easily and quickly (Rochelle Sharpe, "FDA Tries to Find Right Balance on Drug Approvals," *The Wall Street Journal*, April 20, 1999, A24). Consider a null hypothesis that a new, unapproved drug is unsafe and an alternative hypothesis that a new, unapproved drug is safe.
a. Explain the risks of committing a Type I or Type II error.
b. Which type of error are the consumer groups trying to avoid? Explain.
c. Which type of error are the industry lobbyists trying to avoid? Explain.
d. How would it be possible to lower the chance of both Type I and Type II errors?

  9.16 As a result of complaints from both students and faculty about lateness, the registrar at a large university wants to adjust the scheduled class times to allow for adequate travel time between classes and is ready to undertake a study. Until now, the registrar has believed that 20 minutes between scheduled classes should be sufficient. State the null hypothesis H_0 and the alternative hypothesis H_1.

9.17 The director of manufacturing at a clothing factory needs to determine whether a new machine is producing a particular type of cloth according to the manufacturer's specifications, which indicate that the cloth should have a mean breaking strength of 70 pounds. A sample of 49 pieces of cloth reveals a sample mean breaking strength of 69.1 pounds. State the null and alternative hypotheses.

9.18 The manager of a paint supply store wants to determine whether the amount of paint contained in 1-gallon cans purchased from a nationally known manufacturer actually averages 1 gallon. It is known from the manufacturer's specifications that the standard deviation of the amount of paint is 0.02 gallon. A random sample of fifty

1-gallon cans is selected, and the sample mean is 0.995 gallon. State the null and alternative hypotheses.

9.19 The quality-control manager at a lightbulb factory needs to determine whether the mean life of a large shipment of lightbulbs is equal to the specified value of 375 hours. It is known that the population standard deviation is 100 hours. A random sample of 64 lightbulbs indicates a sample mean life of 350 hours. State the null and alternative hypotheses.

9.2 Z TEST OF HYPOTHESIS FOR THE MEAN (σ KNOWN)

Now that you have been introduced to hypothesis-testing methodology, recall that in the "Using Statistics" scenario on page 258, the Oxford Cereal Company wants to determine whether the cereal-filling process is working properly (that is, whether the mean fill throughout the entire packaging process remains at the specified 368 grams and no corrective action is needed). To evaluate the 368-gram requirement, you take a random sample of 25 boxes, weigh each box, and then evaluate the difference between the sample statistic and the hypothesized population parameter by comparing the mean weight (in grams) from the sample to the expected mean of 368 grams specified by the company. For this filling process, the null and alternative hypotheses are

$$H_0: \mu = 368$$

$$H_1: \mu \neq 368$$

When the standard deviation σ is known, you use the Z test if the population is normally distributed. If the population is not normally distributed, you can still use the Z test if the sample size is large enough for the Central Limit Theorem to take effect (see section 7.2). Equation (9.1) defines the **Z-test statistic** for determining the difference between the sample mean $\overline{X}$ and the population mean μ when the standard deviation σ is known.

Z TEST OF HYPOTHESIS FOR THE MEAN (σ KNOWN)

$$Z = \frac{\overline{X} - \mu}{\dfrac{\sigma}{\sqrt{n}}} \tag{9.1}$$

In Equation (9.1) the numerator measures how far (in an absolute sense) the observed sample mean $\overline{X}$ is from the hypothesized mean μ. The denominator is the standard error of the mean, so Z represents the difference between $\overline{X}$ and μ in standard error units.

The Critical Value Approach to Hypothesis Testing

The observed value of the Z test statistic, Equation (9.1), is compared to critical values. These critical values are expressed as standardized Z values (i.e., in standard-deviation units). For example, if you use a level of significance of 0.05, the size of the rejection region is 0.05. Because the rejection region is divided into the two tails of the distribution (this is called a **two-tail test**), you divide the 0.05 into two equal parts of 0.025 each. A rejection region of 0.025 in each tail of the normal distribution results in a cumulative area of 0.025 below the lower critical value and a cumulative area of 0.975 below the upper critical value. According to the cumulative standardized normal distribution table (Table E.2), the critical values that divide the rejection and nonrejection regions are −1.96 and +1.96. Figure 9.2 illustrates that if the mean is actually 368 grams, as H_0 claims, then the values of the test statistic Z have a standardized normal distribution centered at $Z = 0$ (which corresponds to an $\bar{X}$ value of 368 grams). Values of Z greater than +1.96 or less than −1.96 indicate that $\bar{X}$ is so far from the hypothesized $\mu = 368$ that it is unlikely that such a value would occur if H_0 were true.

FIGURE 9.2

Testing a Hypothesis about the Mean (σ Known) at the 0.05 Level of Significance

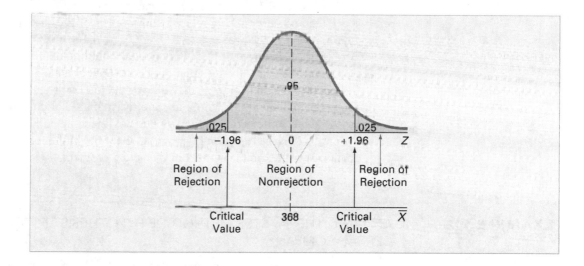

Therefore, the decision rule is

Reject H_0 if $Z > +1.96$

or if $Z < -1.96$;

otherwise do not reject H_0.

Suppose that the sample of 25 cereal boxes indicates a sample mean $\bar{X} = 372.5$ grams and the population standard deviation σ is assumed to be 15 grams. Using Equation (9.1):

$$Z = \frac{\bar{X} - \mu}{\dfrac{\sigma}{\sqrt{n}}} = \frac{372.5 - 368}{\dfrac{15}{\sqrt{25}}} = +1.50$$

Because the test statistic $Z = +1.50$ is between −1.96 and +1.96, you do not reject H_0 (see Figure 9.3). You continue to believe that the mean fill amount is 368 grams. To take into account the possibility of a Type II error, you state the conclusion as "there is insufficient evidence that the mean fill is different from 368 grams."

FIGURE 9.3

Testing a Hypothesis about the Mean (σ Known) at the 0.05 Level of Significance

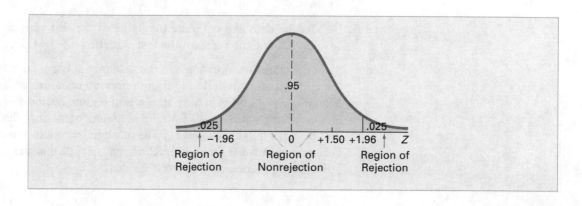

Exhibit 9.1 provides a summary of the critical value approach for hypothesis testing.

EXHIBIT 9.1: THE SIX-STEP METHOD OF HYPOTHESIS TESTING

1. State the null hypothesis, H_0, and the alternative hypothesis, H_1.
2. Choose the level of significance, α, and the sample size, n. The level of significance is specified according to the relative importance of the risks of committing Type I and Type II errors in the problem.
3. Determine the appropriate test statistic and sampling distribution.
4. Determine the critical values that divide the rejection and nonrejection regions.
5. Collect the data and compute the value of the test statistic.
6. Make the statistical decision and state the managerial conclusion. If the test statistic falls into the nonrejection region, you do not reject the null hypothesis H_0. If the test statistic falls into the rejection region, you reject the null hypothesis. The managerial conclusion is written in the context of the actual problem.

EXAMPLE 9.2

APPLYING THE SIX-STEP METHOD OF HYPOTHESIS TESTING AT THE OXFORD CEREAL COMPANY

State the six-step method of hypothesis testing at the Oxford Cereal Company.

SOLUTION

Step 1: State the null and alternative hypotheses. The null hypothesis H_0 is always stated in statistical terms using population parameters. In testing whether the mean fill is 368 grams, the null hypothesis states that μ equals 368. The alternative hypothesis, H_1, is also stated in statistical terms using population parameters. Therefore, the alternative hypothesis states that μ is not equal to 368 grams.

Step 2: Choose the level of significance and the sample size. You choose the level of significance α according to the relative importance of the risks of committing Type I and Type II errors in the problem. The smaller the value of α, the less risk there is of making a Type I error. In this example, a Type I error is to conclude that the population mean is not 368 grams, when it is 368 grams. Here, $\alpha = 0.05$ is selected. The sample $n = 25$.

Step 3: Select the appropriate test statistic. Because σ is known from information about the filling process, you use the normal distribution and the Z-test statistic.

Step 4: Determine the rejection region. Critical values for the appropriate test statistic are selected so that the rejection region contains a total area of α when H_0 is true, and the nonrejection region contains a total area of $1 - \alpha$ when H_0 is true. Since $\alpha = 0.05$ in the cereal example, the critical values of the Z-test statistic are -1.96 and $+1.96$. The rejection region is $Z < -1.96$ or $Z > +1.96$. The nonrejection region is $-1.96 < Z < +1.96$.

Step 5: Collect the data and compute the value of the test statistic. In the cereal example, $\overline{X} = 372.5$ and the value of the test statistic is $Z = +1.50$.

Step 6: State the statistical decision and the managerial conclusion. First, determine whether the test statistic has fallen into the rejection or nonrejection region. For the cereal example, $Z = +1.50$ is in the nonrejection region, because $-1.96 < Z = +1.50 < +1.96$. Since the test statistic falls into the nonrejection region, the statistical decision is do not reject the null hypothesis H_0. The managerial conclusion is that there is insufficient evidence to prove at the 0.05 level of significance that the mean fill is different from 368 grams. No corrective action is needed.

EXAMPLE 9.3   REJECTING A NULL HYPOTHESIS

You are the manager of a fast-food restaurant. You want to determine whether the waiting time to place an order has changed in the last month from its previous population mean value of 4.5 minutes. From past experience, you can assume that the population standard deviation is 1.2 minutes. You select a sample of 25 orders during a one-hour period. The sample mean is 5.1 minutes. Use the six-step approach of Exhibit 9.1 to determine whether there is evidence at the 0.05 level of significance that the mean waiting time to place an order has changed in the last month from its previous population mean value of 4.5 minutes.

SOLUTION

Step 1: The null hypothesis is that the population mean has not changed from its previous value of 4.5 minutes.

$$H_0: \mu = 4.5$$

The alternative hypothesis is the opposite of the null hypothesis. Since the null hypothesis is that the population mean is 4.5 minutes, the alternative hypothesis is that the population mean is not 4.5 minutes.

$$H_1: \mu \neq 4.5$$

Step 2: You have selected a sample of $n = 25$. The level of significance is 0.05 (i.e., $\alpha = 0.05$).

Step 3: Because σ is known, you use the normal distribution and the *Z*-test statistic.

Step 4: Since $\alpha = 0.05$, the critical values of the *Z*-test statistic are -1.96 and $+1.96$. The rejection region is $Z < -1.96$ or $Z > +1.96$. The nonrejection region is $-1.96 < Z < +1.96$.

Step 5: You collect the data and compute $\overline{X} = 5.1$. Using Equation (9.1), you compute the test statistic.

$$Z = \frac{\overline{X} - \mu}{\dfrac{\sigma}{\sqrt{n}}} = \frac{5.1 - 4.5}{\dfrac{1.2}{\sqrt{25}}} = 2.50$$

Step 6: Since $Z = 2.50 > 1.96$, you reject the null hypothesis. You conclude that there is evidence that the waiting time to place an order has changed from its previous population mean value of 4.5 minutes. The mean waiting time for customers is longer now than last month.

The *p*-Value Approach to Hypothesis Testing

Most modern software including Microsoft Excel, Minitab, and SPSS compute the *p*-value when performing a test of hypothesis.

> The ***p*-value** is the probability of getting a test statistic equal to or more extreme than the sample result, given that the null hypothesis H_0 is true.

The *p*-value, often referred to as the *observed level of significance*, is the smallest level at which H_0 can be rejected.

The decision rules for rejecting H_0 in the *p*-value approach are.

- If the *p*-value is greater than or equal to α, you do not reject the null hypothesis.
- If the *p*-value is less than α, you reject the null hypothesis.

Many people confuse these rules, mistakenly believing that a high *p*-value is grounds for rejection. You can avoid this confusion by remembering the following mantra.

If the *p*-value is low, then H_0 must go.

To understand the *p*-value approach, consider the Oxford Cereal Company scenario. You tested whether or not the mean fill was equal to 368 grams. The test statistic resulted in a *Z* value of +1.50 and you did not reject the null hypothesis because +1.50 was less than the upper critical value of +1.96 and more than the lower critical value of −1.96.

To use the *p*-value approach for the *two-tail test*, you find the probability of getting a test statistic *Z* that is equal to or *more extreme than* 1.50 standard deviation units from the center of a standardized normal distribution. In other words, you need to compute the probability of a *Z* value greater than +1.50 along with the probability of a *Z* value less than −1.50. Table E.2 shows that the probability of a *Z* value below −1.50 is 0.0668. The probability of a value below +1.50 is 0.9332 and the probability of a value above +1.50 is 1 − 0.9332 = 0.0668. Therefore, the *p*-value for this two-tail test is 0.0668 + 0.0668 = 0.1336 (see Figure 9.4). Thus, the probability of a result equal to or more extreme than the one observed is 0.1336. Because 0.1336 is greater than α = 0.05, you do not reject the null hypothesis.

FIGURE 9.4

Finding a *p*-Value for a Two-Tail Test

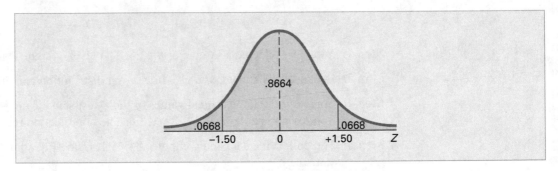

In this example, the observed sample mean is 372.5 grams, 4.5 grams above the hypothesized value and the *p*-value is 0.1336. Thus, if the population mean is 368 grams, there is a 13.36% chance that the sample mean will be more than 4.5 grams away from 368 (i.e., greater than or equal to 372.5 grams or less than or equal to 363.5 grams). Therefore, while 372.5 is above the hypothesized value of 368, a result as extreme or more extreme than 372.5 is not highly unlikely when the population mean is 368.

Unless you are dealing with a test statistic that follows the normal distribution, the computation of the *p*-value can be very difficult. However, software such as Microsoft Excel, Minitab or SPSS routinely presents the *p*-value as part of the output for hypothesis-testing procedures. Figure 9.5 displays a Microsoft Excel worksheet for the cereal-filling example discussed in this section.

FIGURE 9.5

Microsoft Excel Z-Test Worksheet for the Cereal-Filling Example

Exhibit 9.2 provides a summary of the p-value approach for hypothesis testing.

EXHIBIT 9.2: THE FIVE-STEP METHOD OF HYPOTHESIS TESTING USING THE P-VALUE APPROACH

1. State the null hypothesis, H_0, and the alternative hypothesis, H_1.
2. Choose the level of significance, α, and the sample size, n. The level of significance is specified according to the relative importance of the risks of committing Type I and Type II errors in the problem.
3. Determine the appropriate test statistic and sampling distribution.
4. Collect the data, compute the value of the test statistic, and compute the p-value.
5. Make the statistical decision and state the managerial conclusion. If the p-value is greater than or equal to α, you do not reject the null hypothesis H_0. If the p-value is less than α, you reject the null hypothesis. Remember the mantra, if the p-value is low, then H_0 must go. The managerial conclusion is written in the context of the actual problem.

EXAMPLE 9.4

REJECTING A NULL HYPOTHESIS USING THE P-VALUE APPROACH

You are the manager of a fast-food restaurant. You want to determine whether the waiting time to place an order has changed in the last month from its previous population mean value of 4.5 minutes. From past experience, you can assume that the population standard deviation is 1.2 minutes. You select a sample of 25 orders during a one-hour period. The sample mean is 5.1 minutes. Use the five-step approach of Exhibit 9.2 above to determine whether there is evidence that the mean waiting time to place an order has changed in the last month from its previous population mean value of 4.5 minutes.

SOLUTION

Step 1: The null hypothesis is that the population mean has not changed from its previous value of 4.5 minutes.

$$H_0: \mu = 4.5$$

The alternative hypothesis is the opposite of the null hypothesis. Since the null hypothesis is that the population mean is 4.5 minutes, the alternative hypothesis is that the population mean is not 4.5 minutes.

$$H_1: \mu \neq 4.5$$

Step 2: You have selected a sample size of $n = 25$. You choose a 0.05 level of significance (i.e., $\alpha = .05$).

Step 3: Select the appropriate test statistic. Because σ is known you use the normal distribution and the Z-test statistic.

Step 4: You collect the data and compute $\overline{X} = 5.1$. Using Equation (9.1) you compute the test statistic as follows.

$$Z = \frac{\overline{X} - \mu}{\frac{\sigma}{\sqrt{n}}} = \frac{5.1 - 4.5}{\frac{1.2}{\sqrt{25}}} = 2.50$$

To find the probability of getting a test statistic Z that is equal to or *more extreme than* 2.50 standard deviation units from the center of a standardized normal distribution, you compute the probability of a Z value greater than 2.50 along with the probability of a Z value less than -2.50. From Table E.2, the probability of a Z value below -2.50 is 0.0062. The probability of a value below $+2.50$ is 0.9938. Therefore, the probability of a value above $+2.50$ is $1 - 0.9938 = 0.0062$. Thus, the p-value for this two-tail test is $0.0062 + 0.0062 = 0.0124$.

Step 5: Since the p-value $= 0.0124 < \alpha = 0.05$, you reject the null hypothesis. You conclude that there is evidence that the mean waiting time to place an order has changed from its previous population mean value of 4.5 minutes. The mean waiting time for customers is longer now than last month.

A Connection between Confidence Interval Estimation and Hypothesis Testing

This chapter and Chapter 8 discuss the two major components of statistical inference, confidence interval estimation and hypothesis testing. Although they are based on the same set of concepts, they are used for different purposes. In Chapter 8, you used confidence intervals to estimate parameters. In this chapter, hypothesis testing is used for making decisions about specified values of population parameters. Hypothesis tests are used when trying to prove that a parameter is less than, more than, or not equal to a specified value. Proper interpretation of a confidence interval, however, can also indicate whether a parameter is less than, more than, or not equal to a specified value.

For example, in this section you tested whether the population mean fill amount was different from 368 grams by using Equation (9.1):

$$Z = \frac{\overline{X} - \mu}{\dfrac{\sigma}{\sqrt{n}}}$$

Instead of testing the null hypothesis that $\mu = 368$ grams, you can reach the same conclusion by forming a confidence interval estimate of μ. If the hypothesized value of $\mu = 368$ falls into the interval, you do not reject the null hypothesis because 368 would not be considered an unusual value. On the other hand, if the hypothesized value does not fall into the interval, you reject the null hypothesis, because "368 grams" is then considered an unusual value. Using Equation (8.1) and the following data:

$$n = 25, \overline{X} = 372.5 \text{ grams}, \sigma = 15 \text{ grams}$$

For a confidence level of 95% (corresponding to a 0.05 level of significance—i.e., $\alpha = 0.05$),

$$\overline{X} \pm Z \frac{\sigma}{\sqrt{n}}$$

$$372.5 \pm (1.96) \frac{15}{\sqrt{25}}$$

$$372.5 \pm 5.88$$

so that

$$366.62 \leq \mu \leq 378.38$$

Because the interval includes the hypothesized value of 368 grams, you do not reject the null hypothesis. There is insufficient evidence that the mean fill amount over the entire filling process is not 368 grams. You reached the same decision by using hypothesis testing.

PROBLEMS FOR SECTION 9.2

Learning the Basics

 9.20 If you use a 0.05 level of significance in a (two-tail) hypothesis test, what will you decide if the computed value of the test statistic *Z* is +2.21?

 9.21 If you use a 0.10 level of significance in a (two-tail) hypothesis test, what is your decision rule for rejecting a null hypothesis that the population mean is 500 if you use the *Z* test?

 9.22 If you use a 0.01 level of significance in a (two-tail) hypothesis test, what is your decision rule for rejecting H_0: $\mu = 12.5$ if you use the *Z* test?

 9.23 What is your decision in problem 9.22 if the computed value of the test statistic *Z* is −2.61?

 9.24 Suppose that in a two-tail hypothesis test you compute the value of the test statistic *Z* as +2.00. What is the *p*-value?

 9.25 In problem 9.24, what is your statistical decision if you test the null hypothesis at the 0.10 level of significance?

 9.26 Suppose that in a two-tail hypothesis test you compute the value of the test statistic *Z* as −1.38. What is the *p*-value?

 9.27 In problem 9.26, what is your statistical decision if you test the null hypothesis at the 0.01 level of significance?

Applying the Concepts

9.28 The director of manufacturing at a clothing factory needs to determine whether a new machine is producing a particular type of cloth according to the manufacturer's specifications, which indicate that the cloth should have a mean breaking strength of 70 pounds and a standard deviation of 3.5 pounds. A sample of 49 pieces of cloth reveals a sample mean breaking strength of 69.1 pounds.
a. Is there evidence that the machine is not meeting the manufacturer's specifications for mean breaking strength? (Use a 0.05 level of significance.)
b. Compute the *p*-value and interpret its meaning.
c. What is your answer in (a) if the standard deviation is 1.75 pounds?
d. What is your answer in (a) if the sample mean is 69 pounds and the standard deviation is 3.5 pounds?

 9.29 The manager of a paint supply store wants to determine whether the mean amount of paint contained in 1-gallon cans purchased from a nationally known manufacturer is actually 1 gallon. You know from the manufacturer's specifications that the standard deviation of the amount of paint is 0.02 gallon. You select a random sample of 50 cans, and the mean amount of paint per 1-gallon can is 0.995 gallon.
a. Is there evidence that the mean amount is different from 1.0 gallon (use α = 0.01)?
b. Compute the *p*-value and interpret its meaning.
c. Construct a 99% confidence interval estimate of the population mean amount of paint.
d. Compare the results of (a) and (c). What conclusions do you reach?

9.30 The quality-control manager at a lightbulb factory needs to determine whether the mean life of a large shipment of lightbulbs is equal to 375 hours. The population standard deviation is 100 hours. A random sample of 64 lightbulbs indicates a sample mean life of 350 hours.
a. At the 0.05 level of significance, is there evidence that the mean life is different from 375 hours?
b. Compute the *p*-value and interpret its meaning.
c. Construct a 95% confidence interval estimate of the population mean life of the lightbulbs.
d. Compare the results of (a) and (c). What conclusions do you reach?

9.31 The inspection division of the Lee County Weights and Measures Department is interested in determining whether the proper amount of soft drink has been placed in 2-liter bottles at the local bottling plant of a large nationally known soft-drink company. The bottling plant has informed the inspection division that the standard deviation for 2-liter bottles is 0.05 liter. A random sample of one hundred 2-liter bottles selected from this bottling plant indicates a sample mean of 1.99 liters.
a. At the 0.05 level of significance, is there evidence that the mean amount in the bottles is different from 2.0 liters?
b. Compute the *p*-value and interpret its meaning.
c. Construct a 95% confidence interval estimate of the population mean amount in the bottles.
d. Compare the results of (a) and (c). What conclusions do you reach?

9.32 A manufacturer of salad dressings uses machines to dispense liquid ingredients into bottles that move along a filling line. The machine that dispenses dressings is working properly when the mean amount dispensed is 8 ounces. The population standard deviation of the amount dispensed is 0.15 ounce. A sample of 50 bottles is selected periodically, and the filling line is stopped if there is evidence that the mean amount dispensed is different from 8 ounces.

Suppose that the mean amount dispensed in a particular sample of 50 bottles is 7.983 ounces.

a. Is there evidence that the population mean amount is different from 8 ounces? (Use a 0.05 level of significance.)

b. Compute the *p*-value and interpret its meaning.

c. What is your answer in (a) if the standard deviation is 0.05 ounce?

d. What is your answer in (a) if the sample mean is 7.952 ounces and the standard deviation is 0.15 ounce?

9.33 ATMs must be stocked with enough cash to satisfy customers making withdrawals over an entire weekend. But if too much cash is unnecessarily kept in the ATMs, the bank is forgoing the opportunity of investing the money and earning interest. Suppose that at a particular branch the population mean amount of money withdrawn from ATMs per customer transaction over the weekend is $160 with a population standard deviation of $30.

a. If a random sample of 36 customer transactions indicates that the sample mean withdrawal amount is $172, is there evidence to believe that the population mean withdrawal amount is no longer $160? (Use a 0.05 level of significance.)

b. Compute the *p*-value and interpret its meaning.

c. What is your answer in (b) if you use a 0.01 level of significance?

d. What is your answer in (b) if the standard deviation is $24 (use $\alpha = 0.05$)?

9.3   ONE-TAIL TESTS

So far, hypothesis-testing methodology has been used to examine the question of whether or not the population mean amount of cereal filled is 368 grams. The alternative hypothesis (H_1: $\mu \neq 368$) contains two possibilities: Either the mean is less than 368 grams, or the mean is more than 368 grams. For this reason, the rejection region is divided into the two tails of the sampling distribution of the mean.

In many situations, however, the alternative hypothesis focuses on a *particular direction*. One such situation occurs in the following application. A company that makes processed cheese is interested in determining whether some suppliers that provide milk for the processing operation are adding water to their milk to increase the amount supplied to the processing operation. It is known that excess water reduces the freezing point of the milk. The freezing point of natural milk is normally distributed with a mean of $-0.545°$ Celsius (C). The standard deviation of the freezing temperature of natural milk is known to be 0.008°C. Because the cheese company is only interested in determining whether the freezing point of the milk is less than what would be expected from natural milk, the entire rejection region is located in the lower tail of the distribution.

The Critical Value Approach

Suppose you wish to determine whether the mean freezing point of milk is less than $-0.545°$. To perform this one-tail hypothesis test, you use the six-step method listed in Exhibit 9.1.

Step 1: H_0: $\mu \geq -0.545°$
H_1: $\mu < -0.545°$

The alternative hypothesis contains the statement you are trying to prove. If you reject the null hypothesis there is statistical proof that the mean freezing point of the milk is less than the natural freezing point of $-0.545°$. If the conclusion of the test is "do not reject H_0," then there is insufficient evidence to prove that the mean freezing point is below the natural freezing point of $-0.545°$.

Step 2: You have selected a sample size of $n = 25$. You decide to use $\alpha = 0.05$.

Step 3: Because σ is known, you use the normal distribution and the *Z*-test statistic.

Step 4: The rejection region is entirely contained in the lower tail of the sampling distribution of the mean since you want to reject H_0 only when the sample mean is significantly below $-0.545°$. When the entire rejection region is contained in one tail of the sampling distribution of the test statistic, the test is called a **one-tail** or **directional test**.

When the alternative hypothesis includes the *less than* sign, the critical value of Z must be less than zero. As shown from Table 9.2 and Figure 9.6, because the entire rejection region is in the lower tail of the standardized normal distribution and contains an area of 0.05, the critical value of the Z-test statistic is -1.645, the mean of -1.64 and -1.65. The decision rule is

$$\text{Reject } H_0 \text{ if } Z < -1.645;$$

$$\text{otherwise do not reject } H_0.$$

TABLE 9.2

Finding the Critical Value of the Z-Test Statistic from the Standardized Normal Distribution for a One-Tail Test with $\alpha = 0.05$

Z	.00	.01	.02	.03	.04	.05	.06	.07	.08	.09
⋮	⋮	⋮	⋮	⋮	⋮	⋮	⋮	⋮	⋮	⋮
−1.8	.0359	.0351	.0344	.0336	.0329	.0322	.0314	.0307	.0301	.0294
−1.7	.0446	.0436	.0427	.0418	.0409	.0401	.0392	.0384	.0375	.0367
−1.6	.0548	.0537	.0526	.0516	.0505	.0495	.0485	.0475	.0465	.0455

Source: Extracted from Table E.2.

FIGURE 9.6

One-Tail Test of Hypothesis for a Mean (σ Known) at the 0.05 Level of Significance

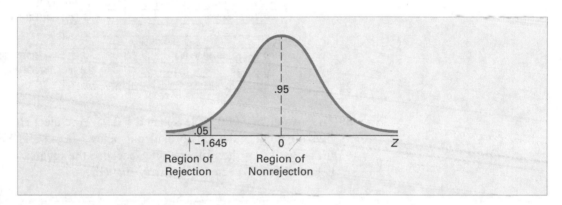

Step 5:   You select a sample of 25 containers of milk and compute the sample mean freezing point to be $-0.550°$. Using $n = 25$, $\overline{X} = -0.550°$, $\sigma = 0.008°$, and Equation (9.1),

$$Z = \frac{\overline{X} - \mu}{\dfrac{\sigma}{\sqrt{n}}} = \frac{-0.550 - (-0.545)}{\dfrac{0.008}{\sqrt{25}}} = -3.125$$

Step 6:   Since $Z = -3.125 < -1.645$, you reject the null hypothesis (see Figure 9.6). You conclude that the mean freezing point of the milk provided is below $-0.545°$. The company should pursue an investigation of the milk supplier because the mean freezing point is significantly below what is expected to occur by chance.

The *p*-Value Approach

Use the five steps listed in Exhibit 9.2 to illustrate the above test using the *p*-value approach.

Steps 1–3:   These steps are the same as in the critical value approach.

Step 4: $Z = -3.125$ (see step 5 of the critical value approach). Since the alternative hypothesis indicates a rejection region entirely in the *lower* tail of the sampling distribution of the Z-test statistic, to compute the *p*-value you need to find the probability that the Z value will be *below* the test statistic of -3.125. From Table E.2, the probability that the Z value will be below -3.125 is 0.0009 (see Figures 9.7 and 9.8).

FIGURE 9.7

Determining the *p*-Value for a One-Tail Test

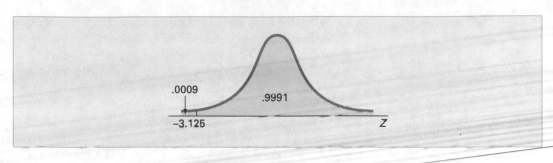

FIGURE 9.8

Microsoft Excel Z-Test Output for the Milk Production Example

	A	B	
1	**Milk Production Hypothesis**		
2			
3	**Data**		
4	Null Hypothesis μ=	-0.545	
5	Level of Significance	0.06	
6	Population Standard Deviation	0.008	
7	Sample Size	25	
8	Sample Mean	-0.55	
9			
10	Intermediate Calculations		
11	Standard Error of the Mean	0.0016	=B6/SQRT(B7)
12	Z Test Statistic	-3.125	=(B8-B4)/B11
13			
14	Lower-Tail Test		
15	Lower Critical Value	-1.6449	=NORMSINV(B5)
16	*p*-Value	0.0009	=NORMSDIST(B12)
17	Reject the null hypothesis		

Step 5: The *p*-value of 0.0009 is less than $\alpha = 0.05$. You reject H_0. You conclude that the mean freezing point of the milk provided is below $-0.545°$. The company should pursue an investigation of the milk supplier because the mean freezing point is significantly below what is expected to occur by chance.

EXAMPLE 9.5

A ONE-TAIL TEST FOR THE MEAN

A company that manufactures chocolate bars is particularly concerned that the mean weight of the chocolate bar not exceed 6.03 ounces. Past experience allows you to assume that the standard deviation is 0.02 ounce. A sample of 50 chocolate bars is selected and the sample mean is 6.034 ounces. Using the $\alpha = 0.01$ level of significance, is there evidence that the population mean weight of the chocolate bars is greater than 6.03 ounces?

SOLUTION Using the critical value approach,

Step 1: $H_0: \mu \leq 6.03$
$H_1: \mu > 6.03$

Step 2: You have selected a sample of $n = 50$. You decide to use $\alpha = 0.01$.

Step 3: Because σ is known, you use the normal distribution and the Z-test statistic.

Step 4: The rejection region is entirely contained in the upper tail of the sampling distribution of the mean since you want to reject H_0 only when the sample mean is significantly above 6.03 ounces. Because the entire rejection region is in the upper tail of the standardized normal distribution and contains an area of 0.01, the critical value of the Z-test statistic is 2.33.

The decision rule is

$$\text{Reject } H_0 \text{ if } Z > 2.33;$$

$$\text{otherwise do not reject } H_0.$$

Step 5: You select a sample of 50 chocolate bars and the sample mean weight is 6.034 ounces. Using $n = 50$, $\overline{X} = 6.034$, $\sigma = 0.02$, and Equation (9.1):

$$Z = \frac{\overline{X} - \mu}{\frac{\sigma}{\sqrt{n}}} = \frac{6.034 - 6.03}{\frac{0.02}{\sqrt{50}}} = 1.414$$

Step 6: Since $Z = 1.414 < 2.33$, you do not reject the null hypothesis. There is insufficient evidence to conclude that the population mean weight is above 6.03 ounces.

To perform one-tail tests of hypotheses, you must properly formulate H_0 and H_1. A summary of the null and alternative hypotheses for one-tail tests is as follows.

1. The null hypothesis H_0 represents the status quo or the current belief in a situation.
2. The alternative hypothesis H_1 is the opposite of the null hypothesis and represents a research claim or specific inference you would like to prove.
3. If you reject the null hypothesis, you have statistical proof that the alternative hypothesis is correct.
4. If you do not reject the null hypothesis, then you have failed to prove the alternative hypothesis. The failure to prove the alternative hypothesis, however, does not mean that you have proven the null hypothesis.
5. The null hypothesis (H_0) always refers to a specified value of the *population parameter* (such as μ), not to a *sample statistic* (such as $\overline{X}$).
6. The statement of the null hypothesis *always* contains an equal sign regarding the specified value of the parameter (e.g., H_0: $\mu \geq -0.545°C$).
7. The statement of the alternative hypothesis *never* contains an equal sign regarding the specified value of the parameter (e.g., H_1: $\mu < -0.545°C$).

PROBLEMS FOR SECTION 9.3

Learning the Basics

 9.34 What is the *upper-tail* critical value of the Z-test statistic at the 0.01 level of significance?

 9.35 In problem 9.34, what is your statistical decision if the computed value of the Z-test statistic is +2.39?

 9.36 What is the *lower-tail* critical value of the Z-test statistic at the 0.01 level of significance?

 9.37 In problem 9.36, what is your statistical decision if the computed value of the Z-test statistic is −1.15?

 9.38 Suppose that in a one-tail hypothesis test where you reject H_0 only in the *upper* tail, you compute the value of the test statistic Z to be +2.00. What is the p-value?

 9.39 In problem 9.38, what is your statistical decision if you tested the null hypothesis at the 0.05 level of significance?

 9.40 Suppose that in a one-tail hypothesis test where you reject H_0 only in the *lower* tail, you compute the value of the test statistic Z as −1.38. What is the p-value?

 9.41 In problem 9.40, what is your statistical decision if you tested the null hypothesis at the 0.01 level of significance?

9.42 In a one-tail hypothesis test where you reject H_0 only in the *lower* tail, you compute the value of the test statistic Z as +1.38. What is the p-value?

9.43 In problem 9.42, what is the statistical decision if you tested the null hypothesis at the 0.01 level of significance?

Applying the Concepts

 9.44 The Glen Valley Steel Company manufactures steel bars. If the production process is working properly, it turns out steel bars with mean length of *at least* 2.8 feet with a standard deviation of 0.20 foot (as determined from engineering specifications on the production equipment involved). Longer steel bars can be used or altered, but shorter bars must be scrapped. You select a sample of 25 bars and the mean length is 2.73 feet. Do you need to adjust the production equipment?

a. If you want to test the null hypothesis at the 0.05 level of significance, what decision would you make using the critical value approach to hypothesis testing?

b. If you want to test the null hypothesis at the 0.05 level of significance, what decision would you make using the p-value approach to hypothesis testing?

c. Interpret the meaning of the p-value in this problem.

d. Compare your conclusions in (a) and (b).

9.45 You are the manager of a restaurant that delivers pizza to college dormitory rooms. You have just changed your delivery process in an effort to reduce the mean time between the order and completion of delivery from the current 25 minutes. From past experience, you can assume that the population standard deviation is 6 minutes. A sample of 36 orders using the new delivery process yields a sample mean of 22.4 minutes.

a. Using the six-step critical value approach, at the 0.05 level of significance, is there evidence that the mean delivery time has been reduced below the previous population mean value of 25 minutes?

b. At the 0.05 level of significance, use the five-step p-value approach.

c. Interpret the meaning of the p-value in (b).

d. Compare your conclusions in (a) and (b).

9.46 Children in the United States account directly for $36 billion in sales annually. When their indirect influence over product decisions from stereos to vacations is considered, the total economic spending impacted by children in the United States is $290 billion. It is estimated that by age 10, a child makes an average of over five trips a week to a store (M. E. Goldberg, G. J. Gorn, L. A. Peracchio, and G. Bamossy, "Understanding Materialism Among Youth,"

Journal of Consumer Psychology, 2003, 13(3):278–288). Suppose that you want to prove that children in your city average more than five trips a week to a store. Let μ represent the population mean number of times children in your city make trips to a store.

a. State the null and alternative hypothesis.

b. Explain in the context of the above scenario the meaning of the Type I and Type II errors.

c. Suppose that you carry out a study in the city in which you live. Based on past studies, you assume that the standard deviation of the number of trips to the store is 1.6. You take a sample of 100 children and find that the mean number of trips to the store is 5.47. At the 0.01 level of significance, is there evidence that the population mean number of trips to the store is greater than 5 per week?

d. Interpret the meaning of the p-value in (c).

9.47 The policy of a particular bank branch is that its ATMs must be stocked with enough cash to satisfy customers making withdrawals over an entire weekend. Customer goodwill depends on such services meeting customer needs. At this branch the population mean amount of money withdrawn from ATMs per customer transaction over the weekend is $160 with a population standard deviation of $30. Suppose that a random sample of 36 customer transactions is examined, and you find that the sample mean withdrawal amount is $172.

a. At the 0.05 level of significance, using the critical value approach to hypothesis testing, is there evidence to believe that the population mean withdrawal amount is greater than $160?

b. At the 0.05 level of significance, using the p-value approach to hypothesis testing, is there evidence to believe that the population mean withdrawal amount is greater than $160?

c. Interpret the meaning of the p-value in this problem.

d. Compare your conclusions in (a) and (b).

9.4   *t* TEST OF HYPOTHESIS FOR THE MEAN (σ UNKNOWN)

In most hypothesis-testing situations dealing with numerical data, you do not know the population standard deviation σ. Instead, you use the sample standard deviation S. If you assume that the population is normally distributed, the sampling distribution of the mean will follow a t distribution with $n - 1$ degrees of freedom. If the population is not normally distributed, you can still use the t test if the sample size is large enough for the Central Limit Theorem to take effect (see section 7.2). Equation (9.2) defines the test statistic t for determining the difference between the sample mean $\overline{X}$ and the population mean μ when the sample standard deviation S is used.

---

t TEST OF HYPOTHESIS FOR THE MEAN (σ UNKNOWN)

$$t = \frac{\overline{X} - \mu}{\dfrac{S}{\sqrt{n}}} \tag{9.2}$$

where the test statistic t follows a t distribution having $n - 1$ degrees of freedom.

To illustrate the use of this *t* test, return to the "Using Statistics" scenario concerning the Saxon Home Improvement Company on page 258. Over the past five years, the mean amount per sales invoice is $120. As an accountant for the company, you need to inform the finance department if this amount changes. In other words, the hypothesis test is used to try to prove that the mean amount per sales invoice is increasing or decreasing.

The Critical Value Approach

To perform this two-tail hypothesis test, you use the six-step method listed in Exhibit 9.1.

Step 1: $H_0: \mu = \$120$
$H_1: \mu \neq \$120$
The alternative hypothesis contains the statement you are trying to prove. If the null hypothesis is rejected, you will have statistical proof that the mean amount per sales invoice is no longer $120. If the statistical conclusion is "do not reject H_0," then you will conclude that there is insufficient evidence to prove that the mean amount differs from the long-term mean of $120.

Step 2: You have selected a sample of $n = 12$. You decide to use $\alpha = 0.05$.

Step 3: Because σ is unknown, you use the *t* distribution and the *t*-test statistic for this example. You must assume that the population of sales invoices is normally distributed. This assumption is discussed on page 279.

Step 4: For a given sample size n, the test statistic *t* follows a *t* distribution with $n - 1$ degrees of freedom. The critical values of the *t* distribution with $12 - 1 = 11$ degrees of freedom are found in Table E.3, as illustrated in Figure 9.9 and Table 9.3. Because the alternative hypothesis H_1 that $\mu \neq \$120$ is *nondirectional*, the area in the rejection region of the *t* distribution's left (lower) tail is 0.025, and the area in the rejection region of the *t* distribution's right (upper) tail is also 0.025.

From the *t* table as given in Table E.3, a portion of which is shown in Table 9.3, the critical values are ±2.2010. The decision rule is

$$\text{Reject } H_0 \text{ if } t < -t_{11} = -2.2010$$
$$\text{or if } t > t_{11} = +2.2010;$$
$$\text{otherwise do not reject } H_0.$$

FIGURE 9.9

Testing a Hypothesis about the Mean (σ Unknown) at the 0.05 Level of Significance with 11 Degrees of Freedom

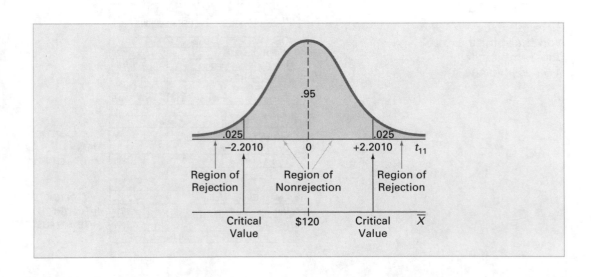

TABLE 9.3

Determining the
Critical Value from the
t Table for an Area of
0.025 in Each Tail with
11 Degrees of Freedom

Degrees of Freedom	Upper-Tail Areas					
	.25	.10	.05	.025	.01	.005
1	1.0000	3.0777	6.3138	12.7062	31.8207	63.6574
2	0.8165	1.8856	2.9200	4.3027	6.9646	9.9248
3	0.7649	1.6377	2.3534	3.1824	4.5407	5.8409
4	0.7407	1.5332	2.1318	2.7764	3.7469	4.6041
5	0.7267	1.4759	2.0150	2.5706	3.3649	4.0322
6	0.7176	1.4398	1.9432	2.4469	3.1427	3.7074
7	0.7111	1.4149	1.8946	2.3646	2.9980	3.4995
8	0.7064	1.3968	1.8595	2.3060	2.8965	3.3554
9	0.7027	1.3830	1.8331	2.2622	2.8214	3.2498
10	0.6998	1.3722	1.8125	2.2281	2.7638	3.1693
11	0.6974	1.3634	1.7959	2.2010	2.7181	3.1058

Source: Extracted from Table E.3.

Step 5: The following data **INVOICES** are the amounts (in dollars) in a random sample of 12
sales invoices.

$$108.98 \quad 152.22 \quad 111.45 \quad 110.59 \quad 127.46 \quad 107.26$$
$$93.32 \quad 91.97 \quad 111.56 \quad 75.71 \quad 128.58 \quad 135.11$$

Using Equations (3.1) and (3.10), or the Microsoft Excel output of Figure 9.10 or the
Minitab output of Figure 9.11

$$\bar{X} = \frac{\sum_{i=1}^{n} X_i}{n} = \$112.85 \quad \text{and} \quad S = \sqrt{\frac{\sum_{i=1}^{n}(X_i - \bar{X})^2}{n-1}} = \$20.80$$

From Equation (9.2),

$$t = \frac{\bar{X} - \mu}{\frac{S}{\sqrt{n}}} = \frac{112.85 - 120}{\frac{20.80}{\sqrt{12}}} = -1.19$$

FIGURE 9.10

Microsoft Excel
Worksheet for the
One-Sample t Test
of Sales Invoices

	A	B	
1	**Mean Amount Per Invoice Hypothesis**		
2			
3	**Data**		
4	**Null Hypothesis** μ=	120	
5	**Level of Significance**	0.05	
6	**Sample Size**	12	
7	**Sample Mean**	112.85	
8	**Sample Standard Deviation**	20.8	
9			
10	**Intermediate Calculations**		
11	Standard Error of the Mean	6.0044	=B8/SQRT(B6)
12	Degrees of Freedom	11	=B6 - 1
13	*t* Test Statistic	-1.1908	=(B7 - B4)/B11
14			
15	**Two-Tail Test**		
16	**Lower Critical Value**	-2.2010	=-(TINV(B5, B12))
17	**Upper Critical Value**	2.2010	=TINV(B5, B12)
18	*p*-Value	0.2588	=TDIST(ABS(B13), B12, 2)
19	**Do not reject the null hypothesis**		

FIGURE 9.11

Minitab Output for the
One-Sample *t* Test of
Sales Invoices

```
Test of mu = 120 vs not = 120


Variable    N    Mean    StDev   SE Mean      95% CI          T      P
Amount     12   112.851  20.790   0.004   (99.636, 126.065)  -1.19  0.259
```

Step 6: Since $-2.201 < t = -1.19 < 2.201$, you do not reject H_0. You have insufficient evidence to conclude that the mean amount per sales invoice differs from \$120. You should inform the finance department that the audit suggests that the mean amount per invoice has not changed.

The *p*-Value Approach

Steps 1–3: These steps are the same as in the critical value approach.

Step 4: $t = -1.19$ (see step 5 of the critical value approach).

Step 5: The Microsoft Excel worksheet of Figure 9.10 and the Minitab output of Figure 9.11 give the *p*-value for this two-tail test as 0.259. Since the *p*-value of 0.259 is greater than $\alpha = 0.05$, you do not reject H_0. The data provide insufficient evidence to conclude that the mean amount per sales invoice differs from \$120. You should inform the finance department that the audit suggests that the mean amount per invoice has not changed. The *p*-value indicates that if the null hypothesis were true, the probability that a sample of 12 invoices could have a monthly mean that differs by \$7.15 or more from the stated \$120 is 0.259. In other words, if the mean amount per sales invoice is truly \$120, then there is a 25.9% chance of observing a sample mean below \$112.85 or above \$127.15.

In the above example it is incorrect to state that there is a 25.9% chance that the null hypothesis is true. This misinterpretation of the *p*-value is sometimes used by those not properly trained in statistics. Remember that the *p*-value is a conditional probability, calculated by *assuming* that the null hypothesis is true. In general, it is proper to state the following. If the null hypothesis is true, then there is a (*p*-value)*100% chance of observing a sample result at least as contradictory to the null hypothesis as the result observed.

Checking Assumptions

[1]When a large sample size is available, S estimates σ precisely enough that there is little difference between the t and Z distributions. Therefore, you can use a Z test instead of a t test when the sample size is greater than 120.

You use the one-sample *t* test when the population standard deviation σ is not known and is estimated using the sample standard deviation[1] *S*. The *t* test is considered a *classical parametric* procedure, one that makes a variety of stringent assumptions that must hold to ensure that the results of the test are valid.

To use the one-sample *t* test, the data are assumed to represent a random sample from a population that is normally distributed. In practice, as long as the sample size is not very small and the population is not very skewed, the *t* distribution provides a good approximation to the sampling distribution of the mean when σ is unknown.

There are several ways to evaluate the normality assumption necessary for using the *t* test. You can observe how closely the sample statistics match the normal distribution's theoretical properties. You can also use a histogram, stem-and-leaf display, box-and-whisker plot, or normal probability plot.

Figure 9.12 presents Microsoft Excel output that provides descriptive statistics. Figure 9.13 is a Minitab box-and-whisker plot. Figure 9.14 is a Minitab normal probability plot.

FIGURE 9.12

Microsoft Excel Descriptive Statistics for the Sales Invoice Data

	A	B
1	*Invoice Amount*	
2		
3	Mean	112.8508333
4	Standard Error	6.003863082
5	Median	111.02
6	Mode	#N/A
7	Standard Deviation	20.7979918
8	Sample Variance	432.5564629
9	Kurtosis	0.172707598
10	Skewness	0.13363802
11	Range	76.51
12	Minimum	75.71
13	Maximum	152.22
14	Sum	1354.21
15	Count	12
16	Largest(1)	152.22
17	Smallest(1)	75.71

FIGURE 9.13

Minitab Box-and-Whisker Plot for the Sales Invoice data

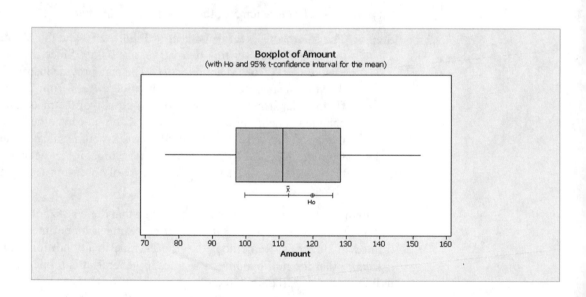

FIGURE 9.14

Minitab Normal Probability Plot for the Sales Invoice Data

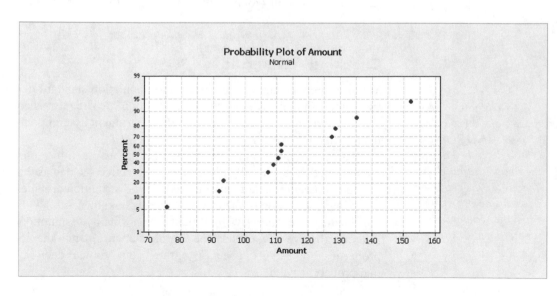

Because the mean is very close to the median, the points on the normal probability plot appear to be increasing approximately in a straight line and the box-and-whisker plot appears approximately symmetrical. You can assume that the population of sales invoices is approximately normally distributed. The normality assumption is valid and therefore the auditor's results are valid.

The *t* test is a **robust test**. It does not lose power if the shape of the population departs somewhat from a normal distribution, particularly when the sample size is large enough to enable the test statistic *t* to be influenced by the Central Limit Theorem (see section 7.2). However, you can make erroneous conclusions and can lose statistical power if you use the *t* test incorrectly. If the sample size *n* is small (i.e., less than 30) and you cannot easily make the assumption that the underlying population is at least approximately normally distributed, other *nonparametric* testing procedures are more appropriate (see references 1 and 2).

PROBLEMS FOR SECTION 9.4

Learning the Basics

 9.48 If, in a sample of *n* = 16 selected from a normal population, $\bar{X} = 56$ and $S = 12$, what is the value of the *t*-test statistic if you are testing the null hypothesis, H_0: $\mu = 50$?

9.49 In problem 9.48, how many degrees of freedom are there in the one-sample *t* test?

9.50 In problems 9.48 and 9.49, what are the critical values from the *t* table if the level of significance $\alpha = 0.05$ and the alternative hypothesis H_1 is:
a. $\mu \neq 50$?
b. $\mu > 50$?

9.51 In problems 9.48, 9.49, and 9.50, what is your statistical decision if the alternative hypothesis H_1 is:
a. $\mu \neq 50$?
b. $\mu > 50$?

9.52 If, in a sample of *n* = 16 selected from a left-skewed population, $\bar{X} = 65$ and $S = 21$, would you use the *t* test to test the null hypothesis, H_0: $\mu = 60$? Discuss.

9.53 If, in a sample of *n* = 160 selected from a left-skewed population, $\bar{X} = 65$ and $S = 21$, would you use the *t* test to test the null hypothesis, H_0: $\mu = 60$? Discuss.

Applying the Concepts
Problems 9.54–9.58 can be solved manually or by using Microsoft Excel, Minitab, or SPSS. We recommend that you use Microsoft Excel, Minitab, or SPSS to solve problems 9.59–9.65.

 9.54 The director of admissions at a large university advises parents of incoming students about the cost of textbooks during a typical semester. He selected a sample of 100 students and recorded their textbook expenses for the semester. He then computed a sample mean cost of $315.40 and a sample standard deviation of $43.20.

a. Using the 0.10 level of significance, is there evidence that the population mean is above $300?
b. What is your answer in (a) if the standard deviation is $75 and the 0.05 level of significance is used?
c. What is your answer in (a) if the sample mean is $305.11 and the sample standard deviation is $43.20?

9.55 In an article (Nanci Hellmich, " 'Supermarket Guru' Has a Simple Mantra," *USA Today*, June 19, 2002, 70) a claim was made that the typical supermarket trip takes a mean of 22 minutes. Suppose that in an effort to test this claim, you select a sample of 50 shoppers at a local supermarket. The mean shopping time for the sample of 50 shoppers was 25.36 minutes with a standard deviation of 7.24 minutes. Using the 0.10 level of significance, is there evidence that the mean shopping time at the local supermarket is different from the claimed value of 22 minutes?

9.56 You are the manager of a restaurant for a fast-food franchise. Last month the mean waiting time at the drive-through window, as measured from the time a customer places an order until the time the customer receives the order, was 3.7 minutes. The franchise helped you institute a new process intended to reduce waiting time. You select a random sample of 64 orders. The sample mean waiting time is 3.57 minutes with a sample standard deviation of 0.8 minute. At the 0.05 level of significance, is there evidence that the population mean waiting time is now less than 3.7 minutes?

9.57 A manufacturer of chocolate candies uses machines to package candies as they move along a filling line. Although the packages are labeled as 8 ounces, the company wants the packages to contain 8.17 ounces so that virtually none of the packages contain less than 8 ounces. A sample of 50 packages is selected periodically, and the packaging process is stopped if there is evidence that the mean amount packaged is different from 8.17 ounces. Suppose that the mean amount dispensed in a particular sample of 50 packages is 8.159 ounces with a sample standard deviation of 0.051 ounce.

a. Is there evidence that the population mean amount is different from 8.17 ounces? (Use a 0.05 level of significance.)

b. Compute the p-value and interpret its meaning.

9.58 A manufacturer of flashlight batteries took a sample of 13 batteries **BATTERIES** from a day's production and used them continuously until they failed to work. The life of the batteries in hours until failure is:

$$342 \quad 426 \quad 317 \quad 545 \quad 264 \quad 451 \quad 1,049$$
$$631 \quad 512 \quad 266 \quad 492 \quad 562 \quad 298$$

a. At the 0.05 level of significance, is there evidence that the mean life of the batteries is more than 400 hours?

b. Determine the p-value in (a) and interpret its meaning.

c. Using the information above, what would you advise if the manufacturer wanted to say in advertisements that these batteries "should last more than 400 hours"?

d. Suppose that the first value was 1,342 instead of 342. Repeat (a) through (c), using this value. Comment on the difference in the results.

9.59 In New York State, savings banks are permitted to sell a form of life insurance called Savings Bank Life Insurance (SBLI). The approval process consists of underwriting, which includes a review of the application, a medical information bureau check, possible requests for additional medical information and medical exams, and a policy compilation stage where the policy pages are generated and sent to the bank for delivery. The ability to deliver approved policies to customers in a timely manner is critical to the profitability of this service. During a period of one month, a random sample of 27 approved policies is selected **INSURANCE** and the total processing time in days recorded:

73 19 16 64 28 28 31 90 60 56 31 56 22 18
45 48 17 17 17 91 92 63 50 51 69 16 17

a. In the past, the mean processing time averaged 45 days. At the 0.05 level of significance, is there evidence that the mean processing time has changed from 45 days?

b. What assumption about the population distribution is needed in (a)?

c. Do you think that the assumption needed in (b) is seriously violated? Explain.

9.60 The following data represent the amount of soft drink filled in a sample of 50 consecutive 2-liter bottles. **DRINK** The results, listed horizontally in the order of being filled, were:

2.109 2.086 2.066 2.075 2.065 2.057 2.052 2.044 2.036 2.038
2.031 2.029 2.025 2.029 2.023 2.020 2.015 2.014 2.013 2.014
2.012 2.012 2.012 2.010 2.005 2.003 1.999 1.996 1.997 1.992
1.994 1.986 1.984 1.981 1.973 1.975 1.971 1.969 1.966 1.967
1.963 1.957 1.951 1.951 1.947 1.941 1.941 1.938 1.908 1.894

a. At the 0.05 level of significance, is there evidence that the mean amount of soft drink filled is different from 2.0 liters?

b. Determine the p-value in (a) and interpret its meaning.

c. Evaluate the assumption you made in (a) graphically. Are the results of (a) valid? Why?

d. Examine the values of the 50 bottles in their sequential order as given in the problem. Is there a pattern to the results? If so, what impact might this pattern have on the validity of the results in (a)?

9.61 One of the major measures of the quality of service provided by any organization is the speed with which it responds to customer complaints. A large family-held department store selling furniture and flooring including carpeting had undergone a major expansion in the past several years. In particular, the flooring department had expanded from 2 installation crews to an installation supervisor, a measurer, and 15 installation crews. Last year there were 50 complaints concerning carpeting installation. The following data **FURNITURE** represent the number of days between the receipt of the complaint and the resolution of the complaint.

54 5 35 137 31 27 152 2 123 81 74 27
11 19 126 110 110 29 61 35 94 31 26 5
12 4 165 32 29 28 29 26 25 1 14 13
13 10 5 27 4 52 30 22 36 26 20 23
33 68

a. The installation supervisor claims that the mean number of days between the receipt of the complaint and the resolution of the complaint is 20 days or less. At the 0.05 level of significance, is there evidence that the claim is not true (i.e., that the mean number of days is greater than 20)?

b. What assumption about the population distribution must you make in (a)?

c. Do you think that the assumption made in (b) is seriously violated? Explain.

d. What effect might your conclusion in (c) have on the validity of the results in (a)?

9.62 In an article in *Quality Engineering*, the viscosity (resistance to flow) of a chemical product produced in batches was examined. The data for 120 batches are in the data file **CHEMICAL**.

Source: Holmes and Mergen, "Parabolic Control Limits for the Exponentially Weighted Moving Average Control Charts," Quality Engineering, 1992, 4(4): 487–495.

a. In the past, the mean viscosity was 15.5. At the 0.10 level of significance, is there evidence that the mean viscosity has changed from 15.5?

b. What assumption about the population distribution do you need to make in (a)?

c. Do you think that the assumption made in (b) has been seriously violated? Explain.

9.63 One operation of a steel mill is to cut pieces of steel into parts that are used in the frame for front seats in an automobile. The steel is cut with a diamond saw and requires the resulting parts to be within ±0.005 inch of the length specified by the automobile company. The data in the file STEEL come from a sample of 100 steel parts. The measurement reported is the difference in inches between the actual length of the steel part, as measured by a laser measurement device, and the specified length of the steel part. For example, a value of −0.002 represents a steel part that is 0.002 inch shorter than the specified length.

a. At the 0.05 level of significance, is there evidence that the mean difference is not equal to 0.0 inches?

b. Determine the *p*-value in (a) and interpret its meaning.

c. What assumption about the differences between the actual length of the steel part and the specified length of the steel part must you make in (a)?

d. Evaluate the assumption in (c) graphically. Are the results of (a) valid? Why?

9.64 In problem 3.86, you were introduced to a tea-bag-filling operation. An important quality characteristic of interest for this process is the weight of the tea in the individual bags. The data in the file TEABAGS is an ordered array of the weight, in grams, of a sample of 50 tea bags produced during an eight-hour shift.

a. Is there evidence that the mean amount of tea per bag is different from 5.5 grams (use α = 0.01)?

b. Construct a 99% confidence interval estimate of the population mean amount of tea per bag. Interpret this interval.

c. Compare the conclusions reached in (a) and (b).

9.65 The following table contains a random sample of 30 mutual funds taken from the mutual funds reported in the *The Wall Street Journal* on June 15, 2004. CHANGE2004 For each mutual fund, "Change" is the change (in dollars) in fund value on June 14, 2004.

Mutual Fund	Change
ABN AMRO Growth I	−0.22
Aim Funds HYld	0.00
Amer Advant Int Plan	−0.42
Artisan Funds SmCap	−0.24
Calif Trust S&P 500	−0.23
Cohen and Steers Inst Rel	0.55
Columbia Balance Z	−0.15
Delaware Large Cap Value A	−0.17
Dimension EmgMkt	−0.38
Dodge&Cox Stock	−1.50
Dreyfus It Inc	−0.09
Dreyfus OHMA	−0.02
Eaton Balanced	−0.06
Emerald Gr A	−0.18
Evergreen GLLeadA	−0.26
Federated Cap App	−0.20
Federated Intl Eq	−0.43
Fidelity Banking	−0.58
FirstAmerican LgCapValue	−0.17
Janus Balanced	−0.16
Kinetics Internet	−0.21
Merrill Lynch Equity Inc	−0.12
Nicholas Group Nich	−0.46
Northern Balanced A	−0.09
One Group DivMidCap	−0.24
Prudential Bear	0.03
Putnam Income	−0.02
South Trust Value	−0.14
Third Avenue Real Est	−0.26
Van Kampen Entc	−0.10

Source: Extracted from The Wall Street Journal, *June 15, 2004.*

a. Is there evidence that the population mean fund value changed on June 14, 2004? Use a level of significance of 0.05.

b. What assumptions are made to perform the test in (a)?

c. Determine the *p*-value and interpret its meaning.

9.5 Z TEST OF HYPOTHESIS FOR THE PROPORTION

In some situations, you want to test a hypothesis about the population proportion π of values that are in a particular category rather than testing the population mean. To begin, you select a random sample and compute the **sample proportion**, $p = X/n$. You then compare the value of this statistic to the hypothesized value of the parameter π in order to decide whether to reject the null hypothesis.

If the number of successes (X) and the number of failures ($n - X$) are each at least five, the sampling distribution of a proportion approximately follows a standardized normal distribution. You use the **Z test for the proportion** given in Equation (9.3) to perform the hypothesis test for the difference between the sample proportion p and the hypothesized population proportion π.

ONE SAMPLE Z TEST FOR THE PROPORTION

$$Z = \frac{p - \pi}{\sqrt{\dfrac{\pi(1 - \pi)}{n}}} \qquad (9.3)$$

where $p = \dfrac{X}{n} = \dfrac{\text{number of successes in the sample}}{\text{sample size}}$

$= $ sample proportion of successes

$\pi = $ hypothesized proportion of successes in the population

The test statistic Z approximately follows a standardized normal distribution,

Alternatively, by multiplying numerator and denominator by n, you can write the Z-test statistic in terms of the number of successes X as shown in Equation (9.4).

Z TEST FOR THE PROPORTION IN TERMS OF THE NUMBER OF SUCCESSES

$$Z = \frac{X - n\pi}{\sqrt{n\pi(1 - \pi)}} \qquad (9.4)$$

To illustrate the one-sample Z test for a proportion, consider the following study reported in *The Wall Street Journal*. In the study, the question posed was "are an equal number of home-based businesses owned by men and women?" The study of 899 home-based businesses reported that 369 were owned by women (Eleena De Lisser and Dan Morse, "More Men Work at Home than Women, Study Shows," *The Wall Street Journal*, May 18, 1999, B2).

For this study, the null and alternative hypotheses are stated as follows:

H_0: $\pi = 0.50$ (i.e., the proportion of home-based businesses owned by females is 0.50)

H_1: $\pi \neq 0.50$ (i.e., the proportion of home-based businesses owned by females is not 0.50)

The Critical Value Approach

Because you are interested in whether or not the proportion of home-based businesses owned by females is 0.50 (and the proportion owned by males is 0.50), you use a two-tail test. If you select the $\alpha = 0.05$ level of significance, the rejection and nonrejection regions are set up as in Figure 9.15, and the decision rule is

Reject H_0 if $Z < -1.96$ or if $Z > +1.96$;

otherwise do not reject H_0.

FIGURE 9.15

Two-Tail Test of Hypothesis for the Proportion at the 0.05 Level of Significance

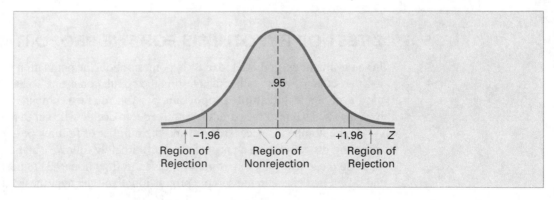

.95

−1.96   0   +1.96   Z

Region of Rejection   Region of Nonrejection   Region of Rejection

Since 369 of the 899 home-based businesses are owned by females,

$$p = \frac{369}{899} = 0.41046$$

Using Equation (9.3),

$$Z \cong \frac{p - \pi}{\sqrt{\dfrac{\pi(1 - \pi)}{n}}} = \frac{0.41046 - 0.50}{\sqrt{\dfrac{0.50(1 - 0.50)}{899}}} = \frac{-0.08954}{0.0167} = -5.37$$

or, using Equation (9.4),

$$Z \cong \frac{X - n\pi}{\sqrt{n\pi(1 - \pi)}} = \frac{369 - (899)(0.50)}{\sqrt{899(0.50)(0.50)}} = \frac{-80.5}{14.99} = -5.37$$

Because $-5.37 < -1.96$, you reject H_0. You can conclude that the proportion of home-based businesses owned by females is not 0.50. Figure 9.16 presents a Microsoft Excel worksheet for these data.

FIGURE 9.16

Microsoft Excel Worksheet for the Study on Home-Based Business Ownership

	A	B	
1	Ownership Proportion Hypothesis		
2			
3	Data		
4	Null Hypothesis p=	0.5	
5	Level of Significance	0.05	
6	Number of Successes	369	
7	Sample Size	899	
8			
9	Intermediate Calculations		
10	Sample Proportion	0.4105	=B6/B7
11	Standard Error	0.0167	=SQRT(B4 * (1 - B4)/B7)
12	Z Test Statistic	-5.3697	=(B10 - B4)/B11
13			
14	Two-Tail Test		
15	Lower Critical Value	-1.9600	=NORMSINV(B5/2)
16	Upper Critical value	1.9600	=NORMSINV(1 - B5/2)
17	p-Value	0.0000	=2 * (1 - NORMSDIST(ABS(B12)))
18	Reject the null hypothesis		

The *p*-Value Approach

As an alternative approach toward making a hypothesis-testing decision, you can compute the *p*-value. For this two-tail test in which the rejection region is located in the lower tail and the upper tail, you need to find the area below a *Z* value of -5.37 and above a *Z* value of $+5.37$. Figure 9.16 and Figure 9.17 report a *p*-value of 0.0000. Because this value is less than the selected level of significance ($\alpha = 0.05$), you reject the null hypothesis. This extremely small *p*-value indicates that there is virtually no chance that the sample proportion will be as small as 0.41046 if the population proportion is 0.50.

FIGURE 9.17

Minitab Output for the Study of Home-Based Business Ownership

```
Test of p = 0.5 vs p not = 0.5


Sample     X    N   Sample p          95% CI           Z-Value   P-Value
1        369  899   0.410456    (0.378300, 0.442612)    -5.37     0.000
```

EXAMPLE 9.6   TESTING A HYPOTHESIS FOR A PROPORTION

A fast-food chain has just developed a new process to make sure that orders at the drive-through are filled correctly. The previous process filled orders correctly 88% of the time. A sample of 100 orders using the new process is selected and 92 were filled correctly. At the 0.01 level of significance, can you conclude that the new process has increased the proportion of orders filled correctly?

SOLUTION The null and alternative hypotheses are

H_0: $\pi \leq 0.88$ (i.e., the proportion of orders filled correctly is less than or equal to 0.88)

H_1: $\pi > 0.88$ (i.e., the proportion of orders filled correctly is greater than 0.88)

Using Equation (9.3),

$$p = \frac{X}{n} = \frac{92}{100} = 0.92$$

$$Z = \frac{p - \pi}{\sqrt{\dfrac{\pi(1 - \pi)}{n}}} = \frac{0.92 - 0.88}{\sqrt{\dfrac{0.88(1 - 0.88)}{100}}} = \frac{0.04}{0.0325} = 1.23$$

The p-value for $Z > 1.23$ is 0.1093.

Using the critical value approach, you reject H_0 if $Z > 2.33$. Using the p-value approach, you reject H_0 if the p-value < 0.01. Since $Z = 1.23 < 2.33$ or the p-value $= 0.1093 > 0.01$, you do not reject H_0. You conclude that there is insufficient evidence that the new process has increased the proportion of correct orders above 0.88.

PROBLEMS FOR SECTION 9.5

Learning the Basics

 9.66 If, in a random sample of 400 items, 88 are defective, what is the sample proportion of defective items?

 9.67 In problem 9.66, if the null hypothesis is that 20% of the items in the population are defective, what is the value of the Z-test statistic?

 9.68 In problems 9.66 and 9.67, suppose you are testing the null hypothesis H_0: $\pi = 0.20$ against the two-tail alternative hypothesis H_1: $\pi \neq 0.20$ and you choose the level of significance $\alpha = 0.05$. What is your statistical decision?

Applying the Concepts

  9.69 An article in *The Wall Street Journal* implies that more than half of all Americans would prefer being given $100 rather than a day off from work. This statement is based on a survey conducted by American Express Incentive Services, in which 593 of 1,040 respondents indicated that they would rather have the $100 (Carlos Tejada, "Work Week," *The Wall Street Journal*, July 25, 2000, A1).
a. At the 0.05 level of significance, is there evidence based on the survey data that more than half of all Americans would rather have $100 than a day off from work?
b. Compute the p-value and interpret its meaning.

9.70 Due to a very weak economy, only an estimated 43% of employers in the United States recruited new employees in 2003. But, by the end of the year, the economy showed signs of improvement. A survey by the Society for Human Resource Management indicated that 181 of 362 human-resources professionals planned to recruit new employees in 2004 (Hane J. Kim, "Finally, 2004 May Be the Time to Seek a Raise," *The Wall Street Journal*, January 8, 2004, D4). Conduct a hypothesis test to try to prove that the proportion of employers that planned to hire new employees in 2004 is larger than the 2003 proportion of 0.43. Use the six-step hypothesis-testing method and a 0.05 level of significance.

9.71 A *Wall Street Journal* article suggests that age bias is becoming an even bigger problem in the corporate world (Carol Hymowitz, "Top Executives Chase Youthful Appearance, But Miss Real Issue," *The Wall Street Journal*, February 17, 2004, B1). In 2001, an estimated 78% of executives believed that age bias was a serious problem. In a 2004 study by ExecuNet, 82% of the executives surveyed considered age bias a serious problem. The sample size for the 2004 study was not disclosed. Suppose 50 executives were surveyed.

a. At the 0.05 level of significance, use the six-step hypothesis method to try and prove that the proportion of executives who believe that age bias is a serious problem is higher than the 2001 value of 0.78.

b. Use the five-step *p*-value approach. Interpret the meaning of the *p*-value.

c. Suppose that the sample size used was 1,000. Redo (a) and (b).

d. Discuss the effect that sample size had on the outcome of this analysis and, in general, on the effect sample size plays in hypothesis-testing.

9.72 A *Wall Street Journal* poll asked respondents if they trusted energy-efficiency ratings on cars and appliances; 552 responded *yes*, and 531 responded *no* ("What's News Online," *The Wall Street Journal*, March 30, 2004, D7).

a. At the 0.05 level of significance, use the six-step hypothesis testing method to try and prove that the percentage of people who trust energy-efficiency ratings differs from 50%.

b. Use the 5-step *p*-value approach. Interpret the meaning of the *p*-value.

9.73 One of the biggest issues facing e-retailers is the ability to turn browsers into buyers (M. Totty, "Making the Sale," *The Wall Street Journal*, September 24, 2001, R6). This is measured by the conversion rate, the percentage of browsers who buy something in their visit to a site. This article reported that the conversion rate for llbean.com was 10.1% and for victoriasecret.com was 8.2%. Suppose that each of these sites were redesigned in an attempt to increase their conversion rates. Samples of 200 browsers at each redesigned site were selected. Suppose that 24 browsers at llbean.com made a purchase and 25 browsers at victoriasecret.com made a purchase.

a. Is there evidence of an increased conversion rate at llbean.com at the 0.05 level of significance?

b. Is there evidence of an increased conversion rate at victoriasecret.com at the 0.05 level of significance?

9.74 More professional women than ever before are foregoing motherhood because of the time constraints of their careers. Yet, many women still manage to find time to climb the corporate ladder *and* set time aside to have children. A survey of 187 attendees at *Fortune Magazine*'s Most Powerful Women in Business summit in March 2002 found that 133 had at least one child (Carol Hymowitz, "Women Plotting Mix of Work and Family Won't Find Perfect Plan," *The Wall Street Journal*, June 11, 2002, B1). Assume that the group of 187 women is a random sample from the population of all successful women executives.

a. What is the sample proportion of successful women executives who have children?

b. At the 0.05 level of significance, can you state that more than half of all successful women executives have children?

c. At the 0.05 level of significance, can you state that more than two-thirds of all successful women executives have children?

d. Do you think the random sample assumption is valid? Explain.

9.6 POTENTIAL HYPOTHESIS-TESTING PITFALLS AND ETHICAL ISSUES

To this point, you have studied the fundamental concepts of hypothesis testing. You used hypothesis testing for analyzing differences between sample estimates (i.e., statistics) and hypothesized population characteristics (i.e., parameters) in order to make decisions about the underlying characteristics. You have also learned how to evaluate the risks involved in making these decisions.

When planning to carry out a test of the hypothesis based on a survey, research study, or designed experiment, you must ask several questions to ensure that proper methodology is used. You need to raise and answer questions like the following ones in the planning stage.

1. What is the goal of the survey, study, or experiment? How can you translate the goal into a null hypothesis and an alternative hypothesis?

2. Is the hypothesis test a two-tail test or one-tail test?
3. Can you select a random sample from the underlying population of interest?
4. What kinds of data will you collect from the sample? Are the variables numerical or categorical?
5. At what significance level, or risk of committing a Type I error, should you conduct the hypothesis test?
6. Is the intended sample size large enough to achieve the desired power of the test for the level of significance chosen?
7. What statistical test procedure should you use and why?
8. What conclusions and interpretations can you make from the results of the hypothesis test?

Therefore, you should consult with a person with substantial statistical training early in the process. All too often such an individual is consulted far too late in the process, after the data have been collected. Typically, all that you can do at such a late stage is to choose the statistical test procedure that is best for the data. You are forced to assume that certain biases built into the study (because of poor planning) are negligible. But this is a large assumption. Good research involves good planning. To avoid biases, adequate controls must be built in from the beginning.

You need to distinguish between poor research methodology and unethical behavior. Ethical considerations arise when the hypothesis-testing process is manipulated. Some of the ethical issues that arise include the data collection method, informed consent from human subjects being "treated," the type of test (one-tail or two-tail), the choice of the level of significance α, data snooping, the cleansing and discarding of data, and the reporting of findings.

Data Collection Method—Randomization

To eliminate the possibility of potential biases in the results, you must use proper data collection methods. To draw meaningful conclusions, the data must be the outcome of a random sample from a population or from an experiment in which a **randomization** process was used. Potential respondents should not be permitted to self-select for a study nor should they be purposely selected. Aside from the potential ethical issues that may arise, such a lack of randomization can result in serious coverage errors or selection biases that destroy the integrity of the study.

Informed Consent from Human Respondents Being "Treated"

Ethical considerations require that any individual who is to be subjected to some "treatment" in an experiment be made aware of the research endeavor and any potential behavioral or physical side effects. The subject should also provide informed consent with respect to participation.

Type of Test—Two-Tail or One-Tail

If prior information is available that leads you to test the null hypothesis against a specifically directed alternative, then a one-tail test is more powerful than a two-tail test. However, if you are interested only in *differences* from the null hypothesis, not in the *direction* of the difference, the two-tail test is the appropriate procedure to use. For example, if previous research and statistical testing have already established the difference in a particular direction, or if an established scientific theory states that it is possible for results to occur in only one direction, then a one-tail test is appropriate. It is never appropriate to change the direction of a test after the data are collected.

Choice of Level of Significance α

In a well-designed study, you select the level of significance α before data collection occurs. You cannot alter the level of significance, after the fact, to achieve a specific result. It is also good practice to always report the p-value, not just the conclusions of the hypothesis test.

Data Snooping   **Data snooping** is never permissible. It is unethical to perform a hypothesis test on a set of data, look at the results, and then decide on the level of significance or decide between a one-tail or two-tail test. You must make these decisions before the data are collected in order for the conclusions to have meaning. In those situations in which you consult a statistician late in the process, with data already available, it is imperative that you establish the null and alternative hypotheses and choose the level of significance prior to carrying out the hypothesis test. In addition, you cannot arbitrarily change or discard extreme or unusual values in order to alter the results of the hypothesis tests.

Cleansing and Discarding of Data   Data cleansing is not data snooping. In the data preparation stage of editing, coding, and transcribing, you have an opportunity to review the data for any value whose measurement appears extreme or unusual. After reviewing the unusual observations, you should construct a stem-and-leaf display and/or a box-and-whisker plot in preparation for further data presentation and confirmatory analysis. This exploratory data analysis stage gives you another opportunity to cleanse the data set by flagging possible outliers to double-check against the original data. In addition, the exploratory data analysis enables you to examine the data graphically with respect to the assumptions underlying a particular hypothesis test procedure.

The process of data cleansing raises a major ethical question. Should you ever remove a value from a study? The answer is a qualified yes. If you can determine that a measurement is incomplete or grossly in error because of some equipment problem or unusual behavioral occurrence unrelated to the study, you can discard the value. Sometimes you have no choice—an individual may decide to quit a particular study he or she has been participating in before a final measurement can be made. In a well-designed experiment or study, you should decide, in advance, on all rules regarding the possible discarding of data.

Reporting of Findings   In conducting research, you should document both good and bad results. It is inappropriate to report the results of hypothesis tests that show statistical significance, but not those for which there is insufficient evidence in the findings. In those instances where there is insufficient evidence to reject H_0, you must make it clear that this does not prove that the null hypothesis is true. What the result does indicate is that with the sample size used, there is not enough information to *disprove* the null hypothesis.

Statistical Significance versus Practical Significance   You need to make the distinction between the existence of a statistically significant result and its practical significance in the context within a field of application. Sometimes, due to a very large sample size, you will get a result that is statistically significant, but has little practical significance. For example, suppose that prior to a national marketing campaign focusing on a series of expensive television commercials, you believe that the proportion of people who recognized your brand was 0.30. At the completion of the campaign, a survey of 20,000 people indicates that 6,168 recognized your brand. A one-tail test trying to prove that the proportion is now greater than 0.30 results in a *p*-value of 0.0047 and the correct statistical conclusion is that the proportion of consumers recognizing your brand name has now increased. Was the campaign successful? The result of the hypothesis test indicates a statistically significant increase in brand awareness, but is this increase practically important? The population proportion is now estimated at 6,168/20,000 = 0.3084 or 30.84%. This increase is less than 1% more than the hypothesized value of 30%. Did the large expenses associated with the marketing campaign produce a result with a meaningful increase in brand awareness? Because of the minimal real-world impact an increase of less than 1% has on the overall marketing strategy, and the huge expenses associated with the marketing campaign, you should conclude that the campaign was not successful. On the other hand, if the campaign increased brand awareness by 20%, you could conclude that the campaign was successful.

To summarize, in discussing ethical issues concerning hypothesis-testing the key is *intent*. You must distinguish between poor data analysis and unethical practice. Unethical practice occurs when researchers *intentionally* create a selection bias in data collection, manipulate the treatment of human subjects without informed consent, use data snooping to select the type of test (two-tail or one-tail) and/or level of significance, hide the facts by discarding values that do not support a stated hypothesis, or fail to report pertinent findings.

KEY FORMULAS

Z Test of Hypothesis for the Mean (σ Known)

$$Z = \frac{\overline{X} - \mu}{\frac{\sigma}{\sqrt{n}}} \quad (9.1)$$

t Test of Hypothesis for the Mean (σ Unknown)

$$t = \frac{\overline{X} - \mu}{\frac{S}{\sqrt{n}}} \quad (9.2)$$

One Sample Z Test for the Proportion

$$Z \cong \frac{p - \pi}{\sqrt{\frac{\pi(1 - \pi)}{n}}} \quad (9.3)$$

Z Test for the Proportion in Terms of the Number of Successes

$$Z \cong \frac{X - n\pi}{\sqrt{n\pi(1 - \pi)}} \quad (9.4)$$

CHAPTER REVIEW PROBLEMS

Checking Your Understanding

9.75 What is the difference between a null hypothesis H_0 and an alternative hypothesis H_1?

9.76 What is the difference between a Type I and a Type II error?

9.77 What is meant by the power of a test?

9.78 What is the difference between a one-tail and a two-tail test?

9.79 What is meant by a *p*-value?

9.80 How can a confidence interval estimate for the population mean provide conclusions to the corresponding hypothesis test for the population mean?

9.81 What is the six-step critical value approach to hypothesis testing?

9.82 What are some of the ethical issues to be concerned with in performing a hypothesis test?

Applying the Concepts

9.83 An article in *Marketing News* (Thomas T. Semon, "Consider a Statistical Insignificance Test," *Marketing News*, February 1, 1999) argues that the level of significance used when comparing two products is often too low, that is, sometimes you should be using an α value greater than 0.05. Specifically, the article recounts testing the pro-

portion of potential customers with a preference for product 1 over product 2. The null hypothesis is that the population proportion of potential customers preferring product 1 is 0.50, and the alternative hypothesis is that it is not equal to 0.50. The *p*-value for the test is 0.22. The article suggests that in some cases this should be enough evidence to reject the null hypothesis.
a. State the null and alternative hypotheses in statistical terms.
b. Explain the risks associated with Type I and Type II errors.
c. What are the consequences if you rejected the null hypothesis for a *p*-value of 0.22?
d. Why do you think the article suggests raising the value of α?
e. What would you do in this situation?
f. What is your answer in (e) if the *p*-value equals 0.12? What if it equals 0.06?

9.84 La Quinta Motor Inns developed a computer model to help predict the profitability of sites that are being considered as locations for new hotels. If the computer model predicts large profits, La Quinta buys the proposed site and builds a new hotel. If the computer model predicts small or moderate profits, La Quinta chooses not to proceed with that site (Sheryl E. Kimes and James A. Fitzsimmons, "Selecting Profitable Hotel Sites at La Quinta Motor Inns," *Interfaces*, Vol. 20,

March–April 1990, 12–20). This decision-making procedure can be expressed in the hypothesis-testing framework. The null hypothesis is that the site is not a profitable location. The alternative hypothesis is that the site is a profitable location.
a. Explain the risks associated with committing a Type I error.
b. Explain the risks associated with committing a Type II error.
c. Which type of error do you think the executives at La Quinta Motor Inns are trying hard to avoid? Explain.
d. How do changes in the rejection criterion affect the probabilities of committing Type I and Type II errors?

9.85 A 1999 General Accounting Office (GAO) study found that about a third of the 23.4 million retirees 65 or older supplemented Medicare with some form of employer coverage (Carlos Tejada, "Work Week," *The Wall Street Journal*, June 26, 2002, B5). The article suggests that this proportion is increasing. Suppose that in a current study, a random sample of 500 retirees 65 or older indicated that 185 supplemented Medicare with some form of employer coverage.
a. At the 0.01 level of significance, is there evidence that the proportion of retirees 65 or older that supplement Medicare with some form of employer coverage is now greater than one-third?
b. Compute the p-value and interpret its meaning.

9.86 The owner of a gasoline station wants to study gasoline purchasing habits by motorists at his station. You select a random sample of 60 motorists during a certain week with the following results:
• Amount purchased: $\overline{X} = 11.3$ gallons, $S = 3.1$ gallons.
• 11 motorists purchased premium-grade gasoline.
a. At the 0.05 level of significance, is there evidence that the mean purchase is different from 10 gallons?
b. Find the p-value in (a).
c. At the 0.05 level of significance, is there evidence that fewer than 20% of all the motorists at his station purchase premium-grade gasoline?
d. What is your answer to (a) if the sample mean equals 10.3 gallons?
e. What is your answer to (c) if seven motorists purchased premium-grade gasoline?

9.87 An auditor for a government agency is assigned the task of evaluating reimbursement for office visits to physicians paid by Medicare. The audit is conducted on a sample of 75 of the reimbursements with the following results:
• In 12 of the office visits, an incorrect amount of reimbursement was provided.
• The amount of reimbursement was: $\overline{X} = \$93.70$, $S = \$34.55$.

a. At the 0.05 level of significance, is there evidence that the mean reimbursement is less than $100?
b. At the 0.05 level of significance, is there evidence that the proportion of incorrect reimbursements in the population is greater than 0.10?
c. Discuss the underlying assumptions of the test used in (a).
d. What is your answer to (a) if the sample mean equals $90?
e. What is your answer to (b) if 15 office visits had incorrect reimbursements?

9.88 A bank branch located in a commercial district of a city has developed an improved process for serving customers during the noon to 1:00 P.M. lunch period. The waiting time (defined as the time the customer enters the line until he or she reaches the teller window) of all customers during this hour is recorded over a period of 1 week. A random sample of 15 customers is selected, and the results are as follows: BANK1

4.21 5.55 3.02 5.13 4.77 2.34 3.54 3.20
4.50 6.10 0.38 5.12 6.46 6.19 3.79

a. At the 0.05 level of significance, is there evidence that the mean waiting time is less than 5 minutes?
b. What assumption must hold in order to perform the test in (a)?
c. Evaluate this assumption through a graphical approach. Discuss.
d. As a customer walks into the branch office during the lunch hour, she asks the branch manager how long she can expect to wait. The branch manager replies, "Almost certainly not longer than 5 minutes." On the basis of the results of (a), evaluate this statement.

9.89 A manufacturing company produces electrical insulators. If the insulators break when in use, a short circuit is likely to occur. To test the strength of the insulators, destructive testing is carried out to determine how much *force* is required to break the insulators. Force is measured by observing how many pounds is applied to the insulator before it breaks. The following data are from 30 observations from this experiment. FORCE

Force (in the Number of Pounds Required to Break the Insulator)

1,870 1,728 1,656 1,610 1,634 1,784 1,522 1,696 1,592 1,662
1,866 1,764 1,734 1,662 1,734 1,774 1,550 1,756 1,762 1,866
1,820 1,744 1,788 1,688 1,810 1,752 1,680 1,810 1,652 1,736

a. At the 0.05 level of significance, is there evidence that the mean force is greater than 1,500 pounds?
b. What assumption must hold in order to perform the test in (a)?

c. Evaluate this assumption through a graphical approach. Discuss.

d. Based on (a), what can you conclude about the strength of the insulators?

9.90 An important quality characteristic used by the manufacturer of "Boston" and "Vermont" asphalt shingles is the amount of moisture the shingles contain when they are packaged. Customers may feel that they have purchased a product lacking in quality if they find moisture and wet shingles inside the packaging. In some cases, excessive moisture can cause the granules attached to the shingle for texture and coloring purposes to fall off the shingle, resulting in appearance problems. To monitor the amount of moisture present, the company conducts moisture tests. A shingle is weighed and then dried. The shingle is then reweighed and, based on the amount of moisture taken out of the product, the pounds of moisture per 100 square feet are calculated. The company would like to show that the mean moisture content is less than 0.35 pounds per 100 square feet. The data file MOISTURE includes 36 measurements (in pounds per 100 square feet) for the "Boston" shingles and 31 for "Vermont" shingles.

a. For the "Boston" shingles, is there evidence at the 0.05 level of significance that the mean moisture content is less than 0.35 pounds per 100 square feet?

b. Interpret the meaning of the p-value in (a).

c. For the "Vermont" shingles, is there evidence at the 0.05 level of significance that the mean moisture content is less than 0.35 pounds per 100 square feet?

d. Interpret the meaning of the p-value in (c).

e. What assumption must hold in order to perform the tests in (a) and (c)?

f. Evaluate the assumption for the "Boston" shingles and the "Vermont" shingles by using a graphical approach. Discuss.

9.91 Studies conducted by a manufacturer of "Boston" and "Vermont" asphalt shingles have shown product weight to be a major factor in the customer's perception of quality. Moreover, the weight represents the amount of raw materials being used and is therefore very important to the company from a cost standpoint. The last stage of the assembly line packages the shingles before the packages are placed on wooden pallets. Once a pallet is full (a pallet for most brands holds 16 squares of shingles), it is weighed and the measurement is recorded. The data file PALLET contains the weight (in pounds) from a sample of 368 pallets of Boston shingles and 330 pallets of Vermont shingles.

a. For the Boston shingles, is there evidence that the mean weight is different from 3,150 pounds?

b. Interpret the meaning of the p-value in (a).

c. For the Vermont shingles, is there evidence that the mean weight is different from 3,700 pounds?

d. Interpret the meaning of the p-value in (c).

e. Is the assumption needed for (a) and (c) seriously violated?

9.92 The manufacturer of "Boston" and "Vermont" asphalt shingles provide their customers with a 20-year warranty on most of their products. To determine whether a shingle will last as long as the warranty period, accelerated-life testing is conducted at the manufacturing plant. Accelerated-life testing exposes the shingle to the stresses it would be subject to in a lifetime of normal use in a laboratory setting via an experiment that takes only a few minutes to conduct. In this test, a shingle is repeatedly scraped with a brush for a short period of time and the amount of shingle granules that are removed by the brushing is weighed (in grams). Shingles that experience low amounts of granule loss are expected to last longer in normal use than shingles that experience high amounts of granule loss. The data file GRANULE contains a sample of 170 measurements made on the company's Boston shingles, and 140 measurements made on Vermont shingles.

a. For the Boston shingles, is there evidence that the mean granule loss is different from 0.50 grams?

b. Interpret the meaning of the p-value in (a).

c. For the Vermont shingles, is there evidence that the mean granule loss is different from 0.50 grams?

d. Interpret the meaning of the p-value in (c).

e. Is the assumption needed for (a) and (c) seriously violated?

Report Writing Exercises

9.93 Referring to the results of problems 9.90–9.92 concerning the "Boston" and "Vermont" shingles, write a report that evaluates the moisture level, weight, and granule loss of the two types of shingles.

RUNNING CASE
MANAGING THE *SPRINGVILLE HERALD*

Continuing its monitoring of the blackness of the newspaper print, first described in the Chapter 6 *Managing the Springville Herald* case, the production department of the newspaper wants to ensure that the mean blackness of the print for all newspapers is at least 0.97 on a standard scale in which the target value is 1.0. A random sample of 50 newspapers has been selected and the blackness of each paper has been measured. Calculate the sample statistics and determine if there is evidence that the mean blackness is less than 0.97. Write a memo to management that summarizes your conclusions.

Blackness of 50 Newspapers

0.854 1.023 1.005 1.030 1.219 0.977 1.044 0.778 1.122 1.114

1.091 1.086 1.141 0.931 0.723 0.934 1.060 1.047 0.800 0.889

1.012 0.695 0.869 0.734 1.131 0.993 0.762 0.814 1.108 0.805

1.223 1.024 0.884 0.799 0.870 0.898 0.621 0.818 1.113 1.286

1.052 0.678 1.162 0.808 1.012 0.859 0.951 1.112 1.003 0.972

SH9

WEB CASE

Apply your knowledge about hypothesis testing in this Web Case that continues the cereal-fill-packaging dispute Web Case from Chapter 7.

Oxford Cereals recently conducted a public experiment in which it claims it has successfully debunked the statements of groups such as the TriCities Consumers Concerned About Cereal Companies That Cheat (TCCACCTC) that claimed that Oxford Cereals was cheating consumers by packaging cereals at less than labeled weights. Review the Oxford Cereals' press release and supporting documents that describe the experiment at the company's Web site **www.prenhall.com/Springville/OC_WinTrust.htm** and then answer the following:

1. Are the results of the independent testing valid? Why, or why not? If you were conducting the experiment, is there anything you would change?
2. Do the results support the claim that Oxford Cereals is not cheating its customers?
3. Is the claim of the Oxford CEO that many cereal boxes contain *more* than 368 grams surprising? True?
4. Could there ever be a circumstance in which the results of the public experiment *and* the TCCACCTC's results are both correct? Explain.

REFERENCES

1. Bradley, J. V., *Distribution-Free Statistical Tests* (Englewood Cliffs, NJ: Prentice Hall, 1968).
2. Daniel, W., *Applied Nonparametric Statistics*, 2nd ed. (Boston, MA: Houghton Mifflin, 1990).
3. *Microsoft Excel 2003* (Redmond, WA: Microsoft Corporation, 2003).
4. *Minitab for Windows Version 14* (State College PA: Minitab, Inc., 2004).
5. *SPSS Base 12.0 Brief Guide* (Upper Saddle River, NJ: Prentice Hall, 2003).

CHAPTER 10

Two-Sample Tests and One-Way ANOVA

USING STATISTICS: Comparing Sales from End-Aisle Displays and Normal Displays

LEARNING OBJECTIVES

In this chapter, you learn hypothesis testing procedures to test:

- The means of two independent populations
- The means of two related populations
- Two proportions
- The variances of two independent populations
- The means of more than two populations

USING STATISTICS

Comparing Sales from End-Aisle Displays and Normal Displays

Does the type of display used in a supermarket affect the sales of products? As the regional sales manager for BLK Foods, you are interested in comparing the sales volume of BLK cola when you display the soft drink in the normal shelf location as compared to an end-aisle promotional display. To test the effectiveness of the end-aisle displays, you select 20 stores from the BLK supermarket chain that all experience similar storewide sales volumes. You then randomly assign 10 of the 20 stores to group 1 and 10 to group 2. The managers of the 10 stores in group 1 place the BLK cola in the regular shelf location alongside the other cola products. The 10 stores in group 2 use the special end-aisle promotional display. At the end of one week, the sales of BLK cola are recorded. How can you determine whether sales of BLK cola using the end-aisle displays are the same as those when the cola is placed in the regular shelf location? How can you decide if the variability in BLK cola sales from store to store is the same for the two types of displays? How could you use the answers to these questions to improve sales of BLK colas?

Hypothesis testing provides a *confirmatory* approach to data analysis. In Chapter 9 the focus was on a variety of commonly used hypothesis-testing procedures that relate to a single sample of data selected from a single population. In this chapter, hypothesis testing is extended to procedures that compare statistics from samples of data drawn from two or more populations. For example, are the mean weekly sales of BLK cola when using an end-aisle display equal to the mean weekly sales of BLK cola when placed in the normal shelf location?

10.1 COMPARING THE MEANS OF TWO INDEPENDENT POPULATIONS

Z Test for the Difference Between Two Means

Suppose that you take a random sample of n_1 from the first population and a random sample of n_2 from the second population, and the data collected in each sample are from a numerical variable. In the first population, the mean is represented by the symbol μ_1 and the standard deviation is represented by the symbol σ_1. In the second population, the mean is represented by the symbol μ_2 and the standard deviation is represented by the symbol σ_2.

The test statistic used to determine the difference between the population means is based on the difference between the sample means $(\overline{X}_1 - \overline{X}_2)$. If you assume that the samples are randomly and independently selected from populations that are normally distributed, this statistic follows the standardized normal distribution. If the populations are not normally distributed, the Z test is still appropriate if the sample sizes are large enough (typically n_1 and $n_2 \geq 30$; see the Central Limit Theorem in section 7.2). Equation (10.1) defines the **Z test for the difference between two means**.

Z TEST FOR THE DIFFERENCE BETWEEN TWO MEANS

$$Z = \frac{(\overline{X}_1 - \overline{X}_2) - (\mu_1 - \mu_2)}{\sqrt{\dfrac{\sigma_1^2}{n_1} + \dfrac{\sigma_2^2}{n_2}}} \qquad (10.1)$$

where $\bar{X}_1$ = mean of the sample taken from population 1

μ_1 = mean of population 1

σ_1^2 = variance of population 1

n_1 = size of the sample taken from population 1

$\bar{X}_2$ = mean of the sample taken from population 2

μ_2 = mean of population 2

σ_2^2 = variance of population 2

n_2 = size of the sample taken from population 2

The test statistic Z follows a standardized normal distribution.

Pooled-Variance t Test for the Difference Between Two Means

In most cases the variances of the two populations are not known. The only information you usually have are the sample means and the sample variances. If you assume that the samples are randomly and independently selected from populations that are normally distributed and that the population variances are equal (that is, $\sigma_1^2 = \sigma_2^2$), you can use a **pooled-variance t test** to determine whether there is a significant difference between the means of the two populations. If the populations are not normally distributed, the pooled-variance t test is still appropriate if the sample sizes are large enough (typically n_1 and $n_2 \geq 30$; see the Central Limit Theorem in section 7.2).

The pooled-variance t test is so named because the test statistic pools (combines) the two sample variances S_1^2 and S_2^2 to compute S_p^2; the best estimate of the variance common to both populations under the assumption that the two population variances are equal.[1]

To test the null hypothesis of no difference in the means of two independent populations:

$$H_0: \mu_1 = \mu_2 \text{ or } \mu_1 - \mu_2 = 0$$

against the alternative that the means are not the same

$$H_1: \mu_1 \neq \mu_2 \text{ or } \mu_1 - \mu_2 \neq 0$$

you use the pooled-variance t-test statistic.

[1] When the two sample sizes are equal (that is, $n_1 = n_2$), the formula for the pooled variance can be simplified to $S_p^2 = \dfrac{S_1^2 + S_2^2}{2}$

POOLED-VARIANCE t TEST FOR THE DIFFERENCE BETWEEN TWO MEANS

$$t = \frac{(\bar{X}_1 - \bar{X}_2) - (\mu_1 - \mu_2)}{\sqrt{S_p^2\left(\dfrac{1}{n_1} + \dfrac{1}{n_2}\right)}} \tag{10.2}$$

where $S_p^2 = \dfrac{(n_1 - 1)S_1^2 + (n_2 - 1)S_2^2}{(n_1 - 1) + (n_2 - 1)}$

and S_p^2 = pooled variance

$\bar{X}_1$ = mean of the sample taken from population 1

S_1^2 = variance of the sample taken from population 1

n_1 = size of the sample taken from population 1

$\bar{X}_2$ = mean of the sample taken from population 2

S_2^2 = variance of the sample taken from population 2

n_2 = size of the sample taken from population 2

The test statistic t follows a t distribution with $n_1 + n_2 - 2$ degrees of freedom.

The pooled-variance t-test statistic follows a t distribution with $n_1 + n_2 - 2$ degrees of freedom. For a given level of significance α, in a two-tail test, you reject the null hypothesis if the computed t-test statistic is greater than the upper-tail critical value from the t distribution or if the computed test statistic is less than the lower-tail critical value from the t distribution. Figure 10.1 displays the regions of rejection. In a one-tail test in which the rejection region is in the lower tail, you reject the null hypothesis if the computed test statistic is less than the lower-tail critical value from the t distribution. In a one-tail test in which the rejection region is in the upper tail, you reject the null hypothesis if the computed test statistic is greater than the upper-tail critical value from the t distribution.

FIGURE 10.1

Regions of Rejection and Nonrejection for the Pooled-Variance t Test for the Difference Between the Means (Two-Tail Test)

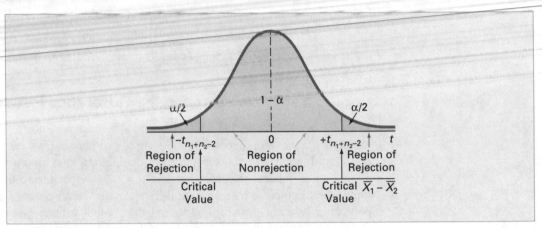

To demonstrate the use of the pooled-variance t test, return to the "Using Statistics" scenario on page 296. The question you want to answer is whether the mean weekly sales of BLK cola are the same when using a normal shelf location and when using an end-aisle display. There are two populations of interest. The first population is the set of all possible weekly sales of BLK cola *if* all the BLK supermarkets used the normal shelf location. The second population is the set of all possible weekly sales of BLK cola *if* all the BLK supermarkets used the end-aisle displays. The first sample contains the weekly sales of BLK cola from the 10 stores selected to use the normal shelf location, while the second sample contains the weekly sales of BLK cola from the 10 stores selected to use the end-aisle display. Table 10.1 contains the cola sales (in number of cases) for the two samples COLA.

TABLE 10.1

Comparing BLK Cola Weekly Sales from Two Different Display Locations (in Number of Cases)

Display Location									
Normal					**End-Aisle**				
22	34	52	62	30	52	71	76	54	67
40	64	84	56	59	83	66	90	77	84

The null and alternative hypotheses are

$$H_0: \mu_1 = \mu_2 \text{ or } \mu_1 - \mu_2 = 0$$

$$H_1: \mu_1 \neq \mu_2 \text{ or } \mu_1 - \mu_2 \neq 0$$

Assuming that the samples are from underlying normal populations having equal variances, you can use the pooled-variance t test. The t-test statistic follows a t distribution with $10 + 10 - 2 = 18$ degrees of freedom. Using $\alpha = 0.05$ level of significance, you divide the rejection region into the two tails for this two-tail test (i.e., two equal parts of 0.025 each). Table E.3 shows that the critical values for this two-tail test are $+2.1009$ and -2.1009. As shown in Figure 10.2, the decision rule is:

$$\text{Reject } H_0 \text{ if } t > t_{18} = +2.1009$$

$$\text{or if } t < -t_{18} = -2.1009;$$

$$\text{otherwise do not reject } H_0.$$

FIGURE 10.2

Two-Tail Test of
Hypothesis for the
Difference Between the
Means at the 0.05 Level
of Significance with
18 Degrees of Freedom

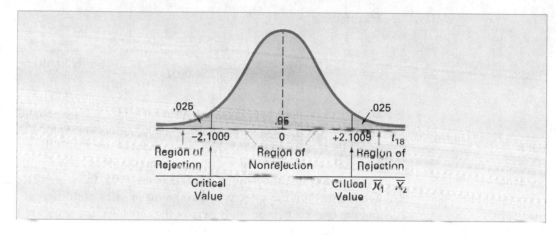

From Figures 10.3 or 10.4, the computed t statistic for this test is -3.04 and the p-value is 0.007.

FIGURE 10.3

Microsoft Excel t-Test
Output for the Two
Display Locations

	A	B	C
1	t-Test: Two-Sample Assuming Equal Variances		
2			
3		*Normal*	*End-Aisle*
4	Mean	50.3	72
5	Variance	350.6778	157.3333
6	Observations	10	10
7	Pooled Variance	254.0055556	
8	Hypothesized Mean Difference	0	
9	df	18	
10	t Stat	-3.04455	
11	P(T<=t) one-tail	0.00349	
12	t Critical one-tail	1.73406	
13	P(T<=t) two-tail	0.00697	
14	t Critical two-tail	2.10092	

FIGURE 10.4

Minitab t-Test Output
for the Two Display
Locations

```
Two-sample T for Sales_Normal vs Sales_EndAisle

                 N   Mean   StDev   SE Mean
Sales_Normal    10   50.3    18.7     5.9
Sales_EndAisle  10   72.0    12.5     4.0


Difference = mu (Sales_Normal) - mu (Sales_EndAisle)
Estimate for difference:  -21.7000
95% CI for difference:   (-36.6743, -6.7257)
T-Test of difference = 0 (vs not =): T-Value = -3.04   P-Value = 0.007   DF = 18
Both use Pooled StDev = 15.9376
```

Using Equation (10.2) and the descriptive statistics provided in Figure 10.3 or 10.4

$$t = \frac{(\bar{X}_1 - \bar{X}_2) - (\mu_1 - \mu_2)}{\sqrt{S_p^2\left(\dfrac{1}{n_1} + \dfrac{1}{n_2}\right)}}$$

where

$$S_p^2 = \frac{(n_1 - 1)S_1^2 + (n_2 - 1)S_2^2}{(n_1 - 1) + (n_2 - 1)}$$

$$= \frac{9(350.6778) + 9(157.3333)}{9 + 9} = 254.0056$$

Therefore,

$$t = \frac{(50.3 - 72.0) - 0.0}{\sqrt{254.0056\left(\dfrac{1}{10} + \dfrac{1}{10}\right)}} = \frac{-21.7}{\sqrt{50.801}} = -3.04$$

You reject the null hypothesis because $t = -3.04 < t_{18} = -2.1009$. The p-value (as computed from Microsoft Excel or Minitab) is 0.00697. In other words, the probability that $t > 3.04$ or $t < -3.04$ is equal to 0.00697. This p-value indicates that if the population means are equal, the probability of observing a difference this large or larger in the two sample means is only 0.00697. Because the p-value is less than $\alpha = 0.05$, there is sufficient evidence to reject the null hypothesis. You can conclude that the mean sales are different for the normal shelf location and the end-aisle location. Based on these results, the sales are lower for the normal location (i.e., higher for the end-aisle location).

EXAMPLE 10.1

TESTING FOR THE DIFFERENCE IN THE MEAN DELIVERY TIMES

A local pizza restaurant located close to a college campus advertises that their delivery time to a college dormitory is less than for a local branch of a national pizza chain. In order to determine whether this advertisement is valid, you and some friends have decided to order 10 pizzas from the local pizza restaurant and 10 pizzas from the national chain, all at different times. The delivery times in minutes PIZZATIME are shown in Table 10.2:

TABLE 10.2

Delivery Times for Local Pizza Restaurant and National Pizza Chain

Local	Chain	Local	Chain
16.8	22.0	18.1	19.5
11.7	15.2	14.1	17.0
15.6	18.7	21.8	19.5
16.7	15.6	13.9	16.5
17.5	20.8	20.8	24.0

At the 0.05 level of significance, is there evidence that the mean delivery time is lower for the local pizza restaurant than for the national pizza chain?

SOLUTION Since you want to know whether the mean is *lower* for the local pizza restaurant than for the national pizza chain, you have a one-tail test with the following null and alternative hypotheses:

$H_0: \mu_1 \geq \mu_2$ (The mean time for the local pizza restaurant is equal to or higher than for the national pizza chain)

$H_1: \mu_1 < \mu_2$ (The mean time for the local pizza restaurant is less than for the national pizza chain)

Figure 10.5 displays Microsoft Excel output of the pooled t-test for these data.

FIGURE 10.5

Microsoft Excel Output of the Pooled t-Test for the Pizza Delivery Time Data

	A	B	C
1	t-Test: Two-Sample Assuming Equal Variances		
2			
3		Local	Chain
4	Mean	16.7	18.88
5	Variance	9.582222	8.215111
6	Observations	10	10
7	Pooled Variance	8.898667	
8	Hypothesized Mean Difference	0	
9	df	18	
10	t Stat	-1.6341	
11	P(T<=t) one-tail	0.059803	
12	t Critical one-tail	1.734063	
13	P(T<=t) two-tail	0.119606	
14	t Critical two-tail	2.100924	

Using Equation (10.2),

$$t = \frac{(\overline{X}_1 - \overline{X}_2) - (\mu_1 - \mu_2)}{\sqrt{S_p^2\left(\dfrac{1}{n_1} + \dfrac{1}{n_2}\right)}}$$

where

$$S_p^2 = \frac{(n_1 - 1)S_1^2 + (n_2 - 1)S_2^2}{(n_1 - 1) + (n_2 - 1)}$$

$$= \frac{9(9.5822) + 9(8.2151)}{9 + 9} = 8.8987$$

Therefore,

$$t = \frac{(16.7 - 18.88) - 0.0}{\sqrt{8.8987\left(\dfrac{1}{10} + \dfrac{1}{10}\right)}} = \frac{-2.18}{\sqrt{1.7797}} = -1.634$$

You do not reject the null hypothesis because $t = -1.634 > t_{18} = -1.734$. The p-value (as computed from Microsoft Excel) is 0.0598. In other words, the probability that $t < -1.634$ is equal to 0.0598. This p-value indicates that if the population means are equal, the probability that the t statistic will be less than -1.634 is 0.0598. Because the p-value is greater than $\alpha = 0.05$, there is insufficient evidence to reject the null hypothesis. Based on these results, there is insufficient evidence for the local pizza restaurant to make the advertising claim that they have a lower delivery time.

In testing for the difference between the means, you assume that the populations are normally distributed with equal variances. For situations in which the two populations have equal variances, the pooled-variance t test is **robust** (i.e., not sensitive) to moderate departures from the assumption of normality, provided that the sample sizes are large. In such situations, you can use the pooled-variance t test without serious effects on its power. However, if you cannot assume that the data in each group are from normally distributed populations, you have two choices. You can use a non-parametric procedure, such as the Wilcoxon rank sum test (see reference 1), that does not depend on the assumption of normality for the two populations, or you can use a normalizing transformation (see reference 9) on each of the outcomes and then use the pooled-variance t test.

To check the assumption of normality in each of the two groups, observe the box-and-whisker plot of the sales for the two aisle locations in Figure 10.6. There appears to be only moderate departure from normality, so the assumption of normality needed for the t test is not seriously violated.

FIGURE 10.6

Minitab Box-and-Whisker Plot of the Sales for Two Aisle Locations

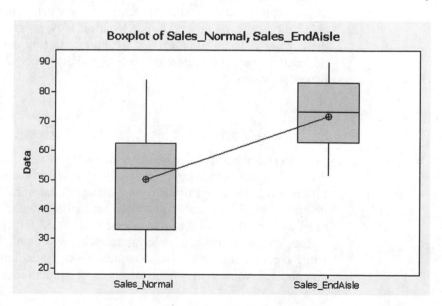

Confidence Interval Estimate for the Difference Between the Means of Two Independent Populations

Instead of, or in addition to, testing for the difference in the means of two independent populations, you can use Equation (10.3) to develop a confidence interval estimate of the difference in the means.

CONFIDENCE INTERVAL ESTIMATE OF THE DIFFERENCE IN THE MEANS OF TWO INDEPENDENT POPULATIONS

$$(\bar{X}_1 - \bar{X}_2) \pm t_{n_1+n_2-2}\sqrt{S_p^2\left(\frac{1}{n_1}+\frac{1}{n_2}\right)} \qquad (10.3)$$

or

$$(\bar{X}_1 - \bar{X}_2) - t_{n_1+n_2-2}\sqrt{S_p^2\left(\frac{1}{n_1}+\frac{1}{n_2}\right)} \leq \mu_1 - \mu_2 \leq (\bar{X}_1 - \bar{X}_2) + t_{n_1+n_2-2}\sqrt{S_p^2\left(\frac{1}{n_1}+\frac{1}{n_2}\right)}$$

where $t_{n_1+n_2-2}$ is the critical value of the t distribution with $n_1 + n_2 - 2$ degrees of freedom for an area of $\alpha/2$ in the upper tail.

Using 95% confidence, the sample statistics reported in Figures 10.3 or 10.4, and Equation (10.3),

$$\bar{X}_1 = 50.3, n_1 = 10, \bar{X}_2 = 72, n_2 = 10, S_p^2 = 254.0056, \text{ and } t_{18} = 2.1009:$$

$$(50.3 - 72) \pm (2.1009)\sqrt{254.0056\left(\frac{1}{10}+\frac{1}{10}\right)}$$

$$-21.7 \pm (2.1009)(7.1275)$$

$$-21.7 \pm 14.97$$

$$-36.67 \leq \mu_1 - \mu_2 \leq -6.73$$

Therefore, you are 95% confident that the difference in mean sales between the normal aisle location and the end-aisle location is between −36.67 cases of cola and −6.73 cases of cola. In other words, the end-aisle location sells, on average, 6.73 to 36.67 cases more than the normal aisle location. From a hypothesis testing perspective, because the interval does not include zero, you reject the null hypothesis of no difference between the means of the two populations.

Separate-Variance t Test for the Difference Between Two Means

In testing for the difference between the means of two independent populations when the population variances are assumed equal, the sample variances are pooled together into a common estimate S_p^2. However, if you cannot make this assumption, then the pooled-variance t test is inappropriate. In this case, it is more appropriate to use the **separate-variance t test** developed by Satterthwaite (see reference 8). In the Satterthwaite approximation procedure, you include the two separate sample variances in the computation of the t-test statistic—hence, the name separate-variance t test. Although the computations for the separate-variance t test are complicated, you can use Microsoft Excel or Minitab to do them.

Figure 10.7 illustrates Microsoft Excel output for this separate-variance t test. Figure 10.8 illustrates Minitab output.

FIGURE 10.7

Microsoft Excel Output of the Separate-Variance t Test for the Aisle Location Data

	A	B	C
1	t-Test: Two-Sample Assuming Unequal Variances		
2			
3		Normal	End-Aisle
4	Mean	50.3	72
5	Variance	350.6778	157.3333
6	Observations	10	10
7	Hypothesized Mean Difference	0	
8	df	16	
9	t Stat	3.04466	
10	P(T<=t) one-tail	0.00386	
11	t Critical one-tail	1.74588	
12	P(T<=t) two-tail	0.00773	
13	t Critical two-tail	2.11990	

FIGURE 10.8

Minitab Output of the Separate-Variance t Test for the Aisle Location Data

```
Two-sample T for Sales_Normal vs Sales_EndAisle

                   N   Mean   StDev   SE Mean
Sales_Normal      10   50.3   18.7      5.9
Sales_EndAisle    10   72.0   12.5      4.0


Difference = mu (Sales_Normal) - mu (Sales_EndAisle)
Estimate for difference:   -21.7000
95% CI for difference:   (-36.8919, -6.5081)
T-Test of difference = 0 (vs not =): T-Value = -3.04  P-Value = 0.008  DF = 15
```

In Figures 10.7 and 10.8 the test statistic is $t = -3.04$ and the p-value is $0.008 < 0.05$. Thus, the results for the separate-variance t test are almost exactly the same as those of the pooled-variance t test. The assumption of equality of population variances had no real effect on the results. Sometimes, however, the results from the pooled-variance and separate-variance t tests conflict because the assumption of equal variances is violated. Therefore, it is important that you evaluate the assumptions and use those results as a guide in appropriately selecting a test procedure. In section 10.4 the F test to determine whether there is evidence of a difference in the two population variances is discussed. The results of that test can help you determine which of the t tests (pooled-variance or separate-variance) is more appropriate.

PROBLEMS FOR SECTION 10.1

Learning the Basics

 10.1 Given a sample of $n_1 = 40$ from a population with known standard deviation $\sigma_1 = 20$, and an independent sample of $n_2 = 50$ from another population with known standard deviation $\sigma_2 = 10$, what is the value of the Z-test statistic for testing H_0: $\mu_1 = \mu_2$ if $\bar{X}_1 = 72$ and $\bar{X}_2 = 66$?

 10.2 What is your decision in problem 10.1 if you are testing H_0: $\mu_1 = \mu_2$ against the two-tail alternative H_1: $\mu_1 \neq \mu_2$ using a level of significance $\alpha = 0.01$?

10.3 What is the p-value in problem 10.1 if you are testing H_0: $\mu_1 = \mu_2$ against the two-tail alternative H_1: $\mu_1 \neq \mu_2$?

 10.4 Assume that you have a sample of $n_1 = 8$ with sample mean $\bar{X}_1 = 42$ and a sample standard deviation of $S_1 = 4$, and you have an independent sample of $n_2 = 15$ from another population with a sample mean of $\bar{X}_2 = 34$ and sample standard deviation $S_2 = 5$,
a. What is the value of the pooled-variance t-test statistic for testing H_0: $\mu_1 = \mu_2$?
b. In finding the critical value of the test statistic t, how many degrees of freedom are there?
c. Using a level of significance $\alpha = 0.01$, what is the critical value for a one-tail test of the hypothesis H_0: $\mu_1 \leq \mu_2$ against the alternative H_1: $\mu_1 > \mu_2$?
d. What is your statistical decision?

10.5 What assumptions about the two populations are necessary in problem 10.4?

10.6 Referring to problem 10.4, construct a 95% confidence interval estimate of the population difference between μ_1 and μ_2.

Applying the Concepts

Problems 10.7–10.17 can be solved manually or by using Microsoft Excel, Minitab, or SPSS. We recommend that you use Microsoft Excel, Minitab, or SPSS to solve problems 10.18–10.21.

PH Grade ASSIST **10.7** The operations manager at a lightbulb factory wants to determine whether there is any difference in the mean life expectancy of bulbs manufactured on two different types of machines. The population standard deviation of machine I is 110 hours and of machine II is 125 hours. A random sample of 25 lightbulbs from machine I indicates a sample mean of 375 hours, and a similar sample of 25 from machine II indicates a sample mean of 362 hours.

a. Using the 0.05 level of significance, is there any evidence of a difference in the mean life of bulbs produced by the two types of machines?

b. Compute the *p*-value in (a) and interpret its meaning.

PH Grade ASSIST **10.8** The purchasing director for an industrial parts factory is investigating the possibility of purchasing a new type of milling machine. She determines that the new machine will be bought if there is evidence that the parts produced have a higher mean breaking strength than those from the old machine. The population standard deviation of the breaking strength for the old machine is 10 kilograms and for the new machine is 9 kilograms. A sample of 100 parts taken from the old machine indicates a sample mean of 65 kilograms and a similar sample of 100 from the new machine indicates a sample mean of 72 kilograms.

a. Using the 0.01 level of significance, is there evidence that the purchasing director should buy the new machine?

b. Compute the *p*-value in (a) and interpret its meaning.

10.9 Millions of dollars are spent each year on diet foods. Trends such as the low-fat diet or the low-carb Atkins diet have led to a host of new products. A study by Dr. Linda Stern of the Philadelphia Veterans Administration Hospital compared weight loss between obese patients on a low-fat diet and obese patients on a low-carb diet (R. Bazell, "Study Casts Doubt on Advantages of Atkins Diet," **msnbc.com**, May 17, 2004). Let μ_1 represent the mean number of pounds obese patients on a low-fat diet lose in six months, and μ_2 represent the mean number of pounds obese patients on a low-carb diet lose in six months.

a. State the null and alternative hypotheses if you want to test whether or not the mean weight loss between the two diets are equal.

b. In the context of this study, what is the meaning of a Type I error?

c. In the context of this study, what is the meaning of a Type II error?

d. Suppose that a sample of 100 obese patients on a low-fat diet lost a mean of 7.6 pounds in six months with a standard deviation of 3.2 pounds, while a sample of 100 obese patients on a low-carb diet lost a mean of 6.7 pounds in six months with a standard deviation of 3.9 pounds. At the 0.05 level of significance, is there evidence of a difference in the mean weight loss of obese patients between the low-fat and low-carb diets?

10.10 When do children in the United States develop preferences for brand-name products? In a study reported in the *Journal of Consumer Psychology* (G. W. Achenreiner and D. R. John, "The Meaning of Brand Names to Children: A Developmental Investigation," *Journal of Consumer Psychology*, 2003, 13(3): 205–219), marketers showed children identical pictures of athletic shoes. One picture was labeled Nike and one was labeled K-Mart. The children were asked to evaluate the shoes based on their appearance, quality, price, prestige, favorableness, and preference for owning. A score from 2 (highest product evaluation possible) to –2 (lowest product evaluation possible) was recorded for each child. The following table reports the results of the study.

Age by Brand	Sample Size	Sample Mean	Sample Standard Deviation
Age 8			
Nike	27	0.89	0.98
K-Mart	22	0.86	1.07
Age 12			
Nike	39	0.88	1.01
K-Mart	41	0.09	1.08
Age 16			
Nike	35	0.41	0.81
K-Mart	33	–0.29	0.92

a. Conduct a pooled-variance *t* test for the difference between two means for each of the three age groups. Use a level of significance of 0.05.

b. Write a brief summary of your findings.

PH Grade ASSIST **10.11** According to a survey conducted in October 2001, consumers were trying to reduce their credit card debt (Margaret Price, "Credit Debts Get Cut Down to Size," *Newsday*, November 25, 2001, F3). Based on a sample of 1,000 consumers in October 2001 and in October 2000, the mean credit card debt was $2,411 in October 2001 as compared to $2,814 in October 2000. Suppose that the standard deviation was $847.43 in October 2001 and $976.93 in October 2000.

a. Assuming that the population variances from both years are equal, is there evidence that the mean credit card debt is lower in October 2001 than in October 2000? (Use the $\alpha = 0.05$ level of significance.)

b. Find the *p*-value in (a) and interpret its meaning.

c. Assuming that the population variances from both years are equal, construct and interpret a 95% confidence interval estimate of the difference between the population means in October 2001 and October 2000.

 10.12 The Computer Anxiety Rating Scale (CARS) measures an individual's level of computer anxiety on a scale from 20 (no anxiety) to 100 (highest level of anxiety). Researchers at Miami University administered CARS to 172 business students. One of the objectives of the study was to determine if there is a difference between the level of computer anxiety experienced by female and male business students.

	Males	Females
$\bar{X}$	40.26	36.85
S	13.35	9.42
n	100	72

Source: Extracted from Travis Broome and Douglas Havelka, "Determinants of Computer Anxiety in Business Students," The Review of Business Information Systems, Spring 2002, 6(2):9–16.

a. At the 0.05 level of significance, is there evidence of a difference in the mean computer anxiety experienced by female and male business students?
b. Determine the p-value and interpret its meaning.
c. What assumptions do you have to make about the two populations in order to justify the use of the t test?

10.13 Shipments of meat, meat by-products, and other ingredients are mixed together in several filling lines at a pet food canning factory. After the ingredients are thoroughly mixed, the pet food is placed in eight-ounce cans. Descriptive statistics concerning fill weights from two production lines, from two independent samples are given in the following table.

	Line A	Line B
$\bar{X}$	8.005	7.997
S	0.012	0.005
n	11	16

Assuming that the population variances are equal, at the 0.05 level of significance, is there evidence of a difference between the mean weight of cans filled on the two lines?

10.14 A bank with a branch located in a commercial district of a city has developed an improved process for serving customers during the noon to 1 P.M. lunch period. The waiting time (operationally defined as the time elapsed from when the customer enters the line until he or she reaches the teller window) of all customers during this hour is recorded over a period of one week. A random sample of 15 customers BANK1 is selected, and the results (in minutes) are as follows:

4.21 5.55 3.02 5.13 4.77 2.34 3.54 3.20
4.50 6.10 0.38 5.12 6.46 6.19 3.79

Suppose that another branch located in a residential area is also concerned with the noon to 1 P.M. lunch period. A random sample of 15 customers is selected BANK2, and the results are as follows:

9.66 5.90 8.02 5.79 8.73 3.82 8.01 8.35
10.49 6.68 5.64 4.08 6.17 9.91 5.47

a. Assuming that the population variances from both banks are equal, is there evidence of a difference in the mean waiting time between the two branches? (Use $\alpha = 0.05$.)
b. Determine the p-value in (a) and interpret its meaning.
c. What other assumption is necessary in (a)?
d. Assuming that the population variances from both branches are equal, construct and interpret a 95% confidence interval estimate of the difference between the population means in the two branches.

10.15 Repeat problem 10.14(a) assuming that the population variances in the two branches are not equal. Compare the results with those of problem 10.14(a).

10.16 A problem with a telephone line that prevents a customer from receiving or making calls is disconcerting to both the customer and the telephone company. The data PHONE represent samples of 20 problems reported to two different offices of a telephone company and the time to clear these problems (in minutes) from the customers' lines:

Central Office I Time to Clear Problems (minutes)
1.48 1.75 0.78 2.85 0.52 1.60 4.15 3.97 1.48 3.10
1.02 0.53 0.93 1.60 0.80 1.05 6.32 3.93 5.45 0.97

Central Office II Time to Clear Problems (minutes)
7.55 3.75 0.10 1.10 0.60 0.52 3.30 2.10 0.58 4.02
3.75 0.65 1.92 0.60 1.53 4.23 0.08 1.48 1.65 0.72

a. Assuming that the population variances from both offices are equal, is there evidence of a difference in the mean waiting time between the two offices? (Use $\alpha = 0.05$.)
b. Find the p-value in (a) and interpret its meaning.
c. What other assumption is necessary in (a)?
d. Assuming that the population variances from both offices are equal, construct and interpret a 95% confidence interval estimate of the difference between the population means in the two offices.

10.17 Repeat problem 10.16(a) assuming that the population variances in the two offices are not equal. Compare the results with those of problem 10.16(a).

10.18 In intaglio printing, a design or figure is carved beneath the surface of hard metal or stone. Suppose that an experiment is designed to compare differences in mean surface hardness of steel plates used in intaglio printing (measured in indentation numbers) based on two different surface conditions—untreated and treated by lightly polishing with emery paper. In the experiment, 40 steel plates are randomly assigned, 20 that are untreated, and 20 that are treated INTAGLIO.

Untreated		Treated	
164.368	177.135	158.239	150.226
159.018	163.903	138.216	155.620
153.871	167.802	168.006	151.233
165.096	160.818	149.654	158.653
157.184	167.433	145.456	151.204
154.496	163.538	168.178	150.869
160.920	164.525	154.321	161.657
164.917	171.230	162.763	157.016
169.091	174.964	161.020	156.670
175.276	166.311	167.706	147.920

a. Assuming that the population variances from both conditions are equal, is there evidence of a difference in the mean surface hardness between untreated and treated steel plates? (Use $\alpha = 0.05$.)
b. Find the p-value in (a) and interpret its meaning.
c. What other assumption is necessary in (a)?
d. Assuming that the population variances from untreated and treated steel plates are equal, construct and interpret a 95% confidence interval estimate of the difference between the population means in the two conditions.

10.19 Repeat problem 10.18(a) assuming that the population variances from untreated and treated steel plates are not equal. Compare the results with those of problem 10.18(a).

10.20 The director of training for an electronic equipment manufacturer is interested in determining whether different training methods have an effect on the productivity of assembly-line employees. She randomly assigns 42 recently hired employees into two groups of 21. The first group receives a computer-assisted, individual-based training program and the other receives a team-based training program. Upon completion of the training, the employees

are evaluated on the time (in seconds) it takes to assemble a part. The results are in the data file TRAINING.

a. Assuming that the variances in the populations of training methods are equal, is there evidence of a difference between the mean assembly times (in seconds) of employees trained in a computer-assisted, individual-based program and those trained in a team-based program? (Use a 0.05 level of significance.)
b. What other assumption is necessary in (a)?
c. Repeat (a), assuming that the population variances are not equal.
d. Compare the results of (a) and (c).
e. Assuming equal variances, construct and interpret a 95% confidence interval estimate of the difference between the population means of the two training methods.

10.21 Nondestructive evaluation (NDE) is a method that is used to describe the properties of components or materials without causing any permanent physical change to the units. It includes the determination of properties of materials and the classification of flaws by size, shape, type, and location. This method is most effective for detecting surface flaws and characterizing surface properties of electrically conductive materials. Recently, data were collected that classified each component as having a flaw based on manual inspection and operator judgment and also reported the size of the crack in the material. Do the components classified as unflawed have a smaller mean crack size than components classified as flawed? The results in terms of crack size (in inches) are in the data file: CRACK (Source: B. D. Olin and W. Q. Meeker, "Applications of Statistical Methods to Nondestructive Evaluation," *Technometrics*, 38, 1996, 101.)

a. Assuming that the population variances are equal, is there evidence that the mean crack size is smaller for the unflawed specimens than for the flawed specimens? (Use $\alpha = 0.05$.)
b. Repeat (a) assuming that the population variances are not equal.
c. Compare the results of (a) and (b).

10.2   COMPARING THE MEANS OF TWO RELATED POPULATIONS

The hypothesis-testing procedures examined in section 10.1 enable you to make comparisons and examine differences in the means of two *independent* populations. In this section, you will learn about a procedure for analyzing the difference between the means of two populations when you collect sample data from populations that are related, that is, when results of the first population are *not* independent of the results of the second population.

Two approaches that involve related data between populations are possible. In the first approach, items or individuals are **paired** or **matched** according to some characteristic. In the second approach you take **repeated measurements** from the same set of items or individuals. In either case, the variable of interest becomes the *difference between the values* rather than the *values* themselves.

The first approach for analyzing related-samples involves matching or pairing items or individuals according to some characteristic of interest. For example, in test-marketing a product under two different advertising campaigns, a sample of test markets can be *matched* on the basis of the test-market population size and/or demographic variables. By controlling these variables, you are better able to measure the effects of the two different advertising campaigns.

The second approach for analyzing related-samples involves taking repeated measurements on the same items or individuals. Under the theory that the same items or individuals will behave alike if treated alike, your objective is to show that any differences between two measurements of the same items or individuals are due to different treatment conditions. For example, when performing a taste-testing experiment, you can use each person in the sample as his or her own control so that you can have *repeated measurements* on the same individual.

Regardless of whether you have matched (paired) samples or repeated measurements, the objective is to study the difference between two measurements by reducing the effect of the variability that is due to the items or individuals themselves. Table 10.3 shows the differences in the individual values for samples taken from two related populations. To read this table, let $X_{11}, X_{12}, \ldots X_{1n}$ represent the n values from a sample. And let $X_{21}, X_{22}, \ldots X_{2n}$ represent either the corresponding n matched values from a second sample or the corresponding n repeated measurements from the initial sample. Then, $D_1, D_2, \ldots D_n$ will represent the corresponding set of n difference *scores* such that

$$D_1 = X_{11} - X_{21}, D_2 = X_{12} - X_{22}, \ldots, \text{ and } D_n = X_{1n} - X_{2n}$$

TABLE 10.3

Determining the Difference Between Two Related Populations

Value	Group 1	Group 2	Difference
1	X_{11}	X_{21}	$D_1 = X_{11} - X_{21}$
2	X_{12}	X_{22}	$D_2 = X_{12} - X_{22}$
.	.	.	.
.	.	.	.
.	.	.	.
i	X_{1i}	X_{2i}	$D_i = X_{1i} - X_{2i}$
.	.	.	.
.	.	.	.
.	.	.	.
n	X_{1n}	X_{2n}	$D_n = X_{1n} - X_{2n}$

To test for the mean difference between two related populations, you treat the difference scores, the D_i's, as values from a single sample. If you know the population standard deviation of the difference scores, you use the Z test defined in Equation (10.4).[2] This Z test for the mean difference using samples from two related populations is equivalent to the one-sample Z test for the mean of the difference scores [see Equation (9.1)].

[2] If the sample size is large, the Central Limit Theorem (see page 213) assures you that the sampling distribution of $\overline{D}$ follows a normal distribution.

Z TEST FOR THE MEAN DIFFERENCE

$$Z = \frac{\overline{D} - \mu_D}{\frac{\sigma_D}{\sqrt{n}}} \qquad (10.4)$$

where

$$\overline{D} = \frac{\sum_{i=1}^{n} D_i}{n}$$

μ_D = hypothesized mean difference

σ_D = population standard deviation of the difference scores

n = sample size

The test statistic Z follows a standardized normal distribution.

Paired t Test

In most cases the population standard deviation is unknown. The only information you usually have are the sample mean and the sample standard deviation.

If you assume that the difference scores are randomly and independently selected from a population that is normally distributed, you can use the **paired t test for the mean difference in related populations** to determine whether there is a significant population mean difference. Thus, like the one-sample t test developed in section 9.4 [see Equation (9.2)], the t-test statistic developed here follows the t distribution with $n - 1$ degrees of freedom. Although you must assume the population is normally distributed, as long as the sample size is not very small and the population is not highly skewed, you can use the paired t test.

To test the null hypothesis that there is no difference in the means of two related populations (i.e., the population mean difference μ_D is 0)

$$H_0: \mu_D = 0 \text{ (where } \mu_D = \mu_1 - \mu_2)$$

against the alternative that the means are not the same (i.e., the population mean difference μ_D is not 0)

$$H_1: \mu_D \neq 0$$

you compute the t-test statistic in Equation (10.5).

PAIRED t TEST FOR THE MEAN DIFFERENCE

$$t = \frac{\overline{D} - \mu_D}{\frac{S_D}{\sqrt{n}}}$$

(10.5)

where

$$\overline{D} = \frac{\sum_{i=1}^{n} D_i}{n}$$

and

$$S_D = \sqrt{\frac{\sum_{i=1}^{n} (D_i - \overline{D})^2}{n - 1}}$$

The test statistic t follows a t distribution with $n - 1$ degrees of freedom.

For a two-tail test with a given level of significance α, you reject the null hypothesis if the computed t-test statistic is greater than the upper-tail critical value t_{n-1} from the t distribution or if the computed test statistic is less than the lower-tail critical value $-t_{n-1}$ from the t distribution. That is, the decision rule is

$$\text{Reject } H_0 \text{ if } t > t_{n-1}$$

$$\text{or if } t < -t_{n-1};$$

$$\text{otherwise do not reject } H_0.$$

To illustrate the use of the t test for the mean difference, suppose that a software applications company is developing a new financial applications package. Because computer-processing time is an important decision criterion, the developer wants the new package to have the same features and capabilities as the current market leader while providing results faster than the current leading package. If the new financial package is effective, it will provide the same results as the current market leader but will use less processing time.

What is the best way to design an experiment to compare the processing speed of the new software package to the processing speed of the current package? One approach is to take two independent samples and then use the hypothesis tests discussed in section 10.1. In this approach, you would use one set of financial applications projects to test the new software package. Then you would use a second set of different financial applications projects to test the current package. However, since the first set of financial applications projects used to test the new package might be faster or slower to process than the second set of financial application projects, this is not the best approach. A better approach is to use a repeated measurements experiment. In this experiment, you use one set of financial applications projects. For each of the projects, the new software package is tested and the current package is tested. Measuring the two processing times for each financial applications project serves to reduce the variability in the processing times compared with what would occur if you used two independent sets of financial applications projects. This approach also focuses on the differences between the two processing times for each financial applications project in order to measure the effectiveness of the new software package.

The results displayed in Table 10.4 are for a sample of $n = 10$ financial applications projects used in the experiment COMPTIME.

TABLE 10.4

Repeated Measurements of Time (in Seconds) to Complete Financial Applications Projects on Two Competing Software Packages

Applications Project	Processing Times (in seconds)		
	By Current Market Leader	By New Software Package	Difference (D_i)
1	9.98	9.88	+0.10
2	9.88	9.86	+0.02
3	9.84	9.75	+0.09
4	9.99	9.80	+0.19
5	9.94	9.87	+0.07
6	9.84	9.84	0.00
7	9.86	9.87	−0.01
8	10.12	9.86	+0.26
9	9.90	9.83	+0.07
10	9.91	9.86	+0.05
			+0.84

The question that you must answer is whether the new software package is faster. In other words, is there evidence that the mean processing time is significantly greater when financial applications projects use the current market leader rather than the new software package? Thus, the null and alternative hypotheses are:

H_0: $\mu_D \leq 0$ (mean processing time for the current package is less than or the same as that for the new package)
H_1: $\mu_D > 0$ (mean processing time for the current package is greater than that for the new package)

Choosing a level of significance of $\alpha = 0.05$ and assuming that the differences are normally distributed, you use the paired t test [Equation (10.5)]. For a sample of $n = 10$ projects, there are $n - 1 = 9$ degrees of freedom. Using Table E.3, the decision rule is:

Reject H_0 if $t > t_9 = 1.8331$;

otherwise do not reject H_0.

For the $n = 10$ differences (see Table 10.4), the sample mean difference is

$$\overline{D} = \frac{\sum_{i=1}^{n} D_i}{n} = \frac{0.84}{10} = 0.084$$

and

$$S_D = \sqrt{\frac{\sum_{i=1}^{n}(D_i - \bar{D})^2}{n-1}} = 0.0844$$

From Equation (10.5),

$$t = \frac{\bar{D} - \mu_D}{\frac{S_D}{\sqrt{n}}} = \frac{0.084 - 0}{\frac{0.0844}{\sqrt{10}}} = 3.15$$

Because $t = 3.15$ is greater than 1.8331, you reject the null hypothesis H_0 (see Figure 10.9). There is evidence that the mean processing time is higher for the current market leader than for the new package.

FIGURE 10.9

One-tail Paired t Test at the 0.05 Level of Significance with 9 Degrees of Freedom

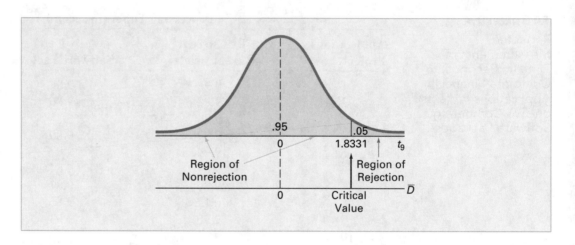

You can compute this test statistic along with the p-value using Microsoft Excel or Minitab (see Figures 10.10 and 10.11). Because the p-value = 0.006 < α = 0.05, you reject H_0. The p-value indicates that if the two packages have the same mean processing time, the probability that the new package would outperform the current package by a mean of 0.084 seconds or more is only 0.006. Because this probability is so small, you have a minimal degree of belief in the null hypothesis and you conclude that the alternative hypothesis (i.e., the current package takes more time) is true.

FIGURE 10.10

Microsoft Excel Paired t Test for the Financial Packages Data

	A	B	C
1	t-Test: Paired Two Sample for Means		
2			
3		*Current*	*New*
4	Mean	9.926	9.842
5	Variance	0.0074	0.0016
6	Observations	10	10
7	Pearson Correlation	0.2798	
8	Hypothesized Mean Difference	0	
9	df	9	
10	t Stat	3.14902	
11	P(T<=t) one-tail	0.00588	
12	t Critical one-tail	1.83311	
13	P(T<=t) two-tail	0.01176	
14	t Critical two-tail	2.26216	

**FIGURE 10.11
PANEL A**

Minitab Paired *t* Test
for the Financial
Packages Data

```
Paired T for Current - New

                N      Mean      StDev     SE Mean
Current        10   9.92600    0.08631    0.02729
New            10   9.84200    0.03994    0.01263
Difference     10   0.084000   0.084354   0.026675


95% lower bound for mean difference: 0.035102
T-Test of mean difference = 0 (vs > 0): T-Value = 3.15  P-Value = 0.006
```

**FIGURE 10.11
PANEL B**

Minitab Boxplot
for the Financial
Packages Data

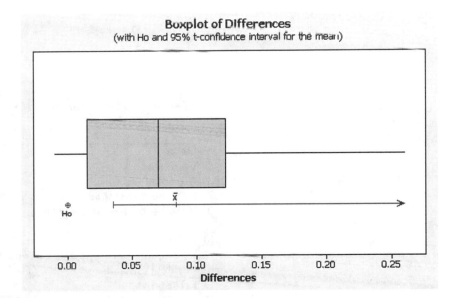

From Figure 10.11, panel B, observe that the box-and-whisker plot shows approximate symmetry between the first and third quartiles, but also has one or more high values. Thus, the data do not greatly contradict the underlying assumption of normality. If an exploratory data analysis reveals that the assumption of underlying normality in the population is severely violated, then the *t* test is inappropriate. If this occurs, you can either use a *nonparametric* procedure that does not make the stringent assumption of underlying normality (see references 1 and 2) or make a data transformation (see reference 9) and then recheck the assumptions to determine whether you should use the *t* test.

EXAMPLE 10.2

PAIRED *t*-TEST OF PIZZA DELIVERY TIMES

Recall from Example 10.1 that a local pizza restaurant located close to a college campus advertises that their delivery time to a college dormitory is less than for a local branch of a national pizza chain. In order to determine whether this advertisement is valid, you and some friends have decided to order 10 pizzas from the local pizza restaurant and 10 pizzas from the national chain. In fact, you and your friends have collected the data at 10 different times. At each time, you ordered a pizza from the local pizza restaurant and also from the national pizza chain. Thus, you have paired data, one measurement for each pizza delivered at each time.

SOLUTION You use the paired *t* test instead of the pooled *t* test to analyze these data **PIZZATIME**. Table 10.5 summarizes the data.

TABLE 10.5

Delivery Times for Local Pizza Restaurant and National Pizza Chain

Time	Local	Chain	Difference
1	16.8	22.0	−5.2
2	11.7	15.2	−3.5
3	15.6	18.7	−3.1
4	16.7	15.6	1.1
5	17.5	20.8	−3.3
6	18.1	19.5	−1.4
7	14.1	17.0	−2.9
8	21.8	19.5	2.3
9	13.9	16.5	−2.6
10	20.8	24.0	−3.2
			−21.8

FIGURE 10.12

Microsoft Excel Paired t Test Output for the Pizza Delivery Data

	A	B	C
1	t-Test: Paired Two Sample for Means		
2			
3		Local	Chain
4	Mean	16.7	18.88
5	Variance	9.582222	8.215111
6	Observations	10	10
7	Pearson Correlation	0.714077	
8	Hypothesized Mean Difference	0	
9	df	9	
10	t Stat	-3.04479	
11	P(T<=t) one-tail	0.006955	
12	t Critical one-tail	1.833114	
13	P(T<=t) two-tail	0.01391	
14	t Critical two-tail	2.262159	

Figure 10.12 illustrates Microsoft Excel paired t test output for the pizza delivery data. The null and alternative hypotheses are:

H_0: $\mu_D \geq 0$ (mean delivery time for the local pizza restaurant is higher than or the same as that for the national pizza chain)

H_1: $\mu_D < 0$ (mean delivery time for the local pizza restaurant is lower than for the national pizza chain)

Choosing a level of significance of $\alpha = 0.05$ and assuming that the differences are normally distributed, you use the paired t test [Equation (10.5)]. For a sample of $n = 10$ delivery times, there are $n - 1 = 9$ degrees of freedom. Using Table E.3, the decision rule is:

Reject H_0 if $t < t_9 = -1.8331$;

otherwise do not reject H_0

For $n = 10$ differences (see Table 10.5), the sample mean difference is

$$\overline{D} = \frac{\sum_{i=1}^{n} D_i}{n} = \frac{-21.8}{10} = -2.18$$

and the sample standard deviation of the difference is

$$S_D = \sqrt{\frac{\sum_{i=1}^{n}(D_i - \overline{D})^2}{n-1}} = 2.2641$$

From Equation (10.5),

$$t = \frac{\overline{D} - \mu_D}{\frac{S_D}{\sqrt{n}}} = \frac{-2.18 - 0}{\frac{2.2641}{\sqrt{10}}} = -3.045$$

Because $t = -3.045$ is less than -1.8331, you reject the null hypothesis H_0 (the p-value is 0.007 < 0.05). There is evidence that the mean delivery time is lower for the local pizza restaurant than for the national pizza chain.

This conclusion is different from the one you reached when you used the pooled-variance t test for these data. By pairing the delivery times, you were able to focus on the differences between the two pizza delivery services and you had a more powerful statistical procedure that was better able to detect the difference between the two restaurants.

Confidence Interval Estimate for the Mean Difference

Instead of, or in addition to, testing for the difference between the means of two related populations, you can construct a confidence interval estimate of the mean difference as shown in Equation (10.6).

CONFIDENCE INTERVAL ESTIMATE FOR THE MEAN DIFFERENCE

$$\overline{D} \pm t_{n-1} \frac{S_D}{\sqrt{n}} \qquad (10.6)$$

or

$$\overline{D} - t_{n-1} \frac{S_D}{\sqrt{n}} \leq \mu_D \leq \overline{D} + t_{n-1} \frac{S_D}{\sqrt{n}}$$

Returning to the example concerning the financial applications projects on pages 308–309, using Equation (10.6) above, $\overline{D} = 0.084$, $S_D = 0.0844$, $n = 10$, and $t = 2.2622$ (for 95% confidence and $n - 1 = 9$ degrees of freedom),

$$0.084 \pm (2.2622) \frac{0.0844}{\sqrt{10}}$$

$$0.084 \pm 0.0604$$

$$0.0236 \leq \mu_D \leq 0.1444$$

Thus, with 95% confidence, the mean difference between the two software packages is between 0.0236 and 0.1444 seconds. Since the interval estimate only contains values greater than zero, you can conclude that the mean processing time for the current package is higher than that for the new package.

PROBLEMS FOR SECTION 10.2

Learning the Basics

PH Grade ASSIST **10.22** An experimental design for a paired t test has, as a matched sample, 20 pairs of identical twins. How many degrees of freedom are there in this t test?

PH Grade ASSIST **10.23** An experimental design for a repeated-measures t test requires a measurement before and after the presentation of a stimulus on each of 15 subjects. How many degrees of freedom are there in this t test?

Applying the Concepts

Problems 10.24–10.29 can be solved manually or by using Microsoft Excel, Minitab, or SPSS. We recommend that you use Microsoft Excel, Minitab, or SPSS to solve problem 10.30.

10.24 Travel expenses paid by companies can increase or decrease dramatically when there are changes in the daily rates for hotel rooms. Did these rates stay the same from June 2002 to March 2004? The following data HOTELPRICE2 give typical daily rates for hotels in 18 cities during March 2004 and June 2002.

City	Hotel 2004	Hotel 2002
Atlanta	78.91	173
Boston	112.92	243
Chicago	96.90	257
Dallas	77.43	167
Denver	74.22	139
Detroit	77.71	141
Houston	76.26	180
Los Angeles	95.78	223
Miami	140.61	116
Minneapolis	78.64	167
New Orleans	121.59	142
New York	167.43	273
Orlando	98.57	133
Phoenix	123.19	124
San Francisco	123.51	178
Seattle	95.09	176
St. Louis	74.68	159
Washington	123.27	262

Source: Extracted from "Travel," The Wall Street Journal, June 7, 2002, W4; and C. Woodyard, "Luxury Costs More These Days," USA Today, April 27, 2004, 5B.

a. At the 0.05 level of significance, is there evidence of a difference in the mean daily hotel rate in March 2004 and June 2002?

b. What assumption is necessary to perform this test?

c. Determine the *p*-value in (a) and interpret its meaning.

d. Construct and interpret a 95% confidence interval estimate of the difference in the mean daily hotel rate for March 2004 and June 2002.

10.25 In industrial settings, alternative methods often exist for measuring variables of interest. The data in the file MEASUREMENT (coded to maintain confidentiality) represent measurements in-line (collected from an analyzer during the production process) and from an analytical lab. (M. Leitnaker, "Comparing Measurement Processes: In-line Versus Analytical Measurements," *Quality Engineering*, 13, 2000–2001, 293–298.)

a. At the 0.05 level of significance, is there evidence of a difference in the mean measurements in-line and from an analytical lab?

b. What assumption is necessary to perform this test?

c. Use a graphical method to evaluate the validity of the assumption in (a).

d. Construct and interpret a 95% confidence interval estimate of the difference in the mean measurements in-line and from an analytical lab.

 10.26 Can students save money by buying their textbooks at Amazon.com? To investigate this possibility, a random sample of 15 textbooks used during a recent semester at Miami University was selected. The prices for these textbooks at both a local bookstore and through Amazon.com were recorded. The prices for the textbooks, including all relevant taxes and shipping are given below TEXTBOOK:

Textbook	Book Store	Amazon
Access 2000 Guidebook	52.22	57.34
HTML 4.0 CD with Java Script	52.74	44.47
Designing the Physical Education Curriculum	39.04	41.48
Service Management: Operations, Strategy and IT	101.28	73.72
Fundamentals of Real Estate Appraisal	37.45	42.04
Investments	113.41	95.38
Intermediate Financial Management	109.72	119.80
Real Estate Principles	101.28	62.48
The Automobile Age	29.49	32.43
Geographic Information Systems in Ecology	70.07	74.43
Geosystems: An Introduction to Physical Geography	83.87	83.81
Understanding Contemporary Africa	23.21	26.48
Early Childhood Education Today	72.80	73.48
System of Transcendental Idealism (1800)	17.41	20.98
Principles and Labs for Fitness and Wellness	37.72	40.43

a. At the 0.01 level of significance, is there evidence of a difference between the mean price of textbooks at the local bookstore and Amazon.com?

b. What assumption is necessary to perform this test?

c. Construct a 99% confidence interval estimate of the mean difference in price. Interpret the interval.

d. Compare the results of (a) and (c).

10.27 A recent article discussed the new Whole Foods Market in the Time-Warner building in New York City. The following data **WHOLEFOODS1** compared the price of some kitchen staples at the new Whole Foods Market and at the Fairway supermarket located about 15 blocks from the Time-Warner building.

Item	Whole Foods	Fairway
Half gallon milk	2.19	1.35
Dozen eggs	2.39	1.69
Tropicana orange juice (64 oz.)	2.00	2.49
Head of Boston lettuce	1.98	1.29
Ground round 1lb.	4.99	3.69
Bumble Bee tuna 6 oz. can	1.79	1.33
Granny Smith apples (1 lb.)	1.69	1.49
Box DeCecco linguini	1.99	1.59
Salmon steak 1 lb.	7.99	5.99
Whole chicken per pound	2.19	1.49

Source: Extracted from W. Grimes, "A Pleasure Palace without the Guilt," The New York Times, February 18, 2004, F1, F5.

a. At the 0.01 level of significance, is there evidence that the mean price is higher at Whole Foods Market than at the Fairway Supermarket?
b. Interpret the meaning of the *p*-value in (a).

10.28 Multiple myeloma or blood plasma cancer is characterized by increased blood vessel formulation (angiogenesis) in the bone marrow that is a prognostic factor in survival. One treatment approach used for multiple myeloma is stem cell transplantation with the patient's own stem cells. The following data **MYELOMA** represent the bone marrow microvessel density for patients who had a complete response to the stem cell transplant as measured by blood and urine tests. The measurements were taken immediately prior to the stem cell transplant and at the time of the complete response.

Patient	Before	After
1	158	284
2	189	214
3	202	101
4	353	227
5	416	290
6	426	176
7	441	290

Source: S. V. Rajkumar, R. Fonseca, T. E. Witzig, M. A. Gertz, and P. R. Greipp, "Bone Marrow Angiogenesis in Patients Achieving Complete Response After Stem Cell Transplantation for Multiple Myeloma," Leukemia, 1999, 13, 469–472.

a. At the 0.05 level of significance, is there evidence that the mean bone marrow microvessel density is higher before the stem cell transplant than after the stem cell transplant?
b. Interpret the meaning of the *p*-value in (a).
c. Construct and interpret a 95% confidence interval estimate of the mean difference in bone marrow microvessel density before and after the stem cell transplant.

10.29 Over the past year the vice president for human resources at a large medical center has run a series of three-month workshops aimed at increasing worker motivation and performance. To check the effectiveness of the workshops, she selected a random sample of 35 employees from the personnel files and recorded their most recent annual performance ratings along with their ratings prior to attending the workshops **PERFORM**. The Microsoft Excel output in panels A and B below provides both descriptive and inferential information so that you can analyze the results and examine the assumptions of the hypothesis test used.

State your findings and conclusions in a report to the vice president for human resources.

	A	B
1	**Difference**	
3	Mean	-5.25714
4	Standard Error	1.947782
5	Median	-5
6	Mode	-10
7	Standard Deviation	11.52323
8	Sample Variance	132.7849
9	Kurtosis	1.103831
10	Skewness	0.110341
11	Range	61
12	Minimum	-34
13	Maximum	27
14	Sum	-184
15	Count	35
16	Largest(1)	27
17	Smallest(1)	-34

PANEL A

	A	B	C
1	t-Test: Paired Two Sample for Means		
3		Before	After
4	Mean	74.54286	79.8
5	Variance	80.90252	37.16471
6	Observations	35	35
7	Pearson Correlation	-0.1342	
8	Hypothesized Mean Difference	0	
9	df	34	
10	t Stat	-2.69904	
11	P(T<=t) one-tail	0.005376	
12	t Critical one-tail	1.690923	
13	P(T<=t) two-tail	0.010752	
14	t Critical two-tail	2.032243	

PANEL B

10.30 The data in the file CONCRETE1 represent the compressive strength in thousands of pounds per square inch (psi) of 40 samples of concrete taken two and seven days after pouring.

Source: O. Carrillo-Gamboa and R. F. Gunst, "Measurement-Error-Model Collinearities," Technometrics, 34, 1992, 454–464.

a. At the 0.01 level of significance, is there evidence that the mean strength is less at two days than at seven days?
b. What assumption is necessary to perform this test?
c. Find the *p*-value in (a) and interpret its meaning.

10.3 COMPARING TWO POPULATION PROPORTIONS

Often you need to make comparisons and analyze differences between two population proportions. You can perform a test for the difference between two proportions selected from independent samples using two different methods. This section presents a procedure whose test statistic Z is approximated by a standardized normal distribution. In section 11.1, a procedure whose test statistic χ^2 is approximated by a chi-square distribution is developed. As you will see, the results from these two tests are equivalent.

Z Test for the Difference Between Two Proportions

In evaluating differences between two population proportions, you can use a **Z test for the difference between two proportions**. The test statistic Z is based on the difference between two sample proportions $(p_1 - p_2)$. This test statistic, given in Equation (10.7), approximately follows a standardized normal distribution for large enough sample sizes.

Z TEST FOR THE DIFFERENCE BETWEEN TWO PROPORTIONS

$$Z = \frac{(p_1 - p_2) - (\pi_1 - \pi_2)}{\sqrt{\bar{p}(1 - \bar{p})\left(\dfrac{1}{n_1} + \dfrac{1}{n_2}\right)}}$$

(10.7)

with

$$\bar{p} = \frac{X_1 + X_2}{n_1 + n_2} \qquad p_1 = \frac{X_1}{n_1} \qquad p_2 = \frac{X_2}{n_2}$$

where
- p_1 = proportion of successes in sample 1
- X_1 = number of successes in sample 1
- n_1 = sample size of sample 1
- π_1 = proportion of successes in population 1
- p_2 = proportion of successes in sample 2
- X_2 = number of successes in sample 2
- n_2 = sample size of sample 2
- π_2 = proportion of successes in population 2
- $\bar{p}$ = pooled estimate of the population proportion of successes

The test statistic Z approximately follows a standardized normal distribution.

Under the null hypothesis, you assume that the two population proportions are equal ($\pi_1 = \pi_2$). Because the pooled estimate for the population proportion is based on the null hypothesis, you combine or pool the two sample proportions to compute an overall estimate of the common population proportion. This estimate is equal to the number of successes in the two samples combined ($X_1 + X_2$) divided by the total sample size from the two sample groups ($n_1 + n_2$).

As shown in the following table, you can use this Z test for the difference between population proportions to determine whether there is a difference in the proportion of successes in the two groups (two-tail test) or whether one group has a higher proportion of successes than the other group (one-tail test).

Two-Tail Test	One-Tail Test	One-Tail Test
$H_0\colon \pi_1 = \pi_2$	$H_0\colon \pi_1 \geq \pi_2$	$H_0\colon \pi_1 \leq \pi_2$
$H_1\colon \pi_1 \neq \pi_2$	$H_1\colon \pi_1 < \pi_2$	$H_1\colon \pi_1 > \pi_2$

where

π_1 = proportion of successes in population 1

π_2 = proportion of successes in population 2

To test the null hypothesis that there is no difference between the proportions of two independent populations:

$$H_0\colon \pi_1 = \pi_2$$

against the alternative that the two population proportions are not the same:

$$H_1\colon \pi_1 \neq \pi_2$$

use the test statistic Z, given by Equation (10.7). For a given level of significance α, reject the null hypothesis if the computed Z-test statistic is greater than the upper-tail critical value from the standardized normal distribution or if the computed test statistic is less than the lower-tail critical value from the standardized normal distribution.

To illustrate the use of the Z test for the equality of two proportions, suppose that you are the manager of T.C. Resort Properties, a collection of five upscale resort hotels located on two resort islands. On one of the islands, T.C. Resort Properties has two hotels, the Beachcomber and the Windsurfer. In tabulating the responses to the single question, "Are you likely to choose this hotel again?" 163 of 227 guests at the Beachcomber responded yes, and 154 of 262 guests at the Windsurfer responded yes. At the 0.05 level of significance, is there evidence of a significant difference in guest satisfaction (as measured by likelihood to return to the hotel) between the two hotels?

The null and alternative hypotheses are

$$H_0\colon \pi_1 = \pi_2 \text{ or } \pi_1 - \pi_2 = 0$$
$$H_1\colon \pi_1 \neq \pi_2 \text{ or } \pi_1 - \pi_2 \neq 0$$

Using the 0.05 level of significance, the critical values are -1.96 and $+1.96$ (see Figure 10.13), and the decision rule is

Reject H_0 if $Z < -1.96$

or if $Z > +1.96$;

otherwise do not reject H_0.

FIGURE 10.13

Regions of Rejection
and Nonrejection When
Testing a Hypothesis for
the Difference Between
Two Proportions
at the 0.05 Level
of Significance

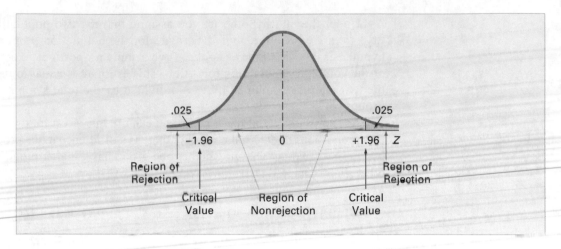

Using Equation (10.7),

$$Z = \frac{(p_1 - p_2) - (\pi_1 - \pi_2)}{\sqrt{\bar{p}(1 - \bar{p})\left(\dfrac{1}{n_1} + \dfrac{1}{n_2}\right)}}$$

where

$$p_1 = \frac{X_1}{n_1} = \frac{163}{227} = 0.718 \qquad p_2 = \frac{X_2}{n_2} = \frac{154}{262} = 0.588$$

and

$$\bar{p} = \frac{X_1 + X_2}{n_1 + n_2} = \frac{163 + 154}{227 + 262} = \frac{317}{489} = 0.648$$

so that

$$Z = \frac{(0.718 - 0.588) - (0)}{\sqrt{0.648(1 - 0.648)\left(\dfrac{1}{227} + \dfrac{1}{262}\right)}}$$

$$= \frac{0.13}{\sqrt{(0.228)(0.0082)}}$$

$$= \frac{0.13}{\sqrt{0.00187}}$$

$$= \frac{0.13}{0.0432} = +3.01$$

Using the 0.05 level of significance, reject the null hypothesis because $Z = +3.01 > +1.96$. The p-value is 0.0026 (calculated from Table E.2 or from the Microsoft Excel worksheet of Figure 10.14 or the Minitab output of Figure 10.15). This indicates that if the null hypothesis is true, the probability that a Z-test statistic is less than −3.01 is 0.0013, and, similarly, the probability that a Z-test statistic is greater than +3.01 is 0.0013. Thus, for this two-tail test, the p-value is 0.0013 + 0.0013 = 0.0026. Because 0.0026 < α = 0.05, you reject the null hypothesis. There is evidence to conclude that the two hotels are significantly different with respect to guest satisfaction; a greater proportion of guests are willing to return to the Beachcomber than to the Windsurfer.

FIGURE 10.14

Microsoft Excel
Worksheet for the
Z Test for the Difference
Between Two
Proportions for the
Hotel Guest Satisfaction
Problem

	A	B	C	D	E	F	G
1	Guest Satisfaction Analysis						
2							
3	Data						
4	Hypothesized Difference	0					
5	Level of Significance	0.05					
6	Group 1						
7	Number of Successes	163					
8	Sample Size	227					
9	Group 2						
10	Number of Successes	154					
11	Sample Size	262					
12							
13	Intermediate Calculations						
14	Group 1 Proportion	0.7181		=B7/B8			
15	Group 2 Proportion	0.5878		=B10/B11			
16	Difference in Two Proportions	0.1303		=B14 - B15			
17	Average Proportion	0.6483		=(B7 + B10)/(B8 + B11)			
18	Z Test Statistic	3.0088		=(B16 - B4)/SQRT(B17 * (1 - B17) * (1/B8 + 1/B11))			
19							
20	Two-Tail Test						
21	Lower Critical Value	-1.9600		=NORMSINV(B5/2)			
22	Upper Critical Value	1.9600		=NORMSINV(1 - B5/2)			
23	p-Value	0.0026		=2 * (1 - NORMSDIST(ABS(B18)))			
24	Reject the null hypothesis						

FIGURE 10.15

Minitab Output for the
Z Test for the Difference
Between Two
Proportions for the
Hotel Guest Satisfaction
Problem

Test and CI for Two Proportions

```
Sample    X     N   Sample p
1       163   227   0.718062
2       154   262   0.587786


Difference = p (1) - p (2)
Estimate for difference:  0.130275
95% CI for difference:  (0.0467379, 0.213813)
Test for difference = 0 (vs not = 0):  Z = 3.01  P-Value = 0.003
```

EXAMPLE 10.3

TESTING FOR THE DIFFERENCE IN TWO PROPORTIONS

Money worries in the United States start at an early age. In a survey, 660 children (330 boys and 330 girls) ages 6 to 14 were asked the question, "Do you worry about having enough money?" Of the boys surveyed, 201 (60.9%) said yes, and 178 (53.9%) of the girls surveyed said yes (Extracted from D. Haralson and K. Simmons, "Snapshots," *USA Today*, May 24, 2004, 1B). At the 0.05 level of significance, is the proportion of boys who worry about having enough money greater than the proportion of girls?

SOLUTION Since you want to know whether there is evidence that the proportion of boys who worry about having enough money is *greater* than the proportion of girls, you have a one-tail test. The null and alternative hypotheses are

$H_0: \pi_1 \leq \pi_2$ (The proportion of boys who worry about having enough money is less than or equal to the proportion of girls)
$H_1: \pi_1 > \pi_2$ (The proportion of boys who worry about having enough money is greater than the proportion of girls)

Using the 0.05 level of significance, for the one-tail test in the upper tail, the critical value is +1.645. The decision rule is

$$\text{Reject } H_0 \text{ if } Z > +1.645;$$

$$\text{otherwise do not reject } H_0.$$

Using Equation (10.7),

$$Z = \frac{(p_1 - p_2) - (\pi_1 - \pi_2)}{\sqrt{\bar{p}(1 - \bar{p})\left(\dfrac{1}{n_1} + \dfrac{1}{n_2}\right)}}$$

where

$$p_1 = \frac{X_1}{n_1} = \frac{201}{330} = 0.609 \qquad p_2 = \frac{X_2}{n_2} = \frac{178}{330} = 0.539$$

and

$$\bar{p} = \frac{X_1 + X_2}{n_1 + n_2} = \frac{201 + 178}{330 + 330} = \frac{379}{660} = 0.5742$$

so that

$$Z = \frac{(0.609 - 0.539) - (0)}{\sqrt{0.5742(1 - 0.5742)\left(\dfrac{1}{330} + \dfrac{1}{330}\right)}}$$

$$= \frac{0.07}{\sqrt{(0.2445)(0.00606)}}$$

$$= \frac{0.07}{\sqrt{0.00148}}$$

$$= \frac{0.07}{0.0385} = +1.818$$

Using the 0.05 level of significance, reject the null hypothesis because $Z = +1.818 > +1.645$. The p-value is 0.0344 (calculated from Table E.2). Therefore, if the null hypothesis is true, the probability that a Z-test statistic is greater than $+1.818$ is 0.0344 (which is less than $\alpha = 0.05$). You conclude that there is evidence that the proportion of boys who worry about having enough money is greater than the proportion of girls.

Confidence Interval Estimate for the Difference Between Two Proportions

Instead of or in addition to testing for the difference between the proportions of two independent populations, you can construct a confidence interval estimate of the difference between the two proportions using Equation (10.8).

CONFIDENCE INTERVAL ESTIMATE FOR THE DIFFERENCE
BETWEEN TWO PROPORTIONS

$$(p_1 - p_2) \pm Z\sqrt{\frac{p_1(1 - p_1)}{n_1} + \frac{p_2(1 - p_2)}{n_2}} \qquad \textbf{(10.8)}$$

or

$$(p_1 - p_2) - Z\sqrt{\frac{p_1(1 - p_1)}{n_1} + \frac{p_2(1 - p_2)}{n_2}} \le (\pi_1 - \pi_2)$$

$$\le (p_1 - p_2) + Z\sqrt{\frac{p_1(1 - p_1)}{n_1} + \frac{p_2(1 - p_2)}{n_2}}$$

To construct a 95% confidence interval estimate of the population difference between the percentages of guests who would return to the Beachcomber and who would return to the Windsurfer, you use the results on page 318 or from Figures 10.14 or 10.15.

$$p_1 = \frac{X_1}{n_1} = \frac{163}{227} = 0.718 \quad p_2 = \frac{X_2}{n_2} = \frac{154}{262} = 0.588$$

Using Equation (10.8),

$$(0.718 - 0.588) \pm (1.96)\sqrt{\frac{0.718(1 - 0.718)}{227} + \frac{0.588(1 - 0.588)}{262}}$$

$$0.13 \pm (1.96)(0.0426)$$

$$0.13 \pm 0.0835$$

$$0.0465 \le (\pi_1 - \pi_2) \le 0.2135$$

Thus, you have 95% confidence that the difference between the population proportion of guests who would return again to the Beachcomber and the Windsurfer is between 0.0465 and 0.2135. In percentages, the difference is between 4.65% and 21.35%. Guest satisfaction is higher at the Beachcomber than at the Windsurfer.

PROBLEMS FOR SECTION 10.3

Learning the Basics

 10.31 Assume that $n_1 = 100$, $X_1 = 50$, $n_2 = 100$, and $X_2 = 30$.
a. At the 0.05 level of significance, is there evidence of a significant difference between the two population proportions?
b. Construct a 95% confidence interval estimate of the difference between the two population proportions.

 10.32 Assume that $n_1 = 100$, $X_1 = 45$, $n_2 = 50$, and $X_2 = 25$.
a. At the 0.01 level of significance, is there evidence of a significant difference between the two population proportions?
b. Construct a 99% confidence interval estimate of the difference between the two population proportions.

Applying the Concepts

 10.33 A sample of 500 shoppers was selected in a large metropolitan area to determine various information concerning consumer behavior. Among the questions asked was, "Do you enjoy shopping for clothing?" Of 240 males, 136 answered yes. Of 260 females, 224 answered yes.
a. Is there evidence of a significant difference between males and females in the proportion who enjoy shopping for clothing at the 0.01 level of significance?

b. Find the p-value in (a) and interpret its meaning.
c. Construct and interpret a 99% confidence interval estimate of the difference between the proportion of males and females who enjoy shopping for clothing.
d. What are your answers to (a) through (c) if 206 males enjoyed shopping for clothing?

 10.34 *The New York Times* reported a study conducted by the Henry J. Kaiser Family Foundation concerning the role of media in the lives of children (Dylan Loeb McClain, "Where Is Today's Child? Probably Watching TV," *The New York Times*, December 6, 1999, C1). In one question of the study, children were asked if they use a computer each day. From a sample of 1,090 children between the ages of 2 and 7, 283 used a computer each day. From a sample of 2,065 children between the ages of 8 and 18, 1,053 used a computer each day.
a. At the 0.05 level of significance, is there evidence of a significant difference between the two age groups in the proportion of children that use a computer each day?
b. Find the p-value in (a) and interpret its meaning.
c. Construct and interpret a 95% confidence interval estimate of the difference between the population proportion of 2- to 7-year-old children and 8- to 18-year-old children who use a computer each day.

PH Grade ASSIST **10.35** The results of a study conducted as part of a yield-improvement effort at a semiconductor manufacturing facility provided defect data for a sample of 450 wafers. The following contingency table presents a summary of the responses to two questions: "Was a particle found on the die that produced the wafer?" and "Is the wafer good or bad?"

	QUALITY OF WAFER		
PARTICLES	**Good**	**Bad**	**Totals**
Yes	14	36	50
No	320	80	400
Totals	334	116	450

Source: Extracted from S.W. Hall, "Analysis of Defectivity of Semiconductor Wafers by Contingency Table," Proceedings Institute of Environmental Sciences, Vol. 1 (1994), 177–183.

a. At the 0.05 level of significance, is there evidence of a significant difference between the proportion of good and bad wafers that have particles?
b. Determine the *p*-value in (a) and interpret its meaning.
c. Construct and interpret a 95% confidence interval estimate of the difference between the population proportion of good and bad wafers that contain particles.
d. What conclusions can you reach from this analysis?

10.36 The percentage of online adults in the United States increased from 63% in 2000 to 69% in December 2003 ("Activities Gaining Popularity on Net," *USA Today Snapshots*, February 3, 2004). In 2000, 25% of online adults used the Internet to gather data about products and services. Suppose that this result was based on a sample of 500 online adults. In December 2003, 299 of 729 online adults who were sampled used the Internet to gather data about products and services.
a. At the 0.05 level of significance, is there evidence that the proportion of online adults who use the Internet to gather data about products and services is higher in December 2003 than in 2000?
b. Find the *p*-value in (a) and interpret its meaning.

10.37 Is good gas mileage a priority for car shoppers? A survey conducted by Progressive Insurance asked this question to both men and women shopping for new cars. The data were reported as percentages, and no sample sizes were given.

	GENDER	
GAS MILEAGE A PRIORITY?	**Men**	**Women**
Yes	76%	84%
No	24%	16%

Source: Extracted from Snapshots, Usatoday.com, June 21, 2004.

a. Assume that 50 men and 50 women were included in the survey. At the 0.05 level of significance, is there evidence of a difference in the population proportion of males and females who make gas mileage a priority?
b. Assume that 500 men and 500 women were included in the survey. At the 0.05 level of significance, is there evidence of a difference between males and females in the proportion who make gas mileage a priority?
c. Discuss the effect of sample size on the *Z* test for the difference between two proportions.

 10.38 Are whites more likely to claim bias? A survey conducted by Barry Goldman ("White Fight: A Researcher Finds Whites are More Likely to Claim Bias," *The Wall Street Journal*, Workweek, April 10, 2001, A1) found that of 56 white workers terminated, 29 claimed bias. Of 407 black workers terminated, 126 claimed bias.
a. At the 0.05 level of significance, is there evidence that white workers are more likely to claim bias than black workers?
b. Find the *p*-value in (a) and interpret its meaning.

10.39 A study conducted by Ariel Mutual Funds and the Charles Schwab Corporation surveyed 500 African Americans with an annual income above $50,000, and 500 whites with an annual income above $50,000. The results indicated that 74% of the African Americans and 84% of the whites owned stocks (Cheryl Winokur Munk, "Stock-Ownership Race Gap Shrinks, *The Wall Street Journal*, June 13, 2002, B11).
a. Is there evidence of a significant difference between the proportion of African Americans with incomes above $50,000 who invest in stocks and the proportion of whites with incomes above $50,000 who invest in stocks? (Use $\alpha = 0.05$.)
b. Determine the *p*-value in (a) and interpret its meaning.
c. Construct and interpret a 95% confidence interval estimate of the difference between the population proportion of African Americans with incomes above $50,000 who invest in stocks and the population proportion of whites with incomes above $50,000 who invest in stocks.

10.4　*F* TEST FOR THE DIFFERENCE BETWEEN TWO VARIANCES

Often you need to test whether two independent populations have the same variability. One important reason to test for the difference between the variances of two populations is to determine whether the pooled-variance *t* test is appropriate.

The test for the difference between the variances of two independent populations is based on the ratio of the two sample variances. If you assume that each population is normally distributed, then the ratio S_1^2/S_2^2 follows the **F distribution** (see Table E.5). The critical values of the *F* distribution in Table E.5 depend on two sets of degrees of freedom. The degrees of freedom in the numerator of the ratio are for the first sample, and the degrees of freedom in the denominator are for the second sample. Equation (10.9) defines the **F-test statistic for testing the equality of two variances**.

F STATISTIC FOR TESTING THE EQUALITY OF TWO VARIANCES

The *F*-test statistic is equal to the variance of sample one divided by the variance of sample two.

$$F = \frac{S_1^2}{S_2^2}$$ (10.9)

where

S_1^2 = variance of sample 1

S_2^2 = variance of sample 2

n_1 = size of sample taken from population 1

n_2 = size of sample taken from population 2

$n_1 - 1$ = degrees of freedom from sample 1 (i.e., the numerator degrees of freedom)

$n_2 - 1$ = degrees of freedom from sample 2 (i.e., the denominator degrees of freedom)

The test statistic *F* follows an *F* distribution with $n_1 - 1$ and $n_2 - 1$ degrees of freedom.

For a given level of significance α, to test the null hypothesis of equality of variances

$$H_0: \sigma_1^2 = \sigma_2^2$$

against the alternative hypothesis that the two population variances are not equal

$$H_1: \sigma_1^2 \neq \sigma_2^2$$

you reject the null hypothesis if the computed *F*-test statistic is greater than the upper-tail critical value F_U from the *F* distribution with $n_1 - 1$ degrees of freedom in the numerator and $n_2 - 1$ degrees of freedom in the denominator, or if the computed *F*-test statistic falls below the lower-tail critical value F_L from the *F* distribution with $n_1 - 1$ and $n_2 - 1$ degrees of freedom in the numerator and denominator, respectively. Thus, the decision rule is

$$\text{Reject } H_0 \text{ if } F > F_U$$
$$\text{or if } F < F_L;$$
$$\text{otherwise do not reject } H_0.$$

This decision rule and rejection regions are displayed in Figure 10.16.

FIGURE 10.16

Regions of Rejection and Nonrejection for the Two-Tail F Test

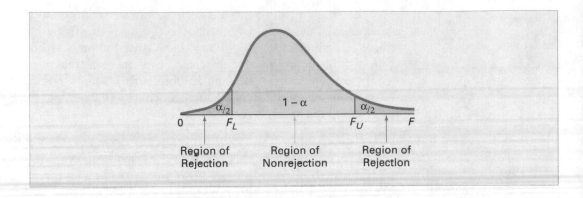

To illustrate how to use the F test to determine whether the two variances are equal, return to the "Using Statistics" scenario concerning the sales of BLK cola in two different aisle locations (see page 296). To determine whether to use the pooled-variance t test or the separate-variance t test in section 10.1, you can test the equality of the two population variances. The null and alternative hypotheses are:

$$H_0: \sigma_1^2 = \sigma_2^2$$
$$H_1: \sigma_1^2 \neq \sigma_2^2$$

Because this is a two-tail test, the rejection region is split into the lower and upper tails of the F distribution. Using a level of significance of $\alpha = 0.05$, each rejection region contains 0.025 of the distribution.

Because there are samples of 10 stores for each of the two display locations, there are $10 - 1 = 9$ degrees of freedom for group 1 and also for group 2. F_U, the upper-tail critical value of the F distribution, is found directly from Table E.5, a portion of which is presented in Table 10.6. Because there are 9 degrees of freedom in the numerator and 9 degrees of freedom in the denominator, you find the upper-tail critical value F_U by looking in the column labeled "9" and the row labeled "9." Thus, the upper-tail critical value of this F distribution is 4.03.

TABLE 10.6

Finding F_U, Upper-Tail Critical Value of F with 9 and 9 Degrees of Freedom for Upper-Tail Area of 0.025

Denominator				Numerator df_1			
df_2	1	2	3	...	7	8	9
1	647.80	799.50	864.20	...	948.20	956.70	963.30
2	38.51	39.00	39.17	...	39.36	39.37	39.39
3	17.44	16.04	15.44	...	14.62	14.54	14.47
.	.	.	.		.	.	.
.	.	.	.		.	.	.
.	.	.	.		.	.	.
7	8.07	6.54	5.89	...	4.99	4.90	4.82
8	7.57	6.06	5.42	...	4.53	4.43	4.36
9	7.21	5.71	5.08	...	4.20	4.10	4.03

Source: Extracted from Table E.5.

Finding Lower-Tail Critical Values

You compute F_L, a lower-tail critical value on the F distribution with $n_1 - 1$ degrees of freedom in the numerator and $n_2 - 1$ degrees of freedom in the denominator, by taking the reciprocal of F_{U*}, an upper-tail critical value on the F distribution with degrees of freedom "switched" (i.e., $n_2 - 1$ degrees of freedom in the numerator and $n_1 - 1$ degrees of freedom in the denominator). This relationship is shown in Equation (10.10).

FINDING LOWER-TAIL CRITICAL VALUES FROM THE *F* DISTRIBUTION

$$F_L = \frac{1}{F_{U*}} \qquad\qquad (10.10)$$

where F_{U*} is from an *F* distribution with $n_2 - 1$ degrees of freedom in the numerator and $n_1 - 1$ degrees of freedom in the denominator.

In the cola sales example, the degrees of freedom are 9 and 9 for the respective numerator sample and denominator sample so there is no "switching" of degrees of freedom, you just take the reciprocal. Therefore, to compute the lower-tail 0.025 critical value, you need to find the upper-tail 0.025 critical value of *F* with 9 degrees of freedom in the numerator and 9 degrees of freedom in the denominator and take its reciprocal. As shown in Table 10.6, this upper-tail value is 4.03. Using Equation (10.10),

$$F_L = \frac{1}{F_{U*}} = \frac{1}{4.03} = 0.248$$

As depicted in Figure 10.17, the decision rule is

Reject H_0 if $F > F_U = 4.03$

or if $F < F_L = 0.248$;

otherwise do not reject H_0

FIGURE 10.17

Regions of Rejection and Nonrejection for the Two-Tail *F* Test for the Equality of Two Variances at the 0.05 Level of Significance with 9 and 9 Degrees of Freedom

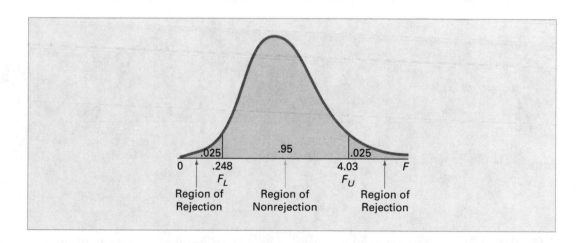

Using Equation (10.9) and the cola sales data (see Table 10.1), the *F*-test statistic is

$$F = \frac{S_1^2}{S_2^2}$$

$$= \frac{350.6778}{157.3333} = 2.23$$

Because $F_L = 0.248 < F = 2.23 < F_U = 4.03$, do not reject H_0. The *p*-value is 0.248 for a two-tail test (twice the *p*-value for the one-tail test shown in the Microsoft Excel output of Figure 10.18). Figure 10.19 illustrates Minitab output. Since $0.248 > 0.05$, you conclude that there is no significant difference in the variability of the sales of cola for the two display locations.

FIGURE 10.18

Microsoft Excel F Test
Output for the Cola
Sales Data

	A	B	C
1	F-Test Two-Sample for Variances		
2			
3		Normal	End-Aisle
4	Mean	50.3	72
5	Variance	350.6777778	157.3333333
6	Observations	10	10
7	df	9	9
8	F	2.228884181	
9	P(F<=f) one-tail	0.124104358	
10	F Critical one-tail	3.178893105	

FIGURE 10.19

Minitab F Test Output
for the Cola Sales Data

95% Bonferroni confidence intervals for standard deviations

Display	N	Lower	StDev	Upper
EndAisle	10	8.2048	12.5433	25.2578
Normal	10	12.2494	18.7264	37.7085

F-Test (normal distribution)
Test statistic = 0.45, p-value = 0.248

In testing for a difference in two variances using the F test described in this section, you assume that each of the two populations are normally distributed. The F test is very sensitive to the normality assumption. If box-and-whisker plots or normal probability plots suggest even a mild departure from normality for either of the two populations, you should not use the F test. In this case, a nonparametric approach is more appropriate (see reference 2).

In testing for the equality of variances, as part of assessing the validity of the pooled-variance t-test procedure, the F test is a two-tail test. However, when you are interested in the variability itself, the F test is often a one-tail test. Thus, in testing the equality of two variances, you can use either a two-tail or one-tail test, depending on whether you are testing whether the two population variances are *different* or whether one variance is *greater than* the other variance. Figure 10.20 illustrates the three possible situations.

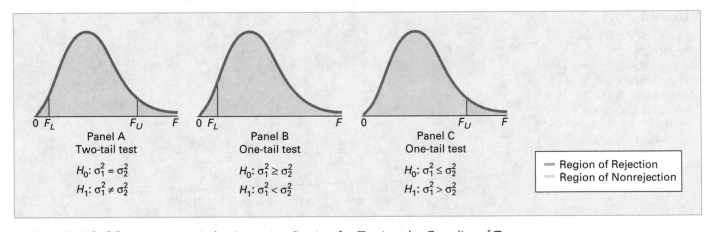

Panel A
Two-tail test

$H_0: \sigma_1^2 = \sigma_2^2$
$H_1: \sigma_1^2 \neq \sigma_2^2$

Panel B
One-tail test

$H_0: \sigma_1^2 \geq \sigma_2^2$
$H_1: \sigma_1^2 < \sigma_2^2$

Panel C
One-tail test

$H_0: \sigma_1^2 \leq \sigma_2^2$
$H_1: \sigma_1^2 > \sigma_2^2$

— Region of Rejection
— Region of Nonrejection

FIGURE 10.20 Determining the Rejection Region for Testing the Equality of Two
Population Variances

Often the sample sizes in the two groups will differ. Example 10.4 demonstrates how to find a lower-tail critical value from the F distribution in this situation.

EXAMPLE 10.4

FINDING THE LOWER-TAIL CRITICAL VALUE FROM THE F DISTRIBUTION
IN A TWO-TAIL TEST OF HYPOTHESIS

You select a sample of $n_1 = 8$ from a normally distributed population. The variance for this sample (S_1^2) is 56.0. You select a sample of $n_2 = 10$ from a second normally distributed population (independent of the first population). The variance for this sample (S_2^2) is 24.0. Using a level of significance of $\alpha = 0.05$, test the null hypothesis of no difference in the two population variances against the two-tail alternative that there is evidence of a significant difference in the population variances.

SOLUTION The null and alternative hypotheses are

$$H_0: \sigma_1^2 = \sigma_2^2$$
$$H_1: \sigma_1^2 \neq \sigma_2^2$$

The *F*-test statistic is given by Equation (10.9).

$$F = \frac{S_1^2}{S_2^2}$$

You use Table E.5 to find the upper and lower critical values of the *F* distribution. With $n_1 - 1 = 7$ degrees of freedom in the numerator and $n_2 - 1 = 9$ degrees of freedom in the denominator and $\alpha = 0.05$ split equally into the lower- and upper-tail rejection regions of 0.025 each, the upper critical value $F_U = 4.20$ (see Table 10.7).

To find the lower critical value F_L with 7 degrees of freedom in the numerator and 9 degrees of freedom in the denominator, take the reciprocal of F_{U*} with degrees of freedom switched to 9 in the numerator and 7 in the denominator. Thus, from Equation (10.10) and Table 10.7,

$$F_L = \frac{1}{F_{U*}} = \frac{1}{4.82} = 0.207$$

TABLE 10.7

Finding F_{U*} and F_L, with 7 and 9 Degrees of Freedom Using a Level of Significance $\alpha = 0.05$

Denominator				Numerator df_1			
df_2	1	2	3	...	7	8	9
1	647.80	799.50	864.20	...	948.20	956.70	963.30
2	38.51	39.00	39.17	...	39.36	39.37	39.39
3	17.44	16.04	15.44	...	14.62	14.54	14.47
.	.	.	.		.	.	.
.	.	.	.		.	.	.
7	8.07	6.54	5.89	...	4.99	4.90	4.82
8	7.57	6.06	5.42	...	4.53	4.43	4.36
9	7.21	5.71	5.08	...	4.20	4.10	4.03

Source: Extracted from Table E.5.

The decision rule is

$$\text{Reject } H_0 \text{ if } F > F_U = 4.20$$

$$\text{or if } F < F_L = 0.207;$$

$$\text{otherwise do not reject } H_0.$$

From Equation (10.9), the *F*-test statistic is

$$F = \frac{S_1^2}{S_2^2}$$

$$= \frac{56.0}{24.0} = 2.33$$

Because $F_L = 0.207 < F = 2.33 < F_U = 4.20$, you do not reject H_0. Using a 0.05 level of significance, you conclude that there is no evidence of a significant difference in the variances in these two independent populations.

PROBLEMS FOR SECTION 10.4

Learning the Basics

 10.40 Determine F_U and F_L, the upper- and lower-tail critical values of F in each of the following two-tail tests:

a. $\alpha = 0.10$, $n_1 = 16$, $n_2 = 21$
b. $\alpha = 0.05$, $n_1 = 16$, $n_2 = 21$
c. $\alpha = 0.02$, $n_1 = 16$, $n_2 = 21$
d. $\alpha = 0.01$, $n_1 = 16$, $n_2 = 21$

10.41 Determine F_U, the upper-tail critical value of F in each of the following one-tail tests:

a. $\alpha = 0.05$, $n_1 = 16$, $n_2 = 21$
b. $\alpha = 0.025$, $n_1 = 16$, $n_2 = 21$
c. $\alpha = 0.01$, $n_1 = 16$, $n_2 = 21$
d. $\alpha = 0.005$, $n_1 = 16$, $n_2 = 21$

10.42 Determine F_L, the lower-tail critical value of F in each of the following one-tail tests:

a. $\alpha = 0.05$, $n_1 = 16$, $n_2 = 21$
b. $\alpha = 0.025$, $n_1 = 16$, $n_2 = 21$
c. $\alpha = 0.01$, $n_1 = 16$, $n_2 = 21$
d. $\alpha = 0.005$, $n_1 = 16$, $n_2 = 21$

 10.43 The following information is available for two samples drawn from independent normally distributed populations:

$$n_1 = 25 \quad S_1^2 = 133.7 \quad n_2 = 25 \quad S_2^2 = 161.9$$

What is the value of the F-test statistic if you are testing the null hypothesis $H_0: \sigma_1^2 = \sigma_2^2$?

 10.44 In problem 10.43, how many degrees of freedom are there in the numerator and denominator of the F test?

 10.45 In problems 10.43 and 10.44, what are the critical values for F_U and F_L from Table E.5 if the level of significance α is 0.05 and the alternative hypothesis is $H_1: \sigma_1^2 \neq \sigma_2^2$?

10.46 In problems 10.43 through 10.45, what is your statistical decision?

10.47 The following information is available for two samples selected from independent but very right-skewed populations.

$$n_1 = 16 \quad S_1^2 = 47.3 \quad n_2 = 13 \quad S_2^2 = 36.4$$

Should you use the F test to test the null hypothesis of equality of variances ($H_0: \sigma_1^2 = \sigma_2^2$)? Discuss.

10.48 If the two samples are drawn from independent normally distributed populations in problem 10.47,

a. At the 0.05 level of significance, is there evidence of a difference between σ_1^2 and σ_2^2?
b. Suppose that you want to perform a one-tail test. At the 0.05 level of significance, what is the upper-tail critical value of the F-test statistic to determine whether there is evidence that $\sigma_1^2 > \sigma_2^2$? What is your statistical decision?
c. Suppose that you want to perform a one-tail test. At the 0.05 level of significance, what is the lower-tail critical value of the F-test statistic to determine whether there is evidence that $\sigma_1^2 < \sigma_2^2$? What is your statistical decision?

Applying the Concepts

Problems 10.49–10.54 can be solved manually or by using Microsoft Excel, Minitab, or SPSS.

 10.49 A professor in the accounting department of a business school claims that there is much more variability in the final exam scores of students taking the introductory accounting course as a requirement than for students taking the course as part of a major in accounting. Random samples of 13 nonaccounting majors (group 1) and 10 accounting majors (group 2) are taken from the professor's class roster in his large lecture, and the following results are computed based on the final exam scores:

$$n_1 = 13 \quad S_1^2 = 210.2 \quad n_2 = 10 \quad S_2^2 = 36.5$$

a. At the 0.05 level of significance, is there evidence to support the professor's claim?
b. Interpret the p-value.
c. What assumptions do you make here about the two populations in order to justify your use of the F test?

 10.50 The Computer Anxiety Rating Scale (CARS) measures an individual's level of computer anxiety on a scale from 20 (no anxiety) to 100 (highest level of anxiety). Researchers at Miami University administered CARS to 172 business students. One of the objectives of the study was to determine if there is a difference between the level of computer anxiety experienced by female students and male students.

	Males	Females
$\overline{X}$	40.26	36.85
S	13.35	9.42
n	100	72

Source: Travis Broome and Douglas Havelka, "Determinants of Computer Anxiety in Business Students," The Review of Business Information Systems, Spring 2002, 6(2):9–16.

a. At the 0.05 level of significance, is there evidence of a difference in the variability of the computer anxiety experienced by females and males?

b. Interpret the *p*-value.

c. What assumptions do you need to make about the two populations in order to justify the use of the *F* test?

d. Based on (a) and (b), which *t* test defined in section 10.1 should you use to test whether there is a significant difference in mean computer anxiety for female and male students?

10.51 A bank with a branch located in a commercial district of a city BANK1 has developed an improved process for serving customers during the noon to 1 P.M. lunch period. The waiting time (defined as the time elapsed from when the customer enters the line until he or she reaches the teller window) of all customers during this hour is recorded over a period of one week. A random sample of 15 customers is selected, and the results (in minutes) are as follows:

4.21 5.55 3.02 5.13 4.77 2.34 3.54 3.20

4.50 6.10 0.38 5.12 6.46 6.19 3.79

Suppose that another branch located in a residential area BANK2 is also concerned with the noon to 1 P.M. lunch period. A random sample of 15 customers is selected, and the results are as follows:

9.66 5.90 8.02 5.79 8.73 3.82 8.01 8.35

10.49 6.68 5.64 4.08 6.17 9.91 5.47

a. Is there evidence of a difference in the variability of the waiting time between the two branches? (Use $\alpha = 0.05$.)

b. Find the *p*-value in (a) and interpret its meaning.

c. What assumption is necessary in (a)? Is the assumption valid for these data?

d. Based on the results of (a), is it appropriate to use the pooled-variance *t*-test to compare the means of the two branches?

PH Grade ASSIST **10.52** A problem with a telephone line that prevents a customer from receiving or making calls is disconcerting to both the customer and the telephone company. The following data PHONE represent samples of 20 problems reported to two different offices of a telephone company and the time to clear these problems (in minutes) from the customers' lines:

Central Office I Time to Clear Problems (minutes)

1.48 1.75 0.78 2.85 0.52 1.60 4.15 3.97 1.48 3.10

1.02 0.53 0.93 1.60 0.80 1.05 6.32 3.93 5.45 0.97

Central Office II Time to Clear Problems (minutes)

7.55 3.75 0.10 1.10 0.60 0.52 3.30 2.10 0.58 4.02

3.75 0.65 1.92 0.60 1.53 4.23 0.08 1.48 1.65 0.72

a. Is there evidence of a difference in the variability of the waiting time between the two offices? (Use $\alpha = 0.05$.)

b. Find the *p*-value in (a) and interpret its meaning.

c. What assumption is necessary in (a)? Is the assumption valid for these data?

d. Based on the results of (a), is it appropriate to use the pooled-variance *t* test to compare the means of the two offices?

10.53 The director of training for a company manufacturing electronic equipment is interested in determining whether different training methods have an effect on the productivity of assembly-line employees. She randomly assigns 42 recently hired employees to two groups of 21. The first group receives a computer-assisted, individual-based training program and the other receives a team-based training program. Upon completion of the training, the employees are evaluated on the time (in seconds) it takes to assemble a part. The results are in the data file: TRAINING.

a. Using a 0.05 level of significance, is there evidence of a difference between the variances in assembly times (in seconds) of employees trained in a computer-assisted, individual-based program and those trained in a team-based program?

b. On the basis of the results in (a), is it appropriate to use the pooled-variance *t* test to compare the means of the two groups? Discuss.

10.54 Shipments of meat, meat by-products, and other ingredients are mixed together in several filling lines at a pet food canning factory. Operations managers suspect that, although the mean amount filled in the can of pet food is usually the same, the variability of the cans filled in line A is greater than that of line B. The following results are from samples of eight-ounce cans:

	Line A	Line B
$\overline{X}$	8.005	7.997
S	0.012	0.005
n	11	16

At the 0.05 level of significance, is there evidence that the variance in line A is greater than the variance in line B? Assume that the population amounts filled are normally distributed.

USING STATISTICS

The Perfect Parachute Company

You are the production manager of the Perfect Parachute Company. Parachutes are woven in your factory using a synthetic fiber purchased from one of four different suppliers. For obvious reasons, one of the most important quality characteristics of a parachute is its strength. You need to decide whether the synthetic fibers from your four suppliers result in parachutes of equal strength. To help answer this question, you have decided to design an experiment to test the strength of parachutes woven from the synthetic fibers from the four suppliers. You will need to incorporate the information from the analysis of the experimental data to determine which supplier to use in order to manufacture the strongest parachutes.

10.5 ONE-WAY ANOVA

In sections 10.1–10.4 you used hypothesis-testing to draw conclusions about possible differences between two populations. Frequently, however, you need to evaluate differences among several populations (referred to as groups in this section). This section examines experiments in which you consider more than two **groups** pertaining to one **factor** of interest. Groups are defined by assigning different **levels** of the factor. For example, a factor such as baking temperature may have several *numerical levels* (e.g., 300°, 350°, 400°, 450°) or a factor such as preferred supplier for a parachute manufacturer may have several *categorical levels* (e.g., Supplier 1, Supplier 2, Supplier 3, Supplier 4).

F Test for Differences Among More Than Two Means

You use the **analysis of variance (ANOVA)** to compare the means of more than two groups. When the groups are different levels of one factor, as is the case in this section, the ANOVA procedure used is referred to as a **one-way ANOVA**. This procedure is an extension of the *t* test for the difference between two means discussed in section 10.1. Although ANOVA is an acronym for **AN**alysis **O**f **VA**riance, the term is misleading because the objective is to analyze differences among the group means *not* the variances. However, by analyzing the variation among and within the groups, you can make conclusions about possible differences in group means. In ANOVA, the total variation is subdivided into variation that is due to differences *among* the groups and variation that is due to differences *within* the groups (see Figure 10.21). **Within-group variation** is considered **random error**. **Among-group variation** is due to differences from group to group, also known as the **treatment effect**. The symbol c is used to indicate the number of groups.

FIGURE 10.21

Partitioning the Total Variation in a Completely Randomized Design

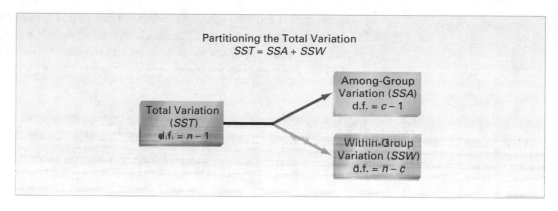

Assuming that the c groups represent populations whose values are randomly and independently selected, follow a normal distribution, and have equal variances, the null hypothesis of no differences in the population means

$$H_0: \mu_1 = \mu_2 = \cdots = \mu_c$$

is tested against the alternative that not all the c population means are equal.

$$H_1: \text{Not all } \mu_j \text{ are equal (where } j = 1, 2, \ldots, c)$$

To perform an ANOVA test of equality of population means, you subdivide the total variation in the values into two parts, that which is due to variation among the groups and that which is due to variation within the groups. The **total variation** is represented by the **sum of squares total (SST)**. Because the population means of the c groups are presumed to be equal under the null hypothesis, you compute the total variation among all the values by summing the squared differences between each individual value and the **grand mean** $\overline{\overline{X}}$. The grand mean is the mean of all the values in all the groups combined. Equation (10.11) shows the computation of the total variation.

TOTAL VARIATION IN ONE-WAY ANOVA

$$SST = \sum_{j=1}^{c} \sum_{i=1}^{n_j} (X_{ij} - \overline{\overline{X}})^2 \qquad \textbf{(10.11)}$$

where

$$\overline{\overline{X}} = \frac{\displaystyle\sum_{j=1}^{c} \sum_{i=1}^{n_j} X_{ij}}{n} = \text{grand mean}$$

$X_{ij} = i$th value in group j

$n_j = $ number of values in group j

$n = $ total number of values in all groups combined
(that is, $n = n_1 + n_2 + \cdots + n_c$)

$c = $ number of groups

You compute the among-group variation, usually called the **sum of squares among groups (SSA)**, by summing the squared differences between the sample mean of each group $\overline{X}_j$ and the grand mean $\overline{\overline{X}}$, weighted by the sample size n_j in each group. Equation (10.12) shows the computation of the among-group variation.

AMONG-GROUP VARIATION IN ONE-WAY ANOVA

$$SSA = \sum_{j=1}^{c} n_j (\overline{X}_j - \overline{\overline{X}})^2 \qquad (10.12)$$

where

c = number of groups

n_j = number of values in group j

$\overline{X}_j$ = sample mean of group j

$\overline{\overline{X}}$ = grand mean

The within-group variation, usually called the **sum of squares within groups (SSW)**, measures the difference between each value and the mean of its own group and sums the squares of these differences over all groups. Equation (10.13) shows the computation of the within-group variation.

WITHIN-GROUP VARIATION IN ONE-WAY ANOVA

$$SSW = \sum_{j=1}^{c} \sum_{i=1}^{n_j} (X_{ij} - \overline{X}_j)^2 \qquad (10.13)$$

where

X_{ij} = ith value in group j

$\overline{X}_j$ = sample mean of group j

Because you are comparing c groups, there are $c - 1$ degrees of freedom associated with the sum of squares among groups. Since each of the c groups contributes $n_j - 1$ degrees of freedom, there are $n - c$ degrees of freedom associated with the sum of squares within groups. In addition, there are $n - 1$ degrees of freedom associated with the sum of squares total because you are comparing each value X_{ij} to the grand mean $\overline{\overline{X}}$ based on all n values.

If you divide each of these sums of squares by its associated degrees of freedom, you have three variances or **mean square** terms—**MSA** (Mean Square Among), **MSW** (Mean Square Within), and **MST** (Mean Square Total).

COMPUTING THE MEAN SQUARES IN ONE-WAY ANOVA

$$MSA = \frac{SSA}{c - 1} \qquad (10.14a)$$

$$MSW = \frac{SSW}{n - c} \qquad (10.14b)$$

$$MST = \frac{SST}{n - 1} \qquad (10.14c)$$

Although you want to compare the means of the c groups to determine whether a difference exists among them, the ANOVA procedure derives its name from the fact that you are comparing variances. If the null hypothesis is true and there are no real differences in the c group means, all three mean square terms—*MSA*, *MSW*, and **MST**—which themselves are *variances*, provide estimates of the overall variance in the data. Thus, to test the null hypothesis

$$H_0: \mu_1 = \mu_2 = \cdots = \mu_c$$

against the alternative

$$H_1: \text{Not all } \mu_j \text{ are equal (where } j = 1, 2, \ldots, c)$$

you compute the **one-way ANOVA F-test statistic** as the ratio of *MSA* to *MSW* as in Equation (10.15).

ONE-WAY ANOVA F-TEST STATISTIC

$$F = \frac{MSA}{MSW} \tag{10.15}$$

The F-test statistic follows an **F distribution** with $c - 1$ degrees of freedom corresponding to *MSA* in the numerator and $n - c$ degrees of freedom corresponding to *MSW* in the denominator. For a given level of significance α, you reject the null hypothesis if the F-test statistic computed in Equation (10.15) is greater than the upper-tail critical value F_U from the F distribution having $c - 1$ degrees of freedom in the numerator and $n - c$ in the denominator (see Table E.5). Thus, as shown in Figure 10.22, the decision rule is

$$\text{Reject } H_0 \text{ if } F > F_U;$$

otherwise do not reject H_0

FIGURE 10.22

Regions of Rejection and Nonrejection When Using ANOVA

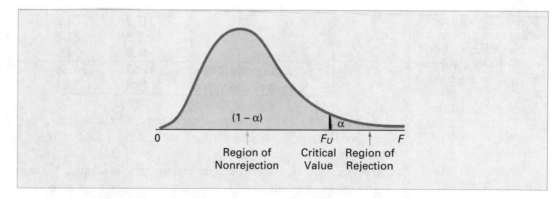

If the null hypothesis is true, the computed F statistic is expected to be approximately equal to 1, because both the numerator and denominator mean square terms are estimating the overall variance in the data. If H_0 is false (and there are real differences in the means), the computed F statistic is expected to be substantially larger than 1 because the numerator, *MSA*, is estimating the treatment effect or differences among groups in addition to the overall variability in the values, while the denominator, *MSW*, is measuring only the overall variability. Thus, the ANOVA procedure provides an F test in which you reject the null hypothesis at a selected α level of significance only if the computed F statistic is greater than F_U, the upper-tail critical value of the F distribution having $c - 1$ and $n - c$ degrees of freedom, as illustrated in Figure 10.22.

The results of an analysis of variance are usually displayed in an **ANOVA summary table**, as shown in Table 10.8. The entries in this table include the sources of variation (i.e., among-group, within-group, and total), the degrees of freedom, the sums of squares, the mean squares (i.e., the variances), and the computed F statistic. In addition, the p-value (i.e., the probability of having an F statistic as large as or larger than the one computed, given that the null hypothesis is true) is included in the ANOVA summary table. The p-value allows you to make direct conclusions about the null hypothesis without referring to a table of critical values of the F distribution. If the p-value is less than the chosen level of significance α, you reject the null hypothesis.

TABLE 10.8

Analysis-of-Variance Summary Table

Source	Degrees of Freedom	Sum of Squares	Mean Square (Variance)	F
Among groups	$c - 1$	SSA	$MSA - \dfrac{SSA}{c-1}$	$F = \dfrac{MSA}{MSW}$
Within groups	$n - c$	SSW	$MSW = \dfrac{SSW}{n-c}$	
Total	$n - 1$	SST		

To illustrate the one-way ANOVA F test, return to the "Using Statistics" scenario concerning the Perfect Parachute Company (see page 330). An experiment was conducted to determine if any significant differences exist in the strength of parachutes woven from synthetic fibers from the different suppliers. Five parachutes were woven for each group—Supplier 1, Supplier 2, Supplier 3, and Supplier 4. The strength of the parachutes is measured by placing them in a testing device that pulls on both ends of a parachute until it tears apart. The amount of force required to tear the parachute is measured on a tensile-strength scale where the larger the value the stronger the parachute. The results of this experiment (in terms of tensile strength) are contained in the data file **PARACHUTE** and are displayed in Figure 10.23 along with the sample mean and sample standard deviation from each supplier.

FIGURE 10.23

Microsoft Excel Worksheet of the Tensile Strength for Parachutes Woven with Synthetic Fibers from Four Different Suppliers Along with the Sample Mean and Sample Standard Deviation

	Supplier 1	Supplier 2	Supplier 3	Supplier 4
	18.5	26.3	20.6	25.4
	24.0	25.3	25.2	19.9
	17.2	24.0	20.8	22.6
	19.9	21.2	24.7	17.5
	18.0	24.5	22.9	20.4
Arithmetic Mean	19.52	24.26	22.84	21.16
Standard Deviation	2.69	1.92	2.13	2.98

In Figure 10.23, observe that there are differences in the sample means for the four suppliers. For Supplier 1, the mean tensile strength is 19.52. For Supplier 2, the mean tensile strength is 24.26. For Supplier 3, the mean tensile strength is 22.84, and, for Supplier 4, the mean tensile strength is 21.16. What you need to determine is whether these sample results are sufficiently different to conclude that the *population* means are not all equal.

In the scatter plot shown in Figure 10.24, you can visually inspect the data and see how the measurements of tensile strength distribute. You can also observe differences among the groups as well as within groups. If the sample sizes in each group were larger, you could develop stem-and-leaf displays, box-and-whisker plots, and normal probability plots.

The null hypothesis states that there is no difference in mean tensile strength among the four suppliers.

$$H_0: \mu_1 = \mu_2 = \mu_3 = \mu_4$$

The alternative hypothesis states that there is a treatment effect; that is, at least one of the suppliers differs with respect to the mean tensile strength.

$$H_1: \text{Not all the means are equal}$$

FIGURE 10.24

Microsoft Excel Scatter Plot of Tensile Strengths for Four Different Suppliers

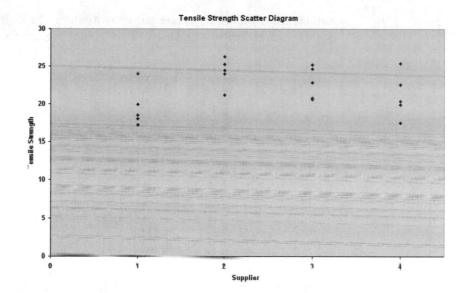

To construct the ANOVA summary table, you first compute the sample means in each group (see Figure 10.23). Then you compute the grand mean by summing all 20 values and dividing by the total number of values.

$$\overline{\overline{X}} = \frac{\sum_{j=1}^{c} \sum_{i=1}^{n_j} X_{ij}}{n} = \frac{438.9}{20} = 21.945$$

Then, using Equations (10.11) through (10.13) you compute the sum of squares:

$$SSA = \sum_{j=1}^{c} n_j(\overline{X}_j - \overline{\overline{X}})^2$$

$$= (5)(19.52 - 21.945)^2 + (5)(24.26 - 21.945)^2 + (5)(22.84 - 21.945)^2$$

$$+ (5)(21.16 - 21.945)^2$$

$$= 63.2855$$

$$SSW = \sum_{j=1}^{c} \sum_{i=1}^{n_j} (X_{ij} - \overline{X}_j)^2$$

$$= (18.5 - 19.52)^2 + \cdots + (18 - 19.52)^2 + (26.3 - 24.26)^2 + \cdots + (24.5 - 24.26)^2$$

$$+ (20.6 - 22.84)^2 + \cdots + (22.9 - 22.84)^2 + (25.4 - 21.16)^2 + \cdots + (20.4 - 21.16)^2$$

$$= 97.504$$

$$SST = \sum_{j=1}^{c} \sum_{i=1}^{n_j} (X_{ij} - \overline{\overline{X}})^2$$

$$= (18.5 - 21.945)^2 + (24 - 21.945)^2 + \cdots + (20.4 - 21.945)^2$$

$$= 160.7895$$

You compute the mean square terms by dividing the sum of squares by the corresponding degrees of freedom [see Equation (10.14)]. Because $c = 4$ and $n = 20$,

$$MSA = \frac{SSA}{c-1} = \frac{63.2855}{4-1} = 21.095$$

$$MSW = \frac{SSW}{n-c} = \frac{97.504}{20-4} = 6.094$$

so that using Equation (10.15)

$$F = \frac{MSA}{MSW} = \frac{21.095}{6.094} = 3.46$$

For a selected level of significance α, you find the upper-tail critical value F_U from the F distribution using Table E.5. A portion of Table E.5 is presented in Table 10.9. In the parachute supplier example, there are 3 degrees of freedom in the numerator of the F ratio and 16 degrees of freedom in the denominator. F_U, the upper-tail critical value at the 0.05 level of significance, is 3.24. Because the computed test statistic $F = 3.46$ is greater than $F_U = 3.24$, you reject the null hypothesis (see Figure 10.25). You conclude that there is a significant difference in the mean tensile strength among the four suppliers.

TABLE 10.9

Finding the Critical Value of F with 3 and 16 Degrees of Freedom at the 0.05 Level of Significance

Denominator, df_2	Numerator, df_1								
	1	2	3	4	5	6	7	8	9
.	.	.		.	.	.	.	.	.
.	.	.		.	.	.	.	.	.
.	.	.		.	.	.	.	.	.
11	4.84	3.98	3.59	3.36	3.20	3.09	3.01	2.95	2.90
12	4.75	3.89	3.49	3.26	3.11	3.00	2.91	2.85	2.80
13	4.67	3.81	3.41	3.18	3.03	2.92	2.83	2.77	2.71
14	4.60	3.74	3.34	3.11	2.96	2.85	2.76	2.70	2.65
15	4.54	3.68	3.29	3.06	2.90	2.79	2.71	2.64	2.59
16	4.49	3.63	3.24	3.01	2.85	2.74	2.66	2.59	2.54

Source: Extracted from Table E.5.

FIGURE 10.25

Regions of Rejection and Nonrejection for the Analysis of Variance at the 0.05 Level of Significance with 3 and 16 Degrees of Freedom

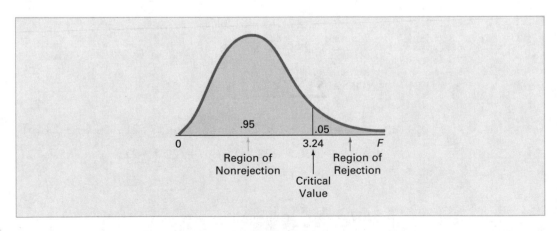

Figure 10.26 shows the Microsoft Excel ANOVA summary table and p-value. Figure 10.27 shows Minitab output. The p-value, or probability of getting an F statistic of 3.46 or larger when the null hypothesis is true, is 0.041. Because this p-value is less than the specified α of

0.05, you reject the null hypothesis. The *p*-value of 0.041 indicates that there is a 4.1% chance of observing differences this large or larger if the population means for the four suppliers are all equal.

FIGURE 10.26

Microsoft Excel Analysis of Variance for the Parachute Example

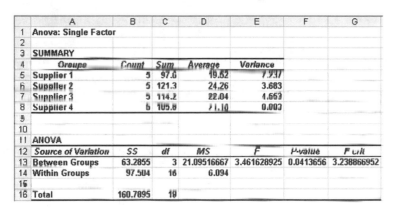

	A	B	C	D	E	F	G
1	Anova: Single Factor						
2							
3	SUMMARY						
4	*Groups*	*Count*	*Sum*	*Average*	*Variance*		
5	Supplier 1	5	97.6	19.52	7.937		
6	Supplier 2	5	121.3	24.26	3.683		
7	Supplier 3	5	114.2	22.84	4.553		
8	Supplier 4	5	105.8	21.16	8.903		
9							
10							
11	ANOVA						
12	*Source of Variation*	*SS*	*df*	*MS*	*F*	*P-value*	*F crit*
13	Between Groups	63.2855	3	21.09516667	3.461628925	0.0413656	3.238866952
14	Within Groups	97.504	16	6.094			
15							
16	Total	160.7895	19				

FIGURE 10.27

Minitab Analysis of Variance for the Parachute Example

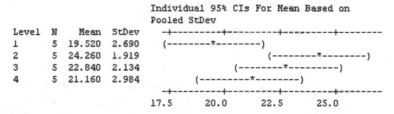

```
One-way ANOVA: 1, 2, 3, 4

Source  DF      SS      MS     F      P
Factor   3   63.29   21.10  3.46  0.041
Error   16   97.50    6.09
Total   19  160.79

S = 2.469   R-Sq = 39.36%   R-Sq(adj) = 27.99%


                              Individual 95% CIs For Mean Based on
                              Pooled StDev
Level  N    Mean   StDev   -+---------+---------+---------+--------
1      5  19.520   2.690   (--------*--------)
2      5  24.260   1.919                        (---------*--------)
3      5  22.840   2.134                  (--------*---------)
4      5  21.160   2.984         (---------*--------)
                              -+---------+---------+---------+--------
                             17.5      20.0      22.5      25.0

Pooled StDev = 2.469
```

After performing the one-way ANOVA and finding a significant difference among the suppliers, what you do not yet know is *which* suppliers differ. All that you know is that there is sufficient evidence to state that the population means are not all the same. In other words, at least one or more population means are significantly different. To determine which suppliers differ, you can use a multiple comparison procedure such as the Tukey-Kramer procedure.

Multiple Comparisons: The Tukey-Kramer Procedure

In the "Using Statistics" scenario concerning the strength of the parachutes, you used the one-way ANOVA *F* test to determine that there was a difference among the suppliers. The next step is to use **multiple comparisons** to determine which groups are different.

Although many procedures are available (see references 5 and 7), this text uses the **Tukey-Kramer multiple comparison procedure** to determine which of the *c* means are significantly different. This procedure was developed by John Tukey (and later modified, independently, by Tukey and by C. Y. Kramer, for situations in which the sample sizes differ—see references 6, 7, and 11). The Tukey-Kramer method is an example of a **post-hoc** comparison procedure, because the hypotheses of interest are formulated *after* the data have been inspected.

The Tukey-Kramer procedure enables you to simultaneously make comparisons between all pairs of groups. First, you compute the differences, $\bar{X}_j - \bar{X}_{j'}$ (where $j \neq j'$), among all $c(c-1)/2$ pairs of means. Then you compute the **critical range** for the Tukey-Kramer procedure using Equation (10.16).

> ## THE CRITICAL RANGE FOR THE TUKEY-KRAMER PROCEDURE
>
> $$\text{Critical range} = Q_U \sqrt{\frac{MSW}{2}\left(\frac{1}{n_j} + \frac{1}{n_{j'}}\right)} \qquad \text{(10.16)}$$
>
> where Q_U is the upper-tail critical value from a **Studentized range distribution** having c degrees of freedom in the numerator and $n - c$ degrees of freedom in the denominator. Values for the Studentized range distribution are found in Table E.8.

If the sample sizes differ, you compute a critical range for each pairwise comparison of sample means. Finally, you compare each of the $c\,(c - 1)/2$ pairs of means against its corresponding critical range. You declare a specific pair significantly different if the absolute difference in the sample means $\left|\overline{X}_j - \overline{X}_{j'}\right|$ is greater than the critical range.

In the parachute example there are four suppliers. Thus, there are $4(4 - 1)/2 = 6$ pairwise comparisons. To apply the Tukey-Kramer procedure, you first compute the absolute mean differences for all six pairwise comparisons. Using Figure 10.23,

1. $\left|\overline{X}_1 - \overline{X}_2\right| = |19.52 - 24.26| = 4.74$

2. $\left|\overline{X}_1 - \overline{X}_3\right| = |19.52 - 22.84| = 3.32$

3. $\left|\overline{X}_1 - \overline{X}_4\right| = |19.52 - 21.16| = 1.64$

4. $\left|\overline{X}_2 - \overline{X}_3\right| = |24.26 - 22.84| = 1.42$

5. $\left|\overline{X}_2 - \overline{X}_4\right| = |24.26 - 21.16| = 3.10$

6. $\left|\overline{X}_3 - \overline{X}_4\right| = |22.84 - 21.16| = 1.68$

You need to compute only one critical range because the sample sizes in the four groups are equal. From the ANOVA summary table (Figure 10.26 or 10.27) $MSW = 6.094$ and $n_j = n_{j'} = 5$. From Table E.8, for $\alpha = 0.05$, $c = 4$ and $n - c = 20 - 4 = 16$, Q_U, the upper-tail critical value of the test statistic is 4.05 (see Table 10.10). From Equation (10.16),

$$\text{Critical range} = 4.05 \sqrt{\left(\frac{6.094}{2}\right)\left(\frac{1}{5} + \frac{1}{5}\right)} = 4.471$$

Because $4.74 > 4.471$, you conclude that there is a significant difference between the means of Suppliers 1 and 2. All other pairwise differences are small enough that they may be due to chance. You can conclude that parachutes woven using fiber from Supplier 1 have a lower mean tensile strength than those from Supplier 2.

TABLE 10.10

Finding the Studentized Range Q_U Statistic for $\alpha = 0.05$ with 4 and 16 Degrees of Freedom

Denominator Degrees of Freedom	Numerator Degrees of Freedom							
	2	3	4	5	6	7	8	9
.	.	.		.	.	.	.	.
.								.
.					.			
11	3.11	3.82	4.26	4.57	4.82	5.03	5.20	5.35
12	3.08	3.77	4.20	4.51	4.75	4.95	5.12	5.27
13	3.06	3.73	4.15	4.45	4.69	4.88	5.05	5.19
14	3.03	3.70	4.11	4.41	4.64	4.83	4.99	5.13
15	3.01	3.67	4.08	4.37	4.60	4.78	4.94	5.08
16	3.00	3.65	4.05	4.33	4.56	4.74	4.90	5.03

Source: Extracted from Table E.8.

These results are summarized in the Microsoft Excel output presented in Figure 10.28 and the Minitab output of Figure 10.29. Minitab gives confidence intervals for the differences between two groups instead of presenting the critical range. For example, the confidence interval for the population mean of supplier 2 minus the population mean for supplier 1,

$$(\bar{X}_2 - \bar{X}_1) \pm Q_U \sqrt{\frac{MSW}{2}\left(\frac{1}{n_j} + \frac{1}{n_{j'}}\right)} = (0.269, 9.211)$$

Since both endpoints of this interval are positive, you can conclude that the population mean of supplier 2 is greater than the population mean of supplier 1

FIGURE 10.28

Microsoft Excel Output of the Tukey-Kramer Procedure for the Parachute Example

	A	B	C	D	E	F	G	H	I
1	Parachute Tensile-Strength Analysis								
2									
3		Sample	Sample			Absolute	Std. Error	Critical	
4	Group	Mean	Size		Comparison	Difference	of Difference	Range	Results
5	1	19.52	5		Group 1 to Group 2	4.74	1.10399275	4.4712	Means are different
6	2	24.28	6		Group 1 to Group 3	3.32	1.10399275	4.4712	Means are not different
7	3	22.84	5		Group 1 to Group 4	1.64	1.10399275	4.4712	Means are not different
8	4	21.16	5		Group 2 to Group 3	1.42	1.10399275	4.4712	Means are not different
9					Group 2 to Group 4	3.1	1.10399275	4.4712	Means are not different
10	Other Data				Group 3 to Group 4	1.68	1.10399275	4.4712	Means are not different
11	Level of significance	0.05							
12	Numerator d.f.	4							
13	Denominator d.f.	16							
14	MSW	6.094							
15	Q Statistic	4.05							

FIGURE 10.29

Minitab Output of the Tukey-Kramer Procedure for the Parachute Example

```
All Pairwise Comparisons

Individual confidence level = 98.87%

1 subtracted from:

     Lower   Center  Upper   -----+---------+---------+---------+----
2    0.269   4.740   9.211                    (-------*--------)
3   -1.151   3.320   7.791               (--------*---------)
4   -2.831   1.640   6.111          (--------*--------)
                             -----+---------+---------+---------+----
                              -5.0      0.0       5.0      10.0

2 subtracted from:

     Lower   Center  Upper   -----+---------+---------+---------+----
3   -5.891  -1.420   3.051       (--------*--------)
4   -7.571  -3.100   1.371   (--------*---------)
                             -----+---------+---------+---------+----
                              -5.0      0.0       5.0      10.0

3 subtracted from:

     Lower   Center  Upper   -----+---------+---------+---------+----
4   -6.151  -1.680   2.791       (--------*--------)
```

ANOVA Assumptions

In Chapter 9 and sections 10.1–10.4, you learned the assumptions made in the application of each hypothesis-testing procedure and the consequences of departures from these assumptions. To use the one-way ANOVA F test, you must also make certain assumptions about the data. These three assumptions are

- Randomness and independence
- Normality
- Homogeneity of variance

The first assumption, **randomness and independence**, is critically important. The validity of any experiment depends on random sampling and/or the randomization process. To avoid biases in the outcomes, you need to either select random samples from the c populations or randomly assign the items or individuals to the c levels of the factor. Selecting a random sample, or randomly assigning the levels, will ensure that a value from one group is independent of any other value in the experiment. Departures from this assumption can seriously affect inferences from the analysis of variance. These problems are discussed more thoroughly in references 5 and 7.

The second assumption, **normality**, states that the sample values in each group are from a normally distributed population. Just as in the case of the t test, the one-way ANOVA F test is fairly robust against departures from the normal distribution. As long as the distributions are not extremely different from a normal distribution, the level of significance of the ANOVA F test is usually not greatly affected, particularly for large samples. You can assess the normality of each of the c samples by constructing a normal probability plot or a box-and-whisker plot.

The third assumption, **homogeneity of variance**, states that the population variances of the c groups are equal (i.e., $\sigma_1^2 = \sigma_2^2 = \cdots = \sigma_c^2$). If you have equal sample sizes in each group, inferences based on the F distribution are not seriously affected by unequal variances. However, if you have unequal sample sizes, then unequal variances can have a serious effect on inferences developed from the ANOVA procedure. Thus, when possible, you should have equal sample sizes in all groups. The Levene test for homogeneity of variance presented below is one method to test whether the variances of the c populations are equal.

When only the normality assumption is violated, the Kruskal-Wallis rank test, a nonparametric procedure (see references 1 and 2) is appropriate. When only the homogeneity-of-variance assumption is violated, procedures similar to those used in the separate-variance t test of section 10.1 are available (see references 1 and 2). When both the normality and homogeneity-of-variance assumptions have been violated, then you need to use an appropriate data transformation that will both normalize the data and reduce the differences in variances (see reference 7) or use a more general nonparametric procedure (see references 1 and 2).

Levene's Test for Homogeneity of Variance

Although the one-way ANOVA F test is relatively robust with respect to the assumption of equal group variances, large differences in the group variances can seriously affect the level of significance and the power of the F test. Many procedures are available to test the assumption of homogeneity of variance. The modified **Levene test** (see references 1, 4, and 10) is a procedure with high statistical power. To test for the equality of the c population variances, you use the following hypotheses:

$$H_0: \sigma_1^2 = \sigma_2^2 = \cdots = \sigma_c^2$$

against the alternative

$$H_1: \text{Not all } \sigma_j^2 \text{ are equal } (j = 1, 2, \ldots, c)$$

To test the null hypothesis of equal variances, you first compute the absolute value of the difference between each value and the median of the group. Then you perform a one-way analysis of variance on these *absolute differences*. To illustrate the modified Levene test, return to the "Using Statistics" scenario concerning the tensile strength of parachutes first presented on page 330. Table 10.11 summarizes the absolute differences from the median of each supplier.

TABLE 10.11

Absolute Differences from the Median Tensile Strength for Four Suppliers

Supplier 1 (Median = 18.5)	Supplier 2 (Median = 24.5)	Supplier 3 (Median = 22.9)	Supplier 4 (Median = 20.4)
$\lvert 18.5 - 18.5 \rvert = 0.0$	$\lvert 26.3 - 24.5 \rvert = 1.8$	$\lvert 20.6 - 22.9 \rvert = 2.3$	$\lvert 25.4 - 20.4 \rvert = 5.0$
$\lvert 24.0 - 18.5 \rvert = 5.5$	$\lvert 25.3 - 24.5 \rvert = 0.8$	$\lvert 25.2 - 22.9 \rvert = 2.3$	$\lvert 19.9 - 20.4 \rvert = 0.5$
$\lvert 17.2 - 18.5 \rvert = 1.3$	$\lvert 24.0 - 24.5 \rvert = 0.5$	$\lvert 20.8 - 22.9 \rvert = 2.1$	$\lvert 22.6 - 20.4 \rvert = 2.2$
$\lvert 19.9 - 18.5 \rvert = 1.4$	$\lvert 21.2 - 24.5 \rvert = 3.3$	$\lvert 24.7 - 22.9 \rvert = 1.8$	$\lvert 17.5 - 20.4 \rvert = 2.9$
$\lvert 18.0 - 18.5 \rvert = 0.5$	$\lvert 24.5 - 24.5 \rvert = 0.0$	$\lvert 22.9 - 22.9 \rvert = 0.0$	$\lvert 20.4 - 20.4 \rvert = 0.0$

Using the absolute differences given in Table 10.11, you perform a one-way analysis of variance. Figure 10.30 presents Microsoft Excel output and Figure 10.31 shows Minitab output.

FIGURE 10.30

Microsoft Excel Output of the Analysis of Variance of the Absolute Differences for the Parachute Data

	A	B	C	D	E	F	G
1	Parachute Tensile-Strength Analysis						
2							
3	SUMMARY						
4	Groups	Count	Sum	Average	Variance		
5	Supplier 1	5	8.7	1.74	4.753		
6	Supplier 2	5	6.4	1.28	1.707		
7	Supplier 3	5	8.5	1.7	0.045		
8	Supplier 4	5	10.6	2.12	4.007		
9							
10							
11	ANOVA						
12	Source of Variation	SS	df	MS	F	P-value	F crit
13	Between Groups	1.77	3	0.59	0.2068	0.890189	3.230067
14	Within Groups	45.648	16	2.853			
15							
16	Total	47.418	19				

FIGURE 10.31

Minitab Output of the Levene Test for the Parachute Data

```
Levene's Test (any continuous distribution)
Test statistic = 0.21, p-value = 0.890
```

From Figures 10.30 and 10.31, observe that $F = 0.21 < 3.238867$ (or the p-value $= 0.89 > 0.05$). Thus, do not reject H_0. There is no evidence of a significant difference among the four variances. In other words, it is reasonable to assume that the materials from the four suppliers produce parachutes with an equal amount of variability. Therefore, the homogeneity of variance assumption for the ANOVA procedure is justified.

EXAMPLE 10.5

ANALYSIS OF VARIANCE OF THE SPEED OF DRIVE-THROUGH SERVICE AT FAST-FOOD CHAINS

For fast-food restaurants, the drive-through window is an increasing source of revenue. The chain that offers the fastest service is likely to attract additional customers. In a study of drive-through times (from menu board to departure) at fast-food chains, the mean time was 150 seconds for Wendy's, 167 seconds for McDonald's, 169 seconds for Checkers, 171 seconds for Burger King, and 172 seconds for Long John Silver's (J. Ordonez, "An Efficiency Drive: Fast-Food Lanes are Getting Even Faster," *The Wall Street Journal*, May 18, 2000, A1, A10). Suppose the study was based on 20 customers for each fast-food chain and the ANOVA table given in Table 10.12 was developed.

TABLE 10.12

Analysis of Variance Table of the Speed of Drive-Through Service at Fast-Food Chains

Source	Degrees of Freedom	Sum of Squares	Mean Squares	F	p-value
Among chains	4	6,536	1,634.0	12.51	0.0000
Within chains	95	12,407	130.6		

At the 0.05 level of significance, is there evidence of a difference in the mean drive-through times of the five chains?

SOLUTION

$H_0: \mu_1 = \mu_2 = \mu_3 = \mu_4 = \mu_5$ where 1 = Wendy's, 2 = McDonald's, 3 = Checkers, 4 = Burger King, 5 = Long John Silver's

H_1: Not all μ_j are equal   where $j = 1, 2, 3, 4, 5$

Decision Rule: If p-value < 0.05, reject H_0. Since the p-value is virtually 0, reject H_0. You have sufficient evidence to conclude that the mean drive-through times of the five chains are not all equal.

To determine which of the means are significantly different from one another, use the Tukey-Kramer procedure [Equation (10.16)] to establish the critical range:

$$Q_{U(c, n-c)} = Q_{U(5,95)} = 3.92$$

$$\text{Critical range} = Q_{U(c, n-c)} \sqrt{\frac{MSW}{2} \cdot \left(\frac{1}{n_j} + \frac{1}{n_{j'}} \right)} = (3.92) \sqrt{\left(\frac{130.6}{2} \right) \left(\frac{1}{20} + \frac{1}{20} \right)}$$

$$= 10.017$$

The drive-through times are different between Wendy's (mean of 150 seconds) and each of the other four chains. With 95% confidence, you can conclude that the drive-through time for Wendy's is faster than McDonald's, Burger King, Checkers, and Long John Silver's, but the drive-through times for McDonald's, Burger King, Checkers, and Long John Silver's are not statistically different.

PROBLEMS FOR SECTION 10.5

Learning the Basics

 10.55 You are working with an experiment that has a single factor with five groups, and seven values in each group.

a. How many degrees of freedom are there in determining the among-group variation?
b. How many degrees of freedom are there in determining the within-group variation?
c. How many degrees of freedom are there in determining the total variation?

 10.56 You are working with the same experiment as in problem 10.55:
a. If $SSA = 60$ and $SST = 210$, what is SSW?
b. What is MSA?
c. What is MSW?
d. What is the value of the test statistic F?

PH Grade ASSIST **10.57** You are working with the same experiment as in problems 10.55 and 10.56:
a. Form the ANOVA summary table and fill in all values in the body of the table.
b. At the 0.05 level of significance, what is the upper-tail critical value from the F distribution?
c. State the decision rule for testing the null hypothesis that all five groups have equal population means.
d. What is your statistical decision?

10.58 You are working with an experiment that has one factor containing three groups with seven values in each:
a. How many degrees of freedom are there in determining the among-group variation?
b. How many degrees of freedom are there in determining the within-group variation?
c. How many degrees of freedom are there in determining the total variation?

 10.59 You are conducting an experiment with one factor containing four groups, with eight values in each group. For the ANOVA summary table below, fill in all the missing results.

Source	Degrees of Freedom	Sum of Squares	Mean Square (Variance)	F
Among groups	$c - 1 = ?$	$SSA = ?$	$MSA = 80$	$F = ?$
Within groups	$n - c = ?$	$SSW = 560$	$MSW = ?$	
Total	$n - 1 = ?$	$SST = ?$		

10.60 You are working with the same experiment as in problem 10.59:
a. At the 0.05 level of significance, state the decision rule for testing the null hypothesis that all four groups have equal population means.
b. What is your statistical decision?
c. At the 0.05 level of significance, what is the upper-tail critical value from the Studentized range distribution?
d. To perform the Tukey-Kramer procedure, what is the critical range?

Applying the Concepts

Problems 10.61–10.68 can be solved manually or by using Microsoft Excel, Minitab, or SPSS.

10.61 The Computer Anxiety Rating Scale (CARS) measures an individual's level of computer anxiety on a scale from 20 (no anxiety) to 100 (highest level of anxiety). Researchers at Miami University administered CARS to 172 business students. One of the objectives of the study was to determine if there are differences in the amount of computer anxiety experienced by students with different majors.

Source	Degrees of Freedom	Sum of Squares	Mean Squares	F
Among Majors	5	3,172		
Within Majors	166	21,246		
Total	171	24,418		

Major	N	Mean
Marketing	19	44.37
Management	11	43.18
Other	14	42.21
Finance	45	41.80
Accountancy	36	37.56
MIS	47	42.21

Source: Travis Broome and Douglas Havelka, "Determinants of Computer Anxiety in Business Students," The Review of Business Information Systems, Spring 2002, 6(2):9–16.

a. Complete the ANOVA summary table.
b. At the 0.05 level of significance, is there evidence of a difference in the mean computer anxiety experienced by different majors?
c. If the results in (b) indicate that it is appropriate, use the Tukey-Kramer procedure to determine which majors differ in mean computer anxiety. Discuss your findings.

PH Grade ASSIST **10.62** Periodically, *The Wall Street Journal* conducted a stock-picking contest. The last one was conducted in March 2001. In this experiment, three different methods were used to select stocks that were expected to perform well during the next five months. Four Wall Street professionals, considered experts on picking stocks, selected four stocks. Four randomly chosen readers of the *Wall Street Journal* also selected four stocks. Finally, four stocks were selected by flinging darts at a table containing a list of stocks. The returns of the selected stocks for March 20, 2001 to August 31, 2001 (in percentage return) are given in the following table. Note that during this period the Dow Jones Industrial Average gained 2.4%. **CONTEST2001**

Experts	Readers	Darts
+39.5	−31.0	+39.0
−1.1	−20.7	+31.9
−4.5	−45.0	+14.1
−8.0	−73.3	+5.4

Source: Extracted from Georgette Jasen, "In Picking Stocks, Dartboard Beats the Pros," The Wall Street Journal, September 27, 2001, C1, C10.

a. Is there evidence of a significant difference in the mean return for the three categories? (Use $\alpha = 0.05$.)
b. If appropriate, determine which categories differ in mean return.

c. Comment on the validity of the inference implied by the title of the article, which suggests that the dartboard was better than the professionals.
d. Is there evidence of a significant difference in the variation in the return for the three categories? (Use $\alpha = 0.05$.)

10.63 The following data represent the price of regular gasoline at self-service stations in four counties in New York City and two suburban counties during the week of May 17, 2004. **GASPRICE**

Counties					
Manhattan	Bronx	Queens	Brooklyn	Nassau	Suffolk
2.339	2.199	2.239	2.159	2.099	2.179
2.299	2.139	2.239	2.199	2.199	2.159
2.239	2.239	2.179	2.359	2.259	2.119
2.199	2.159	2.299	2.159	2.239	2.159
2.199	2.179	2.279	1.999	2.239	2.219

a. At the 0.05 level of significance, is there evidence of a difference in the mean price of gasoline in the six counties?
b. If appropriate, determine which counties differ in mean gasoline price.
c. At the 0.05 level of significance, is there evidence of a difference in the variation in gasoline price among the six counties?

✓SELF Test **10.64** Students in a business statistics course performed an experiment to test the strength of four brands of trash bags. One-pound weights were placed into a bag one at a time until the bag broke. A total of 40 bags, 10 for each brand, were used. The data in the file **TRASHBAGS** give the weight (in pounds) required to break the trash bags.
a. At the 0.05 level of significance, is there evidence of a difference in the mean strength of the four brands of trash bags?
b. If appropriate, determine which brands differ in mean strength.
c. At the 0.05 level of significance, is there evidence of a difference in the variation in strength among the four brands of trash bags?
d. Which brand(s) should you buy and which brand(s) should you avoid? Explain.

10.65 The data below represent the lifetime of four different alloys. **ALLOY**

Alloy			
1	2	3	4
999	1,022	1,026	974
1,010	973	1,008	1,015
995	1,023	1,005	1,009
998	1,023	1,007	1,011
1,001	996	981	995

Source: P. Wludyka, P. Nelson, and P. Silva, "Power Curves for the Analysis of Means for Variances," Journal of Quality Technology, 33, 2001, 60–65.

a. At the 0.05 level of significance, is there evidence of a difference in the mean lifetime of the four alloys?

b. If appropriate, determine which alloys differ in mean lifetime.

c. At the 0.05 level of significance, is there evidence of a difference in the variation in lifetime among the four alloys?

d. What effect does your result in (c) have on the validity of the results in (a) and (b)?

10.66 An advertising agency has been hired by a manufacturer of pens to develop an advertising campaign for the upcoming holiday season. To prepare for this project, the research director decides to initiate a study of the effect of advertising on product perception. An experiment is designed to compare five different advertisements. Advertisement *A* greatly undersells the pen's characteristics. Advertisement *B* slightly undersells the pen's characteristics. Advertisement *C* slightly oversells the pen's characteristics. Advertisement *D* greatly oversells the pen's characteristics. Advertisement *E* attempts to correctly state the pen's characteristics. A sample of 30 adult respondents, taken from a larger focus group, is randomly assigned to the five advertisements (so that there are six respondents to each). After reading the advertisement and developing a sense of "product expectation," all respondents unknowingly receive the same pen to evaluate. The respondents are permitted to test their pen and the plausibility of the advertising copy. The respondents are then asked to rate the pen from 1 to 7 on the product characteristic scales of appearance, durability, and writing performance. The *combined* scores of three ratings (appearance, durability, and writing performance) for the 30 respondents PEN are as follows.

A	B	C	D	E
15	16	8	5	12
18	17	7	6	19
17	21	10	13	18
19	16	15	11	12
19	19	14	9	17
20	17	14	10	14

a. At the 0.05 level of significance, is there evidence of a difference in the mean rating of the five advertisements?

b. If appropriate, determine which advertisements differ in mean rating.

c. At the 0.05 level of significance, is there evidence of a difference in the variation in rating among the five advertisements?

d. Which advertisement(s) should you use and which advertisement(s) should you avoid? Explain.

10.67 The retailing manager of a supermarket chain wants to determine whether product location has any effect on the sale of pet toys. Three different aisle locations are considered: front, middle, and rear. A random sample of 18 stores is selected with 6 stores randomly assigned to each

aisle location. The size of the display area and price of the product are constant for all stores. At the end of a 1-month trial period, the sales volumes (in thousands of dollars) of the product in each store were as follows: LOCATE

Aisle Location		
Front	Middle	Rear
8.6	3.2	4.6
7.2	2.4	6.0
5.4	2.0	4.0
6.2	1.4	2.8
5.0	1.8	2.2
4.0	1.6	2.8

a. At the 0.05 level of significance, is there evidence of a significant difference in mean sales among the various aisle locations?

b. If appropriate, which aisle locations appear to differ significantly in mean sales?

c. At the 0.05 level of significance, is there evidence of a significant difference in the variation in sales among the various aisle locations?

d. What should the retailing manager conclude? Fully describe the retailing manager's options with respect to aisle locations.

10.68 A sporting goods manufacturing company wanted to compare the distance traveled by golf balls produced by each of four different designs. Ten balls were manufactured with each design and were brought to the local golf course for the club professional to test. The order in which the balls were hit with a driver from the first tee was randomized so that the pro did not know which type of ball was being hit. All 40 balls were hit in a short period of time during which the environmental conditions were essentially the same. The results (distance traveled in yards) for the four designs were as follows: GOLFBALL

Designs			
1	2	3	4
206.32	203.81	217.08	213.90
226.77	223.85	230.55	231.10
207.94	206.75	221.43	221.28
224.79	223.97	227.95	221.53
206.19	205.68	218.04	229.43
229.75	234.30	231.84	235.45
204.45	204.49	224.13	213.54
228.51	219.50	224.87	228.35
209.65	210.86	211.82	214.51
221.44	233.00	229.49	225.09

a. At the 0.05 level of significance, is there evidence of a difference in the mean distance traveled by the golf balls with different designs?

b. If the results in (a) indicate that it is appropriate, use the Tukey-Kramer procedure to determine which designs differ in mean distance.

c. What assumptions are necessary in (a)?

d. At the 0.05 level of significance, is there evidence of a difference in the variation of the distance traveled by the golf balls differing in design?

e. What golf ball design should the manufacturing manager choose? Explain.

KEY FORMULAS

Z Test for the Difference Between Two Means

$$Z = \frac{(\bar{X}_1 - \bar{X}_2) - (\mu_1 - \mu_2)}{\sqrt{\dfrac{\sigma_1^2}{n_1} + \dfrac{\sigma_2^2}{n_2}}} \quad (10.1)$$

Pooled-Variance t Test for the Difference Between Two Means

$$t = \frac{(\bar{X}_1 - \bar{X}_2) - (\mu_1 - \mu_2)}{\sqrt{S_p^2\left(\dfrac{1}{n_1} + \dfrac{1}{n_2}\right)}} \quad (10.2)$$

Confidence Interval Estimate of the Difference in the Means of Two Independent Populations

$$(\bar{X}_1 - \bar{X}_2) \pm t_{n_1 + n_2 - 2}\sqrt{S_p^2\left(\dfrac{1}{n_1} + \dfrac{1}{n_2}\right)} \quad (10.3)$$

or

$$(\bar{X}_1 - \bar{X}_2) - t_{n_1 + n_2 - 2}\sqrt{S_p^2\left(\dfrac{1}{n_1} + \dfrac{1}{n_2}\right)} \le \mu_1 - \mu_2$$

$$\le (\bar{X}_1 - \bar{X}_2) + t_{n_1 + n_2 - 2}\sqrt{S_p^2\left(\dfrac{1}{n_1} + \dfrac{1}{n_2}\right)}$$

Z Test for the Mean Difference

$$Z = \frac{\bar{D} - \mu_D}{\dfrac{\sigma_D}{\sqrt{n}}} \quad (10.4)$$

Paired t Test for the Mean Difference

$$t = \frac{\bar{D} - \mu_D}{\dfrac{S_D}{\sqrt{n}}} \quad (10.5)$$

Confidence Interval Estimate for the Mean Difference

$$\bar{D} \pm t_{n-1}\frac{S_D}{\sqrt{n}} \quad (10.6)$$

or

$$\bar{D} - t_{n-1}\frac{S_D}{\sqrt{n}} \le \mu_D \le \bar{D} + t_{n-1}\frac{S_D}{\sqrt{n}}$$

Z Test for the Difference Between Two Proportions

$$Z = \frac{(p_1 - p_2) - (\pi_1 - \pi_2)}{\sqrt{\bar{p}(1 - \bar{p})\left(\dfrac{1}{n_1} + \dfrac{1}{n_2}\right)}} \quad (10.7)$$

Confidence Interval Estimate for the Difference Between Two Proportions

$$(p_1 - p_2) \pm Z\sqrt{\frac{p_1(1 - p_1)}{n_1} + \frac{p_2(1 - p_2)}{n_2}} \quad (10.8)$$

or

$$(p_1 - p_2) - Z\sqrt{\frac{p_1(1 - p_1)}{n_1} + \frac{p_2(1 - p_2)}{n_2}} \le (\pi_1 - \pi_2)$$

$$\le (p_1 - p_2) + Z\sqrt{\frac{p_1(1 - p_1)}{n_1} + \frac{p_2(1 - p_2)}{n_2}}$$

F Statistic for Testing the Equality of Two Variances

$$F = \frac{S_1^2}{S_2^2} \quad (10.9)$$

Finding Lower-Tail Critical Values from the F Distribution

$$F_L = \frac{1}{F_{U*}} \quad (10.10)$$

Total Variation in One-Way ANOVA

$$SST = \sum_{j=1}^{c}\sum_{i=1}^{n_j}(X_{ij} - \bar{\bar{X}})^2 \quad (10.11)$$

Among-Group Variation in One-Way ANOVA

$$SSA = \sum_{j=1}^{c} n_j(\bar{X}_j - \bar{\bar{X}})^2 \quad (10.12)$$

Within-Group Variation in One-Way ANOVA

$$SSW = \sum_{j=1}^{c}\sum_{i=1}^{n_j}(X_{ij} - \bar{X}_j)^2 \quad (10.13)$$

The Mean Squares in One-Way ANOVA

$$MSA = \frac{SSA}{c - 1} \quad (10.14a)$$

$$MSW = \frac{SSW}{n - c} \quad \text{(10.14b)}$$

$$MST = \frac{SST}{n - 1} \quad \text{(10.14c)}$$

One-Way ANOVA *F*-Test Statistic

$$F = \frac{MSA}{MSW} \quad \text{(10.15)}$$

The Critical Range for the Tukey-Kramer Procedure

$$\text{Critical range} = Q_U \sqrt{\frac{MSW}{2}\left(\frac{1}{n_j} + \frac{1}{n_{j'}}\right)} \quad \text{(10.16)}$$

CHAPTER REVIEW PROBLEMS

Checking Your Understanding

10.69 What are some of the criteria used in the selection of a particular hypothesis-testing procedure?

10.70 Under what conditions should you use the pooled-variance *t* test to examine possible differences in the means of two independent populations?

10.71 Under what conditions should you use the *F* test to examine possible differences in the variances of two independent populations?

10.72 What is the difference between two independent and two related populations?

10.73 What is the distinction between repeated measurements and matched (or paired) items?

10.74 Explain the similarities and differences between the test of hypothesis for the difference between the means of two independent populations, and the confidence interval estimate of the difference between the means.

10.75 In a one-way ANOVA, what is the difference between the among-groups variance *MSA* and the within-groups variance *MSW*?

10.76 What are the assumptions of ANOVA?

10.77 Under what conditions should you select the one-way ANOVA *F* test to examine possible differences among the means of *c* independent populations?

10.78 When and how should you use multiple comparison procedures for evaluating pairwise combinations of the group means?

10.79 What is the difference between the one-way ANOVA *F* test and the Levene test?

Applying the Concepts

Problems 10.84–10.87 can be solved manually or by using Microsoft Excel, Minitab, or SPSS. We recommend that you use Microsoft Excel, Minitab, or SPSS to solve problems 10.88–10.105.

10.80 A study reported in the *Journal of Business Strategies* compared music compact disk prices for Internet-based retailers and traditional brick-and-mortar retailers (Lee Zoonky, and Sanjay Gosain, "A Longitudinal Price Comparison for Music CDs in Electronic and Brick-and-Mortar Markets: Pricing Strategies in Emergent Electronic Commerce," Spring 2002, 19(1):55–72). Before collecting the data, the researchers carefully defined several research hypotheses including:
1. Price dispersion on the Internet will be lower than the price dispersion in the brick-and-mortar market.
2. Prices in electronic markets will be lower than prices in physical markets.
a. Consider research hypothesis 1. Write the null and alternative hypotheses in terms of population parameters. Carefully define the population parameters used.
b. Define a Type I and Type II error for the hypotheses in (a).
c. What type of statistical test should you use?
d. What assumptions are needed to perform the test you selected?
e. Repeat (a) through (d) for research hypothesis 2.

10.81 The pet-drug market is growing very rapidly. Before introducing new pet drugs into the marketplace, they must be approved by the U.S. Food and Drug Administration (FDA). In 1999, the Norvatis company was trying to get Anafranil, a drug to reduce dog anxiety, approved. According to an article (Elyse Tanouye, "The Ow in Bowwow: With Growing Market in Pet Drugs, Makers Revamp Clinical Trials," *The Wall Street Journal*,

April 13, 1999), Norvatis had to find a way to translate a dog's anxiety symptoms into numbers that could be used to prove to the FDA that the drug had a *statistically significant effect* on the condition.

a. What is meant by the phrase statistically significant effect?

b. Consider an experiment where dogs suffering from anxiety are divided into two groups. One group will be given Anafranil, and the other will be given a placebo (a drug without active ingredients). How can you translate a dog's anxiety symptoms into numbers? In other words, define a continuous variable X_1, the measurement of effectiveness of the drug Anafranil, and X_2, the measurement of the effectiveness of the placebo.

c. Building on your answer to part (b), define the null and alternative hypotheses for this study.

10.82 In response to lawsuits filed against the tobacco industry, many companies such as Philip Morris are running television advertisements that are supposed to educate teenagers about the dangers of smoking. Are these tobacco industry antismoking campaigns successful? Are state-sponsored antismoking commercials more effective? An article (Gordon Fairclough, "Philip Morris's Antismoking Campaign Draws Fire," *The Wall Street Journal*, April 6, 1999, B1) discussed a study in California that compared commercials made by the state of California and commercials produced by Philip Morris. Researchers showed the state ads and the Philip Morris ads to a group of California teenagers and measured the effectiveness of both. The researchers concluded that the state ads were more effective in relaying the dangers of smoking than the Philip Morris ads. The article suggests, however, that the study is not *statistically reliable* because the sample size was too small and because the study specifically selected participants who were considered more likely to start smoking than others.

a. How do you think the researchers measured effectiveness?

b. Define the null and alternative hypotheses for this study.

c. Explain the risks associated with Type I and Type II errors in this study.

d. What type of test is most appropriate in this situation?

e. What do you think is meant by the phrase *statistically reliable*?

10.83 The FedEx St. Jude Classic professional golf tournament is held each year in Memphis, Tennessee. FedEx sponsors this PGA tournament, and part of the proceeds goes to the St. Jude Children's Research Hospital. In 2003, the tournament raised $679,115 for the hospital. This type of corporate sponsorship is known as cause-related marketing. Spectators at the tournament were surveyed and asked to respond to a series of questions on a 5-point scale (1 = Strongly Disagree, 2 = Disagree, 3 = Neutral, 4 = Agree, and 5 = Strongly Agree). Four of the questions asked are listed below:

1. Cause-related marketing creates a positive company image.
2. I would be willing to pay more for a service that supports a cause I care about.
3. Cause-related marketing should be a standard part of a company's activities.
4. Based on its support of St. Jude, I will be more likely to use FedEx services.

For each question, the researchers tested the null hypothesis that the mean response for males and females is equal. The alternative hypothesis is that the mean response is different for males and females. The following table summarizes the results.

	Sample Mean			
Question	Female (n_1=137)	Male (n_2=305)	t	p-value
1	4.46	4.26	1.907	0.057
2	4.09	3.86	2.105	0.035
3	4.26	3.91	3.258	0.001
4	4.12	4.06	0.567	0.571

Source: Extracted from R. L. Irwin, T. Lachowetz, T. B. Cornwell, and J. S. Cook, 2003, "Cause-Related Sport Sponsorship: An Assessment of Spectator Beliefs, Attitudes, and Behavioral Intentions," Sport Marketing Quarterly, 12(3): 131–139.

a. Interpret the results of the t test for question 1.

b. Interpret the results of the t test for question 2.

c. Interpret the results of the t test for question 3.

d. Interpret the results of the t test for question 4.

e. Write a short summary about the differences between males and females concerning their views toward cause-related sponsorship.

10.84 A large public utility company wants to compare the consumption of electricity during the summer season for single-family houses in two counties that it services. For each household sampled, the monthly electric bill is recorded with the following results:

	County I	County II
$\bar{X}$	$115	$98
S	$30	$18
n	25	21

Use a level of significance of 0.01.

a. Is there evidence that the mean bill in county II is above $80?

b. Is there evidence of a difference between the variances of bills in county I and in county II?

c. Is there evidence that the mean monthly bill is higher in county I than in county II?

d. Construct and interpret a 99% confidence interval estimate of the difference between the mean monthly bill in county I and county II.

10.85 The manager of computer operations of a large company wants to study computer usage of two departments within the company, the accounting department and the research department. A random sample of five jobs from the accounting department in the past week and six jobs from the research department in the past week are selected, and the processing time (in seconds) for each job is recorded. ACCRES

Department	Processing Time (in Seconds)					
Accounting	9	3	8	7	12	
Research	4	13	10	9	9	6

Use a level of significance of 0.05.
a. Is there evidence that the mean processing time in the research department is greater than 6 seconds?
b. Is there evidence of a difference between the variances in the processing time of the two departments?
c. Is there evidence of a difference between the mean processing time of the accounting department and the research department?
d. Determine the p-values in (a), (b), and (c) and interpret their meanings.
e. Construct and interpret a 95% confidence interval estimate of the difference in the mean processing times between the accounting and research departments.

10.86 A computer information systems professor is interested in studying the amount of time it takes students enrolled in the Introduction to Computers course to write and run a program in Visual Basic. The professor hires you to analyze the following results (in minutes) from a random sample of nine students: VB

10 13 9 15 12 13 11 13 12

a. At the 0.05 level of significance, is there evidence that the population mean amount is greater than 10 minutes? What will you tell the professor?
b. Suppose the computer professor, when checking her results, realizes that the fourth student needed 51 minutes rather than the recorded 15 minutes to write and run the Visual Basic program. At the 0.05 level of significance, reanalyze the question posed in (a) using the revised data. What will you tell the professor now?
c. The professor is perplexed by these paradoxical results and requests an explanation from you regarding the justification for the difference in your findings in (a) and (b). Discuss.

d. A few days later, the professor calls to tell you that the dilemma is completely resolved. The original number 15 (the fourth data value) was correct, and therefore your findings in (a) are being used in the article she is writing for a computer journal. Now she wants to hire you to compare the results from that group of Introduction to Computers students against those from a sample of 11 computer majors in order to determine whether there is evidence that computer majors can write a Visual Basic program in less time than introductory students. The sample mean is 8.5 minutes and the sample standard deviation is 2.0 minutes for the computer majors. At the 0.05 level of significance, completely analyze these data. What will you tell the professor?
e. A few days later the professor calls again to tell you that a reviewer of her article wants her to include the p-value for the "correct" result in (a). In addition, the professor inquires about an unequal variances problem, which the reviewer wants her to discuss in her article. In your own words, discuss the concept of p-value and describe the unequal variances problem. Determine the p-value in (a) and discuss whether or not the unequal variances problem had any meaning in the professor's study.

10.87 Over the last several years, the use of cell phones has increased dramatically. An article in *USA Today* (D. Sharp, "Cellphones Reveal Screaming Lack of Courtesy," *USA Today*, September 2001, 4A) reported that according to a poll, the mean talking time per month for cell phones was 372 minutes for men and 275 minutes for women, while the mean talking time per month for traditional home phones was 334 minutes for men and 510 minutes for women. Suppose that the poll was based on a sample of 100 men and 100 women, and that the standard deviation of the talking time per month for cell phones was 120 minutes for men and 100 minutes for women, while the standard deviation of the talking time per month for traditional home phones was 100 minutes for men and 150 minutes for women.
Use a level of significance of 0.05.
a. Is there evidence of a difference in the mean monthly talking time on cell phones for men and women?
b. Is there evidence of a difference in the mean monthly talking time on traditional home phones for men and women?
c. Construct and interpret a 95% confidence interval estimate of the difference in the mean monthly talking time on cell phones for men and women.
d. Construct and interpret a 95% confidence interval estimate of the difference in the mean monthly talking time on traditional home phones for men and women.
e. Is there evidence of a difference in the variance of the monthly talking time on cell phones for men and women?

f. Is there evidence of a difference in the variance of the monthly talking time on traditional home phones for men and women?

g. Based on the results of (a) through (f), what conclusions can you reach concerning cell phone and traditional home phone usage between men and women?

10.88 *Working Woman* magazine conducted a large study to determine typical salaries for men and women in many different types of jobs (Extracted from "Annual Salary Survey," *Working Woman*, July/August 2001, 44–47). A data set containing 114 job titles along with the corresponding typical salaries for men and women is included in the data file SALARIES.

a. At the 0.01 level of significance, is there evidence that the mean salary for men is greater than the mean salary for women?

b. Compute the *p*-value in (a).

10.89 Use the data in the COLLEGES2002 file to compare public and private universities in terms of first quartile of SAT scores, third quartile of SAT scores, total cost, room and board cost, and total indebtedness at graduation. Use the 0.05 level of significance.

10.90 The lengths of life (in hours) of a sample of forty 100-watt lightbulbs produced by manufacturer A and a sample of forty 100-watt lightbulbs produced by manufacturer B are in the file BULBS. Completely analyze the differences between the life of the bulbs produced by two manufacturers (use $\alpha = 0.05$).

10.91 The data contained in the file PETFOOD2 consist of the cost per serving, cups per can, protein in grams, and fat in grams for 97 varieties of dry and canned dog and cat food. Completely analyze the differences between cat food and dog food for the variables of cost per serving, protein in grams, and fat in grams. Do a similar analysis comparing the differences between dry food and canned food (use $\alpha = 0.05$).

Source: Copyright © 1998 by Consumers Union of U.S., Inc., Yonkers, NY 10703-1057. Adapted with permission from Consumer Reports, *February 1998, 18–19.*

10.92 Use the data in the file AUTO2002 to compare 2002 sports utility vehicles (SUVs) and non-SUVs in terms of miles per gallon, length, width, turning-circle requirement, weight, and luggage capacity. Completely analyze differences between SUVs and non-SUVs (use $\alpha = 0.05$).

Source: "The 2002 cars," Copyright © 2002 by Consumers Union of U.S., Inc., Yonkers, NY 10703-1057. Adapted with permission from Consumer Reports, *April 2002.*

10.93 Zagat's publishes restaurant ratings for various locations in the United States. The data file RESTRATE contains the Zagat rating for food, décor, service, and the price per person for a sample of 50 restaurants located in New York City and 50 restaurants located on Long Island. Completely analyze the differences between New York City and Long Island restaurants for the variables food rating, décor rating, service rating, and price per person, using $\alpha = 0.05$.

Source: Extracted from Zagat Survey 2002 New York City Restaurants and Zagat Survey 2001–2002 Long Island Restaurants

10.94 The data found in the file BEER represent the price of a six-pack of 12-ounce bottles, the calories per 12 fluid ounces, the percentage of alcohol content per 12 fluid ounces, the type of beer (i.e., craft lager, craft ale, imported lager, regular or ice beer, and light or nonalcoholic beer), and the country of origin (U.S. versus imported) for each of the 69 beers that were sampled. Completely analyze the differences between beers brewed in the United States and those that were imported in terms of price, calories, and alcohol content (use $\alpha = 0.05$).

Source: "Beers," Copyright © 1996 by Consumers Union of U.S., Inc., Yonkers, NY 10703-1057. Adapted with permission from Consumer Reports, *June 1996.*

10.95 In manufacturing processes there is a term called *work-in-process* (often abbreviated WIP). In a book manufacturing plant WIP represents the time it takes for sheets from a press to be folded, gathered, sewn, tipped on end sheets, and bound. The following data represent samples of 20 books at each of two production plants and the processing time (operationally defined as the time in days from when the books came off the press to when they were packed in cartons). WIP

Plant A

5.62 5.29 16.25 10.92 11.46 21.62 8.45 8.58 5.41 11.42
11.62 7.29 7.50 7.96 4.42 10.50 7.58 9.29 7.54 8.92

Plant B

9.54 11.46 16.62 12.62 25.75 15.41 14.29 13.13 13.71 10.04
5.75 12.46 9.17 13.21 6.00 2.33 14.25 5.37 6.25 9.71

Completely analyze the differences between the processing times for the two plants using $\alpha = 0.05$, and write a summary of your findings to be presented to the vice president for operations of the company.

10.96 Do marketing promotions, such as bobble-head giveaways, increase attendance at Major League Baseball games? An article reported on the effectiveness of marketing promotions (Extracted from T. C. Boyd and T. C. Krehbiel, "Promotion Timing in Major League Baseball and the Stacking Effects of Factors that Increase Game Attractiveness," *Sport Marketing Quarterly*, March 2003, 12, 173–184). The data file ROYALS includes the following variables for the Kansas City Royals during the 2002 baseball season:

GAME = Home games in the order they were played
ATTENDANCE = Paid attendance for the game
PROMOTION – 1 = if a promotion was held; 0 = if no promotion was held

a. At the 0.05 level of significance, is there evidence of a difference between the variances in the attendance at games with promotions and games without promotions?
b. Based on the result of (a), conduct the appropriate test of hypothesis to determine whether there is a difference in the mean attendance at games with promotions and games without promotions. (Use $\alpha = 0.05$.)
c. Write a brief summary of your results.

10.97 The manufacturer of "Boston" and "Vermont" asphalt shingles know that product weight is a major factor in the customer's perception of quality. Moreover, the weight represents the amount of raw materials being used and is therefore very important to the company from a cost standpoint. The last stage of the assembly-line packages the shingles before they are placed on wooden pallets. Once a pallet is full (a pallet for most brands holds 16 squares of shingles), it is weighed and the measurement is recorded. The data file PALLET contains the weight (in pounds) from a sample of 368 pallets of Boston shingles and 330 pallets of Vermont shingles. Completely analyze the differences in the weight of the Boston and Vermont shingles using $\alpha = 0.05$.

10.98 The manufacturer of "Boston" and "Vermont" asphalt shingles provide their customers with a 20-year warranty on most of their products. To determine whether a shingle will last as long as the warranty period, accelerated-life testing is conducted at the manufacturing plant. Accelerated-life testing exposes the shingle to the stresses it would be subject to in a lifetime of normal use in a laboratory setting via an experiment that takes only a few minutes to conduct. In this test, a shingle is repeatedly scraped with a brush for a short period of time and the amount of shingle granules that are removed by the brushing is weighed (in grams). Shingles that experience low amounts of granule loss are expected to last longer in normal use than shingles that experience high amounts of granule loss. In this situation, a shingle should experience no more than 0.8 grams of granule loss if it is expected to last the length of the warranty period. The data file GRANULE contains a sample of 170 measurements made on the company's Boston shingles, and 140 measurements

made on Vermont shingles. Completely analyze the differences in the granule loss of the Boston and Vermont shingles using $\alpha = 0.05$.

10.99 The quality control director for a clothing manufacturer wants to study the effect of machines on the breaking strength (in pounds) of wool serge material. A batch of the material is cut into square-yard pieces and these are randomly assigned, 12 each, to the three machines chosen specifically for the experiment. The results are as follows.
BREAKSTW

Machine		
I	II	III
115	111	109
115	108	110
119	114	107
117	105	110
114	102	113
114	106	114
109	100	103
110	103	102
106	101	105
112	105	108
115	107	111
111	107	110

At the 0.05 level of significance:
a. Is there an effect that is due to machine?
b. Plot the mean breaking strength for each machine.
c. If appropriate, use the Tukey-Kramer procedure to examine differences among the machines.
d. What can you conclude about the effect of machines on breaking strength? Explain.

10.100 An operations manager wants to examine the effect of air-jet pressure (in psi) on the breaking strength of the yarn. Three different levels of air-jet pressure are to be considered: 30 psi, 40 psi, and 50 psi. A random sample of 18 homogeneous filling yarns are selected from the same batch and the yarns are randomly assigned, 6 each, to the 3 levels of air-jet pressure. The breaking strength scores are in the data file: YARN
a. Is there evidence of a significant difference in the variances of the breaking strengths for the three air-jet pressures? (Use $\alpha = 0.05$).
b. At the 0.05 level of significance, is there evidence of a difference among mean breaking strengths for the three air-jet pressures?
c. If appropriate, use the Tukey-Kramer procedure to determine which air-jet pressures significantly differ with respect to mean breaking strength. (Use $\alpha = 0.05$.)
d. What should the operations manager conclude?

10.101 Modern software applications require rapid data access capabilities. An experiment was conducted to test the effect of data file size on the ability to access the files (as measured by read time in milliseconds). Three different levels of data file size were considered: small—50,000 characters; medium—75,000 characters; or large—100,000 characters. A sample of eight files of each size was evaluated. The access read times in milliseconds are in the data file: ACCESS

a. Is there evidence of a significant difference in the variance of the access read times for the three file sizes? (Use $\alpha = 0.05$).

b. At the 0.05 level of significance, is there evidence of a difference among mean access read times for the three file sizes?

c. If appropriate, use the Tukey-Kramer procedure to determine which file sizes significantly differ with respect to mean access read time. (Use $\alpha = 0.05$.)

d. What conclusions can you reach?

Report Writing Exercises

10.102 Referring to the results of problems 10.97 and 10.98 concerning the weight and granule loss of Boston and Vermont shingles, write a report that summarizes your conclusions.

10.103 The data in the file BEER represent the price of a six-pack of 12-ounce bottles, the calories per 12 fluid ounces, the percentage of alcohol content per 12 fluid ounces, the type of beer (craft lager, craft ale, imported lager, regular and ice beer, and light and nonalcoholic beer), and the country of origin (U.S. versus imported) for each of 69 beers.

Your task is to write a report based on a complete evaluation comparing and contrasting price, calories, and alcohol content based on type of beer—craft lager, craft ale, imported lager, regular and ice beer, and light and nonalcoholic beer.

Source: "Beers." Copyright © 1996 by Consumers Union of U.S., Inc., Yonkers, NY 10703-1057. Adapted with permission from Consumer Reports, *June 1996.*

TEAM PROJECT

The data file MUTUALFUNDS2004 contains information regarding 12 variables from a sample of 121 mutual funds. The variables are:

Fund—The name of the mutual fund.

Category—Type of stocks comprising the mutual fund—small cap, mid cap, large cap

Objective—Objective of stocks comprising the mutual fund—growth or value

Assets—In millions of dollars

Fees—Sales charges (no or yes)

Expense ratio—expenses as a percentage of net assets

2003 Return—Twelve-month return in 2003

Three-year return—Annualized return 2001–2003

Five-year return—Annualized return 1999–2003

Risk—Risk-of-loss factor of the mutual fund classified as low, average, or high

Best quarter—Best quarterly performance 1999–2003

Worst quarter—Worst quarterly performance 1999–2003

10.104 Completely analyze the difference between mutual funds without fees and mutual funds with fees in terms of 2003 return, 3-year return, and the 5-year return. Write a report summarizing your findings.

10.105 How did the different types of mutual funds as categorized by their type (small cap, mid cap, large cap) perform during 2003, the three-year period from 2001–2003, and the five-year period from 1999–2003? Completely analyze these data at the 0.05 level of significance and write a report summarizing your conclusions.

RUNNING CASE
MANAGING THE *SPRINGVILLE HERALD*

Phase 1

A marketing department team is charged with improving the telemarketing process in order to increase the number of home-delivery subscriptions sold. After several brainstorming sessions, it was clear that the longer a caller speaks to a respondent the greater is the chance that the caller will sell a home-delivery subscription. Therefore, the team decided to find ways to increase the length of the phone calls.

Initially, the team investigated the impact that time of call might have on the length of the call. Under current arrangements, calls were made in the evening hours between 5:00 P.M. and 9:00 P.M., Monday through Friday. The team wanted to compare length of calls made early in the evening (before 7:00 P.M.) with those made later in the evening (after 7:00 P.M.) to determine whether one of these time periods is more conducive to lengthier calls and, correspondingly, to increased subscription sales. The team selected a sample of 30 female callers who staff the telephone bank on Wednesday evenings and randomly assigned 15 of them to the "early" group and 15 to the "later" group. The callers knew that the team was observing their efforts that evening but didn't know which calls were monitored. The callers had been trained to make their telephone presentations in a structured manner. They were to read from a script and their greeting was personal but informal ("Hi, this is Mary Jones from the *Springville Herald*—may I speak to Bill Richards?").

Measurements were taken on the length of call (defined as the difference, in seconds, between the time the person answers the phone and the time he or she hangs up). The results are presented in Table SH10.1. **SH10-1**

TABLE SH10.1

Length of Calls in Seconds Based on Time of Call— Early Versus Late in the Evening

Time of Call		Time of Call	
Early	**Late**	**Early**	**Late**
41.3	37.1	40.6	40.7
37.5	38.9	33.3	38.0
39.3	42.2	39.6	43.6
37.4	45.7	35.7	43.8
33.6	42.4	31.3	34.9
38.5	39.0	36.8	35.7
32.6	40.9	36.3	47.4
37.3	40.5		

EXERCISES

SH10.1 Analyze the data in Table SH10.1 and write a report to the marketing department team that indicates your findings. Include an attached appendix in which you discuss the reason you selected a particular statistical test to compare the two independent groups of callers.

SH10.2 Suppose that instead of the research design described here, there were only 15 callers sampled and each caller was to be monitored twice in the evening, once in the early time period and once in the later time period. Suppose that in Table SH10.1 each pair of values represents a particular caller's two measurements. Reanalyze these data and write a report for presentation to the team that indicates your findings.

SH10.3 What other variables should be investigated next? Why?

DO NOT CONTINUE UNTIL THE PHASE 1 EXERCISE HAS BEEN COMPLETED.

Phase 2

In studying the home delivery solicitation process the marketing department team determined that the so-called "later" calls made between 7:00 P.M. and 9:00 P.M. were significantly more conducive to lengthier calls than those made earlier in the evening (between 5:00 P.M. to 7:00 P.M.).

Knowing that the 7:00 P.M. to 9:00 P.M. time period is superior, the team sought to investigate the effect of the type of presentation on the length of the call. A group of 24 female callers were randomly assigned, 8 each, to one of three presentation plans—structured, semistructured, and unstructured—and were trained to make the telephone presentation. All calls were made between 7:00 P.M. and 9:00 P.M., the later time period, and the callers were to provide an introductory greeting that was personal but informal ("Hi, this is Mary Jones from the *Springville Herald*—may I speak to Bill Richards?"). The callers knew that the team was observing their efforts that evening but didn't know which particular calls were monitored. Measurements were taken on the length of call (defined as the difference, in seconds, between the time the person answers the phone and the time he or she hangs up). Table SH10.2 presents the results. **SH10-2**

TABLE SH10.2

Length of Calls (in Seconds) Based on Presentation Plan

Presentation Plan		
Structured	**Semi-structured**	**Unstructured**
38.8	41.8	32.9
42.1	36.4	36.1
45.2	39.1	39.2
34.8	28.7	29.3
48.3	36.4	41.9
37.8	36.1	31.7
41.1	35.8	35.2
43.6	33.7	38.1

EXERCISE

SH10.4 Analyze these data and write a report to the team that indicates your findings. Be sure to include your recommendations based on your findings. Also, include an appendix in which you discuss the reason you selected a particular statistical test to compare the three independent groups of callers.

WEB CASE

Apply your knowledge about hypothesis testing in this Web Case that continues the cereal-fill packaging dispute Web Case from Chapters 7 and 9.

After Oxford Cereals conducted its public experiment about cereal box weights, the TriCities Consumers Concerned About Cereal Companies That Cheat (TCCACCTC) remains unconvinced that Oxford Cereals has not misled the public. The group has created and posted a document in which they claim that cereal boxes produced at Plant Number 2 in Springville always weigh less than the claimed 368 grams. Review the group's document and its data sample at the TCCACCTC Web site **www.prenhall.com/Springville/MoreOnCheaters.htm** and then answer the following:

1. Do the TCCACCTC's results prove that there is a statistical difference in the mean weights of cereal boxes produced at Plant Numbers 1 and 2?

2. Perform the appropriate analysis to test the TCCACCTC's hypothesis. What conclusions can you reach based on their data?

After the TCCACCTC's latest posting, Oxford Cereals has complained that the group is guilty of using selective data. Review the company's response on its Web site **www.prenhall.com/Springville/OC_SelectiveData.htm** and then answer the following.

3. Does Oxford Cereals have a legitimate argument? Why, or why not?

4. Assuming that the samples the company has posted were randomly selected, perform the appropriate analysis to resolve the ongoing weight dispute.

5. What conclusions can you draw from your results? If you were called as an expert witness, would you support the claims of the TCCACCTC or the claims of Oxford Cereals? Explain.

REFERENCES

1. Berenson, M., D. Levine, T. Krehbiel, *Basic Business Statistics: Concepts and Applications*, 10th ed. (Upper Saddle River, N.J.: Prentice-Hall, 2006).
2. Conover, W. J., *Practical Nonparametric Statistics*, 3rd ed. (New York: Wiley, 2000).
3. *Microsoft Excel 2003* (Redmond, WA: Microsoft Corp., 2003).
4. *Minitab for Windows Version 14* (State College, PA: Minitab Inc., 2004).
5. Hicks, C. R., and K. V. Turner, *Fundamental Concepts in the Design of Experiments*, 5th ed. (New York: Oxford University Press, 1999).
6. Kramer, C. Y., "Extension of Multiple Range Tests to Group Means with Unequal Numbers of Replications," *Biometrics* 12 (1956): 307–310.
7. Montgomery, D. M., *Design and Analysis of Experiments*, 6th ed. (New York: John Wiley, 2005).
8. Satterthwaite, F. E., "An Approximate Distribution of Estimates of Variance Components," *Biometrics Bulletin*, 2 (1946): 110–114.
9. Snedecor, G. W., and W. G. Cochran, *Statistical Methods*, 7th ed. (Ames, IA: Iowa State University Press, 1980).
10. *SPSS Base 12.0 Brief Guide* (Upper Saddle River, NJ: Prentice Hall, 2003).
11. Tukey, J. W., "Comparing Individual Means in the Analysis of Variance," *Biometrics* 5 (1949): 99–114.
12. Winer, B. J., *Statistical Principles in Experimental Design*, 2nd ed. (New York: McGraw-Hill, 1971).

CHAPTER 11

Chi-Square Tests

USING STATISTICS: Guest Satisfaction at T.C. Resort Properties

LEARNING OBJECTIVES

In this chapter, you learn:

- How and when to use the chi-square test for contingency tables

- How to use the Marascuilo procedure for determining pairwise differences when evaluating more than two proportions

USING STATISTICS

Guest Satisfaction at T.C. Resort Properties

You are the manager of T.C. Resort Properties, a collection of five upscale hotels located on two resort islands. Guests who are satisfied with the quality of services during their stay are more likely to return on a future vacation and to recommend the hotel to friends and relatives. To assess the quality of services being provided by your hotels, guests are encouraged to complete a satisfaction survey when they check out. You need to analyze the data from these surveys to determine the overall satisfaction with the services provided, the likelihood that the guests will return to the hotel, and the reasons some guests indicate that they will not return. For example, on one island, T.C. Resort Properties operates the Beachcomber and Windsurfer hotels. Is the perceived quality at the Beachcomber Hotel the same as the Windsurfer Hotel? If a difference is present, how can you use this information to improve the overall quality of service at T.C. Resort Properties? Furthermore, if guests indicate that they are not planning to return, what are the most common reasons given for this decision? Are the reasons given unique to a certain hotel or common to all hotels operated by T.C. Resort Properties?

In the preceding two chapters you used hypothesis-testing procedures to analyze both numerical and categorical data. Chapter 9 presented a variety of one-sample tests. Chapter 10 developed several two-sample tests as well as the one-way analysis of variance (ANOVA). This chapter extends hypothesis-testing to analyze differences between population proportions based on two or more samples, as well as the hypothesis of *independence* in the joint responses to two categorical variables.

11.1 CHI-SQUARE TEST FOR THE DIFFERENCE BETWEEN TWO PROPORTIONS (INDEPENDENT SAMPLES)

In section 10.3, you studied the Z test for the difference between two proportions. In this section, the data are examined from a different perspective. The hypothesis-testing procedure uses a test statistic that is approximated by a chi-square (χ^2) distribution. The results of this χ^2 test are equivalent to those of the Z test described in section 10.3.

If you are interested in comparing the counts of categorical responses between two independent groups, you can develop a two-way **cross-classification table** (see section 2.4) to display the frequency of occurrence of successes and failures for each group. This table is called a **contingency table**, and was used in Chapter 4 to define and study probability.

To illustrate the contingency table, return to the "Using Statistics" scenario concerning T.C. Resort Properties above. On one of the islands, T.C. Resort Properties has two hotels (the Beachcomber and the Windsurfer). In tabulating the responses to the single question, "Are you likely to choose this hotel again?" 163 of 227 guests at the Beachcomber responded yes, and 154 of 262 guests at the Windsurfer responded yes. At the 0.05 level of significance, is there evidence of a significant difference in guest satisfaction (as measured by likelihood to return to the hotel) between the two hotels?

The contingency table displayed in Table 11.1 has two rows and two columns and is called a **2 × 2 table**. The cells in the table indicate the frequency for each row and column combination.

TABLE 11.1

Layout of a 2 × 2 Contingency Table

	COLUMN VARIABLE (GROUP)		
ROW VARIABLE	**1**	**2**	**Totals**
Successes	X_1	X_2	X
Failures	$n_1 - X_1$	$n_2 - X_2$	$n - X$
Totals	n_1	n_2	n

where

X_1 = number of successes in group 1

X_2 = number of successes in group 2

$n_1 - X_1$ = number of failures in group 1

$n_2 - X_2$ = number of failures in group 2

$X = X_1 + X_2$ is the total number of successes

$n - X = (n_1 - X_1) + (n_2 - X_2)$ is the total number of failures

n_1 = the sample size in group 1

n_2 = the sample size in group 2

$n = n_1 + n_2$ = the total sample size

Table 11.2 contains the contingency table for the hotel guest satisfaction study. The contingency table has two rows, indicating whether the guests would return to the hotel (i.e., success) or would not return to the hotel (i.e., failure), and two columns, one for each hotel. The cells in the table indicate the frequency of each row and column combination. The row totals indicate the number of guests who would return to the hotel and those who would not return to the hotel. The column totals are the sample sizes for each hotel location.

TABLE 11.2

2 × 2 Contingency Table for the Guest Satisfaction Survey

	HOTEL		
CHOOSE HOTEL AGAIN?	**Beachcomber**	**Windsurfer**	**Total**
Yes	163	154	317
No	64	108	172
Total	227	262	489

To test whether the population proportion of guests who would return to the Beachcomber π_1 is equal to the population proportion of guests who would return to the Windsurfer π_2, you can use the χ^2 test for equality of proportions. To test the null hypothesis that there is no difference between the two population proportions:

$$H_0: \pi_1 = \pi_2$$

against the alternative that the two population proportions are not the same:

$$H_1: \pi_1 \neq \pi_2$$

you use the χ^2-test statistic, shown in Equation (11.1).

χ^2 TEST FOR THE DIFFERENCE BETWEEN TWO PROPORTIONS

The χ^2-test statistic is equal to the squared difference between the observed and expected frequencies, divided by the expected frequency in each cell of the table, summed over all cells of the table.

$$\chi^2 = \sum_{all\ cells} \frac{(f_0 - f_e)^2}{f_e} \qquad (11.1)$$

where f_0 = **observed frequency** in a particular cell of a contingency table
          f_e = **expected frequency** in a particular cell if the null hypothesis is true

The test statistic χ^2 approximately follows a chi-square distribution with 1 degree of freedom.

To compute the expected frequency, f_e, in any cell, you need to understand that if the null hypothesis is true, the proportion of successes in the two populations will be equal. Then the sample proportions you compute from each of the two groups would differ from each other only by chance and each would provide an estimate of the common population parameter π. A statistic that combines these two separate estimates together into one overall estimate of the population parameter π provides more information than either one of the two separate estimates could provide by itself. This statistic, given by the symbol $\bar{p}$, represents the estimated overall proportion of successes for the two groups combined (i.e., the total number of successes divided by the total sample size). The complement of $\bar{p}$, $1 - \bar{p}$, represents the overall proportion of failures in the two groups. Using the notation presented in Table 11.1, Equation (11.2) defines $\bar{p}$.

COMPUTING THE ESTIMATED OVERALL PROPORTION

$$\bar{p} = \frac{X_1 + X_2}{n_1 + n_2} = \frac{X}{n} \qquad (11.2)$$

To compute the expected frequency, f_e, for each cell pertaining to success (i.e., the cells in the first row in the contingency table), multiply the sample size (or column total) for a group by $\bar{p}$. To compute the expected frequency, f_e, for each cell pertaining to failure (i.e., the cells in the second row in the contingency table), multiply the sample size (or column total) for a group by $(1 - \bar{p})$.

The test statistic shown in Equation (11.1) approximately follows a **chi-square distribution** (see Table E.4) with one degree of freedom. Using a level of significance α, you reject the null hypothesis if the computed χ^2 test statistic is greater than χ^2_U, the upper-tail critical value from the χ^2 distribution having one degree of freedom. Thus, the decision rule is

$$\text{reject } H_0 \text{ if } \chi^2 > \chi^2_U;$$

otherwise do not reject H_0.

Figure 11.1 illustrates the decision rule.

FIGURE 11.1

Regions of Rejection and Nonrejection When Using the Chi-Square Test for the Difference Between Two Proportions with Level of Significance α

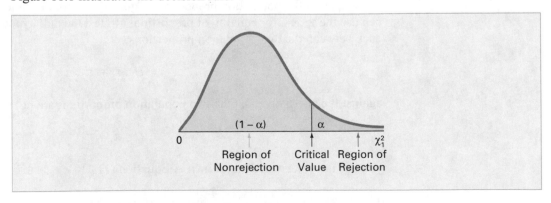

If the null hypothesis is true, the computed χ^2 statistic should be close to zero because the squared difference between what is actually observed in each cell, f_0, and what is theoretically expected, f_e, should be very small. If H_0 is false, and there are real differences in the population proportions, the computed χ^2 statistic is expected to be large. However, what constitutes a large difference in a cell is relative. The same actual difference between f_0 and f_e from a cell with a small number of expected frequencies contributes more to the χ^2 test statistic than a cell with a large number of expected frequencies.

To illustrate the use of the chi-square test for the difference between two proportions, return to the "Using Statistics" scenario, concerning T.C. Resort Properties and the corresponding contingency table displayed in Table 11.2. The null hypothesis (H_0: $\pi_1 = \pi_2$) states that there is no difference between the proportion of guests who are likely to choose either of these hotels again. From Equation (11.2), you use $\bar{p}$ to estimate the common parameter π, the population proportion of guests who are likely to choose the Beachcomber Hotel again and the proportion of guests who are likely to choose the Windsurfer Hotel again. To begin, calculate $\bar{p}$ using Equation (11.2):

$$\bar{p} = \frac{X_1 + X_2}{n_1 + n_2} = \frac{163 + 154}{227 + 262} = \frac{317}{489} = 0.6483$$

$\bar{p}$ is the estimate of the common parameter π, the population proportion of guests who are likely to choose either of these hotels again if the null hypothesis is true. The estimated proportion of guests who are *not* likely to choose these hotels again is the complement of $\bar{p}$, $1 - 0.6483 = 0.3517$. Multiplying these two proportions by the sample size for the Beachcomber Hotel gives the number of guests expected to choose the Beachcomber again and the number not expected to choose this hotel again. In a similar manner, multiplying the two respective proportions by the Windsurfer Hotel's sample size yields the corresponding expected frequencies for that group.

EXAMPLE 11.1

COMPUTING THE EXPECTED FREQUENCIES

Compute the expected frequencies for each of the four cells of Table 11.2.

SOLUTION

Yes—Beachcomber: $\bar{p} = 0.6483$ and $n_1 = 227$, so $f_e = 147.16$
Yes—Windsurfer: $\bar{p} = 0.6483$ and $n_2 = 262$, so $f_e = 169.84$
No—Beachcomber: $1 - \bar{p} = 0.3517$ and $n_1 = 227$, so $f_e = 79.84$
No—Windsurfer: $1 - \bar{p} = 0.3517$ and $n_2 = 262$, so $f_e = 92.16$

Table 11.3 presents these expected frequencies next to the corresponding observed frequencies.

TABLE 11.3

2 × 2 Contingency Table for Comparing the Observed (f_0) and Expected (f_e) Frequencies

HOTEL	BEACHCOMBER		WINDSURFER		
CHOOSE HOTEL AGAIN?	Observed	Expected	Observed	Expected	Total
Yes	163	147.16	154	169.84	317
No	64	79.84	108	92.16	172
Total	227	227.00	262	262.00	489

To test the null hypothesis that the population proportions are equal

$$H_0: \pi_1 = \pi_2$$

against the alternative that the population proportions are not equal

$$H_1: \pi_1 \neq \pi_2$$

you use the observed and expected frequencies from Table 11.3 to compute the χ^2-test statistic given by Equation (11.1). Table 11.4 presents the calculations.

TABLE 11.4

Computation of χ^2-Test Statistic for the Guest Satisfaction Survey

f_o	f_e	$(f_o - f_e)$	$(f_o - f_e)^2$	$(f_o - f_e)^2/f_e$
163	147.16	15.84	250.9056	1.705
154	169.84	−15.84	250.9056	1.477
64	79.84	−15.84	250.9056	3.143
108	92.16	15.84	250.9056	2.723
				9.048

The chi-square distribution is a right-skewed distribution whose shape depends solely on the number of degrees of freedom. As the number of degrees of freedom increases, the chi-square distribution becomes more symmetrical. You find the critical value of the χ^2-test statistic from Table E.4, a portion of which is presented as Table 11.5.

The values in Table 11.5 refer to selected upper-tail areas of the χ^2 distribution. A 2×2 contingency table has $(2 - 1)(2 - 1) = 1$ degree of freedom. Using $\alpha = 0.05$, with one degree of freedom, the critical value of χ^2 from Table 11.5 is 3.841. You reject H_0 if the computed χ^2 statistic is greater than 3.841 (see Figure 11.2). Since $9.048 > 3.841$, you reject H_0. You conclude that there is a difference in the proportion of guests who would return to the Beachcomber and the Windsurfer.

TABLE 11.5

Finding the χ^2 Critical Value from the Chi-Square Distribution with 1 Degree of Freedom Using the 0.05 Level of Significance

			Upper-Tail Area				
Degrees of Freedom	.995	.99	...	.05	.025	.01	.005
1			...	3.841	5.024	6.635	7.879
2	0.010	0.020	...	5.991	7.378	9.210	10.597
3	0.072	0.115	...	7.815	9.348	11.345	12.838
4	0.207	0.297	...	9.488	11.143	13.277	14.860
5	0.412	0.554	...	11.071	12.833	15.086	16.750

FIGURE 11.2

Regions of Rejection and Nonrejection When Finding the χ^2 Critical Value with 1 Degree of Freedom at the 0.05 Level of Significance

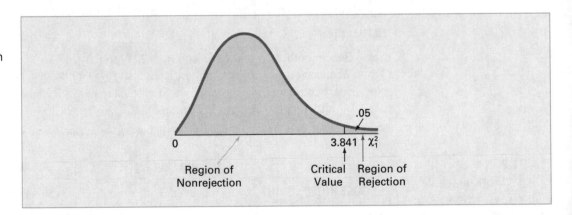

Figure 11.3 represents a Microsoft Excel worksheet for the guest satisfaction contingency table (Table 11.2), while Figure 11.4 illustrates Minitab output. These outputs include the expected frequencies, χ^2-test statistic, degrees of freedom, and p-value. The χ^2-test statistic is 9.05, which is greater than the critical value of 3.841 (or the p-value = 0.0026 < 0.05), so you reject the null hypothesis that there is no difference in guest satisfaction between the two hotels. The p-value of 0.0026 is the probability of observing sample proportions as different as or more different than the actual difference ($0.718 - 0.588 = 0.13$ observed in the sample data), if the population proportions for the Beachcomber and Windsurfer hotels are equal. Thus, there is strong evidence to conclude that the two hotels are significantly different with respect to guest satisfaction as measured by whether the guest is likely to return to the hotel again. An examination of Table 11.3 indicates that a greater proportion of guests at the Beachcomber are likely to return than at the Windsurfer.

FIGURE 11.3

Microsoft Excel Worksheet for the Guest Satisfaction Data

	A	B	C	D	E	F	G
1	**Guest Satisfaction Analysis**						
2							
3		**Observed Frequencies**					
4			Hotel			Calculations	
5	**Choose Again?**	**Beachcomber**	**Windsurfer**	**Total**		fo-fe	
6	Yes	163	154	317		15.84458	-15.8446
7	No	64	108	172		-15.8446	15.84458
8	Total	227	262	489			
9							
10		Expected Frequencies					
11			Hotel				
12	Choose Again?	Beachcomber	Windsurfer	Total		(fo-fe)^2/fe	
13	Yes	147.1554	169.8446	317		1.70602A	1.47012
14	No	79.8446	92.1554	172		3.144243	2.72421
15	Total	227	262	489			
16							
17		**Data**					
18	**Level of Significance**	0.05					
19	Number of Rows	2					
20	Number of Columns	2					
21	Degrees of Freedom	1					
22							
23		**Results**					
24	**Critical Value**	3.8415					
25	**Chi-Square Test Statistic**	9.0526					
26	**p-Value**	0.0026					
27	**Reject the null hypothesis**						
28							
29	*Expected frequency assumption*						
30	*is met.*						

FIGURE 11.4

Minitab Output for the Guest Satisfaction Data

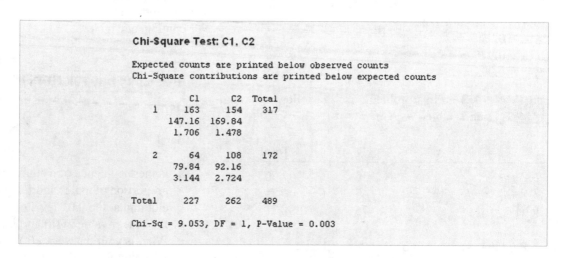

```
Chi-Square Test: C1, C2

Expected counts are printed below observed counts
Chi-Square contributions are printed below expected counts

           C1       C2   Total
    1     163      154    317
       147.16   169.84
        1.706    1.478

    2      64      108    172
        79.84    92.16
        3.144    2.724

Total    227      262    489

Chi-Sq = 9.053, DF = 1, P-Value = 0.003
```

For the χ^2 test to give accurate results for a 2×2 table, you must assume that each expected frequency is at least 5. If this assumption is not satisfied, you can use alternative procedures such as Fisher's exact test (see references 1, 2, and 4).

In the hotel guest satisfaction survey, both the Z test based on the standardized normal distribution (see section 10.3) and the χ^2 test based on the chi-square distribution have led to the same conclusion. You can explain this result by the interrelationship between the standardized normal distribution and a chi-square distribution with 1 degree of freedom. For such situations, the χ^2-test statistic is the square of the Z-test statistic. For instance, in the guest satisfaction study, the computed Z-test statistic is $+3.01$ and the computed χ^2-test statistic is 9.05. Except for rounding error, this latter value is the square of $+3.01$ [i.e., $(+3.01)^2 = 9.05$]. Also, if you compare the critical values of the test statistics from the two distributions, at the 0.05 level of significance, the χ_1^2 value of 3.841 is the square of the Z value of ± 1.96 (i.e., $\chi_1^2 = Z^2$). Furthermore, the p-values for both tests are equal. Therefore, when testing the null hypothesis of equality of proportions:

$$H_0: \pi_1 = \pi_2$$

against the alternative that the population proportions are not equal:

$$H_1: \pi_1 \neq \pi_2$$

the Z test and the χ^2 test are equivalent methods. However, if you are interested in determining whether there is evidence of a *directional* difference, such as $\pi_1 > \pi_2$, then you must use the Z test with the entire rejection region located in one tail of the standardized normal distribution. In section 11.2, the χ^2 test is extended to make comparisons and evaluate differences between the proportions among more than two groups. However, you cannot use the Z test if there are more than two groups.

PROBLEMS FOR SECTION 11.1

Learning the Basics

11.1 Determine the critical value of χ^2 in each of the following circumstances:
a. $\alpha = 0.01, n = 16$
b. $\alpha = 0.025, n = 11$
c. $\alpha = 0.05, n = 8$

11.2 Determine the critical value of χ^2 in each of the following circumstances:
a. $\alpha = 0.95, n = 28$
b. $\alpha = 0.975, n = 21$
c. $\alpha = 0.99, n = 5$

PH Grade ASSIST **11.3** In this problem, use the following contingency table:

	A	B	Total
1	20	30	50
2	30	45	75
Total	50	75	125

a. Find the expected frequency for each cell.
b. Compare the observed and expected frequencies for each cell.
c. Compute the χ^2 statistic. Is it significant at $\alpha = 0.05$?

PH Grade ASSIST **11.4** For this problem, use the following contingency table:

	A	B	Total
1	20	30	50
2	30	20	50
Total	50	50	100

a. Find the expected frequency for each cell.
b. Find the χ^2 statistic for this contingency table. Is it significant at $\alpha = 0.05$?

Applying the Concepts

You can solve problems 11.5–11.10 manually or by using Microsoft Excel or Minitab.

PH Grade ASSIST **11.5** A sample of 500 shoppers was selected in a large metropolitan area to determine various information concerning consumer behavior. Among the questions asked was, "Do you enjoy shopping for clothing?" The results are summarized in the following contingency table:

ENJOY SHOPPING FOR CLOTHING	Male	Female	Total
Yes	136	224	360
No	104	36	140
Total	240	260	500

a. Is there evidence of a significant difference between the proportion of males and females who enjoy shopping for clothing at the 0.01 level of significance?
b. Find the *p*-value in (a) and interpret its meaning.
c. What is your answer to (a) and (b) if 206 males enjoyed shopping for clothing?
d. Compare the results of (a) through (c) to those of problem 10.33 (a) through (c).

11.6 Is good gas mileage a priority for car shoppers? A survey conducted by Progressive Insurance asked this question of both men and women shopping for new cars. The data were reported as percentages, and no sample sizes were given.

GAS MILEAGE A PRIORITY?	Men	Women
Yes	76%	84%
No	24%	16%

Source: Extracted from Snapshots, *USAtoday.com, June 21, 2004.*

a. Assume that 50 men and 50 women were included in the survey. At the 0.05 level of significance, is there a difference between males and females in the proportion who make gas mileage a priority?

b. Assume that 500 men and 500 women were included in the survey. At the 0.05 level of significance, is there a difference between males and females in the proportion who make gas mileage a priority?

c. Discuss the effect of sample size on the chi-square test.

11.7 The results of a yield improvement study at a semiconductor manufacturing facility provided defect data for a sample of 450 wafers. The following contingency table presents a summary of the responses to two questions: "Was a particle found on the die that produced the wafer?" and "Is the wafer good or bad?"

| PARTICLES | QUALITY OF WAFER | | |
	Good	Bad	Totals
Yes	14	36	50
No	320	80	400
Totals	334	116	450

Source: S. W. Hall, "Analysis of Defectivity of Semiconductor Wafers by Contingency Table," Proceedings Institute of Environmental Sciences, Vol. 1 (1994), 177–183.

a. At the 0.05 level of significance, is there a difference between the proportion of good and bad wafers that have particles?

b. Determine the p-value in (a) and interpret its meaning.

c. What conclusions can you draw from this analysis?

d. Compare the results of (a) and (b) to those of problem 10.35.

 11.8 A study conducted by Ariel Mutual Funds and the Charles Schwab Corporation surveyed 500 African Americans with an annual income above $50,000, and 500 whites with an annual income above $50,000. The results indicated that 74% of the African Americans and 84% of the whites owned stocks (Cheryl Winokur Munk, "Stock-Ownership Race Gap Shrinks," *The Wall Street Journal*, June 13, 2002, B11).

a. Is there a difference between the proportion of African Americans with incomes above $50,000 who invest in stocks and the proportion of whites with incomes above $50,000 who invest in stocks? (Use $\alpha = 0.05$.)

b. Determine the p-value in (a) and interpret its meaning.

c. Compare the results of (a) and (b) to those of problem 10.39.

11.9 Nonresponses are a problem for most mail surveys. Researchers at John Carroll University conducted a study to see if prenotification sent via postcards one week prior to sending a survey would decrease the nonresponse rate (Paul R. Murphy and James M. Daley, "Postcard Prenotification in Industrial Surveys: Further evidence," *Mid-American Journal of Business*, Spring 2002, 17(1):51–57). A total of 345 U.S.-based international freight forwarders were divided into two groups. One group was prenotified via a postcard that a mail survey concerning contemporary issues facing international freight forwarders would be arriving in one week. The second group received no prenotification of the mail survey. Results from the study are given in the following table.

| RESULT | TREATMENT GROUP | | |
	Prenotified	Not Prenotified	Total
Responded	39	41	80
Nonresponse	142	123	265
Total	181	164	345

Source: Extracted from Paul R. Murphy and James M. Daley, "Postcard Prenotification in Industrial Surveys: Further Evidence," Mid-American Journal of Business, Spring 2002, 17(1):51–57.

a. At the 0.05 level of significance, is there a difference between the two groups in the proportion of survey recipients who responded to the survey?

b. Find the p-value in (a) and interpret its meaning.

PH Grade ASSIST **11.10** A survey suggests that brand names are less important to consumers when purchasing clothing than they used to be. Of 7,500 apparel customers, 57% said that logos, labels, and trademarks of clothing have less personal importance today than a few years ago, while only 10% said they have more (Shelly Branch, "What's in a Name? Not Much According to Clothes Shoppers," *The Wall Street Journal*, July 16, 2002, B4). The study also investigated whether this change in the importance of brand name differed between female shoppers and male shoppers. The following table indicates the gender of respondents and whether they said that logos, labels, and trademarks of clothing have more personal importance today than a few years ago:

| IMPORTANCE OF BRAND NAME | GENDER | | |
	Male	Female	Total
More	450	300	750
Equal or less	3,300	3,450	6,750
Total	3,750	3,750	7,500

Source: Extracted from Shelly Branch, "What's in a Name? Not Much According to Clothes Shoppers," The Wall Street Journal, July 16, 2002, B4.

a. Is there a difference between the proportion of males and females who place more importance on brand names today than a few years ago? (Use $\alpha = 0.05$.)

b. Find the p-value in (a) and interpret its meaning.

11.2   CHI-SQUARE TEST FOR DIFFERENCES AMONG MORE THAN TWO PROPORTIONS

In this section, the χ^2 test is extended to compare more than two independent populations. The letter c is used to represent the number of independent populations under consideration. Thus, the contingency table now has two rows and c columns. To test the null hypothesis that there are no differences among the c proportions:

$$H_0 : \pi_1 = \pi_2 = \cdots = \pi_c$$

against the alternative that not all the c population proportions are equal:

$$H_1 : \text{Not all } \pi_j \text{ are equal (where } j = 1, 2, \ldots, c)$$

use Equation (11.1)

$$\chi^2 = \sum_{all \text{ cells}} \frac{(f_0 - f_e)^2}{f_e}$$

where f_0 = observed frequency in a particular cell of a $2 \times c$ contingency table

f_e = expected frequency in a particular cell if the null hypothesis is true

If the null hypothesis is true and the proportions are equal across all c populations, then the c sample proportions should differ only by chance. In such a situation, a statistic that combines these c separate estimates into one overall estimate of the population proportion π provides more information than any one of the c separate estimates alone. To expand on Equation (11.2), the statistic $\bar{p}$ in Equation (11.3) represents the estimated overall proportion for all c groups combined.

COMPUTING THE ESTIMATED OVERALL PROPORTION FOR c GROUPS

$$\bar{p} = \frac{X_1 + X_2 + \cdots + X_c}{n_1 + n_2 + \cdots + n_c} = \frac{X}{n} \qquad \textbf{(11.3)}$$

To compute the expected frequency f_e for each cell in the first row in the contingency table, multiply each sample size (or column total) by $\bar{p}$. To compute the expected frequency f_e for each cell in the second row in the contingency table, multiply each sample size (or column total) by $(1 - \bar{p})$. The test statistic shown in Equation (11.1) approximately follows a chi-square distribution with degrees of freedom equal to the number of rows in the contingency table minus 1, times the number of columns in the table minus 1. For a **$2 \times c$ contingency table**, there are $c - 1$ degrees of freedom:

$$\text{Degrees of freedom} = (2 - 1)(c - 1) = c - 1$$

Using a level of significance α, you reject the null hypothesis if the computed χ^2-test statistic is greater than χ_U^2, the upper-tail critical value from a chi-square distribution having $c - 1$ degrees of freedom. Therefore, the decision rule is

$$\text{Reject } H_0 \text{ if } \chi^2 > \chi_U^2;$$

otherwise do not reject H_0.

Figure 11.5 illustrates the decision rule.

FIGURE 11.5

Regions of Rejection and Nonrejection When Testing for Differences Among c Proportions Using the χ^2 Test

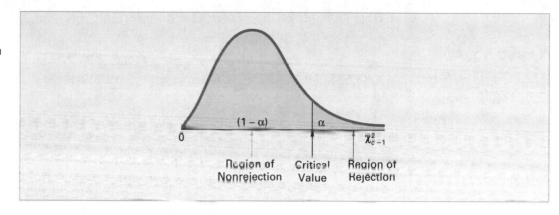

To illustrate the χ^2 test for equality of proportions when there are more than two groups, return to the "Using Statistics" scenario concerning T.C. Resort Properties. A similar survey was recently conducted on a different island in which T.C. Resort Properties has three different hotels. Table 11.6 presents the responses to a question concerning whether guests would be likely to choose their hotel again.

TABLE 11.6

2 × 3 Contingency Table for the Guest Satisfaction Survey

	HOTEL			
CHOOSE HOTEL AGAIN	**Golden Palm**	**Palm Royale**	**Palm Princess**	**Total**
Yes	128	199	186	513
No	88	33	66	187
Total	216	232	252	700

Since the null hypothesis states that there are no differences among the three hotels with respect to the proportion of guests who would likely return again, use Equation (11.3) to calculate an estimate of π, the population proportion of guests who would likely return again.

$$\bar{p} = \frac{X_1 + X_2 + \cdots + X_c}{n_1 + n_2 + \cdots + n_c} = \frac{X}{n}$$

$$= \frac{(128 + 199 + 186)}{(216 + 232 + 252)} = \frac{513}{700}$$

$$= 0.733$$

The estimated overall proportion of guests who would *not* be likely to return again is the complement $(1 - \bar{p})$, or 0.267. Multiplying these two proportions by the sample size taken at each hotel yields the expected number of guests who would and would not likely return.

EXAMPLE 11.2

COMPUTING THE EXPECTED FREQUENCIES

Compute the expected frequencies for each of the six cells in Table 11.6.

SOLUTION

Yes—Golden Palm: $\bar{p} = 0.733$ and $n_1 = 216$, so $f_e = 158.30$
Yes—Palm Royale: $\bar{p} = 0.733$ and $n_2 = 232$, so $f_e = 170.02$
Yes—Palm Princess: $\bar{p} = 0.733$ and $n_3 = 252$, so $f_e = 184.68$
No—Golden Palm: $1 - \bar{p} = 0.267$ and $n_1 = 216$, so $f_e = 57.70$
No—Palm Royale: $1 - \bar{p} = 0.267$ and $n_2 = 232$, so $f_e = 61.98$
No—Palm Princess: $1 - \bar{p} = 0.267$ and $n_3 = 252$, so $f_e = 67.32$

Table 11.7 presents these expected frequencies.

TABLE 11.7

Cross-Classification of Expected Frequencies from a Guest Satisfaction Survey of Three Hotels

	HOTEL			
CHOOSE HOTEL AGAIN?	**Golden Palm**	**Palm Royale**	**Palm Princess**	**Total**
Yes	158.30	170.02	184.68	513
No	57.70	61.98	67.32	187
Total	216.00	232.00	252.00	700

To test the null hypothesis that the proportions are equal:

$$H_0: \pi_1 = \pi_2 = \pi_3$$

against the alternative that not all three proportions are equal:

$$H_1: \text{Not all } \pi_j \text{ are equal (where } j = 1, 2, 3)$$

use the observed and expected frequencies from Table 11.6 and Table 11.7 above to compute the χ^2-test statistic given by Equation (11.1). Table 11.8 presents the computations.

TABLE 11.8

Computation of χ^2-Test Statistic for the Guest Satisfaction Survey of Three Hotels

f_O	f_e	$(f_O - f_e)$	$(f_O - f_e)^2$	$(f_O - f_e)^2/f_e$
128	158.30	−30.30	918.0900	5.800
199	170.02	28.98	839.8404	4.940
186	184.68	1.32	1.7424	0.009
88	57.70	30.30	918.0900	15.911
33	61.98	−28.98	839.8404	13.550
66	67.32	−1.32	1.7424	0.026
				40.236

You find the critical value of the χ^2-test statistic from Table E.4. In the guest satisfaction survey, because three hotels are evaluated, there are $(2 - 1)(3 - 1) = 2$ degrees of freedom. Using $\alpha = 0.05$, the χ^2 critical value with 2 degrees of freedom is 5.991. Because the computed test statistic ($\chi^2 = 40.236$) is greater than this critical value, you reject the null hypothesis (see Figure 11.6). Microsoft Excel (see Figure 11.7) and Minitab (see Figure 11.8) also report the p-value. Since the p-value is approximately 0.0000, which is less than $\alpha = 0.05$, you reject the null hypothesis. Further, this p-value indicates that there is virtually no chance to see differences this large or larger among the three sample proportions, if the population proportions for the three hotels are equal. Thus, there is sufficient evidence to conclude that the hotel properties are different with respect to the proportion of guests who are likely to return.

FIGURE 11.6

Regions of Rejection and Nonrejection When Testing for Differences in Three Proportions at the 0.05 Level of Significance with 2 Degrees of Freedom

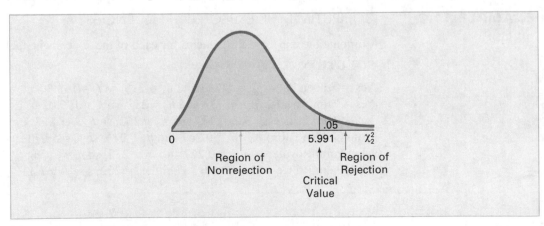

FIGURE 11.7

Microsoft Excel
Worksheet for the
Guest Satisfaction
Data of Table 11.6

	A	B	C	D	E	F	G	H	I
1	Guest Satisfaction (3-Hotels) Analysis								
2									
3		Observed Frequencies							
4			Hotel				Calculations		
5	Choose Again?	Golden Palm	Palm Royale	Palm Princess	Total			fo-fe	
6	Yes	128	199	186	513		-30.2971	28.97714	1.32
7	No	88	33	66	187		30.29714	-28.9771	-1.32
8	Total	216	232	252	700				
9									
10		Expected Frequencies							
11			Hotel						
12	Choose Again?	Golden Palm	Palm Royale	Palm Princess	Total			(fo-fe)^2/fo	
13	Yes	158.2971	170.0229	184.68	513		5.798695	4.9386	0.009435
14	No	57.7029	61.9771	67.32	187		15.90766	13.54814	0.026002
15	Total	216	232	252	700				
16									
17	Data								
18	Level of Significance	0.05							
19	Number of Rows	2							
20	Number of Columns	3							
21	Degrees of Freedom	2							
22									
23	Results								
24	Critical Value	5.9915							
25	Chi-Square Test Statistic	40.2284							
26	p-Value	0.0000							
27	Reject the null hypothesis								
28									
29	Expected frequency assumption								
30	is met.								

FIGURE 11.8

Minitab Output for the
Guest Satisfaction Data
of Table 11.6

```
Chi-Square Test: C1, C2, C3

Expected counts are printed below observed counts
Chi-Square contributions are printed below expected counts

             C1      C2      C3   Total
    1       128     199     186    513
         158.30  170.02  184.68
          5.799   4.939   0.009

    2        88      33      66    187
          57.70   61.98   67.32
         15.908  13.548   0.026

Total    216     232     252     700

Chi-Sq = 40.228, DF = 2, P-Value = 0.000
```

For the χ^2 test to give accurate results when dealing with $2 \times c$ contingency tables, all expected frequencies must be large. For such situations there is much debate among statisticians about the definition of *large*. Some statisticians (see reference 5) have found that the test gives accurate results as long as all expected frequencies equal or exceed 0.5. Other statisticians, more conservative in their approach, require that no more than 20% of the cells contain expected frequencies less than 5 and no cells have expected frequencies less than 1 (see reference 3). A reasonable compromise between these points of view is to make sure that each expected frequency is at least 1. To accomplish this, you may need to collapse two or more low-expected frequency categories into one category in the contingency table before performing the test. Such merging of categories usually results in expected frequencies sufficiently large to conduct the χ^2 test accurately. If the combining of categories is undesirable, alternative procedures are available (see references 2 and 7).

PROBLEMS FOR SECTION 11.2

Learning the Basics

PH Grade ASSIST **11.11** Consider a contingency table with two rows and five columns.
a. Find the degrees of freedom.
b. Find the critical value for $\alpha = 0.05$.
c. Find the critical value for $\alpha = 0.01$.

PH Grade ASSIST **11.12** For this problem, use the following contingency table:

	A	B	C	Total
1	10	30	50	90
2	40	45	50	135
Total	50	75	100	225

a. Compute the expected frequencies for each cell.
b. Compute the χ^2 statistic for this contingency table. Is it significant at $\alpha = 0.05$?
c. If appropriate, use the Marascuilo procedure and $\alpha = 0.05$ to determine which groups are different.

11.13 For this problem, use the following contingency table:

	A	B	C	Total
1	20	30	25	75
2	30	20	25	75
Total	50	50	50	150

a. Compute the expected frequencies for each cell.
b. Compute the χ^2 statistic for this contingency table. Is it significant at $\alpha = 0.05$?

Applying the Concepts

You can solve problems 11.14–11.23 manually or by using Microsoft Excel or Minitab.

11.14 A survey was conducted in five countries. The percentages of respondents who said that they eat out once a week or more are as follows:

Germany	10%
France	12%
United Kingdom	28%
Greece	39%
United States	57%

Source: Adapted from M. Kissel, "Americans Are Keen on Cocooning," The Wall Street Journal, July 22, 2003, D3.

Suppose that the survey was based on 1,000 respondents in each country.

a. At the 0.05 level of significance, determine whether there is a significant difference in the proportion of people who eat out at least once a week in the various countries.
b. Find the *p*-value in (a) and interpret its meaning.
c. If appropriate, use the Marascuilo procedure and $\alpha = 0.05$ to determine which countries are different. Discuss your results.

11.15 Is the degree to which students withdraw from introductory business statistics courses the same for online courses and traditional courses taught in a classroom? Professor Constance McLaren at Indiana State University collected data for five semesters to investigate this question. The following table cross-classifies introductory business statistics students by the type of course (classroom, online) and student persistence (active, dropped, vanished).

	STUDENT PERSISTENCE		
TYPE OF COURSE	**Active**	**Dropped**	**Vanished**
Classroom	127	8	4
Online	81	51	20

Source: Constance McLaren, "A Comparison of Student Persistence and Performance in Online and Classroom Business Statistics Experiences," Decision Sciences Journal of Innovative Education, Spring 2004, 2(1):1–10. Published by the Decision Sciences Institute, headquartered at Georgia State University, Atlanta, GA.

a. Is there evidence of a difference in student persistence (active, dropped, vanished) based on type of course? (Use $\alpha = 0.01$.)
b. Compute the *p*-value and interpret its meaning.

SELF Test **11.16** More shoppers do their majority of grocery shopping on Saturday than any other day of the week. However, is the day of the week a person does the majority of grocery shopping dependent on age? A study cross-classified grocery shoppers by age and major shopping day ("Major Shopping by Day," *Progressive Grocer Annual Report*, April 30, 2002). The data were reported as percentages and no sample sizes were given.

	AGE		
MAJOR SHOPPING DAY	**Under 35**	**35–54**	**Over 54**
Saturday	24%	28%	12%
A day other than Saturday	76%	72%	88%

Source: Extracted from "Major Shopping by Day," Progressive Grocer Annual Report, April 30, 2002.

Assume that 200 shoppers for each age category were surveyed.

a. Is there evidence of a significant difference among the age groups with respect to major grocery shopping day? (Use $\alpha = 0.05$.)
b. Determine the p-value in (a) and interpret its meaning.
c. If appropriate, use the Marascuilo procedure and $\alpha = 0.05$ to determine which age groups are different. Discuss your results.
d. Discuss the managerial implications of (a) and (c). How can grocery stores use this information to improve marketing and sales? Be specific.

11.17 Repeat (a) through (b) of problem 11.16 assuming that only 50 shoppers for each age category were surveyed. Discuss the implications of sample size on the χ^2 test for differences among more than two populations.

11.18 The health care industry and consumer advocacy groups are at odds over the sharing of a patient's medical records without the patient's consent. The health care industry believes that no consent should be necessary to openly share data among doctors, hospitals, pharmacies, and insurance companies. A phone survey by the Gallup Organization asked respondents if they objected to their medical records being shared without consent to a variety of different types of companies or institutions (Laura Landro, "Medical-Privacy Rules Leave Consumers' Data Vulnerable," *The Wall Street Journal*, June 6, 2002, D3). The following table contains a partial listing of the results:

OBJECT TO SHARING?	ORGANIZATION		
	Insurance Companies	Pharmacies	Medical Researchers
Yes	820	590	670
No	180	410	330

Source: Extracted from Laura Landro, "Medical-Privacy Rules Leave Consumers' Data Vulnerable," The Wall Street Journal, June 6, 2002, D3.

a. Determine whether there is a difference in the proportion of people who object to their medical records being shared with the three organizations listed in the table. (Use $\alpha = 0.05$.)
b. If appropriate, use the Marascuilo procedure and $\alpha = 0.05$ to determine which organizations are different. Discuss your results.

11.19 J. C. Schaefer travels the world to rate the services of luxury hotels. Some of his results appear to vary with the city where the hotel is located. Three of the items he rates the hotels on and results from his findings are as fol-

lows. The data were reported as percentages, and no sample sizes were given.

(1) Front Desk Uses the Guest's Name During Check-In

	Hong Kong	New York	Paris
Yes	26%	39%	28%
No	74%	61%	72%

(2) Minibar Charges Are Correctly Posted at Checkout

	Hong Kong	New York	Paris
Yes	86%	76%	78%
No	14%	24%	22%

(3) Bathroom Tub and Shower Are Spotlessly Clean

	Hong Kong	New York	Paris
Yes	81%	76%	79%
No	19%	24%	21%

Source: Extracted from N. Templin, "Undercover with a Hotel Spy," The Wall Street Journal, May 12, 1999.

Assume that 100 luxury hotels in each city were rated.
a. At the 0.05 level of significance, is there evidence of a difference in the proportion of hotels that use the guest's name among the three cities?
b. Find the p-value in (a) and interpret its meaning.

11.20 Referring to problem 11.19,
a. At the 0.05 level of significance, is there evidence of a difference in the proportion of hotels that correctly post minibar charges among the three cities?
b. Find the p-value in (a) and interpret its meaning.

11.21 Referring to problem 11.19,
a. At the 0.05 level of significance, is there evidence of a difference in the proportion of hotels with spotless bathroom tub and shower among the three cities?
b. Find the p-value in (a) and interpret its meaning.

11.22 Referring to problems 11.19 through 11.21, if appropriate, use the Marascuilo procedure and $\alpha = 0.05$ to determine which hotels are different in the proportion that use the guest's name, the proportion of hotels that correctly post minibar charges, and the proportion of hotels with spotless bathroom tub and shower.

11.23 Referring to problems 11.19 through 11.22, assume that the sample size in each city was 200 instead of 100.
a. Repeat problems 11.19 through 11.22 with this sample size.
b. Discuss the effect that sample size has on tests for differences among the three proportions.

11.3 CHI-SQUARE TEST OF INDEPENDENCE

In sections 11.1 and 11.2 you used the χ^2 test to evaluate potential differences among population proportions. For a contingency table that has r rows and c columns, you can generalize the χ^2 test as a *test of independence* for two categorical variables.

As a test of independence, the null and alternative hypotheses follow:

H_0: The two categorical variables are independent (i.e., there is no relationship between them).
H_1: The two categorical variables are dependent (i.e., there is a relationship between them).

Once again you use Equation (11.1) to compute the test statistic:

$$\chi^2 = \sum_{all\ cells} \frac{(f_0 - f_e)^2}{f_e}$$

You reject the null hypothesis at the α level of significance if the computed value of the χ^2-test statistic is greater than χ^2_U, the upper-tail critical value from a chi-square distribution with $(r-1)(c-1)$ degrees of freedom (see Figure 11.9). Thus, the decision rule is

Reject H_0 if $\chi^2 > \chi^2_U$;

otherwise do not reject H_0.

FIGURE 11.9

Regions of Rejection and Nonrejection When Testing for Independence in an $r \times c$ Contingency Table Using the χ^2 Test

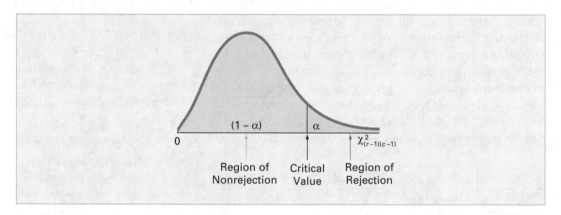

The χ^2 **test of independence** is similar to the χ^2 test for equality of proportions. The test statistics and the decision rules are the same, but the stated hypotheses and the conclusion to be drawn are different. For example, in the guest satisfaction survey of sections 11.1 and 11.2, there is evidence of a significant difference between the hotels with respect to the proportion of guests who would return. From a different viewpoint, you could conclude that there is a significant relationship between the hotels and the likelihood that the guest would return. Nevertheless, there is a fundamental difference between the two types of tests. The major difference is in the sampling scheme used.

In a test for equality of proportions, there is one factor of interest with two or more levels. These levels represent samples drawn from independent populations. The categorical responses in each sample group or level are classified into two categories—*success* and *failure*. The objective is to make comparisons and evaluate differences between the proportions of success among the various levels.

However, in a test for independence, there are two factors of interest, each of which has two or more levels. You select one sample, and tally the joint responses to the two categorical variables into the cells of a contingency table.

To illustrate the χ^2 test for independence, suppose that in the survey on hotel guest satisfaction, a second question was asked of all respondents who indicated that they were not likely to return. These guests were asked to indicate the primary reason for their response. Table 11.9 presents the resulting 4×3 contingency table.

TABLE 11.9

Observed Frequency of Responses Cross-Classifying Primary Reason for Not Returning and Hotel

PRIMARY REASON FOR NOT RETURNING	HOTEL			
	Golden Palm	Palm Royale	Palm Princess	Total
Price	23	7	37	67
Location	39	13	8	60
Room accommodation	13	5	13	31
Other	13	8	8	29
Total	88	33	66	187

In Table 11.9 observe that of the primary reasons for not planning to return to the hotel, 67 were due to price, 60 were due to location, 31 were due to room accommodation, and 29 were due to other reasons. As in Table 11.6, there were 88 guests in the Golden Palm, 33 guests in the Palm Royale, and 66 guests in the Palm Princess who were not planning to return. The observed frequencies in the cells of the 4×3 contingency table represent the joint tallies of the sampled guests with respect to primary reason for not returning and the hotel.

The null and alternative hypotheses are:

H_0: There is no relationship between the primary reason for not returning and the hotel.
H_1: There is a relationship between the primary reason for not returning and the hotel.

To test this null hypothesis of independence against the alternative that there is a relationship between the two categorical variables, use Equation (11.1) to compute the test statistic:

$$\chi^2 = \sum_{all \, cells} \frac{(f_0 - f_e)^2}{f_e}$$

where

f_0 = observed frequency in a particular cell of the $r \times c$ contingency table

f_e = expected frequency in a particular cell if the null hypothesis of independence were true

To compute the expected frequency f_e in any cell, use the multiplication rule for independent events discussed on page 128 [see Equation (4.7)]. For example, under the null hypothesis of independence, the probability of responses expected in the upper-left-corner cell representing primary reason of price for the Golden Palm is the product of the two separate probabilities:

$$P(\text{price and Golden Palm}) = P(\text{price}) \times P(\text{Golden Palm})$$

Here, the proportion of reasons that are due to price, $P(\text{price})$, is $67/187 = 0.3583$, and the proportion of all responses from the Golden Palm, $P(\text{Golden Palm})$, is $88/187 = 0.4706$. If the null hypothesis is true, then the primary reason for not returning and the hotel are independent, and the probability $P(\text{price and Golden Palm})$ is the product of the separate probabilities, $0.3583 \times 0.4706 = 0.1686$. The expected frequency is the product of the overall sample size n and this probability, $187 \times 0.1686 = 31.53$. The f_e values for the remaining cells are calculated in a similar manner (see Table 11.10).

Equation (11.4) presents a simpler way to compute expected frequencies.

COMPUTING THE EXPECTED FREQUENCIES

The expected frequency in a cell is the product of its row total and column total divided by the overall sample size.

$$f_e = \frac{\text{row total} \times \text{column total}}{n} \qquad \textbf{(11.4)}$$

where

row total = sum of all the frequencies in the row

column total = sum of all the frequencies in the column

n = overall sample size

For example, using Equation (11.4) for the upper-left-corner cell (price for the Golden Palm),

$$f_e = \frac{\text{row total} \times \text{column total}}{n} = \frac{(67)(88)}{187} = 31.53$$

and for the lower-right-corner cell (other reason for the Palm Princess),

$$f_e = \frac{\text{row total} \times \text{column total}}{n} = \frac{(29)(66)}{187} = 10.24$$

Table 11.10 lists the entire set of f_e values.

TABLE 11.10

Expected Frequency of Responses to the Survey Cross-Classifying Primary Reason for Not Returning with Hotel

PRIMARY REASON FOR NOT RETURNING	HOTEL			
	Golden Palm	Palm Royale	Palm Princess	Total
Price	31.53	11.82	23.65	67
Location	28.24	10.59	21.18	60
Room accommodation	14.59	5.47	10.94	31
Other	13.65	5.12	10.24	29
Total	88.00	33.00	66.00	187

To perform the test of independence, you use the χ^2-test statistic shown in Equation (11.1). Here the test statistic approximately follows a chi-square distribution with degrees of freedom equal to the number of rows in the contingency table minus 1, times the number of columns in the table minus 1. Thus, for an $r \times c$ contingency table:

Degrees of freedom = $(r - 1)(c - 1)$

Table 11.11 illustrates the computations for the χ^2-test statistic.

TABLE 11.11

Computation of χ^2-Test Statistic for the Test of Independence

Cell	f_O	f_e	$(f_O - f_e)$	$(f_O - f_e)^2$	$(f_O - f_e)^2 / f_e$
Price/Golden Palm	23	31.53	−8.53	72.7609	2.308
Price/Palm Royale	7	11.82	−4.82	23.2324	1.966
Price/Palm Princess	37	23.65	13.35	178.2225	7.536
Location/Golden Palm	39	28.24	10.76	115.7776	4.100
Location/Palm Royale	13	10.59	2.41	5.8081	0.548
Location/Palm Princess	8	21.18	−13.18	173.7124	8.202
Room/Golden Palm	13	14.59	−1.59	2.5281	0.173
Room/Palm Royale	5	5.47	−0.47	0.2209	0.040
Room/Palm Princess	13	10.94	2.06	4.2436	0.388
Other/Golden Palm	13	13.65	−0.65	0.4225	0.031
Other/Palm Royale	8	5.12	2.88	8.2944	1.620
Other/Palm Princess	8	10.24	−2.24	5.0176	0.490
					27.402

Using a level of significance of $\alpha = 0.05$, the upper-tail critical value from the chi-square distribution with $(4 − 1)(3 − 1) = 6$ degrees of freedom is 12.592 (see Table E.4). Since the computed test statistic $\chi^2 = 27.402 > 12.592$, you reject the null hypothesis of independence (see Figure 11.10). Similarly, you can use the Microsoft Excel output in Figure 11.11 or the Minitab output in Figure 11.12 to use the p-value approach. Since the p-value $= 0.00012 < 0.05$, you reject the null hypothesis of independence. This p-value indicates that there is virtually no chance of having a relationship this large or larger between hotels and primary reasons for not returning in a sample, if the primary reasons for not returning are independent of the specific hotels in the entire population. Thus, there is strong evidence of a relationship between primary reason for not returning and the hotel. Examination of the observed and expected frequencies (see Table 11.11) reveals that price is underrepresented as a reason for not returning to the Golden Palm (i.e., $f_0 = 23$ and $f_e = 31.53$) but is overrepresented at the Palm Princess.

FIGURE 11.10

Regions of Rejection and Nonrejection When Testing for Independence in the Hotel Guest Satisfaction Survey Example at the 0.05 Level of Significance with 6 Degrees of Freedom

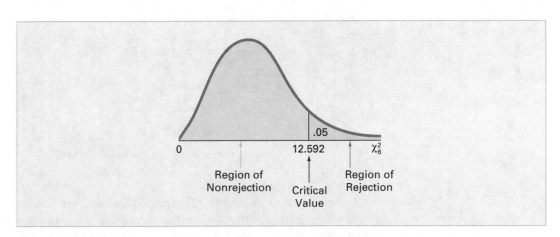

Guests are more satisfied with the price at the Golden Palm compared to the Palm Princess. Location is overrepresented as a reason for not returning to the Golden Palm but greatly underrepresented at the Palm Princess. Thus, guests are much more satisfied with the location of the Palm Princess than the Golden Palm.

FIGURE 11.11

Microsoft Excel
Worksheet for the 4 × 3
Contingency Table for
Primary Reason for Not
Returning and Hotel

FIGURE 11.11

Microsoft Excel
Worksheet for the 4 × 3
Contingency Table for
Primary Reason for Not
Returning and Hotel

	A	B	C	D	E	F	G	H	I
1	Cross-Classification Hotel Analysis								
2									
3		Observed Frequencies							
4		Hotel					Calculations		
5	Reason for Not Returning	Golden Palm	Palm Royale	Palm Princess	Total			fo-fe	
6	Price	23	7	37	67		-8.52941	-4.82353	13.35294
7	Location	39	13	8	60		10.76471	2.411765	-13.1765
8	Room accommodation	13	5	13	31		-1.58824	-0.47059	2.058824
9	Other	13	8	8	29		-0.64706	2.882353	-2.23529
10	Total	88	33	66	187				
11									
12		Expected Frequencies							
13		Hotel							
14	Reason for Not Returning	Golden Palm	Palm Royale	Palm Princess	Total			(fo-fe)^2/fe	
15	Price	31.5294	11.8235	23.6471	67		2.307397	1.967808	7.540094
16	Location	28.2353	10.5882	21.1765	60		4.104044	0.548346	8.196693
17	Room accommodation	14.5882	5.4706	10.9412	31		0.172913	0.040491	0.387413
18	Other	13.6471	5.1176	10.2353	29		0.03068	1.623394	0.488168
19	Total	88	33	66	187				
20									
21		Data							
22	Level of Significance	0.05							
23	Number of Rows	4							
24	Number of Columns	3							
25	Degrees of Freedom	6							
26									
27		Results							
28	Critical Value	12.5916							
29	Chi-Square Test Statistic	27.4104							
30	p-Value	0.00012							
31	Reject the null hypothesis								
32									
33	Expected frequency assumption								
34	is met.								

FIGURE 11.12

Minitab Output for
the 4 × 3 Contingency
Table for Primary
Reason for Not
Returning and Hotel

```
     Chi-Square contributions are printed below expected counts

              C1      C2      C3   Total
        1     23       7      37      67
            31.53   11.82   23.65
            2.307   1.968   7.540

        2     39      13       8      60
            28.24   10.59   21.18
            4.104   0.549   8.199

        3     13       5      13      31
            14.59    5.47   10.94
            0.173   0.040   0.387

        4     13       8       8      29
            13.65    5.12   10.24
            0.031   1.623   0.488

     Total    88      33      66     187

     Chi-Sq = 27.410, DF = 6, P-Value = 0.000
```

To ensure accurate results, all expected frequencies need to be large in order to use the χ^2 test when dealing with $r \times c$ contingency tables. As in the case of $2 \times c$ contingency tables on page 367, all expected frequencies should be at least 1. For cases in which one or more expected frequencies are less than 1, you can use the test after collapsing two or more low-frequency rows into one row (or collapsing two or more low-frequency columns into one column). Merging of rows or columns usually results in expected frequencies sufficiently large to conduct the χ^2 test accurately.

PROBLEMS FOR SECTION 11.3

Learning the Basics

11.24 If a contingency table has three rows and four columns, how many degrees of freedom are there for the χ^2 test for independence?

11.25 When performing a χ^2 test for independence in a contingency table with r rows and c columns, determine the upper-tail critical value of the χ^2-test statistic in each of the following circumstances:

a. $\alpha = 0.05$, $r = 4$ rows, $c = 5$ columns
b. $\alpha = 0.01$, $r = 4$ rows, $c = 5$ columns
c. $\alpha = 0.01$, $r = 4$ rows, $c = 6$ columns
d. $\alpha = 0.01$, $r = 3$ rows, $c = 6$ columns
e. $\alpha = 0.01$, $r = 6$ rows, $c = 3$ columns

Applying the Concepts

You can solve problems 11.26–11.31 manually or by using Microsoft Excel or Minitab.

11.26 During the Vietnam War a lottery system was instituted to choose males to be drafted into the military. Numbers representing days of the year were "randomly" selected; men born on days of the year with low numbers were drafted first; those with high numbers were not drafted. The following shows how many low (1–122), medium (123–244), and high (245–366) numbers were drawn for birth dates in each quarter of the year:

NUMBER SET	QUARTER OF YEAR				
	Jan.–Mar.	Apr.–Jun.	Jul.–Sep.	Oct.–Dec.	Total
Low	21	28	35	38	122
Medium	34	22	29	37	122
High	36	41	28	17	122
Total	91	91	92	92	366

a. Is there evidence that the numbers selected were significantly related to the time of year? (Use $\alpha = 0.05$.)
b. Would you conclude that the lottery drawing appears to have been random?
c. What are your answers to (a) and (b) if the frequencies are

23	30	32	37
27	30	34	31
41	31	26	24

11.27 *USA Today* reported on preferred types of office communication by different age groups. Suppose the results were based on a survey of 500 respondents in each age group. The results are cross-classified in the following table.

TYPE OF COMMUNICATION PREFERRED					
AGE GROUP	Group Meetings	Face-to-face Meetings with Individuals	E-Mails	Other	Total
Generation Y	180	260	50	10	500
Generation X	210	190	65	35	500
Boomer	205	195	65	35	500
Maturo	200	195	50	55	500
Total	795	840	230	135	2,000

Source: Extracted from "Talking Face to Face vs. Group Meetings," USA Today, October 13, 2003, A1.

At the 0.05 level of significance, is there evidence of a relationship between age group and type of communication preferred?

11.28 A large corporation is interested in determining whether a relationship exists between the commuting time of its employees and the level of stress-related problems observed on the job. A study of 116 assembly-line workers reveals the following:

COMMUTING TIME	STRESS LEVEL			
	High	Moderate	Low	Total
Under 15 min	9	5	18	32
15–45 min	17	8	28	53
Over 45 min	18	6	7	31
Total	44	19	53	116

a. At the 0.01 level of significance, is there evidence of a significant relationship between commuting time and stress level?
b. What is your answer to (a) if you used the 0.05 level of significance?

11.29 With business moving at lightning speed, marketing managers often struggle with demands that they reduce the time it takes to craft and launch (cycle time) a marketing campaign. A survey of 175 U.S. and U.K. marketing managers revealed that a marketing campaign has an average cycle time of 2.5 months and slightly more than 16% have cycle times less than one month. The study results suggest that longer is not necessarily better. The marketing managers indicated that a long development time might miss the mark because the data become outdated. On the other hand, they indicated that development time of less than one month can also impair the campaign's effectiveness. Suppose that a cross-classification of the most recent marketing campaign by cycle time and effectiveness resulted in the cross-classification table shown at the top of page 376.

	CYCLE TIME				
EFFECTIVENESS	<1 month	1–2 months	2–4 months	>4 months	Total
Highly Effective	15	28	24	6	73
Effective	9	26	33	19	87
Ineffective	5	2	3	5	15
Total	29	56	60	30	175

*Source: Extracted from Dana James, "Picking Up the Pace,"
Marketing News, April 1, 2002, 3.*

At the 0.05 level of significance, is there evidence of a significant relationship between the length of cycle time and the effectiveness of a marketing campaign? If so, explain the relationship.

11.30 *USA Today* reported on when the decision of what to have for dinner is made. Suppose the results were based on a survey of 1,000 respondents and considered whether the household included any children under 18 years old. The results were cross-classified in the following table:

WHEN DECISION MADE	TYPE OF HOUSEHOLD		
	One Adult/ No Children	Adult/ Children	Two or More Adults/ No Children
Just before eating	162	54	154
In the afternoon	73	38	69
In the morning	59	58	53
A few days before	21	64	45
The night before	15	50	45
Always eat the same thing on this night	2	16	2
Not sure	7	6	7

Source: Extracted from "What's for Dinner," USA Today, January 10, 2000.

At the 0.05 level of significance, is there evidence of a significant relationship between when the decision is made of what to have for dinner and the type of household?

11.31 An article in *USA Today* reported on what drivers most want in a car to make driving time as enjoyable as possible. The survey also considered whether they primarily drove a sedan, a sporty car, or a sports utility vehicle. Suppose the results were based on a survey of 1,000 respondents and the results are cross-classified into the following table:

TECHNOLOGY DESIRED	TYPE OF CAR DRIVEN		
	Sedan	Sporty Car	Sports Utility Vehicle
CD player/change	178	58	54
Quality stereo system	80	54	46
Cell phone	100	8	22
Global positioning system	70	4	16
Movie/game player	68	6	6
Internet access	24	6	10
Radar detector	16	34	20
Don't know	80	26	14

Source: Extracted from "Drivers Just Want to Have Fun," USA Today, May 25, 2000.

At the 0.05 level of significance, is there evidence of a significant relationship between the type of technology desired and the type of car driven?

KEY FORMULAS

χ^2 Test for the Difference Between Two Proportions

$$\chi^2 = \sum_{all\ cells} \frac{(f_0 - f_e)^2}{f_e} \quad (11.1)$$

Computing the Estimated Overall Proportion

$$\bar{p} = \frac{X_1 + X_2}{n_1 + n_2} = \frac{X}{n} \quad (11.2)$$

Computing the Estimated Overall Proportion for c Groups

$$\bar{p} = \frac{X_1 + X_2 + \cdots + X_c}{n_1 + n_2 + \cdots + n_c} = \frac{X}{n} \quad (11.3)$$

Computing the Expected Frequencies

$$f_e = \frac{row\ total \times column\ total}{n} \quad (11.4)$$

CHAPTER REVIEW PROBLEMS

Checking Your Understanding

11.32 Under what conditions should you use the χ^2 test to determine whether there is a difference between the proportions of two independent populations?

11.33 Under what conditions should you use the χ^2 test of independence?

Applying the Concepts

11.34 Undergraduate students at Miami University in Oxford, Ohio, were surveyed in order to evaluate the effect of gender and price on purchasing a pizza from Pizza Hut. Students were told to suppose that they were planning on having a large two-topping pizza delivered to their residence that evening. The students had to decide between ordering from Pizza Hut at a reduced price of $8.49 (the regular price for a large two-topping pizza from the Oxford Pizza Hut at this time was $11.49) and ordering a pizza from a different pizzeria. The results from this question are summarized in the following contingency table.

	PIZZERIA		
GENDER	Pizza Hut	Other	Total
Female	4	13	17
Male	6	12	18
Total	10	25	35

The survey also evaluated purchase decisions at other prices. These results are summarized in the following contingency table.

	PRICE			
PIZZERIA	8.49	11.49	14.49	Total
Pizza Hut	10	5	2	17
Other	25	23	27	75
Total	35	28	29	92

a. Using a level of significance of 0.05 and using the data in the first contingency table, is there evidence of a significant relationship between a student's gender and his or her pizzeria selection?

b. What is your answer to (a) if 9 of the male students had selected Pizza Hut and 9 selected other?

c. Using a level of significance of 0.05 and using the data in the second contingency table, is there evidence of a difference in pizzeria selection based on price?

d. Determine the *p*-value in (c) and interpret its meaning.

e. If appropriate, use the Marascuilo procedure and $\alpha = 0.05$ to determine which prices are different in terms of pizzeria preference.

11.35 A 2004 study by the American Society for Quality investigated executives' views toward quality. Top executives were asked whether they view quality as a profession in the way law, medicine, engineering, and accounting are viewed, or whether they see practicing quality more as the ability to understand and use a variety of tools and techniques to produce a result. Table (1) provides the responses to this question, cross-classified by the type of industry with which the executive is involved. A second question asked whether their companies actually measure the impact of process improvement initiatives designed to raise the quality of their products or services. Table (2) provides the results to this question.

(1) Do you believe that quality is a profession?

	Manufacturing	Service	Healthcare
Yes	108	88	49
No	72	132	50

(2) Does your company measure the impact of process improvement initiatives?

	Manufacturing	Service	Healthcare
Yes	132	129	54
No	48	91	46

Source: Adapted from Greg Weiler, "What Do CEOs Think About Quality?" Quality Progress, May 2004, 37(5):52–56.

a. Is there a significant difference among the three industries with respect to the proportion of top executives who believe quality is a profession? (Use $\alpha = 0.05$.)

b. If appropriate, apply the Marascuilo procedure to (a) using $\alpha = 0.05$.

c. Is there a significant difference among the different industries with respect to the proportion of companies that measure the impact of process improvement initiatives? (Use $\alpha = 0.05$.)

d. If appropriate, apply the Marascuilo procedure to question (c) using $\alpha = 0.05$.

11.36 Money worries in the United States start at an early age. In a survey 660 children (330 boys and 330 girls) ages 6 to 14 were asked the question, "Do you worry about having enough money?" Of the boys surveyed, 61% said yes, and 54% of the girls surveyed said yes (D. Haralson and K. Simmons, "Snapshots," *USA Today*, May 24, 2004, 1B).

a. At the 0.05 level of significance, is there a significant difference between the proportion of boys and girls who worry about having enough money?

b. Find the *p*-value in (a) and interpret its meaning.

11.37 A company that produces and markets video-taped continuing education programs for the financial industry has traditionally mailed sample tapes that contain previews of the programs to prospective customers. Customers then agree to purchase the program tapes or return the sample tapes. A group of sales representatives studied how to increase sales and found that many prospective customers believed it was difficult to tell from the sample tape alone whether the educational programs would meet their needs. The sales representatives performed an experiment to test whether sending the complete program tapes for review by customers would increase sales. They selected 80 customers from the mailing list and randomly assigned 40 to receive the sample tapes and 40 to receive the full-program tapes for review. They then determined the number of tapes that were purchased and returned in each group. The results of the experiment are in the following table.

	TYPE OF VIDEOTAPE RECEIVED		
ACTION	Sample	Full	Total
Purchased	6	14	20
Returned	34	26	60
Total	40	40	80

a. At the 0.05 level of significance, is there evidence of a difference in the proportion of tapes purchased on the basis of the type of tape sent to the customer?
b. On the basis of the results of (a), which tape do you think a representative should send in the future? Explain the rationale for your decision.

The sales representatives also wanted to determine which of three initial sales approaches result in the most sales: (1) a video sales-information tape mailed to prospective customers, (2) a personal sales call to prospective customers, and (3) a telephone call to prospective customers. A random sample of 300 prospective customers was selected, and 100 were randomly assigned to each of the three sales approaches. The results in terms of purchases of the full-program tapes are as follows:

	SALES APPROACH			
ACTION	Videotape	Personal Sales Call	Telephone	Total
Purchase	19	27	14	60
Don't purchase	81	73	86	240
Total	100	100	100	300

c. At the 0.05 level of significance, is there evidence of a difference in the proportion of tapes purchased on the basis of the sales strategy used?
d. If appropriate, use the Marascuilo procedure and α = 0.05 to determine which sales approaches are different.
e. On the basis of the results of (c) and (d), which sales approach do you think a representative should use in the future? Explain the rationale for your decision.

11.38 In October 2000, the Markle Foundation sponsored a telephone survey concerning important issues facing the Internet. One part of the survey separated the respondents into either "general public" or "Internet experts." They were then read statements concerning common Internet practices and asked if they thought the statement was a serious concern or not. The responses to two of these statements, cross-classified by type of user, are given in the following tables:

Statement 1: "Most Web sites place a small file in your computer, called a cookie, that makes it possible for Internet businesses to keep track of all the Web sites you have visited."

	SERIOUSNESS OF CONCERN OVER STATEMENT 1		
TYPE OF USER	Serious	Not Serious	Total
General Public	67	28	95
Internet Experts	46	54	100
Total	113	82	195

Source: Extracted from www.markle.com.

Statement 2: "Three quarters of all large companies repeatedly monitor the e-mail and Internet use of their employees."

	SERIOUSNESS OF CONCERN OVER STATEMENT 2		
TYPE OF USER	Serious	Not Serious	Total
General Public	54	42	96
Internet Experts	37	63	100
Total	91	105	196

Source: Extracted from www.markle.com.

a. At the 0.05 level of significance, is there evidence of a significant relationship between type of user and the seriousness of concern over the first statement?
b. Determine the *p*-value in (a) and interpret its meaning.
c. At the 0.05 level of significance, is there evidence of a significant relationship between type of user and the seriousness of concern over the second statement?
d. Determine the *p*-value in (c) and interpret its meaning.

11.39 The National Coffee Association conducts an annual winter survey of 3,300 people 10 years of age or older. An article discussing this survey (Nikhil Drogun, "Joe Wakes Up, Smells the Soda," *The Wall Street Journal*, June 8, 1999, B1, B16) indicates that soft drinks have become the nation's beverage of choice and that coffee is primarily a breakfast beverage.

a. The survey indicated that 49% of Americans drank coffee the previous day as compared to 75% in 1959. Suppose that the 1959 survey was based on 2,000 respondents. At the 0.01 level of significance, is there evidence of a significant difference between the percentage of Americans who drank coffee in 1999 and the percentage that drank coffee in 1959?

b. Find the p-value in (a) and interpret its meaning.

c. The survey indicated that about 23% of 18- to 24-year-olds in the survey drank coffee the previous day as compared to 74% of those over 60 years of age. Suppose there were 300 respondents 18 to 24 years old in the survey and 500 respondents over 60 years of age. At the 0.01 level of significance, is there evidence of a significant difference in the percentage of 18- to 24-year-olds and those over 60 years of age who drank coffee the previous day?

d. Find the p-value in (c) and interpret its meaning.

e. The survey indicated that of meals at home in 1998, 35% of breakfast meals, 4% of lunch meals, and 3% of supper meals were served with coffee. This compared to 40% of breakfast meals, 9% of lunch meals, and 7% of supper meals in 1988. Suppose that the 1988 survey also was based on 3,300 respondents. At the 0.01 level of significance, is there evidence of a significant difference in the proportion of meals served with coffee between 1988 and 1998? (*Hint*: Do a separate analysis for breakfast, lunch, and supper.)

f. Find the p-values in (e) and interpret its meaning.

11.40 A company is considering an organizational change by adopting the use of self-managed work teams. To assess the attitudes of employees of the company toward this change, a sample of 400 employees is selected and asked whether they favor the institution of self-managed work teams in the organization. Three responses were permitted: favor, neutral, or oppose. The results of the survey, cross-classified by type of job and attitude toward self-managed work teams, are summarized as follows:

ATTITUDE TOWARD SELF-MANAGED WORK TEAMS

TYPE OF JOB	Favor	Neutral	Oppose	Total
Hourly worker	108	46	71	225
Supervisor	18	12	30	60
Middle management	35	14	26	75
Upper management	24	7	9	40
Total	185	79	136	400

a. At the 0.05 level of significance, is there evidence of a relationship between attitude toward self-managed work teams and type of job?

The survey also asked respondents about their attitudes toward instituting a policy whereby an employee could take one additional vacation day per month without pay. The results, cross-classified by type of job, are as follows:

ATTITUDE TOWARD VACATION TIME WITHOUT PAY

TYPE OF JOB	Favor	Neutral	Oppose	Total
Hourly worker	135	23	67	225
Supervisor	39	7	14	60
Middle management	47	6	22	75
Upper management	26	6	8	40
Total	247	42	111	400

b. At the 0.05 level of significance, is there evidence of a relationship between attitude toward vacation time without pay and type of job?

11.41 Researchers studied the goals and outcomes of 349 work teams from various manufacturing companies in Ohio. In the first table, teams are categorized as to whether or not they had specified environmental improvements as a goal and also according to one of four types of manufacturing processes that best described their workplace. The following three tables indicate different outcomes the teams accomplished based on whether or not the team had specified cost cutting as one of the team goals.

TYPE OF MANUFACTURING PROCESS	ENVIRONMENTAL GOAL		
	Yes	No	Total
Job shop or batch	2	42	44
Repetitive batch	4	57	61
Discrete process	15	147	162
Continuous process	17	65	82
Total	38	311	349

OUTCOME	COST-CUTTING GOAL		
	Yes	No	Total
Improved environmental performance	77	52	129
Environmental performance not improved	91	129	220
Total	168	181	349

OUTCOME	COST-CUTTING GOAL		
	Yes	No	Total
Improved profitability	70	68	138
Profitability not improved	98	113	211
Total	168	181	349

	COST-CUTTING GOAL		
OUTCOME	Yes	No	Total
Improved morale	67	55	122
Morale not improved	101	126	227
Total	168	181	349

Source: Extracted from M. Hanna, W. Newman and P. Johnson, "Linking Operational and Environmental Improvement Thru Employee Involvement," International Journal of Operations and Production Management 20, (2000), 148–165.

a. At the 0.05 level of significance, determine whether there is evidence of a significant relationship between the presence of environmental goals and the type of manufacturing process.

b. Calculate the p-value in (a) and interpret its meaning.

c. At the 0.05 level of significance, is there evidence of a difference in improved environmental performance for teams with a specified goal of cutting costs?

d. Calculate the p-value in (c) and interpret its meaning.

e. At the 0.05 level of significance, is there evidence of a difference in improved profitability for teams with a specified goal of cutting costs?

f. Calculate the p-value in (e) and interpret its meaning.

g. At the 0.05 level of significance, is there evidence of a difference in improved morale for teams with a specified goal of cutting costs?

h. Calculate the p-value in (g) and interpret its meaning.

11.42 In summer 2000, a growing number of warranty claims on Firestone tires sold on Ford SUVs prompted Firestone and Ford to issue a major recall. The 2,030 warranty claims for the 23575R15 tires can be categorized into ATX models and Wilderness models. The type of incident leading to a warranty claim, by model type, is summarized in the following table.

Incident	ATX Model Warranty Claims	Wilderness Warranty Claims
Tread Separation	1,365	59
Blow out	77	41
Other/Unknown	422	66
Total	1,864	166

Source: Extracted from Robert L. Simison, "Ford Steps Up Recall Without Firestone," The Wall Street Journal, August 14, 2000, A3.

At the 0.05 level of significance, is there evidence of a significant relationship between type of incident and type of model?

 TEAM PROJECT

The data file MUTUALFUNDS2004 contains information regarding 12 variables from a sample of 121 mutual funds. The variables are:

Fund—The name of the mutual fund
Category—Type of stocks comprising the mutual fund—small cap, mid cap, large cap
Objective—Objective of stocks comprising the mutual fund—growth or value
Assets—In millions of dollars
Fees—Sales charges (no or yes)
Expense ratio—ratio of expenses to net assets in percentage
2003 Return—Twelve-month return in 2003
Three-year return—Annualized return 2001–2003
Five-year return—Annualized return 1999–2003
Risk—Risk-of-loss factor of the mutual fund classified as low, average, or high
Best quarter—Best quarterly performance 1999–2003
Worst quarter—Worst quarterly performance 1999–2003

11.43 a. Construct a 2×2 contingency table using fees as the row variable and objective as the column variable.

b. At the 0.05 level of significance, is there evidence of a significant relationship between the objective of a mutual fund and whether or not there is a fee?

11.44 a. Construct a 2×3 contingency table using fees as the row variable and risk as the column variable.

b. At the 0.05 level of significance, is there evidence of a significant relationship between the perceived risk of a mutual fund and whether there is a fee?

11.45 a. Construct a 3×2 contingency table using risk as the row variable and objective as the column variable.

b. At the 0.05 level of significance, is there evidence of a significant relationship between the objective of a mutual fund and its perceived risk?

RUNNING CASE
MANAGING THE *SPRINGVILLE HERALD*

Phase 1

Reviewing the results of their research, the marketing department concluded that a segment of Springville households might be interested in a discounted trial home subscription to the *Herald*. The team decided to test various discounts before determining the type of discount to offer during the trial period. They decided to conduct an experiment using three types of discounts plus a plan that offered no discount during the trial period. These plans were:

1. No discount for the newspaper. Subscribers would pay $4.50 per week for the newspaper during the 90-day trial period.
2. Moderate discount for the newspaper. Subscribers would pay $4.00 per week for the newspaper during the 90-day trial period.
3. Substantial discount for the newspaper. Subscribers would pay $3.00 per week for the newspaper during the 90-day trial period.
4. Discount restaurant card. Subscribers would be given a card providing a discount of 15% at selected restaurants in Springville during the trial period.

Each participant in the experiment was randomly assigned to a discount plan. A random sample of 100 subscribers to each plan during the trial period was tracked to determine how many would continue to subscribe to the *Herald* after the trial period. Table SH11.1 summarizes the results.

TABLE SH11.1
Number of Subscribers Who Continue Subscriptions after Four Trial Discount Plans

CONTINUE SUBSCRIPTIONS AFTER TRIAL PERIOD	No Discount	Moderate Discount	Substantial Discount	Restaurant Card	Total
Yes	34	37	38	61	170
No	66	63	62	39	230
Total	100	100	100	100	400

EXERCISE

SH11.1 Analyze the results of the experiment. Write a report to the team that includes your recommendation for which discount plan to use. Be prepared to discuss the limitations and assumptions of the experiment.

DO NOT CONTINUE UNTIL THE PHASE 1 EXERCISE HAS BEEN COMPLETED.

Phase 2

The marketing department team discussed the results of the survey presented in Chapter 8. The team realized that the evaluation of individual questions were providing only limited information. In order to further understand the market for home-delivery subscriptions, the data were organized in the following cross-classification tables.

READ OTHER NEWSPAPER

HOME DELIVERY	Yes	No	Total
Yes	61	75	136
No	77	139	216
Total	138	214	352

RESTAURANT CARD

HOME DELIVERY	Yes	No	Total
Yes	26	110	136
No	40	176	216
Total	66	286	352

MONDAY–SATURDAY PURCHASE BEHAVIOR

INTEREST IN TRIAL SUBSCRIPTION	Every Day	Most Days	Occasionally or Never	Total
Yes	29	14	3	46
No	49	81	40	170
Total	78	95	43	216

SUNDAY PURCHASE BEHAVIOR

INTEREST IN TRIAL SUBSCRIPTION	Every Sunday	2–3/ Month	No More Than Once/ Month	Total
Yes	35	10	1	46
No	103	44	23	170
Total	138	54	24	216

INTEREST IN TRIAL SUBSCRIPTION

WHERE PURCHASED	Yes	No	Total
Convenience store	12	62	74
Newstand/candy store	15	80	95
Vending machine	10	11	21
Supermarket	5	8	13
Other locations	4	9	13
Total	46	170	216

MONDAY–SATURDAY PURCHASE BEHAVIOR

SUNDAY PURCHASE BEHAVIOR	Every Day	Most Days	Occasionally or Never	Total
Every Sunday	55	65	18	138
2–3/month	19	23	12	54
Once/month	4	7	13	24
Total	78	95	43	216

EXERCISE

SH11.2 Analyze the results of the cross-classification tables. Write a report for the marketing department team, and discuss the marketing implications of the results for the *Springville Herald*.

WEB CASE

Apply your knowledge of testing for the difference between two proportions in this Web Case that extends the T.C. Resort Properties "Using Statistics" scenario of this chapter.

As it tries to improve its customer service, T.C. Resort Properties faces new competition from SunLow Resorts. SunLow has recently opened resort hotels on the islands where T.C. Resorts Properties has its five hotels. SunLow is currently advertising that a random survey of 300 customers revealed that about 60% percent of the customers preferred its "Concierge Class" travel reward program over T.C. Resorts' "TCPass Plus" program.

Visit the SunLow Web site **www.prenhall.com/ Springville/SunLowHome.htm**, and examine the survey data. Then answer the following:

1. Are the claims made by SunLow valid?
2. What analyses of the survey data would lead to a more favorable impression about T.C. Resort Properties?
3. Perform one of the analyses identified in your answer to step 2.
4. Given the data about T.C. Resorts Properties' customers discussed in this chapter, are there any other factors that you might include in a future survey of travel reward programs? Explain.

REFERENCES

1. Conover, W. J., *Practical Nonparametric Statistics*, 3rd ed. (New York: John Wiley, 2000).
2. Daniel, W. W., *Applied Nonparametric Statistics*, 2nd ed. (Boston: PWS Kent, 1990).
3. Dixon, W. J., and F. J. Massey, Jr., *Introduction to Statistical Analysis*, 4th ed. (New York: McGraw-Hill, 1983).
4. Hollander, M., and D. A. Wolfe, *Nonparametric Statistical Methods* (New York: John Wiley and Sons, 1973).
5. Lewontin, R. C., and J. Felsenstein, "Robustness of Homogeneity Tests in $2 \times n$ Tables," *Biometrics* 21 (March 1965): 19–33.
6. Marascuilo, L. A., "Large-Sample Multiple Comparisons," *Psychological Bulletin* 65 (1966): 280–290.
7. Marascuilo, L. A., and M. McSweeney, *Nonparametric and Distribution-Free Methods for the Social Sciences* (Monterey, CA: Brooks/Cole, 1977).
8. *Microsoft Excel 2003* (Redmond, WA: Microsoft Corp., 2003).
9. *Minitab for Windows Version 14* (State College, PA: Minitab, Inc., 2004).
10. *SPSS 12.0 for Students Brief Guide* (Upper Saddle River, NJ: Prentice Hall, 2003).
11. Winer, B. J., *Statistical Principles in Experimental Design*, 2nd ed. (New York: McGraw-Hill, 1971).

CHAPTER 12

Simple Linear Regression

LEARNING OBJECTIVES

In this chapter, you learn:

- How to use regression analysis to predict the value of a dependent variable based on an independent variable
- The meaning of the regression coefficients b_0 and b_1
- How to evaluate the assumptions of regression analysis and know what to do if the assumptions are violated
- To make inferences about the slope and correlation coefficient
- To estimate mean values and predict individual values

USING STATISTICS

Forecasting Sales for a Clothing Store

The sales for Sunflowers, a chain of apparel stores for women, have increased during the past 12 years as the chain expanded the number of stores open. Until now, Sunflowers senior managers selected sites based on subjective factors such as the availability of a good lease or the perception that a location seemed ideal for an apparel store. As the new director of planning, you need to develop a systematic approach to selecting new sites that will allow Sunflowers to make better-informed decisions for opening additional stores. This plan must be able to forecast annual sales for all potential stores under consideration. You believe that the size of the store significantly contributes to the success of a store and you want to use this relationship in the decision-making process. How can you use statistics so that you can forecast the annual sales of a proposed store based on the size of that store?

In this and the following chapter, you will learn how **regression analysis** allows you to develop a model to predict the values of a numerical variable based on the values of one or more other variables. For example, in the "Using Statistics" scenario above, you may wish to predict sales for a Sunflowers store based on the size of the store. Other examples include predicting your college GPA based on your S.A.T. score, and predicting a professor's salary based on his or her years of experience.

In regression analysis, the variable you wish to predict is called the **dependent variable**. The variables used to make the prediction are called **independent variables**. In addition to predicting values of the dependent variable, regression analysis also allows you to identify the type of mathematical relationship that exists between a dependent and independent variable, to quantify the effect that changes in the independent variable have on the dependent variable, and to identify unusual observations. This chapter discusses **simple linear regression** in which a *single* numerical independent variable X is used to predict the numerical dependent variable Y, such as using the size of a store to predict the annual sales of the store. Chapter 13 discusses *multiple regression models* that use several independent variables to predict a numerical dependent variable Y.

12.1   TYPES OF REGRESSION MODELS

The nature of the relationship between two variables can take many forms, ranging from simple to extremely complicated mathematical functions. The simplest relationship consists of a straight-line or **linear relationship**. An example of this relationship is shown in Figure 12.1.

FIGURE 12.1

A Positive Straight-Line Relationship

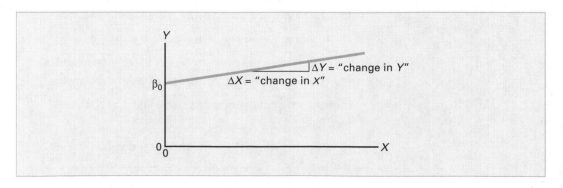

Equation (12.1) represents the straight-line (linear) model.

SIMPLE LINEAR REGRESSION MODEL

$$Y_i = \beta_0 + \beta_1 X_i + \varepsilon_i \qquad (12.1)$$

where $\beta_0 = Y$ intercept for the population

$\beta_1 = $ slope for the population

$\varepsilon_i = $ random error in Y for observation i

$Y_i = $ dependent variable (sometimes referred to as the **response variable**)

$X_i = $ independent variable (sometimes referred to as the **explanatory variable**)

$Y_i = \beta_0 + \beta_1 X_i$ is the equation of a straight line. The **slope** of the line β_1 represents the expected change in Y per unit change in X. It represents the mean amount that Y changes (either positively or negatively) for a one-unit change in X. The **Y intercept** β_0 represents the mean value of Y when X equals 0. The last component of the model, ε_i, represents the random error in Y for each observation i that occurs. In other words, ε_i is the vertical distance Y_i is above or below the line.

The selection of the proper mathematical model depends on the distribution of the X and Y values on the scatter diagram. In panel A of Figure 12.2, the values of Y are generally increasing linearly as X increases. This panel is similar to Figure 12.3, which illustrates the positive relationship between the square footage (i.e., store size available) and the annual sales at branches of the Sunflowers women's clothing store chain.

FIGURE 12.2

Examples of Types of Relationships Found in Scatter Diagrams

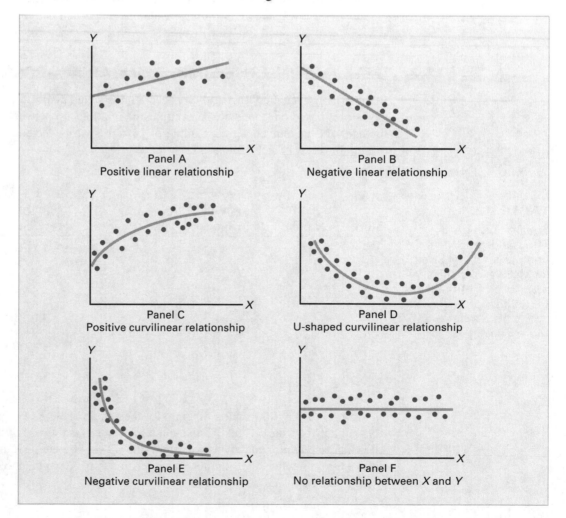

Panel A
Positive linear relationship

Panel B
Negative linear relationship

Panel C
Positive curvilinear relationship

Panel D
U-shaped curvilinear relationship

Panel E
Negative curvilinear relationship

Panel F
No relationship between X and Y

Panel B is an example of a negative linear relationship. As X increases, the values of Y are generally decreasing. An example of this type of relationship might be the price of a particular product and the amount of sales.

The data in panel C show a positive curvilinear relationship between X and Y. The values of Y increase as X increases, but this increase tapers off beyond certain values of X. An example of this positive curvilinear relationship might be the age and maintenance cost of a machine. As a machine gets older, the maintenance cost may rise rapidly at first but then level off beyond a certain number of years.

Panel D shows a U-shaped relationship between X and Y. As X increases, at first Y generally decreases; but as X continues to increase, Y not only stops decreasing but actually increases above its minimum value. An example of this type of relationship might be the number of errors per hour at a task and the number of hours worked. The number of errors per hour decreases as the individual becomes more proficient at the task but then it increases beyond a certain point because of factors such as fatigue and boredom.

Panel E indicates an exponential relationship between X and Y. In this case, Y decreases very rapidly as X first increases, but then it decreases much less rapidly as X increases further. An example of this exponential relationship could be the resale value of an automobile and its age. In the first year the resale value drops drastically from its original price; however, the resale value then decreases much less rapidly in subsequent years.

Finally, Panel F shows a set of data in which there is very little or no relationship between X and Y. High and low values of Y appear at each value of X.

In this section, a variety of different models that represent the relationship between two variables were briefly examined. Although scatter diagrams are useful in visually showing the mathematical form of a relationship, more sophisticated statistical procedures are available to determine the most appropriate model for a set of variables. The rest of this chapter discusses the model used when there is a *linear* relationship between variables.

12.2   DETERMINING THE SIMPLE LINEAR REGRESSION EQUATION

In the "Using Statistics" scenario on page 384, the stated goal is to forecast annual sales for all new stores based on store size. To examine the relationship between the store size (i.e., square footage) and its annual sales, a sample of 14 stores was selected. Table 12.1 summarizes the results for these 14 stores SITE.

TABLE 12.1

Square Footage (in Thousands of Square Feet) and Annual Sales (in Millions of Dollars) for a Sample of 14 Branches of the Sunflowers Women's Clothing Store Chain

Store	Square Feet (000)	Annual Sales (in Millions of Dollars)	Store	Square Feet (000)	Annual Sales (in Millions of Dollars)
1	1.7	3.7	8	1.1	2.7
2	1.6	3.9	9	3.2	5.5
3	2.8	6.7	10	1.5	2.9
4	5.6	9.5	11	5.2	10.7
5	1.3	3.4	12	4.6	7.6
6	2.2	5.6	13	5.8	11.8
7	1.3	3.7	14	3.0	4.1

Figure 12.3 displays the scatter diagram for the data in Table 12.1. Observe the increasing relationship between square feet (X) and annual sales (Y). As the size of the store increases, annual sales increase approximately as a straight line. Thus, you can assume that a straight line provides a useful mathematical model of this relationship. Now you need to determine the specific straight line that is the *best* fit to these data.

FIGURE 12.3

Microsoft Excel Scatter Diagram for the Site Selection Data

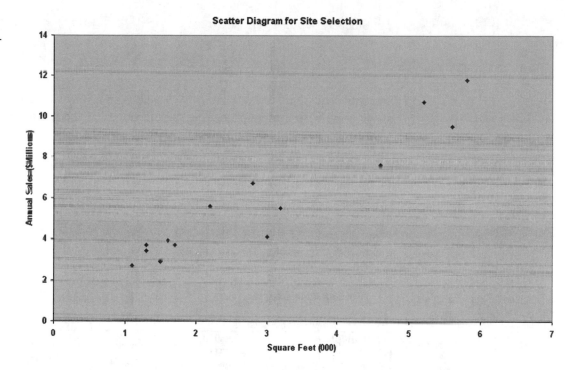

The Least-Squares Method

In the preceding section, a statistical model is hypothesized to represent the relationship between two variables, square footage and sales, in the entire population of Sunflowers women's clothing stores. However, as shown in Table 12.1, the data are from only a random sample of stores. If certain assumptions are valid (see section 12.4), you can use the sample Y intercept b_0 and the sample slope b_1 as estimates of the respective population parameters β_0 and β_1. Equation (12.2) uses these estimates to form the **simple linear regression equation**. This straight line is often referred to as the **prediction line**.

SIMPLE LINEAR REGRESSION EQUATION: THE PREDICTION LINE

The predicted value of Y equals the Y intercept plus the slope times the value of X.

$$\hat{Y}_i = b_0 + b_1 X_i \qquad \textbf{(12.2)}$$

where

$\hat{Y}_i$ = predicted value of Y for observation i

X_i = value of X for observation i

b_0 = sample Y intercept

b_1 = sample slope

Equation (12.2) requires the determination of two **regression coefficients**—b_0 (the sample Y intercept) and b_1 (the sample slope). The most common approach to find b_0 and b_1 is the method of least squares. This method minimizes the sum of the squared differences between the actual values (Y_i) and the predicted values ($\hat{Y}_i$) using the simple linear regression equation [i.e., the prediction line; see Equation (12.2)]. This sum of squared differences is equal to:

$$\sum_{i=1}^{n} (Y_i - \hat{Y}_i)^2$$

Since $\hat{Y}_i = b_0 + b_1 X_i$

$$\sum_{i=1}^{n}(Y_i - \hat{Y}_i)^2 = \sum_{i=1}^{n}[Y_i - (b_0 + b_1 X_i)]^2$$

Since this equation has two unknowns, b_0 and b_1, the sum of squared differences is a function of the sample Y-intercept b_0 and the sample slope b_1. The **least-squares method** determines what values of b_0 and b_1 minimize the sum of squared differences. Any values for b_0 and b_1 other than those determined by the least-squares method result in a greater sum of squared differences between the actual value of Y and the predicted value of Y.

In this text, Microsoft Excel spreadsheet software and Minitab statistical software are used to perform the computations involved in the least-squares method. For the data of Table 12.1, Figure 12.4 represents Microsoft Excel output and Figure 12.5 illustrates Minitab output. However, to understand how the results are computed, many of the computations involved are illustrated in Examples 12.3 and 12.4.

FIGURE 12.4

Microsoft Excel Output for the Site Selection Problem

	A	B	C	D	E	F	G
1	Site Selection Analysis						
2							
3	Regression Statistics						
4	Multiple R	0.95088					
5	R Square	0.90418					
6	Adjusted R Square	0.89619					
7	Standard Error	0.96638	S_{yx}				
8	Observations	14	n				
9						p-value	
10	ANOVA			SSR			
11		df	SS	MS	F	Significance F	
12	Regression	SSE 1	105.74761	105.74761	113.23351	1.82269E-07	
13	Residual	12	11.20668	0.93389			
14	Total	13	116.95429	SST			
15							
16		Coefficients	Standard Error	t Stat	P-value	Lower 95%	Upper 95%
17	Intercept b_0	0.96447	0.52619	1.83293	0.09173	-0.18200	2.11095
18	Square Feet b_1	1.66986	0.15693	10.64112	0.00000	1.32795	2.01177

FIGURE 12.5

Minitab Output for the Site Selection Problem

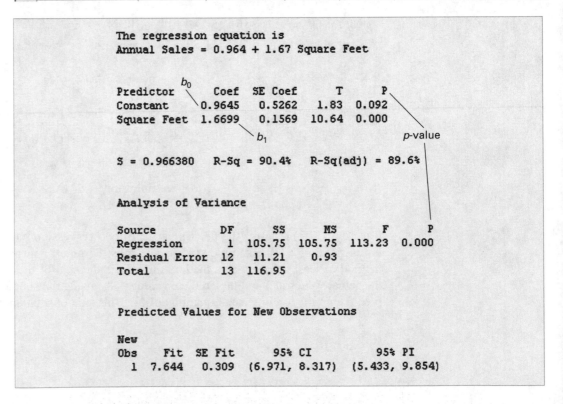

```
The regression equation is
Annual Sales = 0.964 + 1.67 Square Feet


              b0
Predictor      Coef    SE Coef      T       P
Constant      0.9645   0.5262     1.83    0.092
Square Feet   1.6699   0.1569    10.64    0.000
                  b1                          p-value

S = 0.966380   R-Sq = 90.4%   R-Sq(adj) = 89.6%


Analysis of Variance

Source          DF      SS      MS       F       P
Regression       1   105.75  105.75   113.23  0.000
Residual Error  12    11.21    0.93
Total           13   116.95


Predicted Values for New Observations

New
Obs    Fit   SE Fit       95% CI            95% PI
  1  7.644   0.309   (6.971, 8.317)   (5.433, 9.854)
```

In Figure 12.4 or 12.5, observe that $b_0 = 0.964$ and $b_1 = 1.670$. Thus, the prediction line [see Equation (12.2)] for these data is

$$\hat{Y}_i = 0.964 + 1.670X_i$$

The slope b_1 is $+1.670$. This means that for each increase of 1 unit in X, the mean value of Y is estimated to increase by 1.670 units. In other words, for each increase of 1.0 thousand square feet in the size of the store, the mean annual sales are estimated to increase by 1.670 millions of dollars. Thus, the slope represents the portion of the annual sales that are estimated to vary according to the size of the store.

The Y intercept b_0 is $+0.964$. The Y intercept represents the mean value of Y when X equals 0. Because the square footage of the store cannot be 0, this Y intercept has no practical interpretation. Also, the Y intercept for this example is outside the range of the observed values of the X variable, and therefore interpretations of the value of b_0 should be made cautiously. Figure 12.6 displays the actual observations and the prediction line. To illustrate a situation where there is a direct interpretation for the Y intercept b_0, see Example 12.1.

FIGURE 12.6

Microsoft Excel Scatter Diagram and Prediction Line for Site Selection Data

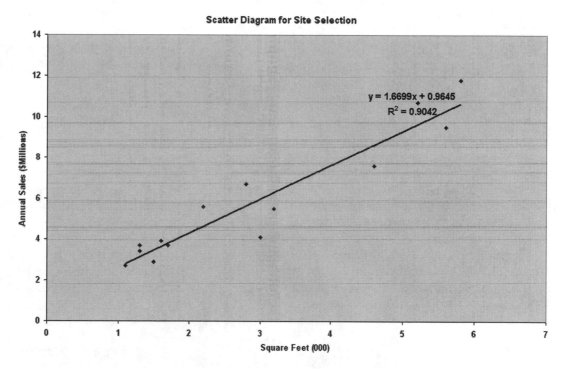

EXAMPLE 12.1   INTERPRETING THE Y INTERCEPT b_0 AND THE SLOPE b_1

A statistics professor wants to use the number of hours a student studies for a statistics final exam (X) to predict the final exam score (Y). A regression model was fit based upon data collected for a class during the previous semester with the following results:

$$\hat{Y}_i = 35.0 + 3X_i$$

What is the interpretation of the Y intercept b_0 and the slope b_1?

SOLUTION The Y intercept $b_0 = 35.0$ indicates that when the student does not study for the final exam, the mean final exam score is 35.0. The slope $b_1 = 3$ indicates that for each increase of one hour in studying time, the mean change in the final exam score is predicted to be $+3.0$. In other words, the final exam score is predicted to increase by 3 points for each one hour increase in studying time.

VISUAL EXPLORATIONS: Exploring Simple Linear Regression Coefficients

Use the Visual Explorations Simple Linear Regression procedure to produce a prediction line that is as close as possible to the prediction line defined by the least-squares solution. Open the **Visual Explorations.xla** macro workbook and:

Select **VisualExplorations → Simple Linear Regression** from the Microsoft Excel menu bar.

When a scatter diagram of the site selection data of Table 12.1 with an initial prediction line appears (shown below), click the spinner buttons to change the values for b_1, the slope of the prediction line, and b_0, the Y intercept of the prediction line.

Try to produce a prediction line that is as close as possible to the prediction line defined by the least-squares estimates, using the chart display and the Difference from Target SSE value as feedback (see page 397 for an explanation of SSE). Click **Finish** when you are done with this exploration.

At anytime, click **Reset** to reset the b_1 and b_0 values, **Help** for more information, or **Solution** to reveal the prediction line defined by the least-squares estimates.

Using Your own regression data. To use Visual Explorations to find a prediction line for your own data, open the **Visual Explorations.xla** workbook (if it is not already open) and then:

Select **VisualExplorations → Simple Linear Regression with your worksheet data**.

In the Simple Linear Regression (your data) dialog box (shown below).

Enter the Y variable cell range in the **Y Variable Cell Range** edit box.

Enter the X variable cell range in the **X Variable Cell Range** edit box.

Select the **First cells in both ranges contain a label** check box, if appropriate.

Enter a title in the **Title** edit box.

Click the **OK** button.

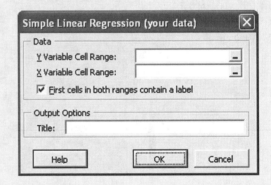

When the scatter diagram with an initial prediction line appears, use the instructions in the first part of this section to try to produce the prediction line defined by the least-squares estimate.

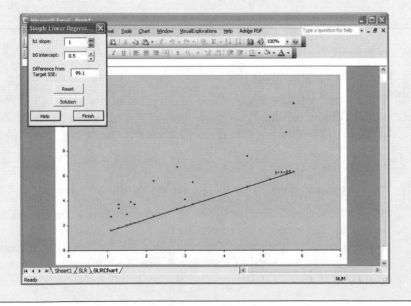

Return to the "Using Statistics" scenario concerning the Sunflowers clothing stores. Example 12.2 illustrates how you use the prediction equation to predict the mean annual sales.

EXAMPLE 12.2

PREDICTING MEAN ANNUAL SALES BASED ON SQUARE FOOTAGE

Use the prediction line to predict the mean annual sales for a store with 4,000 square feet.

SOLUTION You can determine the predicted value by substituting $X = 4$ (thousands of square feet) into the simple linear regression equation,

$$\hat{Y}_i = 0.964 + 1.670 X_i$$

$$\hat{Y}_i = 0.964 + 1.670(4) = 7.644 \text{ or } \$7,644,000$$

Thus, the predicted mean annual sales of a store with 4,000 square feet is $7,644,000.

Predictions in Regression Analysis: Interpolation versus Extrapolation

When using a regression model for prediction purposes, you need to consider only the **relevant range** of the independent variable in making predictions. This relevant range includes all values from the smallest to the largest X used in developing the regression model. Hence, when predicting Y for a given value of X, you can interpolate within this relevant range of the X values, but you should not extrapolate beyond the range of X values. When you use the square footage to predict annual sales, the square footage (in thousands of square feet) varies from 1.1 to 5.8 (see Table 12.1). Therefore, you should predict annual sales *only* for stores whose size is between 1.1 and 5.8 thousands of square feet. Any prediction of annual sales for stores outside this range assumes that the observed relationship between sales and store size for store sizes from 1.1 to 5.8 thousand square feet is the same as for stores outside this range. For example, you cannot extrapolate the linear relationship beyond 5,800 square feet in Example 12.2. It would be improper to use the prediction line to forecast the sales for a new store containing 8,000 square feet. It is quite possible that store size has a point of diminishing returns. If that were true, as square footage increases beyond 5,800 square feet, the effect on sales might become smaller and smaller.

Computing the Y Intercept b_0 and the Slope b_1

For small data sets it is possible to perform the least squres method using a hand calculator. Equations (12.3) and (12.4) give the values of b_0 and b_1, which minimize

$$\sum_{i=1}^{n}(Y_i - \hat{Y}_i)^2 = \sum_{i=1}^{n}[Y_i - (b_0 + b_1 X_i)]^2$$

COMPUTATIONAL FORMULA FOR THE SLOPE b_1

$$b_1 = \frac{SSXY}{SSX} \tag{12.3}$$

where

$$SSXY = \sum_{i=1}^{n}(X_i - \bar{X})(Y_i - \bar{Y}) = \sum_{i=1}^{n}X_iY_i - \frac{\left(\sum_{i=1}^{n}X_i\right)\left(\sum_{i=1}^{n}Y_i\right)}{n}$$

$$SSX = \sum_{i=1}^{n}(X_i - \bar{X})^2 = \sum_{i=1}^{n}X_i^2 - \frac{\left(\sum_{i=1}^{n}X_i\right)^2}{n}$$

COMPUTATIONAL FORMULA FOR THE Y INTERCEPT b_0

$$b_0 = \bar{Y} - b_1\bar{X} \qquad \qquad (12.4)$$

where

$$\bar{Y} = \frac{\sum\limits_{i=1}^{n} Y_i}{n} \text{ and } \bar{X} = \frac{\sum\limits_{i=1}^{n} X_i}{n}$$

EXAMPLE 12.3

COMPUTING THE Y INTERCEPT b_0 AND THE SLOPE b_1

Compute the Y intercept b_0 and the slope b_1 for the site selection problem.

SOLUTION Examining Equations (12.3) and (12.4), you see that five quantities must be calculated to determine b_1 and b_0. These are n, the sample size; $\sum\limits_{i=1}^{n} X_i$, the sum of the X values; $\sum\limits_{i=1}^{n} Y_i$, the sum of the Y values; $\sum\limits_{i=1}^{n} X_i^2$, the sum of the squared X values; and $\sum\limits_{i=1}^{n} X_iY_i$, the sum of the product of X and Y. For the site selection data, the number of square feet is used to predict the annual sales in a store. Table 12.2 presents the computations of the various sums needed (including $\sum\limits_{i=1}^{n} Y_i^2$, the sum of the squared Y values that will be used to compute SST in section 12.3).

TABLE 12.2

Computations for the Site Selection Problem

Store	Square Feet(X)	Annual Sales(Y)	X^2	Y^2	XY
1	1.7	3.7	2.89	13.69	6.29
2	1.6	3.9	2.56	15.21	6.24
3	2.8	6.7	7.84	44.89	18.76
4	5.6	9.5	31.36	90.25	53.20
5	1.3	3.4	1.69	11.56	4.42
6	2.2	5.6	4.84	31.36	12.32
7	1.3	3.7	1.69	13.69	4.81
8	1.1	2.7	1.21	7.29	2.97
9	3.2	5.5	10.24	30.25	17.60
10	1.5	2.9	2.25	8.41	4.35
11	5.2	10.7	27.04	114.49	55.64
12	4.6	7.6	21.16	57.76	34.96
13	5.8	11.8	33.64	139.24	68.44
14	3.0	4.1	9.00	16.81	12.30
Totals	40.9	81.8	157.41	594.90	302.30

Using Equations (12.3) and (12.4), you can compute the values of b_0 and b_1:

$$b_1 = \frac{SSXY}{SSX}$$

$$SSXY = \sum_{i=1}^{n}(X_i - \bar{X})(Y_i - \bar{Y}) = \sum_{i=1}^{n} X_iY_i - \frac{\left(\sum\limits_{i=1}^{n} X_i\right)\left(\sum\limits_{i=1}^{n} Y_i\right)}{n}$$

$$SSXY = 302.3 - \frac{(40.9)(81.8)}{14}$$

$$= 302.3 - 238.97285$$

$$= 63.32715$$

$$SSX = \sum_{i=1}^{n}(X_i - \bar{X})^2 = \sum_{i=1}^{n}X_i^2 - \frac{\left(\sum_{i=1}^{n}X_i\right)^2}{n}$$

$$= 157.41 - \frac{(40.9)^2}{14}$$

$$= 157.41 - 119.48642$$

$$= 37.92358$$

so that

$$b_1 = \frac{63.32715}{37.92358}$$

$$= 1.66986$$

and

$$b_0 = \bar{Y} - b_1\bar{X}$$

$$\bar{Y} = \frac{\sum_{i=1}^{n}Y_i}{n} = \frac{81.8}{14} = 5.842857$$

$$\bar{X} = \frac{\sum_{i=1}^{n}X_i}{n} = \frac{40.9}{14} = 2.92143$$

$$b_0 = 5.842857 - (1.66986)(2.92143)$$

$$= 0.964478$$

PROBLEMS FOR SECTION 12.2

Learning the Basics

PH Grade ASSIST **12.1** Fitting a straight line to a set of data yields the following prediction line

$$\hat{Y}_i = 2 + 5X_i$$

a. Interpret the meaning of the Y intercept b_0.
b. Interpret the meaning of the slope b_1.
c. Predict the mean value of Y for $X = 3$.

PH Grade ASSIST **12.2** If the values of X in problem 12.1 range from 2 to 25, should you use this model to predict the mean value of Y when X equals

a. 3?   c. 0?
b. −3?   d. 24?

12.3 Fitting a straight line to a set of data yields the following prediction line

$$\hat{Y}_i = 16 - 0.5X_i$$

a. Interpret the meaning of the Y intercept b_0.
b. Interpret the meaning of the slope b_1.
c. Predict the mean value of Y for $X = 6$.

Applying the Concepts

Problems 12.4–12.10 can be solved manually or by using Microsoft Excel, Minitab, or SPSS.

  12.4 The marketing manager of a large supermarket chain would like to use shelf space to predict the sales of pet food. A random sample of 12 equal-sized stores PETFOOD is selected, with the following results:

Store	Shelf Space (X) (Feet)	Weekly Sales (Y) (Hundreds of Dollars)
1	5	1.6
2	5	2.2
3	5	1.4
4	10	1.9
5	10	2.4
6	10	2.6
7	15	2.3
8	15	2.7
9	15	2.8
10	20	2.6
11	20	2.9
12	20	3.1

a. Construct a scatter diagram.
For these data $b_0 = 1.45$ and $b_1 = 0.074$.
b. Interpret the meaning of the slope b_1 in this problem.
c. Predict the mean weekly sales (in hundreds of dollars) of pet food for stores with 8 feet of shelf space for pet food.

12.5 Circulation is the lifeblood of the publishing business. The larger the sales of a magazine, the more it can charge advertisers. Recently, a circulation gap has appeared between the publishers' reports of magazines newsstand sales and subsequent audits by the Audit Bureau of Circulations. The following data CIRCULATION represent the reported and audited newsstand sales (in thousands) in 2001 for the following ten magazines.

Magazine	Reported (X)	Audited (Y)
YM	621.0	299.6
CosmoGirl	359.7	207.7
Rosie	530.0	325.0
Playboy	492.1	336.3
Esquire	70.5	48.6
TeenPeople	567.0	400.3
More	125.5	91.2
Spin	50.6	39.1
Vogue	353.3	268.6
Elle	263.6	214.3

Source: Extracted from M. Rose, "In Fight for Ads, Publishers Often Overstate Their Sales," The Wall Street Journal, August 6, 2003, A1, A10.

a. Construct a scatter diagram.
For these data $b_0 = 26.724$ and $b_1 = 0.5719$.
b. Interpret the meaning of the slope b_1 in this problem.

c. Predict the mean audited newsstand sales for a magazine that reports newsstand sales of 400,000.

12.6 The owner of an intracity moving company typically has his most experienced manager predict the total number of labor hours that will be required to complete an upcoming move. This approach has proved useful in the past, but he would like to be able to develop a more accurate method of predicting the labor hours by using the amount of cubic feet moved. In a preliminary effort to provide a more accurate method, he has collected data for 36 moves in which the origin and destination were within the borough of Manhattan in New York City, and the travel time was an insignificant portion of the hours worked. MOVING
a. Construct a scatter diagram.
b. Assuming a linear relationship, use the least-squares method to find the regression coefficients b_0 and b_1.
c. Interpret the meaning of the slope b_1 in this problem.
d. Predict the mean labor hours for moving 500 cubic feet.

PH Grade ASSIST **12.7** A large mail-order house believes that there is a linear relationship between the weight of the mail it receives and the number of orders to be filled. It would like to investigate the relationship in order to predict the number of orders based on the weight of the mail. From an operational perspective, knowledge of the number of orders will help in the planning of the order-fulfillment process. A sample of 25 mail shipments is selected within a range of 200 to 700 pounds. The results are as follows. MAIL

Weight of Mail (Pounds)	Orders (In Thousands)	Weight of Mail (Pounds)	Orders (In Thousands)
216	6.1	432	13.6
283	9.1	409	12.8
237	7.2	553	16.5
203	7.5	572	17.1
259	6.9	506	15.0
374	11.5	528	16.2
342	10.3	501	15.8
301	9.5	628	19.0
365	9.2	677	19.4
384	10.6	602	19.1
404	12.5	630	18.0
426	12.9	652	20.2
482	14.5		

a. Construct a scatter diagram.
b. Assuming a linear relationship, use the least-squares method to find the regression coefficients b_0 and b_1.
c. Interpret the meaning of the slope b_1 in this problem.

d. Predict the mean number of orders when the weight of the mail is 500 pounds.

12.8 The value of a sports franchise is directly related to the amount of revenue that a franchise can generate. The data in the file **BBREVENUE** represent the estimated value in 2004 (in millions of dollars) and the estimated annual revenue (in millions of dollars) for the 30 baseball franchises. Suppose you want to develop a simple linear regression model to predict franchise value based on annual revenue generated.
a. Construct a scatter diagram.
b. Use the least-squares method to find the regression coefficients b_0 and b_1.
c. Interpret the meaning of b_0 and b_1 in this problem.
d. Predict the mean value of a baseball franchise that generates $150 million of annual revenue.

12.9 An agent for a residential real estate company in a large city would like to be able to predict the monthly rental cost for apartments based on the size of the apartment as defined by square footage. A sample of 25 apartments **RENT** in a particular residential neighborhood was selected, and the information gathered revealed the following:

Apartment	Monthly Rent ($)	Size (Square Feet)	Apartment	Monthly Rent ($)	Size (Square Feet)
1	950	850	9	875	700
2	1,600	1,450	10	1,150	956
3	1,200	1,085	11	1,400	1,100
4	1,500	1,232	12	1,650	1,285
5	950	718	13	2,300	1,985
6	1,700	1,485	14	1,800	1,369
7	1,650	1,136	15	1,400	1,175
8	935	726	16	1,450	1,225

Apartment	Monthly Rent ($)	Size (Square Feet)	Apartment	Monthly Rent ($)	Size (Square Feet)
17	1,100	1,245	22	1,650	1,040
18	1,700	1,259	23	1,200	755
19	1,200	1,150	24	800	1,000
20	1,150	896	25	1,750	1,200
21	1,600	1,361			

a. Construct a scatter diagram.
b. Use the least-squares method to find the regression coefficients b_0 and b_1.
c. Interpret the meaning of b_0 and b_1 in this problem.
d. Predict the mean monthly rent for an apartment that has 1,000 square feet.
e. Why would it not be appropriate to use the model to predict the monthly rent for apartments that have 500 square feet?
f. Your friends Jim and Jennifer are considering signing a lease for an apartment in this residential neighborhood. They are trying to decide between two apartments, one with 1,000 square feet for a monthly rent of $1,275 and the other with 1,200 square feet for a monthly rent of $1,425. What would you recommend to them? Why?

12.10 The data in the file **HARDNESS** provide measurements on the hardness and tensile strength for 35 specimens of die-cast aluminum. It is believed that hardness (measured in Rockwell E units) can be used to predict tensile strength (measured in thousands of pounds per square inch).
a. Construct a scatter diagram.
b. Assuming a linear relationship, use the least-squares method to find the regression coefficients b_0 and b_1.
c. Interpret the meaning of the slope b_1 in this problem.
d. Predict the mean tensile strength for die-cast aluminum that has a hardness of 30 Rockwell E units.

12.3   MEASURES OF VARIATION

Computing the Sum of Squares

When using the least squares method to find the regression coefficients for a set of data, there are three measures of variation that you need to compute. The first measure, the **total sum of squares (SST)**, is a measure of variation of the Y_i values around their mean $\overline{Y}$. In a regression analysis, the **total variation** or total sum of squares is subdivided into **explained variation** or **regression sum of squares (SSR)**, that which is due to the relationship between X and Y, and **unexplained variation** or **error sum of squares (SSE)**, that which is due to factors other than the relationship between X and Y. Figure 12.7 shows these different measures of variation.

FIGURE 12.7

Measures of Variation

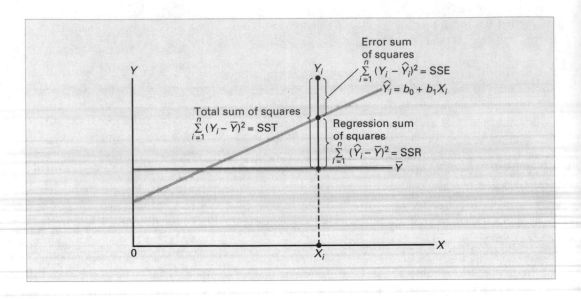

The regression sum of squares (*SSR*) is equal to the difference between $\hat{Y}_i$ (the value of Y that is predicted from the prediction line) and $\bar{Y}$ (the mean value of Y). The error sum of squares (*SSE*) represents the part of the variation in Y that is not explained by the regression. It is based on the difference between Y_i and $\hat{Y}_i$. Equations (12.5), (12.6), (12.7), and (12.8) define these measures of variation.

MEASURES OF VARIATION IN REGRESSION

Total sum of squares = regression sum of squares + error sum of squares.

$$SST = SSR + SSE \qquad (12.5)$$

TOTAL SUM OF SQUARES (*SST*)

The total sum of squares (*SST*) is equal to the sum of the squared differences between each observed Y value and $\bar{Y}$, the mean value of Y.

$$SST = \text{total sum of squares} = \sum_{i=1}^{n}(Y_i - \bar{Y})^2 \qquad (12.6)$$

REGRESSION SUM OF SQUARES (*SSR*)

The regression sum of squares (*SSR*) is equal to the sum of the squared differences between the predicted value of Y and $\bar{Y}$, the mean value of Y.

$$SSR = \text{explained variation or regression sum of squares} \qquad (12.7)$$

$$= \sum_{i=1}^{n}(\hat{Y}_i - \bar{Y})^2$$

ERROR SUM OF SQUARES (*SSE*)

The error sum of squares (*SSE*) is equal to the sum of the squared differences between the observed value of Y and the predicted value of Y.

$$SSE = \text{unexplained variation or error sum of squares} \qquad \textbf{(12.8)}$$

$$= \sum_{i=1}^{n} (Y_i - \hat{Y}_i)^2$$

Figure 12.8 represents the sum of squares portion of the Microsoft Excel output for the site selection problem, while Figure 12.9 illustrates Minitab output.

FIGURE 12.8

Microsoft Excel Sum of Squares for the Site Selection Problem

10	ANOVA					
11		df	SS	MS	F	Significance F
12	Regression	1	105.74761	105.74761	113.23351	1.82269E-07
13	Residual	12	11.20668	0.93389		
14	Total	13	116.95429			

FIGURE 12.9

Minitab Sum of Squares for the Site Selection Problem

```
Analysis of Variance

Source           DF     SS       MS       F       P
Regression        1   105.75   105.75   113.23   0.000
Residual Error   12    11.21     0.93
Total            13   116.95
```

From Figure 12.8 or 12.9, you see that

$$SSR = 105.7476, \; SSE = 11.2067, \text{ and } SST = 116.9543$$

From Equation (12.5),

$$SST = SSR + SSE$$

$$116.9543 = 105.7476 + 11.2067$$

The *SST* is equal to 116.9543. This amount is subdivided into the sum of squares that is explained by the regression (*SSR*), equal to 105.7476, and the sum of squares that is unexplained by the regression (*SSE*), equal to 11.2067.

   In data sets with a large number of significant digits, the output may be displayed using a numerical format known as *scientific notation*. This type of format is used to display very small or very large values. The number after the letter E represents the number of digits that the decimal point needs to be moved to the left (for a negative number) or to the right (for a positive number). For example, the number 3.7431E+02 means that the decimal point should be moved two places to the right, producing the number 374.31. The number 3.7431E−02 means that the decimal point should be moved two places to the left, producing the number 0.037431. When scientific notation is used, fewer significant digits are usually displayed, and the numbers may appear to be rounded.

The Coefficient of Determination

By themselves, *SSR, SSE,* and *SST* provide little information. However, the ratio of the regression sum of squares (*SSR*) to the total sum of squares (*SST*) measures the proportion of variation in *Y* that is explained by the independent variable *X* in the regression model. This ratio is called the **coefficient of determination** r^2 and is defined in Equation (12.9).

COEFFICIENT OF DETERMINATION

The coefficient of determination is equal to the regression sum of squares (i.e., explained variation) divided by the total sum of squares (i.e., total variation).

$$r^2 = \frac{\text{regression sum of squares}}{\text{total sum of squares}} = \frac{SSR}{SST} \qquad (12.9)$$

The coefficient of determination measures the proportion of variation in *Y* that is explained by the independent variable *X* in the regression model. For the site selection example, with *SSR* = 105.7476; *SSE* = 11.2067; and *SST* = 116.9543,

$$r^2 = \frac{105.7476}{116.9543} = 0.904$$

Therefore, 90.4% of the variation in annual sales is explained by the variability in the size of the store as measured by the square footage. This large r^2 indicates a strong positive linear relationship between two variables because the use of a regression model has reduced the variability in predicting annual sales by 90.4%. Only 9.6% of the sample variability in annual sales is due to factors other than what is accounted for by the linear regression model that uses square footage.

Figure 12.10 represents the coefficient of determination portion of the Microsoft Excel output for the site selection problem and Figure 12.11 illustrates Minitab output.

FIGURE 12.10

Partial Microsoft Excel Regression Output for the Site Selection Problem

3	*Regression Statistics*	
4	**Multiple R**	0.95088
5	**R Square**	0.90418
6	**Adjusted R Square**	0.89619
7	**Standard Error**	S_{YX} 0.96638
8	**Observations**	14.00000

FIGURE 12.11

Partial Minitab Regression Output for the Site Selection Problem

```
Predictor      Coef   SE Coef      T       P
Constant     0.9645   0.5262    1.83   0.092
Square Feet  1.6699   0.1569   10.64   0.000


S = 0.966380   R-Sq = 90.4%   R-Sq(adj) = 89.6%
```

EXAMPLE 12.4

COMPUTING THE COEFFICIENT OF DETERMINATION

Compute the coefficient of determination r^2 for the site selection problem.

SOLUTION You can compute *SST, SSR,* and *SSE* that were defined in Equations (12.6), (12.7), and (12.8) by using Equations (12.10), (12.11), and (12.12).

COMPUTATIONAL FORMULA FOR SST

$$SST = \sum_{i=1}^{n} (Y_i - \bar{Y})^2 = \sum_{i=1}^{n} Y_i^2 - \frac{\left(\sum_{i=1}^{n} Y_i\right)^2}{n} \qquad \textbf{(12.10)}$$

COMPUTATIONAL FORMULA FOR SSR

$$SSR = \sum_{i=1}^{n} (\hat{Y}_i - \bar{Y})^2 \qquad \textbf{(12.11)}$$

$$= b_0 \sum_{i=1}^{n} Y_i + b_1 \sum_{i=1}^{n} X_i Y_i - \frac{\left(\sum_{i-1}^{n} Y_i\right)^2}{n}$$

COMPUTATIONAL FORMULA FOR SSE

$$SSE = \sum_{i=1}^{n} (Y_i - \hat{Y})^2 \qquad \textbf{(12.12)}$$

$$= \sum_{i=1}^{n} Y_i^2 - b_0 \sum_{i=1}^{n} Y_i - b_1 \sum_{i=1}^{n} X_i Y_i$$

Using the summary results from Table 12.2,

$$SST = \sum_{i=1}^{n} (Y_i - \bar{Y})^2 = \sum_{i=1}^{n} Y_i^2 - \frac{\left(\sum_{i=1}^{n} Y_i\right)^2}{n}$$

$$= 594.9 - \frac{(81.8)^2}{14}$$

$$= 594.9 - 477.94571$$

$$= 116.95429$$

$$SSR = \sum_{i=1}^{n} (\hat{Y}_i - \bar{Y})^2$$

$$= b_0 \sum_{i=1}^{n} Y_i + b_1 \sum_{i=1}^{n} X_i Y_i - \frac{\left(\sum_{i=1}^{n} Y_i\right)^2}{n}$$

$$= (0.964478)(81.8) + (1.66986)(302.3) - \frac{(81.8)^2}{14}$$

$$= 105.74726$$

$$SSE = \sum_{i=1}^{n}(Y_i - \hat{Y}_i)^2$$

$$= \sum_{i=1}^{n}Y_i^2 - b_0\sum_{i=1}^{n}Y_i - b_1\sum_{i=1}^{n}X_iY_i$$

$$= 594.9 - (0.964478)(81.8) - (1.66986)(302.3)$$

$$= 11.207$$

Therefore,

$$r^2 = \frac{105.74726}{116.9543} = 0.904$$

Standard Error of the Estimate

Although the least-squares method results in the line that fits the data with the minimum amount of variation, unless all the observed data points fall on a straight line, the prediction line is not a perfect predictor. Just as all data values cannot be expected to be exactly equal to their mean, neither can they be expected to fall exactly on the prediction line. Therefore, a statistic that measures the variability of the actual Y values from the predicted Y values needs to be developed, in the same way that the standard deviation was developed in Chapter 3 as a measure of the variability of each value around the mean. This standard deviation around the prediction line is called the **standard error of the estimate**.

Figure 12.6 illustrates the variability around the prediction line for the site selection data. Observe that, although many of the actual values of Y fall near the prediction line, no values are exactly on the line.

The standard error of the estimate, represented by the symbol S_{YX}, is defined in Equation (12.13).

STANDARD ERROR OF THE ESTIMATE

$$S_{YX} = \sqrt{\frac{SSE}{n-2}} = \sqrt{\frac{\sum_{i=1}^{n}(Y_i - \hat{Y}_i)^2}{n-2}} \qquad (12.13)$$

where

Y_i = actual value of Y for a given X_i

$\hat{Y}_i$ = predicted value of Y for a given X_i

SSE = error sum of squares

From Equation (12.8), with $SSE = 11.2067$,

$$S_{YX} = \sqrt{\frac{11.2067}{14-2}} = 0.9664$$

This standard error of the estimate, equal to 0.9664 millions of dollars (i.e., $966,400), is labeled Standard Error on the Microsoft Excel output of Figure 12.10 and as S in the Minitab output of Figure 12.11. The standard error of the estimate represents a measure of the variation around the prediction line. It is measured in the same units as the dependent variable Y. The interpretation of the standard error of the estimate is similar to that of the standard deviation. Just as the standard deviation measures variability around the mean, the standard error of the estimate measures variability around the prediction line. As you will see in sections 12.7 and 12.8, the standard error of the estimate is used to determine whether a statistically significant relationship exists between the two variables and also to make inferences about future values of Y.

PROBLEMS FOR SECTION 12.3

Learning the Basics

 12.11 How do you interpret a coefficient of determination r^2 equal to 0.80?

 12.12 If $SSR = 36$ and $SSE = 4$, find SST, and then compute the coefficient of determination r^2 and interpret its meaning.

 12.13 If $SSR = 66$ and $SST = 88$, compute the coefficient of determination r^2 and interpret its meaning.

 12.14 If $SSE = 10$ and $SSR = 30$, compute the coefficient of determination r^2 and interpret its meaning.

12.15 If $SSR = 120$, why is it impossible for SST to equal 110?

Applying the Concepts

Problems 12.16–12.22 can be solved manually or by using Microsoft Excel, Minitab, or SPSS.

  12.16 In problem 12.4, the marketing manager used shelf space for pet food to predict weekly sales. PETFOOD For that data, $SSR = 2.0535$ and $SST = 3.0025$.
a. Determine the coefficient of determination r^2 and interpret its meaning.
b. Determine the standard error of the estimate.
c. How useful do you think this regression model is for predicting sales?

12.17 In problem 12.5, you used reported magazine newsstand sales to predict audited sales. CIRCULATION For that data, $SSR = 130,301.41$ and $SST = 144,538.64$.
a. Determine the coefficient of determination r^2 and interpret its meaning.
b. Determine the standard error of the estimate.
c. How useful do you think this regression model is for predicting audited sales?

12.18 In problem 12.6, an owner of a moving company wanted to predict labor hours based on the cubic feet moved. MOVING Using the results of that problem,

a. Determine the coefficient of determination r^2 and interpret its meaning.
b. Determine the standard error of the estimate.
c. How useful do you think this regression model is for predicting labor hours?

 12.19 In problem 12.7, you used the weight of mail to predict the number of orders received. MAIL Using the results of that problem,
a. Determine the coefficient of determination r^2 and interpret its meaning.
b. Find the standard error of the estimate.
c. How useful do you think this regression model is for predicting the number of orders?

12.20 In problem 12.8, you used annual revenues to predict the value of a baseball franchise. BBREVENUE Using the results of that problem,
a. Determine the coefficient of determination r^2 and interpret its meaning.
b. Determine the standard error of the estimate.
c. How useful do you think this regression model is for predicting the value of a baseball franchise?

12.21 In problem 12.9, an agent for a real estate company wanted to predict the monthly rent for apartments based on the size of the apartment. RENT Using the results of that problem,
a. Determine the coefficient of determination r^2 and interpret its meaning.
b. Determine the standard error of the estimate.
c. How useful do you think this regression model is for predicting the monthly rent?

12.22 In problem 12.10, you used hardness to predict the tensile strength of die-cast aluminum. HARDNESS Using the results of that problem,
a. Determine the coefficient of determination r^2 and interpret its meaning.
b. Find the standard error of the estimate.
c. How useful do you think this regression model is for predicting the tensile strength of die-cast aluminum?

12.4 ASSUMPTIONS

The discussion of hypothesis testing and the analysis of variance emphasized the importance of the assumptions to the validity of any conclusions reached. The assumptions necessary for regression are similar to those of the analysis of variance because both topics fall under the general heading of *linear models* (reference 5).

The four **assumptions of regression** (known by the acronym LINE) are as follows.

- Linearity
- Independence of errors
- Normality of error
- Equal variance (also called homoscedasticity)

The first assumption, **linearity**, states that the relationship between variables is linear. Relationships between variables that are not linear are discussed in Chapter 13.

The second assumption, **independence of errors**, requires that the errors (ε_i's) are independent from one another. This assumption is particularly important when data are collected over a period of time. In such situations, the errors for a specific time period are often correlated with those of the previous time period.

The third assumption, **normality**, requires that the errors (ε_i's) are normally distributed at each value of X. Like the t test and the ANOVA F test, regression analysis is fairly robust to departures from the normality assumption. As long as the distribution of the errors at each level of X is not extremely different from a normal distribution, inferences about β_0 and β_1 are not seriously affected.

The fourth assumption, **equal variance** or **homoscedasticity**, requires that the variance of the errors (ε_i's) are constant for all values of X. In other words, the variability of Y values will be the same when X is a low value as when X is a high value. The equal variance assumption is important when making inferences about β_0 and β_1. If there are serious departures from this assumption, you can use either data transformations or weighted least-squares methods (see reference 5).

12.5 RESIDUAL ANALYSIS

In section 12.1 regression analysis was introduced. In sections 12.2 and 12.3, a model was developed and estimated using the least-squares approach for the site selection data. Is this the correct model for these data? Are the assumptions introduced in section 12.4 valid? In this section, a graphical approach called **residual analysis** is used to evaluate the assumptions and thus determine whether the regression model selected is an appropriate model.

The **residual** or estimated error value e_i is the difference between the observed (Y_i) and predicted ($\hat{Y}_i$) values of the dependent variable for a given value of X_i. Graphically, a residual appears on a scatter diagram as the vertical distance between an observed value of Y and the prediction line. Equation (12.14) defines the residual.

THE RESIDUAL

The residual is equal to the difference between the observed value of Y and the predicted value of Y.

$$e_i = Y_i - \hat{Y}_i \qquad (12.14)$$

Evaluating the Assumptions

Recall from section 12.4 that the four assumptions of regression (known by the acronym LINE) are linearity, independence, normality, and equal variance.

Linearity   To evaluate linearity, plot the residuals on the vertical axis against the corresponding X_i values of the independent variable on the horizontal axis. If the linear model is appropriate for the data, there will be no apparent pattern in this plot. However, if the linear model is not appropriate, there will be a relationship between the X_i values and the residuals e_i. You can see such a pattern in Figure 12.12. Panel A shows a situation in which, although there is an increasing trend in Y as X increases, the relationship seems curvilinear because the upward trend decreases for increasing values of X. This quadratic effect is highlighted in panel B where there is a clear relationship between X_i and e_i. By plotting the residuals, the linear trend of X with Y has been removed, thereby exposing the lack of fit in the simple linear model. Thus, a quadratic model is a better fit and should be used in place of the simple linear model.

FIGURE 12.12

Studying the Appropriateness of the Simple Linear Regression Model

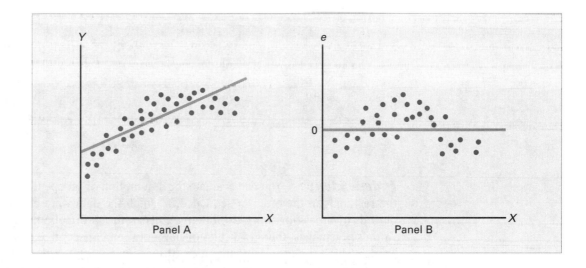

| Panel A | Panel B |

[1]*Other more computationally complex residuals are available in Minitab and SPSS (see references 7 and 9)*

To determine whether the simple linear regression model is appropriate, return to the evaluation of the site selection data. Figure 12.13 provides the predicted and residual values of the response variable (annual sales) computed by Microsoft Excel.[1]

FIGURE 12.13

Microsoft Excel Residual Statistics for the Site Selection Problem

22	RESIDUAL OUTPUT		
23			
24	*Observation*	*Predicted Annual Sales*	*Residuals*
25	1	3.803239598	-0.103239598
26	2	3.636253367	0.263746633
27	3	5.640088147	1.059911853
28	4	10.31570263	-0.815702635
29	5	3.135294672	0.264705328
30	6	4.638170757	0.961829243
31	7	3.135294672	0.564705328
32	8	2.801322208	-0.101322208
33	9	6.308033074	-0.808033074
34	10	3.469267135	-0.569267135
35	11	9.647757708	1.052242292
36	12	8.645840318	-1.045840318
37	13	10.6496751	1.150324902
38	14	5.974060611	-1.874060611

To assess linearity, the residuals are plotted against the independent variable (store size in thousands of square feet) in Figure 12.14. Although there is widespread scatter in the residual plot, there is no apparent pattern or relationship between the residuals and X_i. The residuals appear to be evenly spread above and below 0 for the differing values of X. You can conclude that the linear model is appropriate for the site selection data.

FIGURE 12.14

Microsoft Excel Plot
of Residuals Against
the Square Footage
of a Store for the Site
Selection Problem

Square Feet Residual Plot

Independence   You can evaluate the assumption of independence of the errors by plotting the residuals in the order or sequence in which the data were collected. Data collected over periods of time sometimes exhibit an *autocorrelation* effect among successive observations. In these instances, there is a relationship between consecutive residuals. If this relationship exists (which violates the assumption of independence), it will be apparent in the plot of the residuals versus the time in which the data were collected. You can also test for autocorrelation using the Durbin-Watson statistic, which is the subject of section 12.6. For the site selection data considered thus far in this chapter, the data were collected during the same time period. Therefore, you do not need to evaluate the independence assumption for these data.

Normality   You can evaluate the assumption of normality in the errors by tallying the residuals into a frequency distribution and displaying the results in a histogram (see section 2.3). For the site selection data, the residuals have been tallied into a frequency distribution as shown in Table 12.3. (There are an insufficient number of values, however, to construct a histogram.) You can also evaluate the normality assumption by comparing the actual versus theoretical values of the residuals, or by constructing a normal probability plot, a stem-and-leaf display, or a box-and-whisker plot of the residuals. Figure 12.15 is a normal probability plot of the residuals for the site selection data.

TABLE 12.3

Frequency Distribution
of 14 Residual Values
for the Site Selection
Data

Residuals	Frequency
−2.25 but less than −1.75	1
−1.75 but less than −1.25	0
−1.25 but less than −0.75	3
−0.75 but less than −0.25	1
−0.25 but less than +0.25	2
+0.25 but less than +0.75	3
+0.75 but less than +1.25	4
Total	14

FIGURE 12.15

Minitab Normal
Probability Plot of
Residuals for the Site
Selection Data

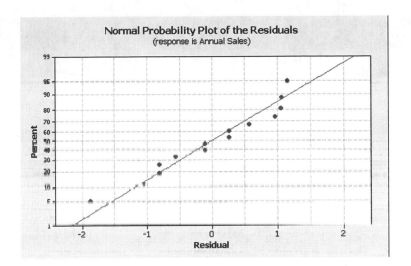

It is difficult to evaluate the normality assumption for a sample of only 14 values regardless of whether you use a histogram, stem-and-leaf display, box-and-whisker plot, or normal probability plot. You can see from Figure 12.15 that the data do not appear to depart substantially from a normal distribution. The robustness of regression analysis to modest departures from normality enables you to conclude that you should not be overly concerned about departures from this normality assumption in the site selection data.

Equal Variance You can evaluate the assumption of equal variance from a plot of the residuals with X_i. For the site selection data of Figure 12.14 there do not appear to be major differences in the variability of the residuals for different X_i values. Thus, you can conclude that there is no apparent violation in the assumption of equal variance at each level of X.

To examine a case in which the equal variance assumption is violated, observe Figure 12.16, which is a plot of the residuals with X_i for a hypothetical set of data. In this plot, the variability of the residuals increases dramatically as X increases, demonstrating the lack of homogeneity in the variances of Y_i at each level of X. For these data, the equal variance assumption is invalid.

FIGURE 12.16

Violation of Equal
Variance

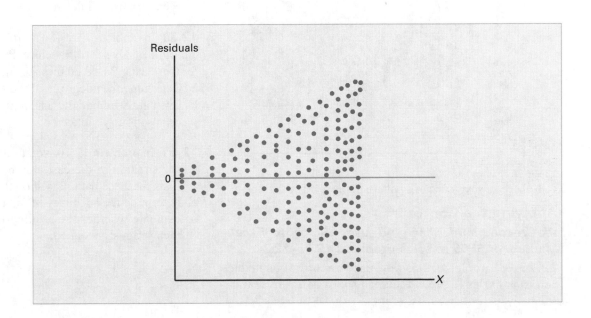

PROBLEMS FOR SECTION 12.5

Learning the Basics

12.23 The following computer output contains the X values, residuals, and a residual plot from a regression analysis.

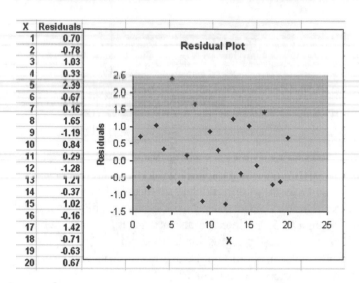

X	Residuals
1	0.70
2	-0.78
3	1.03
4	0.33
5	2.39
6	-0.67
7	0.16
8	1.65
9	-1.19
10	0.84
11	0.29
12	-1.28
13	1.21
14	-0.37
15	1.02
16	-0.16
17	1.42
18	-0.71
19	-0.63
20	0.67

Is there any evidence of a pattern in the residuals? Explain.

12.24 The following computer output contains the X values, residuals, and a residual plot from a regression analysis.

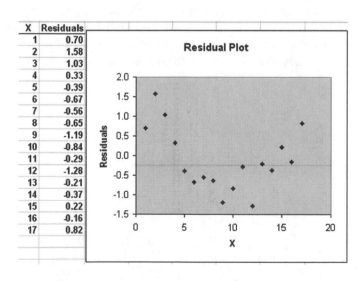

X	Residuals
1	0.70
2	1.58
3	1.03
4	0.33
5	-0.39
6	-0.67
7	-0.56
8	-0.65
9	-1.19
10	-0.84
11	-0.29
12	-1.28
13	-0.21
14	-0.37
15	0.22
16	-0.16
17	0.82

Is there any evidence of a pattern in the residuals? Explain.

Applying the Concepts

We recommend that you use Microsoft Excel, Minitab, or SPSS to solve problems 12.25–12.31.

12.25 In problem 12.5, you used reported magazine newsstand sales to predict audited sales. Perform a residual analysis for these data. CIRCULATION

a. Determine the adequacy of the fit of the model.
b. Evaluate whether the assumptions of regression have been seriously violated.

 12.26 In problem 12.4, the marketing manager used shelf space for pet food to predict weekly sales. Perform a residual analysis for these data.
PETFOOD
a. Determine the adequacy of the fit of the model.
b. Evaluate whether the assumptions of regression have been seriously violated.

12.27 In problem 12.7, you used the weight of mail to predict the number of orders received. Perform a residual analysis for these data. Based on these results, MAIL
a. Determine the adequacy of the fit of the model.
b. Evaluate whether the assumptions of regression have been seriously violated.

12.28 In problem 12.6, the owner of a moving company wanted to predict labor hours based on the cubic feet moved. Perform a residual analysis for these data. Based on these results, MOVING
a. Determine the adequacy of the fit of the model.
b. Evaluate whether the assumptions of regression have been seriously violated.

12.29 In problem 12.9, an agent for a real estate company wanted to predict the monthly rent for apartments based on the size of the apartment. Perform a residual analysis for these data. Based on these results, RENT
a. Determine the adequacy of the fit of the model.
b. Evaluate whether the assumptions of regression have been seriously violated.

12.30 In problem 12.8, you used annual revenues to predict the value of a baseball franchise. Perform a residual analysis for these data. Based on these results, BBREVENUE
a. Determine the adequacy of the fit of the model.
b. Evaluate whether the assumptions of regression have been seriously violated.

12.31 In problem 12.10, you used hardness to predict the tensile strength of die-cast aluminum. Perform a residual analysis for these data. Based on these results, HARDNESS
a. Determine the adequacy of the fit of the model.
b. Evaluate whether the assumptions of regression have been seriously violated.

12.6   MEASURING AUTOCORRELATION: THE DURBIN-WATSON STATISTIC

One of the basic assumptions of the regression model is the independence of the errors. This assumption is sometimes violated when data are collected over sequential periods of time because a residual at any one point in time may tend to be similar to residuals at adjacent points in time. This pattern in the residuals is called **autocorrelation**. When a set of data has substantial autocorrelation, the validity of a regression model can be in serious doubt.

Residual Plots to Detect Autocorrelation

As mentioned in section 12.5, one way to detect autocorrelation is to plot the residuals in time order. If a positive autocorrelation effect is present, there will be clusters of residuals with the same sign and you will readily detect an apparent pattern. If negative autocorrelation exists, residuals will tend to jump back and forth from positive to negative to positive, and so on. This type of pattern is very rarely seen in regression analysis. Thus, the focus of this section is on positive autocorrelation. To illustrate positive autocorrelation, consider the following example.

The manager of a package delivery store wants to predict weekly sales based on the number of customers making purchases for a period of 15 weeks. In this situation, because data are collected over a period of 15 consecutive weeks at the same store, you need to determine whether autocorrelation is present. Table 12.4 summarizes the data for this store CUSTSALE. Figure 12.17 illustrates Excel output and Figure 12.18 illustrates Minitab output.

TABLE 12.4

Customers and Sales for Period of 15 Consecutive Weeks

Week	Customers	Sales (in thousands of dollars)	Week	Customers	Sales (in thousands of dollars)
1	794	9.33	9	880	12.07
2	799	8.26	10	905	12.55
3	837	7.48	11	886	11.92
4	855	9.08	12	843	10.27
5	845	9.83	13	904	11.80
6	844	10.09	14	950	12.15
7	863	11.01	15	841	9.64
8	875	11.49			

FIGURE 12.17

Microsoft Excel Output for the Package Delivery Store Data of Table 12.4

	A	B	C	D	E	F	G
1	**Package Delivery Store Sales Analysis**						
2							
3	*Regression Statistics*						
4	**Multiple R**	0.81083					
5	**R Square**	0.65745					
6	**Adjusted R Square**	0.63109					
7	**Standard Error**	0.93604					
8	**Observations**	15					
9							
10	**ANOVA**						
11		*df*	*SS*	*MS*	*F*	*Significance F*	
12	**Regression**	1	21.86043	21.86043	24.95014	0.00025	
13	**Residual**	13	11.39014	0.87616			
14	**Total**	14	33.25057333				
15							
16		*Coefficients*	*Standard Error*	*t Stat*	*P-value*	*Lower 95%*	*Upper 95%*
17	**Intercept**	-16.03219	5.31017	-3.01915	0.00987	-27.50411	-4.56028
18	**Customers**	0.03076	0.00616	4.99501	0.00025	0.01746	0.04406

FIGURE 12.18

Minitab Output for the
Package Delivery Store
Data of Table 12.4

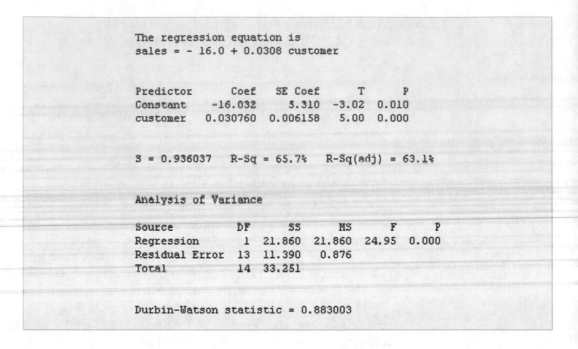

```
The regression equation is
sales = - 16.0 + 0.0308 customer


Predictor       Coef    SE Coef       T      P
Constant     -16.032      5.310   -3.02  0.010
customer    0.030760   0.006158    5.00  0.000



S = 0.936037   R-Sq = 65.7%   R-Sq(adj) = 63.1%


Analysis of Variance


Source          DF      SS      MS      F      P
Regression       1  21.860  21.860  24.95  0.000
Residual Error  13  11.390   0.876
Total           14  33.251


Durbin-Watson statistic = 0.883003
```

From Figure 12.17 or 12.18 observe that r^2 is 0.657, indicating that 65.7% of the variation in sales is explained by variation in the number of customers. In addition, the Y intercept b_0 is -16.032, and the slope b_1 is 0.03076. However, before using this model for prediction, you must undertake proper analyses of the residuals. Because the data have been collected over a consecutive period of 15 weeks, in addition to checking the linearity, normality, and equal variance assumptions, you must investigate the independence of errors assumption. Figure 12.19 plots the residuals versus time to see whether a pattern exists. In Figure 12.19, the residuals tend to fluctuate up and down in a cyclical pattern. This cyclical pattern provides strong cause for concern about the autocorrelation of the residuals and, hence, a violation of the independence of errors assumption.

FIGURE 12.19

Microsoft Excel
Residual Plot for the
Package Delivery Store
Data of Table 12.4

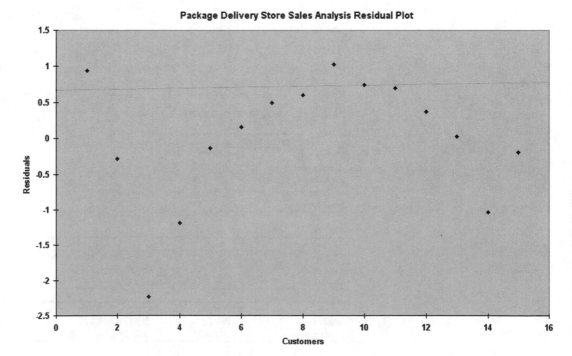

Package Delivery Store Sales Analysis Residual Plot

PROBLEMS FOR SECTION 12.6

Learning the Basics

 12.32 The residuals for 10 consecutive time periods are as follows:

Time Period	Residual	Time Period	Residual
1	5	6	+1
2	-4	7	+2
3	-3	8	+3
4	-2	9	+4
5	-1	10	+5

a. Plot the residuals over time. What conclusion can you reach about the pattern of the residuals over time?
b. Based on (a), what conclusion can you reach about the autocorrelation of the residuals?

 12.33 The residuals for 15 consecutive time periods are as follows:

Time Period	Residual	Time Period	Residual
1	+4	9	+6
2	-6	10	-3
3	-1	11	+1
4	-5	12	+3
5	+2	13	0
6	+5	14	-4
7	-2	15	-7
8	+7		

a. Plot the residuals over time. What conclusion can you reach about the pattern of the residuals over time?
b. Compute the Durbin-Watson statistic. At the 0.05 level of significance, is there evidence of positive autocorrelation among the residuals?
c. Based on (a) and (b), what conclusion can you reach about the autocorrelation of the residuals?

Applying the Concepts

We recommend that you use Microsoft Excel, Minitab, or SPSS to solve problems 12.35–12.39.

12.34 In problem 12.4 (pet food sales), the marketing manager used shelf space for pet food to predict weekly sales.
a. Is it necessary to compute the Durbin-Watson statistic? Explain.
b. Under what circumstances is it necessary to compute the Durbin-Watson statistic before proceeding with the least-squares method of regression analysis?

12.35 The owner of a single-family home in a suburban county in the northeastern United States would like to develop a model to predict electricity consumption in his all-electric house (lights, fans, heat, appliances, and so on) based on average atmospheric temperature (in degrees Fahrenheit). Monthly kilowatt usage and temperature information are available for a period of 24 consecutive months in the file ELECUSE.
a. Assuming a linear relationship, use the least-squares method to find the regression coefficients b_0 and b_1.
b. Predict the mean kilowatt usage when the average atmospheric temperature is 50 degrees Fahrenheit.
c. Plot the residuals versus the time period.
d. Compute the Durbin-Watson statistic. At the 0.05 level of significance, is there evidence of positive autocorrelation among the residuals?
e. Based on the results of (c) and (d), is there reason to question the validity of the model?

12.36 A mail-order catalog business that sells personal computer supplies, software, and hardware maintains a centralized warehouse for the distribution of products ordered. Management is currently examining the process of distribution from the warehouse and is interested in studying the factors that affect warehouse distribution costs. Currently, a small handling fee is added to the order, regardless of the amount of the order. Data have been collected over the past 24 months indicating the warehouse distribution costs and the number of orders received. WARECOST The results are as follows:

Months	Distribution Cost (Thousands of Dollars)	Number of Orders
1	52.95	4,015
2	71.66	3,806
3	85.58	5,309
4	63.69	4,262
5	72.81	4,296
6	68.44	4,097
7	52.46	3,213
8	70.77	4,809
9	82.03	5,237
10	74.39	4,732
11	70.84	4,413
12	54.08	2,921
13	62.98	3,977
14	72.30	4,428
15	58.99	3,964
16	79.38	4,582
17	94.44	5,582
18	59.74	3,450
19	90.50	5,079
20	93.24	5,735
21	69.33	4,269
22	53.71	3,708
23	89.18	5,387
24	66.80	4,161

a. Assuming a linear relationship, use the least-squares method to find the regression coefficients b_0 and b_1.

b. Predict the monthly warehouse distribution costs when the number of orders is 4,500.

c. Plot the residuals versus the time period.

d. Compute the Durbin-Watson statistic. At the 0.05 level of significance, is there evidence of positive autocorrelation among the residuals?

e. Based on the results of (c) and (d), is there reason to question the validity of the model?

12.37 A freshly brewed shot of espresso has three distinct components, the heart, body, and crema. The separation of these three components typically lasts only 10 to 20 seconds. To use the espresso shot in making a latte, cappuccino, or other drinks, the shot must be poured into the beverage during the separation of the heart, body, and crema. If the shot is used after the separation occurs, the drink becomes excessively bitter and acidic, ruining the final drink. Thus, a longer separation time allows the drink-maker more time to pour the shot and ensure that the beverage will meet expectations. An employee at a coffee shop hypothesized that the harder the espresso grounds were tamped down into the portafilter before brewing, the longer the separation time would be. An experiment using 24 observations was conducted to test this relationship.

ESPRESSO The independent variable Tamp measures the distance in inches between the espresso grounds and the top of the portafilter (i.e., the harder the tamp the larger the distance). The dependent variable Time is the number of seconds the heart, body, and crema are separated (i.e., the amount of time after the shot is poured before it must be used for the customer's beverage).

Shot	Tamp	Time	Shot	Tamp	Time
1	0.20	14	13	0.50	18
2	0.50	14	14	0.50	13
3	0.50	18	15	0.35	19
4	0.20	16	16	0.35	19
5	0.20	16	17	0.20	17
6	0.50	13	18	0.20	18
7	0.20	12	19	0.20	15
8	0.35	15	20	0.20	16
9	0.50	9	21	0.35	18
10	0.35	15	22	0.35	16
11	0.50	11	23	0.35	14
12	0.50	16	24	0.35	16

a. Determine the prediction line using Time as the dependent variable and Tamp as the independent variable.

b. Predict the mean separation time for a Tamp distance of 0.50 inch.

c. Plot the residuals versus the time order of experimentation. Are there any noticeable patterns?

d. Compute the Durbin-Watson statistic. At the 0.05 level of significance, is there evidence of positive autocorrelation among the residuals?

e. Based on the results of (c) and (d), is there reason to question the validity of the model?

12.38 The owner of a chain of ice cream stores would like to study the effect of atmospheric temperature on sales during the summer season. A sample of 21 consecutive days is selected, with the results stored in the data file ICECREAM.

(*Hint:* Determine which are the independent and dependent variables.)

a. Assuming a linear relationship, use the least-squares method to find the regression coefficients b_0 and b_1.

b. Predict the sales per store for a day in which the temperature is 83°F.

c. Plot the residuals versus the time period.

d. Compute the Durbin-Watson statistic. At the 0.05 level of significance, is there evidence of positive autocorrelation among the residuals?

e. Based on the results of (c) and (d), is there reason to question the validity of the model?

12.39 Gasoline prices in the United States hit record highs in May of 2004. Experts blamed the high demand for gasoline worldwide, a lack of production capacity in U.S. refineries, geopolitical unrest, and most importantly, the high price of crude oil on the world market. The data file OIL-GAS contains the U.S. retail price for regular gasoline (cents/gallon) and the world crude oil price (dollars/barrel) for 100 weeks ending May 17, 2004 (U.S. Department of Energy, Energy Information Administration, **www.eia.doe.gov**, May 25, 2004.)

a. Construct a scatter diagram with crude oil price on the X axis and gasoline price on the Y axis. Discuss any patterns present in the data.

b. Determine the prediction line using crude oil price as the independent variable and gasoline price as the dependent variable.

c. Plot the residuals versus the time period and interpret the plot.

d. Compute the Durbin-Watson statistic. At the 0.05 level of significance, is there evidence of positive autocorrelation among the residuals?

e. Based on the result of (c) and (d), is there reason to question the validity of the model?

12.7 INFERENCES ABOUT THE SLOPE AND CORRELATION COEFFICIENT

In sections 12.1 through 12.3, you used regression solely for the purpose of description. You learned how the least-squares method determines the regression coefficients, and how to predict Y for a given value of X. In addition, you learned how to compute and interpret the standard error of the estimate and the coefficient of determination.

When residual analysis, as discussed in section 12.5, indicates that the assumptions of a least-squares regression model are not seriously violated and that the straight-line model is appropriate, you can make inferences about the linear relationship between the variables in the population.

t Test for the Slope

To determine the existence of a significant linear relationship between the X and Y variables, you can test whether β_1 (the population slope) is equal to 0. The null and alternative hypotheses are as follows:

$$H_0: \beta_1 = 0 \text{ (There is no linear relationship.)}$$

$$H_1: \beta_1 \neq 0 \text{ (There is a linear relationship.)}$$

If you reject the null hypothesis, you conclude that there is evidence of a linear relationship. Equation (12.15) defines the test statistic.

TESTING A HYPOTHESIS FOR A POPULATION SLOPE β_1 USING THE t TEST

The t statistic equals the difference between the sample slope and hypothesized value of the population slope divided by the standard error of the slope.

$$t = \frac{b_1 - \beta_1}{S_{b_1}} \tag{12.15}$$

where

$$S_{b_1} = \frac{S_{YX}}{\sqrt{SSX}}$$

$$SSX = \sum_{i=1}^{n}(X_i - \bar{X})^2$$

The test statistic t follows a t distribution with $n - 2$ degrees of freedom.

Return to the "Using Statistics" scenario concerning the site selection data. To test whether there is a significant relationship between the size of the store and the annual sales at the 0.05 level of significance, refer to the Microsoft Excel output for the t test presented in Figure 12.20 or the Minitab output presented in Figure 12.21. From Figure 12.20 or 12.21,

$$b_1 = +1.670 \quad n = 14 \quad S_{b_1} = 0.157$$

and

$$t = \frac{b_1 - \beta_1}{S_{b_1}}$$

$$= \frac{1.670 - 0}{0.157} = 10.64$$

Microsoft Excel labels this t statistic t Stat (see Figure 12.20) and Minitab labels it T (see Figure 12.21). Using the 0.05 level of significance, the critical value of t with $n - 2 = 12$ degrees of freedom is 2.1788. Because $t = 10.64 > 2.1788$, reject H_0 (see Figure 12.22). Using the p-value, you reject H_0 because the p-value is approximately 0. Hence, you can conclude that there is a significant linear relationship between mean annual sales and the size of the store.

FIGURE 12.20

Microsoft Excel t Test for the Slope for the Site Selection Data

16		Coefficients	Standard Error	t Stat	P-value	Lower 95%	Upper 95%
17	Intercept	0.96447	0.52619	1.83293	0.09173	-0.18200	2.11095
18	Square Feet	1.66986	0.15693	10.64112	0.00000	1.32795	2.01177

FIGURE 12.21

Minitab t Test for the Slope for the Site Selection Data

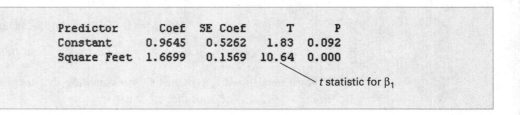

```
Predictor      Coef    SE Coef       T       P
Constant      0.9645    0.5262    1.83   0.092
Square Feet   1.6699    0.1569   10.64   0.000
                                   └── t statistic for β₁
```

FIGURE 12.22

Testing a Hypothesis About the Population Slope at the 0.05 Level of Significance with 12 Degrees of Freedom

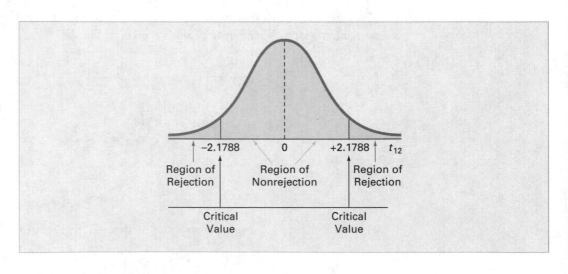

F Test for the Slope

You can also use an F test to determine whether the slope in simple linear regression is statistically significant. Recall from section 10.4 that you use the F distribution to test the ratio of two variances. In testing for the significance of the slope, the F test, defined in Equation (12.16), is the ratio of the variance that is due to the regression (MSR) divided by the error variance ($MSE = S_{YX}^2$).

TESTING A HYPOTHESIS FOR A POPULATION SLOPE β_1 USING THE F TEST

The F statistic is equal to the regression mean square (MSR) divided by the error mean square (MSE).

$$F = \frac{MSR}{MSE} \qquad (12.16)$$

where

$$MSR = \frac{SSR}{k}$$

$$MSE = \frac{SSE}{n - k - 1}$$

k = number of independent variables in the regression model

The test statistic F follows an F distribution with k and $n - k - 1$ degrees of freedom.

Using a level of significance α, the decision rule is

Reject H_0 if $F > F_U$;

otherwise do not reject H_0.

Table 12.5 organizes the complete set of results into an ANOVA table.

TABLE 12.5

ANOVA Table for Testing the Significance of a Regression Coefficient

Source	df	Sum of Squares	Mean Square (Variance)	F
Regression	k	SSR	$MSR = \dfrac{SSR}{k}$	$F = \dfrac{MSR}{MSE}$
Error	$n - k - 1$	SSE	$MSE = \dfrac{SSE}{n - k - 1}$	
Total	$n - 1$	SST		

The completed ANOVA table is also part of the output from Microsoft Excel (see Figure 12.23) and Minitab (see Figure 12.24). Figures 12.23 and 12.24 show that the computed F statistic is 113.23 and the p-value is approximately zero (Excel computes the p-value as 0.000000182).

FIGURE 12.23

Microsoft Excel F Test for the Site Selection Data

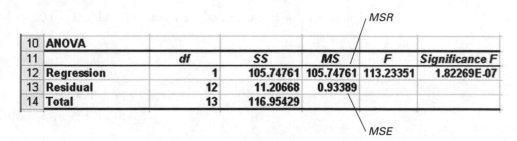

		df	SS	MS	F	Significance F
10	**ANOVA**					
11		df	SS	MS	F	Significance F
12	**Regression**	1	105.74761	105.74761	113.23351	1.82269E-07
13	**Residual**	12	11.20668	0.93389		
14	**Total**	13	116.95429			

FIGURE 12.24

Minitab *F* Test for the Site Selection Data

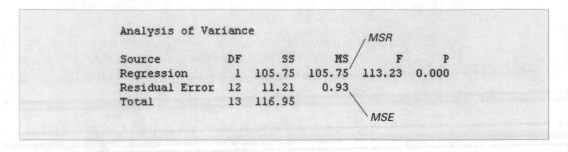

```
Analysis of Variance                          MSR

Source           DF      SS      MS      F       P
Regression        1   105.75  105.75  113.23  0.000
Residual Error   12    11.21    0.93
Total            13   116.95
                                          MSE
```

Using a level of significance of 0.05, from Table E.5 the critical value of the *F* distribution with 1 and 12 degrees of freedom is 4.75 (see Figure 12.25). Because $F = 113.23 > 4.75$ or because the *p*-value = 0.000000182 < 0.05, you reject H_0 and conclude that the size of the store is significantly related to annual sales.

FIGURE 12.25

Regions of Rejection and Nonrejection When Testing for the Significance of the Slope at the 0.05 Level of Significance with 1 and 12 Degrees of Freedom

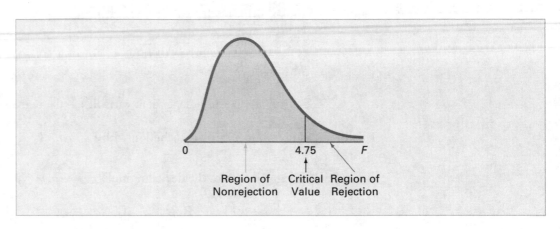

0   4.75   *F*

Region of   Critical   Region of
Nonrejection   Value   Rejection

Confidence Interval Estimate of the Slope (β_1)

As an alternative to testing the existence of a linear relationship between the variables, you can construct a confidence interval estimate of β_1 and determine whether the hypothesized value ($\beta_1 = 0$) is included in the interval. Equation (12.17) defines the confidence interval estimate of β_1.

CONFIDENCE INTERVAL ESTIMATE OF THE SLOPE β_1

The confidence interval estimate for the slope can be constructed by taking the sample slope b_1 and adding and subtracting the critical *t* value multiplied by the standard error of the slope.

$$b_1 \pm t_{n-2}S_{b_1} \tag{12.17}$$

From the Microsoft Excel output of Figure 12.20 or the Minitab output of Figure 12.21,

$$b_1 = +1.670 \quad n = 14 \quad S_{b_1} = 0.157$$

To construct a 95% confidence interval estimate, $\alpha/2 = 0.025$, and from Table E.3, $t_{12} = 2.1788$. Thus,

$$b_1 \pm t_{n-2}S_{b_1} = +1.670 \pm (2.1788)(0.157)$$

$$= +1.670 \pm 0.342$$

$$+1.328 \le \beta_1 \le +2.012$$

Therefore, you estimate with 95% confidence that the population slope is between +1.328 and +2.012 (i.e., $1,328,000 to $2,012,000). Because these values are above 0, you conclude that there is a significant linear relationship between annual sales and square footage size of the store. Had the interval included 0, you would have concluded that no significant relationship exists between the variables. The confidence interval indicates that for each increase of 1,000 square feet, mean annual sales are estimated to increase by at least $1,328,000 but no more than $2,012,000.

t Test for a Correlation Coefficient

You can use the correlation coefficient to determine whether there is a statistically significant linear relationship between X and Y. You hypothesize that the population correlation coefficient ρ is 0. Thus, the null and alternative hypotheses are

$$H_0: \rho = 0 \text{ (No correlation)}$$

$$H_1: \rho \neq 0 \text{ (Correlation)}$$

Equation (12.18) defines the test statistic for determining the existence of a significant correlation.

TESTING FOR THE EXISTENCE OF CORRELATION

$$t = \frac{r - \rho}{\sqrt{\dfrac{1 - r^2}{n - 2}}} \qquad (12.18)$$

where

$$r = +\sqrt{r^2} \text{ if } b_1 > 0$$

or

$$r = -\sqrt{r^2} \text{ if } b_1 < 0$$

The test statistic t follows a t distribution with $n - 2$ degrees of freedom.

In the site selection problem, $r^2 = 0.904$ and $b_1 = +1.670$ (see Figure 12.4 or 12.5). Since $b_1 > 0$, the correlation coefficient for annual sales and store size is the positive square root of r^2, that is, $r^2 = +\sqrt{0.904} = +0.951$. Testing the null hypothesis that there is no correlation between these two variables results in the following observed t statistic:

$$t = \frac{r - 0}{\sqrt{\dfrac{1 - r^2}{n - 2}}}$$

$$= \frac{0.951 - 0}{\sqrt{\dfrac{1 - (0.951)^2}{14 - 2}}} = 10.64$$

Using the 0.05 level of significance, since $t = 10.64 > 2.1788$, you reject the null hypothesis. You conclude that there is evidence of an association between annual sales and store size. This t statistic is equivalent to the t statistic found when testing whether the population slope β_1 is equal to zero (Figures 12.20 and 12.21).

When inferences concerning the population slope were discussed, confidence intervals and tests of hypothesis were used interchangeably. However, developing a confidence interval for the correlation coefficient is more complicated because the shape of the sampling distribution of the statistic r varies for different values of the population correlation coefficient. Methods for developing a confidence interval estimate for the correlation coefficient are presented in reference 5.

PROBLEMS FOR SECTION 12.7

Learning the Basics

 12.40 You are testing the null hypothesis that there is no relationship between two variables X and Y. From your sample of $n = 18$, you determine that $b_1 = +4.5$ and $S_{b_1} = 1.5$.
a. What is the value of the t-test statistic?
b. At the $\alpha = 0.05$ level of significance, what are the critical values?
c. Based on your answers to (a) and (b), what statistical decision should you make?
d. Construct a 95% confidence interval estimate of the population slope β_1.

 12.41 You are testing the null hypothesis that there is no relationship between two variables X and Y. From your sample of $n = 20$, you determine that $SSR = 60$ and $SSE = 40$.
a. What is the value of the F-test statistic?
b. At the $\alpha = 0.05$ level of significance, what is the critical value?
c. Based on your answers to (a) and (b), what statistical decision should you make?
d. Calculate the correlation coefficient by first calculating r^2 and assuming b_1 is negative.
e. At the 0.05 level of significance, is there a significant correlation between X and Y?

Applying the Concepts

Problems 12.42–12.48 and 12.51–12.54 can be solved manually or by using Microsoft Excel, Minitab, or SPSS.

 12.42 In problem 12.4, the marketing manager used shelf space for pet food to predict weekly sales. PETFOOD Using the results of that problem, $b_1 = 0.074$ and $S_{b_1} = 0.0159$.
a. At the 0.05 level of significance, is there evidence of a linear relationship between shelf space and sales?
b. Construct a 95% confidence interval estimate of the population slope β_1.

12.43 In problem 12.5, you used reported magazine newsstand sales to predict audited sales. CIRCULATION Using the results of that problem, $b_1 = 0.5719$ and $S_{b_1} = 0.0668$.

a. At the 0.05 level of significance, is there evidence of a linear relationship between reported sales and audited sales?
b. Construct a 95% confidence interval estimate of the population slope β_1.

12.44 In problem 12.6, the owner of a moving company wanted to predict labor hours based on the number of cubic feet moved. MOVING Using the results of that problem,
a. At the 0.05 level of significance, is there evidence of a linear relationship between the number of cubic feet moved and labor hours?
b. Construct a 95% confidence interval estimate of the population slope β_1.

 12.45 In problem 12.7, you used the weight of mail to predict the number of orders received. MAIL Using the results of that problem,
a. At the 0.05 level of significance, is there evidence of a linear relationship between the weight of mail and the number of orders received?
b. Construct a 95% confidence interval estimate of the population slope β_1.

12.46 In problem 12.8, you used annual revenues to predict the value of a baseball franchise. BBREVENUE Using the results of that problem,
a. At the 0.05 level of significance, is there evidence of a linear relationship between annual revenue and franchise value?
b. Construct a 95% confidence interval estimate of the population slope β_1.

12.47 In problem 12.9, an agent for a real estate company wanted to predict the monthly rent for apartments based on the size of the apartment. RENT Using the results of that problem,
a. At the 0.05 level of significance, is there evidence of a linear relationship between the size of the apartment and the monthly rent?
b. Construct a 95% confidence interval estimate of the population slope β_1.

12.48 In problem 12.10, you used hardness to predict the tensile strength of die-cast aluminum. HARDNESS Using the results of that problem,

a. At the 0.05 level of significance, is there evidence of a linear relationship between hardness and tensile strength?

b. Construct a 95% confidence interval estimate of the population slope β_1.

12.49 The volatility of a stock is often measured by its beta value. You can estimate the beta value of a stock by developing a simple linear regression model using the percentage weekly change in the stock as the dependent variable and the percentage weekly change in a market index as the independent variable. The Standard & Poor's (S&P) 500 Index is a common index to use. For example, if you wanted to estimate the beta for IBM, you could use the following model, which is sometimes referred to as a *market model*.

(% weekly change in IBM) = $\beta_0 + \beta_1$
    (% weekly change in S & P 500 index) + ε

The least-squares regression estimate of the slope b_1 is the estimate of the beta for IBM. A stock with a beta of 1.0 tends to move the same as the overall market. A stock with a beta value of 1.5 tends to move 50% more than the overall market, and a stock with a beta of 0.6 tends to move only 60% as much as the overall market. Stocks with negative betas tend to move in a direction opposite to that of the overall market. The following table gives some beta values for some widely held stocks.

Company	Beta
Sears, Roebuck and Company	0.603
Disney Company	1.109
Ford Motor Company	1.340
IBM	1.449
LSI Logic	2.421

Source: Extracted from finance.yahoo.com, July 27, 2004.

a. For each of the five companies, interpret the value of the beta.

b. How can investors use the beta value as a guide for investing?

12.50 Index funds are mutual funds that try to mimic the movement of leading indexes such as the S&P 500 index, the NASDAQ index, or the Russell 2000 Index. The beta values for these funds (as described in problem 12.49) are therefore approximately 1.0. The estimated market models for these funds are approximately:

(% weekly change in index fund) = 0.0 + 1.0
    (% weekly change in the index)

Leveraged index funds are designed to magnify the movement of major indexes. An article in *Mutual Funds* (Lynn O'Shaughnessy, "Reach for Higher Returns," *Mutual Funds*, July 1999, 44–49) described some of the risks and rewards associated with these funds and gave details on some of the most popular leveraged funds including those in the following table.

Name (Ticker Symbol)	Fund Description
Potomac Small Cap Plus (POSCX)	125% of Russell 2000 Index
Rydex "Inv" Nova (RYNVX)	150% of the S&P 500 Index
ProFund UltraOTC "Inv" (UOPIX)	Double (200%) the NASDAQ 100 Index

Thus, estimated market models for these funds are approximately:

(% weekly change in POSCX) = 0.0 + 1.25
    (% weekly change in the Russell 2000 index)

(% weekly change in RYNVX) = 0.0 + 1.50
    (% weekly change in the S&P 500 index)

(% weekly change in UOPIX fund) = 0.0 + 2.0
    (% weekly change in the NASDAQ 100 index)

Thus, if the Russell 2000 Index gains 10% over a period of time, the leveraged mutual fund POSCX gains approximately 12.5%. On the downside, if the same index loses 20%, POSCX loses approximately 25%.

a. Consider the leveraged mutual fund ProFund UltraBull "Inv" (ULPIX), whose description is 200% of the performance of the S&P 500 Index. What is its approximate market model?

b. If the S&P gains 30% in a year, what return do you expect ULPIX to have?

c. If the S&P loses 35% in a year, what return do you expect ULPIX to have?

d. What type of investors should be attracted to leveraged funds? Which type of investors should stay away from these funds?

12.51 The data in the file REFRIGERATOR represent the approximate retail price and the energy cost per year of 16 medium-size top-freezer refrigerators.

Source: "For the Chill of It," Copyright © 2002 by Consumers Union of U.S., Inc., Yonkers, NY 10703–1057. Adapted with permission from Consumer Reports, August 2002, 26.

a. Compute the coefficient of correlation r.

b. At the 0.05 level of significance, is there a significant linear relationship between the retail price (in $) and the energy cost per year (in $) of medium-size top-freezer refrigerators?

12.52 The data in the file SECURITY represent the turnover rate of pre-boarding screeners at airports in 1998–1999 and the security violations detected per million passengers.

Source: Extracted from *Alan B. Krueger, "A Small Dose of Common Sense Would Help Congress Break the Gridlock Over Airport Security," The New York Times, November 15, 2001, C2.*

a. Compute the coefficient of correlation r.
b. At the 0.05 level of significance, is there a significant linear relationship between the turnover rate of pre-boarding screeners and the security violations detected?
c. What conclusions can you reach about the relationship between the turnover rate of pre-boarding screeners and the security violations detected?

12.53 The data in the file CELLPHONE represents the digital-mode talk time in hours and the battery capacity in millampere-hours of cellphones.

Talk Time	Battery Capacity	Talk Time	Battery Capacity
4.50	800	1.50	450
4.00	1,500	2.25	900
3.00	1,300	2.25	900
2.00	1,550	3.25	900
2.75	900	2.25	700
1.75	875	2.25	800
1.75	750	2.50	800
2.25	1,100	2.25	900
1.75	850	2.00	900

Source: "Service Shortcomings," Copyright 2002 by Consumers Union of U.S., Inc., Yonkers, NY 10703-1057. Adapted with permission from Consumer Reports, February 2002, 25.

a. Compute the coefficient of correlation r.
b. At the 0.05 level of significance, is there a significant linear relationship between the battery capacity and the digital-mode talk time?
c. What conclusions can you reach about the relationship between the battery capacity and the digital-mode talk time?
d. You would expect the cellphones with higher battery capacity to have a higher talk time. Do the data support your expectations?

12.54 The data in the file BATTERIES2 represent the price and cold cranking amps (which denotes the starting current the battery can deliver) of automobile batteries.

Source: "Leading the Charge," Copyright 2001 by Consumers Union of U.S., Inc., Yonkers, NY 10703-1057. Adapted with permission from Consumer Reports, October 2001, 25.

a. Compute the coefficient of correlation r.
b. At the 0.05 level of significance, is there a significant linear relationship between the cold-cranking amps and the price?
c. What conclusions can you reach about the relationship between the cold-cranking amps and the price?
d. You would expect the batteries with higher cold-cranking amps to have a higher price. Do the data support your expectations?

12.8 ESTIMATION OF MEAN VALUES AND PREDICTION OF INDIVIDUAL VALUES

This section presents methods of making inferences about the mean of Y and the prediction of individual values of Y.

The Confidence Interval Estimate

In Example 12.2, you used the prediction line to make predictions about the value of Y for a given X. The mean yearly sales for stores with 4,000 square feet was predicted to be 7.644 millions of dollars ($7,644,000). This estimate, however, is a *point estimate* of the population mean value. In Chapter 8, you studied the concept of the confidence interval as an estimate of the population mean. In a similar fashion, Equation (12.19) defines the **confidence interval estimate for the mean response** for a given X.

CONFIDENCE INTERVAL ESTIMATE FOR THE MEAN OF Y

$$\hat{Y}_i \pm t_{n-2} S_{YX} \sqrt{h_i} \qquad (12.19)$$

$$\hat{Y}_i - t_{n-2} S_{YX} \sqrt{h_i} \le \mu_{Y|X=X_i} \le \hat{Y}_i + t_{n-2} S_{YX} \sqrt{h_i}$$

where

$$h_i = \frac{1}{n} + \frac{(X_i - \bar{X})^2}{SSX}$$

$\hat{Y}_i$ = predicted value of Y; $\hat{Y}_i = b_0 + b_1 X_i$

S_{YX} = standard error of the estimate

n = sample size

X_i = given value of X

$\mu_{Y|X=X_i}$ = mean value of Y when $X = X_i$

$$SSX = \sum_{i=1}^{n}(X_i - \bar{X})^2$$

The width of the confidence interval in Equation (12.19) depends on several factors. For a given level of confidence, increased variation around the prediction line, as measured by the standard error of the estimate, results in a wider interval. However, as you would expect, increased sample size reduces the width of the interval. In addition, the width of the interval also varies at different values of X. When you predict Y for values of X close to $\bar{X}$, the interval is narrower than for predictions for X values more distant from $\bar{X}$.

In the site selection example, suppose you want a 95% confidence interval estimate of the mean annual sales for the entire population of stores that contain 4,000 square feet ($X = 4$). Using the simple linear regression equation:

$$\hat{Y}_i = 0.964 + 1.670 X_i$$

$$= 0.964 + 1.670(4) = 7.644 \text{(millions of dollars)}$$

Also, given the following

$$\bar{X} = 2.9214 \qquad S_{YX} = 0.9664$$

$$SSX = \sum_{i=1}^{n}(X_i - \bar{X})^2 = 37.9236$$

From Table E.3, $t_{12} = 2.1788$. Thus,

$$\hat{Y}_i \pm t_{n-2} S_{YX} \sqrt{h_i}$$

where

$$h_i = \frac{1}{n} + \frac{(X_i - \bar{X})^2}{SSX}$$

so that

$$\hat{Y}_i \pm t_{n-2} S_{YX} \sqrt{\frac{1}{n} + \frac{(X_i - \bar{X})^2}{SSX}}$$

$$= 7.644 \pm (2.1788)(0.9664) \sqrt{\frac{1}{14} + \frac{(4 - 2.9214)^2}{37.9236}}$$

$$= 7.644 \pm 0.673$$

so

$$6.971 \le \mu_{Y|X=4} \le 8.317$$

Therefore, the 95% confidence interval estimate is that the mean annual sales are between 6.971 and 8.317 (millions of dollars) for the population of stores with 4,000 square feet.

The Prediction Interval

In addition to the need for a confidence interval estimate for the mean value, you often want to predict the response for an individual value. Although the form of the prediction interval is similar to the confidence interval estimate of Equation (12.19), the prediction interval is predicting an individual value, not estimating a parameter. Equation (12.20) defines the **prediction interval for an individual response** Y, at a particular value X_i, denoted by $Y_{X=X_i}$.

PREDICTION INTERVAL FOR AN INDIVIDUAL RESPONSE Y

$$\hat{Y}_i \pm t_{n-2} S_{YX} \sqrt{1 + h_i} \qquad\qquad \text{(12.20)}$$

$$\hat{Y}_i - t_{n-2} S_{YX} \sqrt{1 + h_i} \le Y_{X=X_i} \le \hat{Y}_i + t_{n-2} S_{YX} \sqrt{1 + h_i}$$

where h_i, $\hat{Y}_i$, S_{YX}, n, and X_i are defined as in Equation (12.20) and $Y_{X=X_i}$ = a future value of Y when $X = X_i$.

To construct a 95% prediction interval of the annual sales for an individual store that contains 4,000 square feet ($X = 4$), you first compute $\hat{Y}_i$. Using the prediction line:

$$\hat{Y}_i = 0.964 + 1.670 X_i$$

$$= 0.964 + 1.670(4)$$

$$= 7.644 \text{ (millions of dollars)}$$

Also, given the following:

$$\bar{X} = 2.9214 \qquad S_{YX} = 0.9664$$

$$SSX = \sum_{i=1}^{n} (X_i - \bar{X})^2 = 37.9236$$

From Table E.3, $t_{12} = 2.1788$. Thus,

$$\hat{Y}_i \pm t_{n-2} S_{YX} \sqrt{1 + h_i}$$

where

$$h_i = \frac{1}{n} + \frac{(X_i - \bar{X})^2}{\sum_{i=1}^{n}(X_i - \bar{X})^2}$$

so that

$$\hat{Y}_i \pm t_{n-2} S_{YX} \sqrt{1 + \frac{1}{n} + \frac{(X_i - \bar{X})^2}{SSX}}$$

$$= 7.644 \pm (2.1788)(0.9664)\sqrt{1 + \frac{1}{14} + \frac{(4 - 2.9214)^2}{37.9236}}$$

$$- 7.644 \pm 2.210$$

so

$$5.433 \le Y_{X=4} \le 9.854$$

Therefore, with 95% confidence you predict that the annual sales for an individual store with 4,000 square feet is between $5,433,000 and $9,854,000.

Figure 12.26 is a Microsoft Excel worksheet that illustrates the confidence interval estimate and the prediction interval for the site selection problem, and Figure 12.27 shows Minitab output. If you compare the results of the confidence interval estimate and the prediction interval, you see that the width of the prediction interval for an individual store is much wider than the confidence interval estimate for the mean store. Remember that there is much more variation in predicting an individual value than in estimating a mean value.

FIGURE 12.26

Microsoft Excel Confidence Interval Estimate and Prediction Interval for the Site Selection Problem

	A	B	
1	Site Selection Analysis		
2			
3	Data		
4	X Value	4	
5	Confidence Level	95%	
6			
7	Intermediate Calculations		
8	Sample Size	14	=DataCopy!F2
9	Degrees of Freedom	12	=B8 - 2
10	t Value	2.1788	=TINV(1 - B5, B9)
11	Sample Mean	2.9214	=DataCopy!F3
12	Sum of Squared Difference	37.9236	=DataCopy!F4
13	Standard Error of the Estimate	0.9664	(regression worksheet cell B7 value)
14	h Statistic	0.1021	=1/B8 + (B4 - B11)^2/B12
15	Predicted Y (YHat)	7.6439	=DataCopy!F5
16			
17	For Average Y		
18	Interval Half Width	0.6728	=B10 * B13 * SQRT(B14)
19	Confidence Interval Lower Limit	6.9711	=B15 - B18
20	Confidence Interval Upper Limit	8.3167	=B15 + B18
21			
22	For Individual Response Y		
23	Interval Half Width	2.2104	=B10 * B13 * SQRT(1 + B14)
24	Prediction Interval Lower Limit	5.4335	=B15 - B23
25	Prediction Interval Upper Limit	9.8544	=B15 + B23

FIGURE 12.27

Minitab Confidence
Interval Estimate and
Prediction Interval for
the Site Selection
Problem

```
Predicted Values for New Observations

New
Obs    Fit  SE Fit      95% CI           95% PI
  1  7.644   0.309  (6.971, 8.317)  (5.433, 9.854)


Values of Predictors for New Observations

New  Square
Obs   Feet
  1   4.00
```

PROBLEMS FOR SECTION 12.8

Learning the Basics

 12.55 Based on a sample of $n = 20$, the least-squares method was used to develop the following prediction line: $\hat{Y}_i = 5 + 3X_i$. In addition,

$$S_{YX} = 1.0, \ \bar{X} = 2, \text{ and } \sum_{i=1}^{n}(X_i - \bar{X})^2 = 20$$

a. Construct a 95% confidence interval estimate of the mean response for $X = 2$.
b. Construct a 95% prediction interval of an individual response for $X = 2$.

 12.56 Based on a sample of $n = 20$, the least-squares method was used to develop the following prediction line: $\hat{Y}_i = 5 + 3X_i$. In addition,

$$S_{YX} = 1.0, \ \bar{X} = 2, \text{ and } \sum_{i=1}^{n}(X_i - \bar{X})^2 = 20$$

a. Construct a 95% confidence interval estimate of the population mean response for $X = 4$.
b. Construct a 95% prediction interval of an individual response for $X = 4$.
c. Compare the results of (a) and (b) with those of problem 12.55 (a) and (b). Which interval is wider? Why?

Applying the Concepts

Problems 12.57–12.63 can be solved manually or by using Microsoft Excel, Minitab, or SPSS.

12.57 In problem 12.5, you used reported sales to predict audited sales of magazines. CIRCULATION For these data S_{YX} = 42.186 and for $X_i = 400$, $h_i = 0.108$.
a. Construct a 95% confidence interval estimate of the mean audited sales for magazines that report newsstand sales of 400,000.
b. Construct a 95% prediction interval of the audited sales for an individual magazine that reports newsstand sales of 400,000.
c. Explain the difference in the results in (a) and (b).

  12.58 In problem 12.4, the marketing manager used shelf space for pet food to predict weekly sales. PETFOOD For these data $S_{YX} = 0.3081$ and for $X_i = 8$, $h_i = 0.1373$.
a. Construct a 95% confidence interval estimate of the mean weekly sales for all stores that have 8 feet of shelf space for pet food.
b. Construct a 95% prediction interval of the weekly sales of an individual store that has 8 feet of shelf space for pet food.
c. Explain the difference in the results in (a) and (b).

12.59 In problem 12.7, you used the weight of mail to predict the number of orders received. MAIL
a. Construct a 95% confidence interval estimate of the mean number of orders received for all packages with a weight of 500 pounds.
b. Construct a 95% prediction interval of the number of orders received for an individual package with a weight of 500 pounds.
c. Explain the difference in the results in (a) and (b).

12.60 In problem 12.6, the owner of a moving company wanted to predict labor hours based on the number of cubic feet moved. MOVING
a. Construct a 95% confidence interval estimate of the mean labor hours for all moves of 500 cubic feet.
b. Construct a 95% prediction interval of the labor hours of an individual move that has 500 cubic feet.
c. Explain the difference in the results in (a) and (b).

12.61 In problem 12.9, an agent for a real estate company wanted to predict the monthly rent for apartments based on the size of the apartment. RENT
a. Construct a 95% confidence interval estimate of the mean monthly rent for all apartments that are 1,000 square feet in size.
b. Construct a 95% prediction interval of the monthly rent of an individual apartment that is 1,000 square feet in size.
c. Explain the difference in the results in (a) and (b).

12.62 In problem 12.8 , you predicted the value of a baseball franchise based on current revenue. BBREVENUE
a. Construct a 95% confidence interval estimate of the mean value of all baseball franchises that generate $150 million of annual revenue.
b. Construct a 95% prediction interval of the value of an individual baseball franchise that generates $150 million of annual revenue.
c. Explain the difference in the results in (a) and (b).

12.63 In problem 12.10, you used hardness to predict the tensile strength of die-cast aluminum. HARDNESS
a. Construct a 95% confidence interval estimate of the mean tensile strength for all specimens with a hardness of 30 Rockwell E units.
b. Construct a 95% prediction interval of the tensile strength for an individual specimen that has a hardness of 30 Rockwell E units.
c. Explain the difference in the results in (a) and (b).

12.9   PITFALLS IN REGRESSION AND ETHICAL ISSUES

Some of the pitfalls involved in using regression analysis are as follows.

- Lacking an awareness of the assumptions of least-squares regression
- Not knowing how to evaluate the assumptions of least-squares regression
- Not knowing what the alternatives to least-squares regression are if a particular assumption is violated
- Using a regression model without knowledge of the subject matter
- Extrapolating outside the relevant range
- Concluding that a significant relationship identified in an observational study is due to a cause-and-effect relationship

The widespread availability of spreadsheet and statistical software has removed the computational hurdle that prevented many users from applying regression analysis. However, for many users this enhanced availability of software has not been accompanied by an understanding of how to use regression analysis properly. A user who is not familiar with either the assumptions of regression or how to evaluate the assumptions cannot be expected to know what the alternatives to least-squares regression are if a particular assumption is violated.

The data in Table 12.6 illustrates the necessity of using scatter plots and residual analysis to go beyond the basic number crunching of computing the Y intercept, the slope, and r^2.

TABLE 12.6

Four Sets of Artificial Data ANSCOMBE

Data Set A		Data Set B		Data Set C		Data Set D	
X_i	Y_i	X_i	Y_i	X_i	Y_i	X_i	Y_i
10	8.04	10	9.14	10	7.46	8	6.58
14	9.96	14	8.10	14	8.84	8	5.76
5	5.68	5	4.74	5	5.73	8	7.71
8	6.95	8	8.14	8	6.77	8	8.84
9	8.81	9	8.77	9	7.11	8	8.47
12	10.84	12	9.13	12	8.15	8	7.04
4	4.26	4	3.10	4	5.39	8	5.25
7	4.82	7	7.26	7	6.42	19	12.50
11	8.33	11	9.26	11	7.81	8	5.56
13	7.58	13	8.74	13	12.74	8	7.91
6	7.24	6	6.13	6	6.08	8	6.89

Source: F. J. Anscombe, "Graphs in Statistical Analysis," American Statistician, Vol. 27 (1973), 17–21.

Anscombe (reference 1) showed that all four data sets given in Table 12.6 have the following identical results:

$$\hat{Y}_i = 3.0 + 0.5X_i$$

$$S_{YX} = 1.237$$

$$S_{b_1} = 0.118$$

$$r^2 = 0.667$$

$$SSR = \text{explained variation} = \sum_{i=1}^{n}(\hat{Y}_i - \bar{Y})^2 = 27.51$$

$$SSE = \text{unexplained variation} = \sum_{i=1}^{n}(Y_i - \hat{Y}_i)^2 = 13.76$$

$$SST = \text{total variation} = \sum_{i=1}^{n}(Y_i - \bar{Y})^2 = 41.27$$

Thus, with respect to these statistics associated with a simple linear regression, the four data sets are identical. Were you to stop the analysis at this point, you would lose valuable information in the data. By examining Figure 12.28, which represents scatter diagrams for the four data sets, and Figure 12.29, which represents residual plots for the four data sets, you can clearly see that each of the four data sets has a different relationship between X and Y.

From the scatter diagrams of Figure 12.28 and the residual plots of Figure 12.29, you see how different the data sets are. The only data set that seems to follow an approximate straight line is data set A. The residual plot for data set A does not show any obvious patterns or outlying residuals. This is certainly not true for data sets B, C, and D. The scatter plot for data set B shows that a quadratic regression model is more appropriate. This conclusion is reinforced by the clear parabolic form of the residual plot for B. The scatter diagram and the residual plot for data set C clearly show an outlying observation. If this is the case, you may want to remove the outlier and reestimate the regression model. Reestimating the model will uncover a much different relationship. Similarly, the scatter diagram for data set D also represents the situation in which the model is heavily dependent on the outcome of a single response ($X_8 = 19$ and $Y_8 = 12.50$). You would have to cautiously evaluate any regression model since its regression coefficients are heavily dependent on a single observation.

FIGURE 12.28

Scatter Diagrams for Four Data Sets

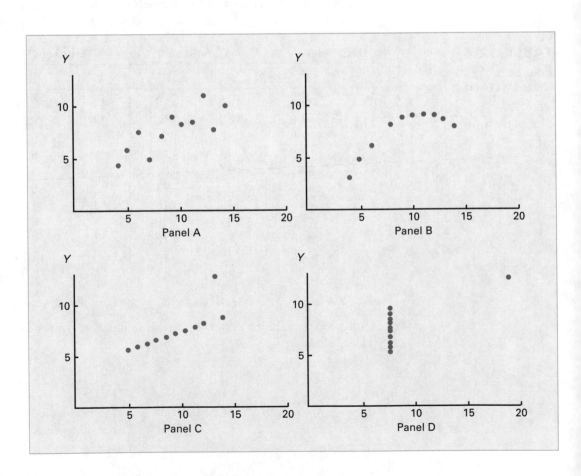

FIGURE 12.29
Residual Plots for Four Data Sets

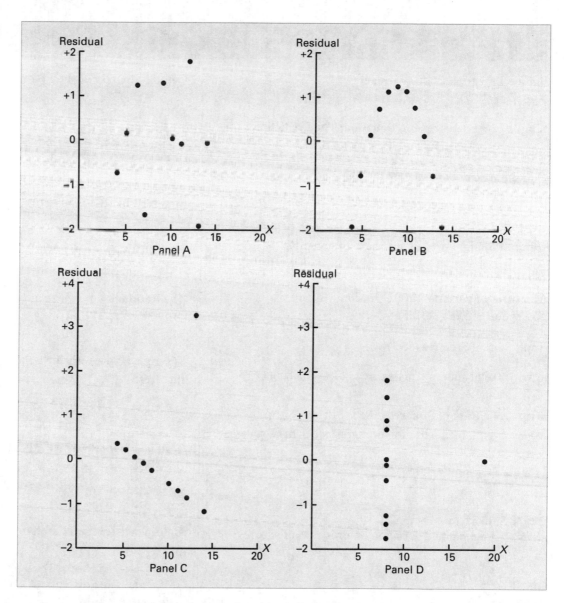

In summary, scatter diagrams and residual plots are of vital importance to a complete regression analysis. The information they provide is so basic to a credible analysis that you should always include these graphical methods as part of a regression analysis. Thus, a strategy that you can use to help avoid the pitfalls of regression is as follows.

- Start with a scatter plot to observe the possible relationship between X and Y.
- Check the assumptions of regression before moving on to using the results of the model.
- Plot the residuals versus the independent variable to determine whether the linear model is appropriate and to check the equal variance assumption.
- Use a histogram, stem-and-leaf display, box-and-whisker plot, or normal probability plot of the residuals to check the normality assumption.
- If you collected the data over time, plot the residuals versus time and use the Durbin-Watson test to check the independence assumption.
- If there are violations of the assumptions, use alternative methods to least-squares regression or alternative least-squares models.
- If there are no violations of the assumptions, then you can carry out tests for the significance of the regression coefficients and develop confidence and prediction intervals.
- Avoid making predictions and forecasts outside the relevant range of the independent variable.
- Always note that the relationships identified in observational studies may or may not be due to a cause-and-effect relationship. Remember that while causation implies correlation, correlation does not imply causation.

KEY FORMULAS

Simple Linear Regression Model

$$Y_i = \beta_0 + \beta_1 X_i + \varepsilon_i \quad \text{(12.1)}$$

Simple Linear Regression Equation: The Prediction Line

$$\hat{Y}_i = b_0 + b_1 X_i \quad \text{(12.2)}$$

Computational Formula for the Slope b_1

$$b_1 = \frac{SSXY}{SSX} \quad \text{(12.3)}$$

Computational Formula for the Y Intercept b_0

$$b_0 = \bar{Y} - b_1 \bar{X} \quad \text{(12.4)}$$

Measures of Variation in Regression

$$SST = SSR + SSE \quad \text{(12.5)}$$

Total Sum of Squares (SST)

$$SST = \text{total sum of squares} = \sum_{i=1}^{n}(Y_i - \bar{Y})^2 \quad \text{(12.6)}$$

Regression Sum of Squares (SSR)

$SSR = $ explained variation or regression sum of squares

$$= \sum_{i=1}^{n}(\hat{Y}_i - \bar{Y})^2 \quad \text{(12.7)}$$

Error Sum of Squares (SSE)

$SSE = $ unexplained variation or error sum of squares

$$= \sum_{i=1}^{n}(Y_i - \hat{Y}_i)^2 \quad \text{(12.8)}$$

Coefficient of Determination

$$r^2 = \frac{\text{regression sum of squares}}{\text{total sum of squares}} = \frac{SSR}{SST} \quad \text{(12.9)}$$

Computational Formula for SST

$$SST = \sum_{i=1}^{n}(Y_i - \bar{Y})^2 = \sum_{i=1}^{n}Y_i^2 - \frac{\left(\sum_{i=1}^{n}Y_i\right)^2}{n} \quad \text{(12.10)}$$

Computational Formula for SSR

$$SSR = \sum_{i=1}^{n}(\hat{Y}_i - \bar{Y})^2 \quad \text{(12.11)}$$

$$= b_0\sum_{i=1}^{n}Y_i + b_1\sum_{i=1}^{n}X_iY_i - \frac{\left(\sum_{i=1}^{n}Y_i\right)^2}{n}$$

Computational Formula for SSE

$$SSE = \sum_{i=1}^{n}(Y_i - \hat{Y})^2 \quad \text{(12.12)}$$

$$= \sum_{i=1}^{n}Y_i^2 - b_0\sum_{i=1}^{n}Y_i - b_1\sum_{i=1}^{n}X_iY_i$$

Standard Error of the Estimate

$$S_{YX} = \sqrt{\frac{SSE}{n-2}} = \sqrt{\frac{\sum_{i=1}^{n}(Y_i - \hat{Y}_i)^2}{n-2}} \quad \text{(12.13)}$$

The Residual

$$e_i = Y_i - \hat{Y}_i \quad \text{(12.14)}$$

Testing a Hypothesis for a Population Slope β_1 Using the t Test

$$t = \frac{b_1 - \beta_1}{S_{b_1}} \quad \text{(12.15)}$$

Testing a Hypothesis for a Population Slope β_1 Using the F Test

$$F = \frac{MSR}{MSE} \quad \text{(12.16)}$$

Confidence Interval Estimate of the Slope β_1

$$b_1 \pm t_{n-2}S_{b_1} \quad \text{(12.17)}$$

Testing for the Existence of Correlation

$$t = \frac{r - \rho}{\sqrt{\frac{1-r^2}{n-2}}} \quad \text{(12.18)}$$

Confidence Interval Estimate for the Mean of Y

$$\hat{Y}_i \pm t_{n-2}S_{YX}\sqrt{h_i} \quad \text{(12.19)}$$

$$\hat{Y}_i - t_{n-2}S_{YX}\sqrt{h_i} \leq \mu_{Y|X=X_i} \leq \hat{Y}_i + t_{n-2}S_{YX}\sqrt{h_i}$$

Prediction Interval for an Individual Response Y

$$\hat{Y}_i \pm t_{n-2}S_{YX}\sqrt{1+h_i} \quad \text{(12.20)}$$

$$\hat{Y}_i - t_{n-2}S_{YX}\sqrt{1+h_i} \leq Y_{X=X_i} \leq \hat{Y}_i + t_{n-2}S_{YX}\sqrt{1+h_i}$$

CHAPTER REVIEW PROBLEMS

Checking Your Understanding

12.64 What is the interpretation of the Y intercept and the slope in the simple linear regression equation?

12.65 What is the interpretation of the coefficient of determination?

12.66 When will the unexplained variation (i.e., error sum of squares) be equal to 0?

12.67 When will the explained variation (i.e., sum of squares due to regression) be equal to 0?

12.68 Why should you always carry out a residual analysis as part of a regression model?

12.69 What are the assumptions of regression analysis?

12.70 How do you evaluate the assumptions of regression analysis?

12.71 When and how do you use the Durbin-Watson statistic?

12.72 What is the difference between a confidence interval estimate of the mean response $\mu_{Y|X=X_i}$ and a prediction interval of $Y_{X=X_i}$?

Applying the Concepts

Problems 12.74–12.92 can be solved manually or by using Microsoft Excel, Minitab, or SPSS.

12.73 Researchers from the Lubin School of Business at Pace University in New York City conducted a study on Internet-supported courses. In one part of the study, four numerical variables were collected on 108 students in an introductory management course that met once a week for an entire semester. One variable collected was *hit consistency*. To measure hit consistency, the researchers did the following:

If a student did not visit the Internet site between classes, the student was given a zero for that time period. If a student visited the Internet site one or more times between classes, the student was given a one for that time period. Since there were 13 time periods, a student's score on hit consistency could range from 0 to 13.

The other three variables included the student's course average, the student's cumulative GPA, and the total number of hits the student had on the Internet site supporting the course. The following table gives the correlation coefficient for all pairs of variables. Note that correlations marked with an * are statistically significant using $\alpha = 0.001$.

Variables	Correlation
Course Average, Cumulative GPA	0.72*
Course Average, Total Hits	0.08
Course Average, Hit Consistency	0.37*
Cumulative GPA, Total Hits	0.12
Cumulative GPA, Hit Consistency	0.32*
Total Hits, Hit Consistency	0.64*

Source: Adapted from Daugher, D., Varanelli, A. and E. Weisbord, "Student Hits in an Internet-Supported Course: How Can Instructors Use Them and What Do They Mean?" Decision Sciences Journal of Innovative Education, Fall 2003, 1(2): 159–179.

a. What conclusions can you reach from this correlation analysis?

b. Are you surprised by the results or are they consistent with your own observations and experiences?

12.74 Management of a soft-drink bottling company wants to develop a method for allocating delivery costs to customers. Although one cost clearly relates to travel time within a particular route, another variable cost reflects the time required to unload the cases of soft drink at the delivery point. A sample of 20 deliveries within a territory was selected. The delivery time and the number of cases delivered were recorded: **DELIVERY**

Customer	Number of Cases	Delivery Time (Minutes)	Customer	Number of Cases	Delivery Time (Minutes)
1	52	32.1	11	161	43.0
2	64	34.8	12	184	49.4
3	73	36.2	13	202	57.2
4	85	37.8	14	218	56.8
5	95	37.8	15	243	60.6
6	103	39.7	16	254	61.2
7	116	38.5	17	267	58.2
8	121	41.9	18	275	63.1
9	143	44.2	19	287	65.6
10	157	47.1	20	298	67.3

Develop a regression model to predict delivery time based on the number of cases delivered.

a. Use the least-squares method to compute the regression coefficients b_0 and b_1.

b. Interpret the meaning of b_0 and b_1 in this problem.

c. Predict the delivery time for 150 cases of soft drink.

d. Would it be appropriate to use the model to predict the delivery time for a customer who is receiving 500 cases of soft drink? Why?

e. Determine the coefficient of determination r^2 and explain its meaning in this problem.

f. Perform a residual analysis. Is there any evidence of a pattern in the residuals? Explain.

g. At the 0.05 level of significance, is there evidence of a linear relationship between delivery time and the number of cases delivered?

h. Construct a 95% confidence interval estimate of the mean delivery time for 150 cases of soft drink.

i. Construct a 95% prediction interval of the delivery time for a single delivery of 150 cases of soft drink.

j. Construct a 95% confidence interval estimate of the population slope.

k. Explain how the results in (a) through (j) can help allocate delivery costs to customers.

12.75 A brokerage house wants to predict the number of trade executions per day using the number of incoming phone calls as a predictor variable. Data were collected over a period of 35 days. TRADES

a. Use the least-squares method to compute the regression coefficients b_0 and b_1.

b. Interpret the meaning of b_0 and b_1 in this problem.

c. Predict the number of trades executed for a day in which the number of incoming calls is 2,000.

d. Is it appropriate to use the model to predict the number of trades executed for a day in which the number of incoming calls is 5,000? Why?

e. Determine the coefficient of determination r^2 and explain its meaning in this problem.

f. Plot the residuals against the number of incoming calls and also against the days. Is there any evidence of a pattern in the residuals with either of these variables? Explain.

g. Determine the Durbin-Watson statistic for these data.

h. Based on the results of (f) and (g), is there reason to question the validity of the model? Explain.

i. At the 0.05 level of significance, is there evidence of a linear relationship between the volume of trade executions and the number of incoming calls?

j. Construct a 95% confidence interval estimate of the mean number of trades executed for days in which the number of incoming calls is 2,000.

k. Construct a 95% prediction interval of the number of trades executed for a particular day in which the number of incoming calls is 2,000.

l. Construct a 95% confidence interval estimate of the population slope.

m. Based on the results of (a) through (l), do you think the brokerage house should focus on a strategy of increasing the total number of incoming calls or on a strategy that relies on trading by a small number of heavy traders? Explain.

12.76 You want to develop a model to predict the selling price of homes based on assessed value. A sample of 30 recently sold single-family houses in a small city is selected to study the relationship between selling price (in thousands of dollars) and assessed value (in thousands of dollars). The houses in the city had been reassessed at full value one year prior to the study. The results are in the file HOUSE1. (*Hint:* First, determine which are the independent and dependent variables.)

a. Plot a scatter diagram and, assuming a linear relationship, use the least-squares method to compute the regression coefficients b_0 and b_1.

b. Interpret the meaning of the Y intercept b_0 and the slope b_1 in this problem.

c. Use the prediction line developed in (a) to predict the selling price for a house whose assessed value is $70,000.

d. Determine the coefficient of determination r^2 and interpret its meaning in this problem.

e. Perform a residual analysis on your results and determine the adequacy of the fit of the model.

f. At the 0.05 level of significance, is there evidence of a linear relationship between selling price and assessed value?

g. Construct a 95% confidence interval estimate of the mean selling price for houses with an assessed value of $70,000.

h. Construct a 95% prediction interval of the selling price of an individual house with an assessed value of $70,000.

i. Construct a 95% confidence interval estimate of the population slope.

12.77 You want to develop a model to predict the assessed value of houses based on heating area. A sample of 15 single-family houses is selected in a city. The assessed value (in thousands of dollars) and the heating area of the houses (in thousands of square feet) are recorded with the following results: HOUSE2

House	Assessed Value ($000)	Heating Area of Dwelling (Thousands of Square Feet)
1	84.4	2.00
2	77.4	1.71
3	75.7	1.45
4	85.9	1.76
5	79.1	1.93
6	70.4	1.20
7	75.8	1.55
8	85.9	1.93
9	78.5	1.59
10	79.2	1.50
11	86.7	1.90
12	79.3	1.39
13	74.5	1.54
14	83.8	1.89
15	76.8	1.59

(*Hint:* First, determine which are the independent and dependent variables.)

a. Plot a scatter diagram and, assuming a linear relationship, use the least-squares method to compute the regression coefficients b_0 and b_1.

b. Interpret the meaning of the Y intercept b_0 and the slope b_1 in this problem.

c. Use the prediction line developed in (a) to predict the assessed value for a house whose heating area is 1,750 square feet.

d. Determine the coefficient of determination r^2 and interpret its meaning in this problem.

e. Perform a residual analysis on your results and determine the adequacy of the fit of the model.

f. At the 0.05 level of significance, is there evidence of a linear relationship between assessed value and heating area?

g. Construct a 95% confidence interval estimate of the mean assessed value for houses with a heating area of 1,750 square feet.

h. Construct a 95% prediction interval of the assessed value of an individual house with a heating area of 1,750 square feet.

i. Construct a 95% confidence interval estimate of the population slope.

12.78 The director of graduate studies at a large college of business would like to predict the grade point index (GPI) of students in an MBA program based on the Graduate Management Aptitude Test (GMAT) score. A sample of 20 students who had completed two years in the program is selected. The results are as follows: **GPIGMAT**

Observation	GMAT Score	GPI	Observation	GMAT Score	GPI
1	688	3.72	11	567	3.07
2	647	3.44	12	542	2.86
3	652	3.21	13	551	2.91
4	608	3.29	14	573	2.79
5	680	3.91	15	536	3.00
6	617	3.28	16	639	3.55
7	557	3.02	17	619	3.47
8	599	3.13	18	694	3.60
9	616	3.45	19	718	3.88
10	594	3.33	20	759	3.76

(*Hint:* First, determine which are the independent and dependent variables.)

a. Plot a scatter diagram and, assuming a linear relationship, use the least-squares method to compute the regression coefficients b_0 and b_1.

b. Interpret the meaning of the Y intercept b_0 and the slope b_1 in this problem.

c. Use the prediction line developed in (a) to predict the GPI for a student with a GMAT score of 600.

d. Determine the coefficient of determination r^2 and interpret its meaning in this problem.

e. Perform a residual analysis on your results and determine the adequacy of the fit of the model.

f. At the 0.05 level of significance, is there evidence of a linear relationship between GMAT score and GPI?

g. Construct a 95% confidence interval estimate for the mean GPI of students with a GMAT score of 600.

h. Construct a 95% prediction interval for a particular student with a GMAT score of 600.

i. Construct a 95% confidence interval estimate of the population slope.

12.79 The manager of the purchasing department of a large banking organization would like to develop a model to predict the amount of time it takes to process invoices. Data are collected from a sample of 30 days, and the number of invoices processed and completion time in hours is recorded. **INVOICE** (*Hint:* First, determine which are the independent and dependent variables.)

a. Assuming a linear relationship, use the least-squares method to compute the regression coefficients b_0 and b_1.

b. Interpret the meaning of the Y intercept b_0 and the slope b_1 in this problem.

c. Use the prediction line developed in (a) to predict the amount of time it would take to process 150 invoices.

d. Determine the coefficient of determination r^2 and interpret its meaning.

e. Plot the residuals against the number of invoices processed and also against time.

f. Based on the plots in (e), does the model seem appropriate?

g. Compute the Durbin-Watson statistic and, at the 0.05 level of significance, determine whether there is any autocorrelation in the residuals.

h. Based on the results of (e) through (g), what conclusions can you reach concerning the validity of the model?

i. At the 0.05 level of significance, is there evidence of a linear relationship between the amount of time and the number of invoices processed?

j. Construct a 95% confidence interval estimate of the mean amount of time it would take to process 150 invoices.

k. Construct a 95% prediction interval of the amount of time it would take to process 150 invoices on a particular day.

12.80 On January 28, 1986, the space shuttle *Challenger* exploded and seven astronauts were killed. Prior to the launch, the predicted atmospheric temperature was for freezing weather at the launch site. Engineers for Morton Thiokol (the manufacturer of the rocket motor) prepared charts to make the case that the launch should not take place due to the cold weather. These arguments were rejected and the launch tragically took place. Upon investigation after the tragedy, experts agreed that the disaster occurred because of leaky rubber O-rings that did not seal properly due to the cold temperature. Data indicating the atmospheric temperature at the time of 23 previous launches and the O-ring damage index are as follows: **O-RING**

Flight Number	Temperature (°F)	O-Ring Damage Index
1	66	0
2	70	4
3	69	0
5	68	0
6	67	0
7	72	0
8	73	0
9	70	0
41-B	57	4
41-C	63	2
41-D	70	4
41-G	78	0
51-A	67	0
51-B	75	0
51-C	53	11
51-D	67	0
51-F	81	0
51-G	70	0
51-I	67	0
51-J	79	0
61-A	75	4
61-B	76	0
61-C	58	4

Note: Data from flight 4 is omitted due to unknown O-ring condition.
Source: Extracted from Report of the Presidential Commission on the Space Shuttle Challenger Accident, *Washington, DC, 1986, Vol. II (H1–H3) and Vol. IV (664),* Post Challenger Evaluation of Space Shuttle Risk Assessment and Management, *Washington, DC, 1988, 135–136.*

a. Construct a scatter diagram for the seven flights in which there was O-ring damage (O-ring damage index $\neq 0$). What conclusions, if any, can you draw about the relationship between atmospheric temperature and O-ring damage?
b. Construct a scatter diagram for all 23 flights.
c. Explain any differences in the interpretation of the relationship between atmospheric temperature and O-ring damage in (a) and (b).
d. Based on the scatter diagram in (b), provide reasons for why a prediction should not be made for an atmospheric temperature of 31°F, the temperature on the morning of the launch of the *Challenger*.
e. Although the assumption of a linear relationship may not be valid, fit a simple linear regression model to predict O-ring damage based on atmospheric temperature.
f. Plot the straight line found in (e) on the scatter diagram developed in (b).

g. Based on the results of (f), do you think a straight line is an appropriate model for these data? Explain.
h. Perform a residual analysis. What conclusions do you reach?

12.81 Crazy Dave, a well-known baseball analyst, would like to study various team statistics for the 2003 baseball season to determine which variables might be useful in predicting the number of wins achieved by teams during the season. He has decided to begin by using the team earned run average (ERA), a measure of pitching performance, to predict the number of wins. The data for the 30 major league teams are in the file **BB2003**.

(*Hint:* First, determine which are the independent and dependent variables.)
a. Assuming a linear relationship, use the least-squares method to compute the regression coefficients b_0 and b_1.
b. Interpret the meaning of the Y intercept b_0 and the slope b_1 in this problem.
c. Use the prediction line developed in (a) to predict the number of wins for a team with an ERA of 4.50.
d. Compute the coefficient of determination r^2 and interpret its meaning.
e. Perform a residual analysis on your results and determine the adequacy of the fit of the model.
f. At the 0.05 level of significance, is there evidence of a linear relationship between the number of wins and the ERA?
g. Construct a 95% confidence interval estimate of the mean number of wins expected for teams with an ERA of 4.50.
h. Construct a 95% prediction interval of the number of wins for an individual team that has an ERA of 4.50.
i. Construct a 95% confidence interval estimate of the slope.
j. The 30 teams constitute a population. In order to use statistical inference [as in (f)–(i)], the data must be assumed to represent a random sample. What "population" would this sample be drawing conclusions about?
k. What other independent variables might you consider for inclusion in the model?

12.82 During the fall harvest season in the United States, pumpkins are sold in large quantities at farm stands. Often, instead of weighing the pumpkins prior to sale, the farm stand operator will just place the pumpkin in the appropriate circular cutout on the counter. When asked why this was done, one farmer replied, "I can tell the weight of the pumpkin from its circumference." To determine whether this was really true, a sample of 23 pumpkins were measured for circumference and weighed with the following results. **PUMPKIN**

Circumference (cm)	Weight (Grams)	Circumference (cm)	Weight (Grams)
50	1,200	57	2,000
55	2,000	66	2,500
54	1,500	82	4,600
52	1,700	83	4,600
37	500	70	3,100
52	1,000	34	600
53	1,500	51	1,500
47	1,400	50	1,500
51	1,500	49	1,600
63	2,500	60	2,300
33	500	59	2,100
43	1,000		

a. Assuming a linear relationship, use the least-squares method to compute the regression coefficients b_0 and b_1.
b. Interpret the meaning of the slope b_1 in this problem.
c. Predict the mean weight for a pumpkin that is 60 centimeters in circumference.
d. Do you think it is a good idea for the farmer to sell pumpkins by circumference instead of weight? Explain.
e. Determine the coefficient of determination r^2 and interpret its meaning.
f. Perform a residual analysis for these data and determine the adequacy of the fit of the model.
g. At the 0.05 level of significance, is there evidence of a linear relationship between the circumference and the weight of a pumpkin?
h. Construct a 95% confidence interval estimate of the population slope β_1.
i. Construct a 95% confidence interval estimate of the population mean weight for pumpkins that have a circumference of 60 centimeters.
j. Construct a 95% prediction interval of the weight for an individual pumpkin that has a circumference of 60 centimeters.

12.83 Can demographic information be helpful in predicting the sales for sporting goods stores? The data stored in SPORTING are the monthly sales totals from a random sample of 38 stores in a large chain of nationwide sporting goods stores. All stores in the franchise, and thus within the sample, are approximately the same size and carry the same merchandise. The county, or in some cases counties, in which the store draws the majority of its customers is referred to here as the customer base. For each of the 38 stores, demographic information about the customer base is provided. The data are real but the name of the franchise is not used at the request of the company. The variables in the data set are:

   Sales: Latest one-month sales total (dollars)
   Age: Median age of customer base (years)

HS: Percentage of customer base with a high school diploma
College: Percentage of customer base with a college diploma
Growth: Annual population growth rate of customer base over the past 10 years
Income: Median family income of customer base (dollars)

a. Construct a scatter diagram using sales as the dependent variable and median family income as the independent variable. Discuss the scatter diagram.
b. Assuming a linear relationship, use the least-squares method to compute the regression coefficients b_0 and b_1.
c. Interpret the meaning of the Y intercept b_0 and the slope b_1 in this problem.
d. Compute the coefficient of determination r^2 and interpret its meaning.
e. Perform a residual analysis on your results and determine the adequacy of the fit of the model.
f. At the 0.05 level of significance, is there evidence of a linear relationship between the independent variable and the dependent variable?
g. Construct a 95% confidence interval estimate of the slope and interpret its meaning.

12.84 For the data of problem 12.83, repeat (a) through (g) using age as the independent variable.

12.85 For the data of problem 12.83, repeat (a) through (g) using high school graduation rate as the independent variable.

12.86 For the data of problem 12.83, repeat (a) through (g) using college graduation rate as the independent variable.

12.87 For the data of problem 12.83, repeat (a) through (g) using growth as the independent variable.

12.88 Zagat's publishes restaurant ratings for various locations in the United States. The data file RESTRATE contains the Zagat rating for food, décor, service, and the price per person for a sample of 50 restaurants located in New York City and 50 restaurants located on Long Island. Develop a regression model to predict the price per person based on a variable that represents the sum of the ratings for food, décor, and service.

Source: Extracted from Zagat Survey 2002 New York City Restaurants and Zagat Survey 2001–2002, Long Island Restaurants.

a. Assuming a linear relationship, use the least-squares method to compute the regression coefficients b_0 and b_1.
b. Interpret the meaning of the Y intercept b_0 and the slope b_1 in this problem.
c. Use the prediction line developed in (a) to predict the price per person for a restaurant with a summated rating of 50.
d. Compute the coefficient of determination r^2 and interpret its meaning.

e. Perform a residual analysis on your results and determine the adequacy of the fit of the model.

f. At the 0.05 level of significance, is there evidence of a linear relationship between the price per person and the summated rating?

g. Construct a 95% confidence interval estimate of the mean price per person for all restaurants with a summated rating of 50.

h. Construct a 95% prediction interval of the price per person for a restaurant with a summated rating of 50.

i. Construct a 95% confidence interval estimate of the slope.

j. How useful do you think the summated rating is as a predictor of price? Explain.

12.89 Refer to the discussion of beta values and market models in problem 12.49. The 2003 weekly data for the S&P 500 and three individual stocks are in the data file **SP500**. Note that the *weekly percentage change* for both the S&P 500 and the individual stocks is measured as the percentage change from the previous week's closing value to the current week's closing value. The variables included are:

Week: Current week
SP500: Weekly percentage change in the S&P 500 Index
SEARS: Weekly percentage change in stock price of Sears, Roebuck, and Company
TARGET: Weekly percentage change in stock price of the Target Corporation
SARALEE: Weekly percentage change in stock price of the Sara Lee Corporation

Source: Extracted from **finance.yahoo.com**, January 20, 2004.

a. Estimate the market model for Sears, Roebuck, and Company (*Hint:* Use the percentage change in the S&P 500 Index as the independent variable and the percentage change in Sears' stock price as the dependent variable.)

b. Interpret the beta value for Sears, Roebuck, and Company.

c. Repeat (a) and (b) for Target, Inc.

d. Repeat (a) and (b) for Sara Lee, Inc.

e. Write a brief summary of your findings.

12.90 The data file **RETURNS** contains the stock price of four companies collected weekly for 53 consecutive weeks ending July 26, 2004. The variables are:

Week: Closing date for stock prices
MSFT: Stock price for Microsoft, Inc.
Ford: Stock price of Ford Motor Company
GM: Stock price of General Motors, Inc.
IAL: Stock price of International Aluminum, Inc.

Source: Extracted from **finance.yahoo.com**, July 30, 2004.

a. Calculate the correlation coefficient r for each pair of stocks. (There are six of them.)

b. Interpret the meaning of r for each pair.

c. Is it a good idea to have all the stocks in an individual's portfolio be strongly positively correlated among each other? Explain.

12.91 Is the daily performance of stocks and bonds correlated? The data file **STOCKS&BONDS** contains information concerning the closing value of the Dow Jones Industrial Average and the Vanguard Long-Term Bond Index Fund for 60 consecutive business days ending July 29, 2004. The variables included are:

Date: Current day
Bonds: Closing price of Vanguard Long-Term Bond Index Fund DJIA
Stocks: Closing price of the Dow Jones Industrial Average

Source: Extracted from **finance.yahoo.com**, July 29, 2004.

a. Compute and interpret the correlation coefficient r for the variables stocks and bonds.

b. At the 0.05 level of significance, is there a relationship between these two variables? Explain.

Report Writing Exercise

12.92 In problems 12.83–12.87, you developed regression models to predict monthly sales at a sporting goods store. Now, write a report based on the models you developed. Append to your report all appropriate charts and statistical information.

RUNNING CASE
MANAGING THE *SPRINGVILLE HERALD*

To ensure that as many trial subscriptions as possible are converted to regular subscriptions, the *Herald* marketing department works closely with the distribution department to accomplish a smooth initial delivery process for the trial subscription customers. To assist in this effort, the marketing department needs to accurately forecast the number of new regular subscriptions for the coming months.

A team consisting of managers from the marketing and distribution departments was convened to develop a better method of forecasting new subscriptions. Previously, after examining new subscription data for the prior three months, a group of three managers would develop a subjective forecast of the number of new subscriptions. Lauren Hall, who was recently hired by the company to provide special skills in quantitative forecasting methods, suggested that the department look for factors that might help in predicting new subscriptions.

Members of the team found that the forecasts in the last year had been particularly inaccurate because in some months much more time was spent on telemarketing than in other months. In particular, in the last month, only 1,055 hours were completed since callers were busy during the first week of the month attending training sessions on the personal but formal greeting style and a new standard presentation guide (see "Managing the Springville Herald" for Chapter 10). Lauren collected the data for the number of new subscriptions and hours spent on telemarketing for each month for the past two years. SH12

EXERCISES

SH12.1 What criticism can you make concerning the method of forecasting that involved taking the new subscriptions for the past three months as the basis for future projections?

SH12.2 What factors other than number of telemarketing hours spent might be useful in predicting the number of new subscriptions? Explain.

SH12.3 **a.** Analyze the data and develop a statistical model to predict the mean number of new subscriptions for a month based on the number of hours spent on telemarketing for new subscriptions.

b. If you expect to spend 1,200 hours on telemarketing per month, estimate the mean number of new subscriptions for the month. Indicate the assumptions upon which this prediction is based. Do you think these assumptions are valid? Explain.

c. What would be the danger of predicting the number of new subscriptions for a month in which 2,000 hours were spent on telemarketing?

WEB CASE

Apply your knowledge of simple linear regression in this Web Case that extends the Sunflowers Clothing Stores "Using Statistics" scenario from this chapter.

Leasing agents from the Triangle Mall Management Corporation have suggested that Sunflowers consider several locations in some of Triangle's newly renovated "lifestyle" malls located in areas of higher than mean disposable income. Although the locations are smaller than the typical Sunflowers location, the leasing agents argue that higher than mean disposable income in the surrounding community is a better predictor of higher sales than store size. The leasing agents maintain that sample data from 14 Sunflowers stores prove that this is true.

Review the leasing agents' proposal and supporting documents that describe the data at the company's Web site **www.prenhall.com/Springville/Triangle_Sunflower.htm** and then answer the following:

1. Should mean disposable income be used to predict sales based on the sample of 14 Sunflowers stores?
2. Should the management of Sunflowers accept the claims of Triangle's leasing agents? Why or why not?
3. Is it possible that the mean disposable income of the surrounding area is not an important factor in leasing new locations? Explain.
4. Are there any other factors not mentioned by the leasing agents that might be relevant to the store leasing decision?

REFERENCES

1. Anscombe, F. J., "Graphs in Statistical Analysis," *The American Statistician* 27 (1973): 17–21.
2. Hoaglin, D. C., and R. Welsch, "The Hat Matrix in Regression and ANOVA," *The American Statistician* 32 (1978): 17–22.
3. Hocking, R. R., "Developments in Linear Regression Methodology: 1959–1982," *Technometrics* 25 (1983): 219–250.
4. Hosmer, D. W., and S. Lemeshow, *Applied Logistic Regression*, 2nd ed. (New York: Wiley, 2001).
5. Kutner, M. H., C. J. Nachtsheim, J. Neter, and W. Li, *Applied Linear Statistical Models*, 5th ed. (New York: McGraw-Hill/Irwin, 2005).
6. *Microsoft Excel 2003* (Redmond, WA: Microsoft Corporation, 2002).
7. *Minitab for Windows Version 14* (State College, PA: Minitab Inc., 2004).
8. Ramsey, P. P., and P. H. Ramsey, "Simple Tests of Normality in Small Samples," *Journal of Quality Technology* 22 (1990): 299–309.
9. *SPSS Base 12 Brief Guide* (Upper Saddle River, NJ: Prentice Hall, 2003).

CHAPTER 13

Multiple Regression

USING STATISTICS: Predicting OmniPower Sales

LEARNING OBJECTIVES

In this chapter, you learn:

- How to develop a multiple regression model
- How to interpret the regression coefficients
- How to determine which independent variables to include in the regression model
- How to use categorical independent variables in a regression model
- How to use quadratic terms in a regression model

USING STATISTICS

Predicting OmniPower Sales

You are the marketing manager for Omni Foods, a large food products company. Omni Foods is preparing a nationwide introduction for a new product, a high-energy bar called OmniPower. Although originally marketed to runners, mountain climbers, and other athletes, high-energy bars are now popular with college students, young business professionals, and other individuals who never seem to have enough time for a traditional breakfast or lunch.

Sales of competitors' high-energy bars have skyrocketed. Before introducing the bar nationwide, you need to determine the effect that price and in-store promotions will have on the sales of OmniPower. You plan to use a sample of 34 stores in a supermarket chain for a test-market study of OmniPower sales. How can you extend the linear regression methods discussed in Chapter 12 to incorporate the effects of price *and* promotion into the same model? How can you use this model to improve the success of the nationwide introduction of OmniPower?

Chapter 12 focused on simple linear regression models that use *one* numerical independent variable X to predict the value of a numerical dependent variable Y. Often you can make better predictions by using *more than one* independent variable. This chapter introduces you to **multiple regression models** that use two or more independent variables to predict the value of a dependent variable.

13.1 DEVELOPING THE MULTIPLE REGRESSION MODEL

A sample of 34 stores in a supermarket chain is selected for a test-market study of OmniPower. All the stores selected have approximately the same monthly sales volume. Two independent variables are considered here—the price of an OmniPower bar as measured in cents (X_1) and the monthly budget for in-store promotional expenditures measured in dollars (X_2). In-store promotional expenditures typically include signs and displays, in-store coupons, and free samples. The dependent variable Y is the number of OmniPower bars sold in a month. Table 13.1 presents the results OMNI of the test-market study.

TABLE 13.1

Monthly OmniPower Sales, Price, and Promotional Expenditures

Store	Sales	Price	Promotion	Store	Sales	Price	Promotion
1	4,141	59	200	18	2,730	79	400
2	3,842	59	200	19	2,618	79	400
3	3,056	59	200	20	4,421	79	400
4	3,519	59	200	21	4,113	79	600
5	4,226	59	400	22	3,746	79	600
6	4,630	59	400	23	3,532	79	600
7	3,507	59	400	24	3,825	79	600
8	3,754	59	400	25	1,096	99	200
9	5,000	59	600	26	761	99	200
10	5,120	59	600	27	2,088	99	200
11	4,011	59	600	28	820	99	200
12	5,015	59	600	29	2,114	99	400
13	1,916	79	200	30	1,882	99	400
14	675	79	200	31	2,159	99	400
15	3,636	79	200	32	1,602	99	400
16	3,224	79	200	33	3,354	99	600
17	2,295	79	400	34	2,927	99	600

With two independent variables and a dependent variable, the data are in three dimensions. Figure 13.1 illustrates a three-dimensional graph constructed by Minitab.

FIGURE 13.1

Minitab Three-Dimensional Graph of Monthly Omnipower Sales, Price, and Promotional Expenditures

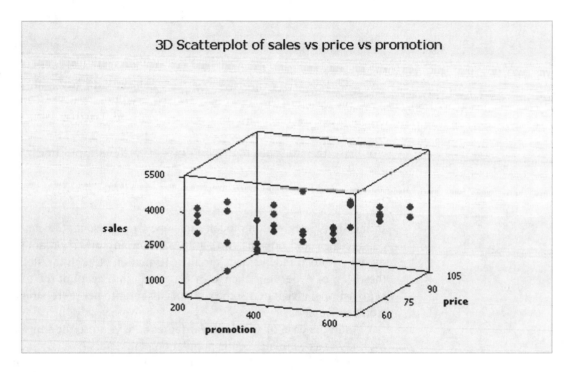

Interpreting the Regression Coefficients

When there are several independent variables, you can extend the simple linear regression model of Equation (12.1) by assuming a linear relationship between each independent variable and the dependent variable. For example, with k independent variables, the multiple regression model is expressed in Equation (13.1).

MULTIPLE REGRESSION MODEL WITH k INDEPENDENT VARIABLES
$$Y_i = \beta_0 + \beta_1 X_{1i} + \beta_2 X_{2i} + \beta_3 X_{3i} + \cdots + \beta_k X_{ki} + \varepsilon_i \qquad \textbf{(13.1)}$$

where $\beta_0 = Y$ intercept

$\beta_1 =$ slope of Y with variable X_1 holding variables $X_2, X_3, \ldots, X_k$ constant

$\beta_2 =$ slope of Y with variable X_2 holding variables $X_1, X_3, \ldots, X_k$ constant

$\beta_3 =$ slope of Y with variable X_3 holding variables $X_1, X_2, X_4, \ldots, X_k$ constant

.

.

.

$\beta_k =$ slope of Y with variable X_k holding variables $X_1, X_2, X_3, \ldots, X_{k-1}$ constant

$\varepsilon_i =$ random error in Y for observation i

Equation (13.2) defines the multiple regression model with two independent variables.

MULTIPLE REGRESSION MODEL WITH TWO INDEPENDENT VARIABLES

$$Y_i = \beta_0 + \beta_1 X_{1i} + \beta_2 X_{2i} + \varepsilon_i \qquad (13.2)$$

where

$\beta_0 = Y$ intercept

$\beta_1 = $ slope of Y with variable X_1 holding variable X_2 constant

$\beta_2 = $ slope of Y with variable X_2 holding variable X_1 constant

$\varepsilon_i = $ random error in Y for observation i

Compare the multiple regression model to the simple linear regression model [Equation (12.1)],

$$Y_i = \beta_0 + \beta_1 X_i + \varepsilon_i$$

In the simple regression model, the slope β_1 represents the change in the mean of Y per unit change in X and does not take into account any other variables. In the multiple regression model with two independent variables [Equation (13.2)], the slope β_1 represents the change in the mean of Y per unit change in X_1, taking into account the effect of X_2. β_1 is called a **net regression coefficient**. (Some statisticians refer to net regression coefficients as partial regression coefficients.)

As in the case of simple linear regression, you use the sample regression coefficients (b_0, b_1, and b_2) as estimates of the population parameters (β_0, β_1, and β_2). Equation (13.3) defines the regression equation for a multiple regression model with two independent variables.

MULTIPLE REGRESSION EQUATION WITH TWO INDEPENDENT VARIABLES

$$\hat{Y}_i = b_0 + b_1 X_{1i} + b_2 X_{2i} \qquad (13.3)$$

You can use Microsoft Excel or Minitab to compute the values of the three regression coefficients using the least-squares method. Figure 13.2 presents Microsoft Excel output for the OmniPower sales data and Figure 13.3 illustrates Minitab output.

From Figure 13.2 or 13.3, the computed values of the regression coefficients are

$$b_0 = 5{,}837.52 \qquad b_1 = -53.2173 \qquad b_2 = 3.6131$$

FIGURE 13.2

Partial Microsoft Excel Output for OmniPower Sales Data

	A	B	C	D	E	F	G
1	OmniPower Sales Analysis						
2							
3	*Regression Statistics*						
4	Multiple R	0.870475					
5	R Square	0.757726					
6	Adjusted R Square	0.742095					
7	Standard Error	638.06529					
8	Observations	34					
9							
10	ANOVA		*SSR*				
11		*df*	*SS*	*MS*	*F*	*Significance F*	
12	Regression	*SSE* 2	39472730.77	19736365.387	48.47713433	2.86258E-10	
13	Residual	31	12620946.67	407127.312			
14	Total	33	52093677.44				
15				*SST*			
16		Coefficients	Standard Error	t Stat	P-value	Lower 95%	Upper 95%
17	Intercept b_0	5837.5208	628.150	9.29319	1.79101E-10	4556.39921	7118.64230
18	Price b_1	-53.21734	6.85222	-7.76644	9.20016E-09	-67.19254	-39.24213
19	Promotion b_2	3.61306	0.68522	5.27283	9.82196E-06	2.21554	5.01058

FIGURE 13.3

Partial Minitab Output for OmniPower Sales Data

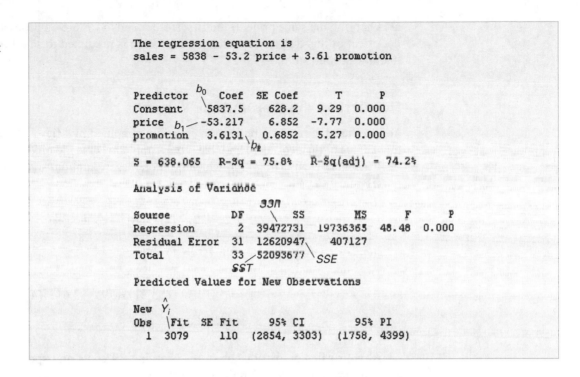

Therefore, the multiple regression equation is

$$\hat{Y}_i = 5{,}837.52 - 53.2173X_{1i} + 3.6131X_{2i}$$

where $\hat{Y}_i$ = predicted monthly sales of OmniPower bars for store i

   X_{1i} = price of OmniPower bar (in cents) for store i

   X_{2i} = monthly in-store promotional expenditures (in dollars) for store i

The sample Y intercept ($b_0 = 5{,}837.52$) estimates the number of OmniPower bars sold in a month if the price is \$0.00 and the total amount spent on promotional expenditures is also \$0.00. Because these values of price and promotion are outside the range of price and promotion used in the test-market study, and are nonsensical, the value of b_0 has no practical interpretation.

The slope of price with OmniPower sales ($b_1 = -53.2173$) indicates that, for a given amount of monthly promotional expenditures, the mean sales of OmniPower are estimated to decrease by 53.2173 bars per month for each 1-cent increase in the price. The slope of monthly promotional expenditures with OmniPower sales ($b_2 = 3.6131$) indicates that, for a given price, the mean sales of OmniPower are estimated to increase by 3.6131 bars for each additional \$1 spent on promotions. These estimates allow you to better understand the likely effect that price and promotion decisions will have in the marketplace. For example, a 10-cent decrease in price is estimated to increase mean sales by 532.173 bars, with a fixed amount of monthly promotional expenditures. A \$100 increase in promotional expenditures is estimated to increase mean sales by 361.31 bars, for a given price.

Regression coefficients in multiple regression are called net regression coefficients and measure the mean change in Y per unit change in a particular X, *holding constant the effect of the other X variables*. For example, in the study of OmniPower bar sales, for a store with a given amount of promotional expenditures, the mean sales are estimated to decrease by 53.22 bars per month for each 1-cent increase in the price of the OmniPower bar. Another way to interpret this "net effect" is to think of two stores with an equal amount of promotional expenditures. If the first store charges 1-cent more than the other store, the "net effect" of this difference is that the first store is predicted to sell 53.22 less bars per month than the second store. To interpret the net effect of promotional expenditures, you can consider two stores that are charging the same price. If the first store spends $1 more on promotional expenditures, the net effect of this difference is that the first store is predicted to sell 3.61 more bars per month than the second store.

Predicting the Dependent Variable Y

You can use the multiple regression equation computed by Microsoft Excel or Minitab to predict values of the dependent variable. For example, what is the predicted sales for a store charging 79 cents during a month in which promotional expenditures are $400? Using the multiple regression equation

$$\hat{Y}_i = 5,837.52 - 53.2173X_{1i} + 3.6131X_{2i}$$

with $X_{1i} = 79$ and $X_{2i} = 400$,

$$\hat{Y}_i = 5,837.52 - 53.2173(79) + 3.6131(400)$$

$$= 3,078.57$$

Thus, your sales prediction for stores charging 79 cents and spending $400 in promotional expenditures is 3,078.57 OmniPower bars per month.

After you have predicted Y and done a residual analysis (see section 13.3), the next step often involves a confidence interval estimate of the mean response and a prediction interval for an individual response. The computation of these intervals is too complex to perform by hand, and you should use Minitab or Microsoft Excel to perform the calculations. Figure 13.3 presents confidence and prediction intervals computed using Minitab for predicting the sales of OmniPower bars. Figure 13.4 illustrates Microsoft Excel output.

FIGURE 13.4

Microsoft Excel Confidence Interval Estimate and Prediction Interval for the OmniPower Example

	A	B	C	D
1	Confidence Interval Estimate and Prediction Interval			
2				
3	Data			
4	Confidence Level	95%		
5		1		
6	Price given value	79		
7	Promotion given value	400		
8				
9	XX	34	2646	13200
10		2646	214674	1018800
11		13200	1018800	6000000
12				
13	Inverse of XX	0.969163	-0.00941	-0.00053
14		-0.009408	0.000115	1.12E-06
15		-0.000535	1.12E-06	1.15E-06
16				
17	X'G times Inverse of XX	0.012054	0.000149	1.49E-05
18				
19	[X'G times Inverse of XX] times XG	0.029762		
20	t Statistic	2.0395		
21	Predicted Y (YHat)	3078.57		
22				
23	For Average Predicted Y (YHat)			
24	Interval Half Width	224.50		
25	Confidence Interval Lower Limit	2854.07		
26	Confidence Interval Upper Limit	3303.08		
27				
28	For Individual Response Y			
29	Interval Half Width	1320.57		
30	Prediction Interval Lower Limit	1758.01		
31	Prediction Interval Upper Limit	4399.14		

The 95% confidence interval estimate of the mean OmniPower sales for all stores charging 79 cents and spending $400 in promotional expenditures is 2,854.07 to 3,303.08 bars. The prediction interval for an individual store is 1,758.01 to 4,399.14 bars.

PROBLEMS FOR SECTION 13.1

Learning the Basics

 13.1 For this problem, use the following multiple regression equation:

$$\hat{Y}_i = 10 + 5X_{1i} + 3X_{2i}$$

a. Interpret the meaning of the slopes.
b. Interpret the meaning of the Y intercept.

 13.2 For this problem, use the following multiple regression equation:

$$\hat{Y}_i = 50 + 2X_{1i} + 7X_{2i}$$

a. Interpret the meaning of the slopes.
b. Interpret the meaning of the Y intercept.

Applying the Concepts

You need to use Microsoft Excel, Minitab, or SPSS to solve problems 13.4–13.8.

13.3 A marketing analyst for a shoe manufacturer is considering the development of a new brand of running shoes. The marketing analyst wants to determine which variables to use in predicting durability (i.e., the effect of long-term impact). Two independent variables under consideration are X_1 (FOREIMP), a measurement of the forefoot shock-absorbing capability, and X_2 (MIDSOLE), a measurement of the change in impact properties over time. The dependent variable Y is LTIMP, a measure of the shoe's durability after a repeated impact test. A random sample of 15 types of currently manufactured running shoes was selected for testing with the following results.

ANOVA	df	SS	MS	F	Significance F
Regression	2	12.61020	6.30510	97.69	0.0001
Error	12	0.77453	0.06454		
Total	14	13.38473			

Variable	Coefficients	Standard Error	t Stat	p-Value
Intercept	−0.02686	0.06905	−0.39	0.7034
Foreimp	0.79116	0.06295	12.57	0.0000
Midsole	0.60484	0.07174	8.43	0.0000

a. State the multiple regression equation.
b. Interpret the meaning of the slopes in this problem.

 13.4 A mail-order catalog business selling personal computer supplies, software, and hardware maintains a centralized warehouse. Management is currently examining the process of distribution from the warehouse and wants to study the factors that affect warehouse distribution costs. Currently, a small handling fee is added to each order, regardless of the amount of the order.

Data collected over the past 24 months indicate the warehouse distribution costs (in thousands of dollars), the sales (in thousands of dollars), and the number of orders received. **WARECOST**
a. State the multiple regression equation.
b. Interpret the meaning of the slopes b_1 and b_2 in this problem.
c. Explain why the regression coefficient b_0 has no practical meaning in the context of this problem.
d. Predict the mean monthly warehouse distribution cost when sales are $400,000 and the number of orders is 4,500.
e. Construct a 95% confidence interval estimate for the mean monthly warehouse distribution cost when sales are $400,000 and the number of orders is 4,500.
f. Construct a 95% prediction interval for the monthly warehouse distribution cost for a particular month when sales are $400,000 and the number of orders is 4,500.

 13.5 A consumer organization wants to develop a regression model to predict gasoline mileage (as measured by miles per gallon) based on the horsepower of the car's engine and the weight of the car in pounds. A sample of 50 recent car models was selected and the results recorded. **AUTO**
a. State the multiple regression equation.
b. Interpret the meaning of the slopes b_1 and b_2 in this problem.
c. Explain why the regression coefficient b_0 has no practical meaning in the context of this problem.
d. Predict the mean miles per gallon for cars that have 60 horsepower and weigh 2,000 pounds.
e. Construct a 95% confidence interval estimate for the mean miles per gallon for cars that have 60 horsepower and weigh 2,000 pounds.
f. Construct a 95% prediction interval for the miles per gallon for an individual car that has 60 horsepower and weighs 2,000 pounds.

 13.6 A consumer products company wants to measure the effectiveness of different types of advertising media in the promotion of its products. Specifically, the company is interested in the effectiveness of radio advertising and newspaper advertising (including the cost of discount coupons). A sample of 22 cities with approximately equal populations is selected for study during a test period of one month. Each city is allocated a specific expenditure level both for radio advertising and for newspaper advertising. The sales of the product (in thousands of dollars) and also the levels of media expenditure (in thousands of dollars) during the test month are recorded with the following results: **ADVERTISE**

City	Sales ($000)	Radio Advertising ($000)	Newspaper Advertising ($000)
1	973	0	40
2	1,119	0	40
3	875	25	25
4	625	25	25
5	910	30	30
6	971	30	30
7	931	35	35
8	1,177	35	35
9	882	40	25
10	982	40	25
11	1,628	45	45
12	1,577	45	45
13	1,044	50	0
14	914	50	0
15	1,329	55	25
16	1,330	55	25
17	1,405	60	30
18	1,436	60	30
19	1,521	65	35
20	1,741	65	35
21	1,866	70	40
22	1,717	70	40

a. State the multiple regression equation.
b. Interpret the meaning of the slopes b_1 and b_2 in this problem.
c. Interpret the meaning of the regression coefficient b_0.
d. Predict the sales for a city in which radio advertising is $20,000 and newspaper advertising is $20,000.
e. Construct a 95% confidence interval estimate for the mean sales for cities in which radio advertising is $20,000 and newspaper advertising is $20,000.
f. Construct a 95% prediction interval for the sales for an individual city in which radio advertising is $20,000 and newspaper advertising is $20,000.

13.7 The director of broadcasting operations for a television station wants to study the issue of standby hours, i.e., hours in which unionized graphic artists at the station are paid but are not actually involved in any activity. The variables in the study include:

Standby hours (Y)—the total number of standby hours in a week
Total staff present (X_1)—the weekly total of people-days in a week.
Remote hours (X_2)—the total number of hours worked by employees at locations away from the central plant
The results for a period of 26 weeks are in the data file STANDBY.
a. State the multiple regression equation.
b. Interpret the meaning of the slopes b_1 and b_2 in this problem.
c. Explain why the regression coefficient b_0 has no practical meaning in the context of this problem.
d. Predict the standby hours for a week in which the total staff present is 310 people-days and the remote hours are 400.
e. Construct a 95% confidence interval estimate for the mean standby hours for weeks in which the total staff present is 310 people-days and the remote hours are 400.
f. Construct a 95% prediction interval for the standby hours for a single week in which the total staff present is 310 people-days and the remote hours are 400.

13.8 Nassau County is located approximately 25 miles east of New York City. Until all residential property was reassessed in 2002, property taxes were assessed based on actual value in 1938 or when the property was built if it was constructed after 1938. Data in the file GLENCOVE include the appraised value (in 2002), land area of the property (acres), and age in years for a sample of 30 single-family homes located in Glen Cove, a small city in Nassau County. Develop a multiple linear regression model to predict appraised value based on land area of the property and age in years.
a. State the multiple regression equation.
b. Interpret the meaning of the slopes b_1 and b_2 in this problem.
c. Explain why the regression coefficient b_0 has no practical meaning in the context of this problem.
d. Predict the appraised value for a house that has a land area of 0.25 acres and is 45 years old.
e. Construct a 95% confidence interval estimate for the mean appraised value for houses that have a land area of 0.25 acres and are 45 years old.
f. Construct a 95% prediction interval estimate for the appraised value for an individual house that has a land area of 0.25 acres and is 45 years old.

13.2 r^2, ADJUSTED r^2, AND THE OVERALL F TEST

Coefficient of Multiple Determination

Recall from section 12.3 that the coefficient of determination r^2 measures the variation in Y that is explained by the independent variable X in the simple linear regression model. In multiple regression, the **coefficient of multiple determination** represents the proportion of the variation in Y that is explained by the set of independent variables. Equation (13.4) defines the coefficient of multiple determination for a multiple regression model with two or more independent variables.

THE COEFFICIENT OF MULTIPLE DETERMINATION

The coefficient of multiple determination is equal to the regression sum of squares (SSR) divided by the total sum of squares (SST).

$$r^2 = \frac{SSR}{SST} \qquad (13.4)$$

where

SSR = regression sum of squares

SST = total sum of squares

In the OmniPower example, from Figure 13.2 or 13.3, $SSR = 39,472,730.77$, and $SST = 52,093,677.44$. Thus,

$$r^2 = \frac{SSR}{SST} = \frac{39,472,730.77}{52,093,677.44} = 0.7577$$

The coefficient of multiple determination ($r^2 = 0.7577$) indicates that 75.77% of the variation in sales is explained by the variation in the price and the variation in the promotional expenditures.

However, when dealing with multiple regression models, some statisticians suggest that you should use the **adjusted r^2** to reflect both the number of independent variables in the model and the sample size. Reporting the adjusted r^2 is extremely important when you are comparing two or more regression models that predict the same dependent variable but have a different number of independent variables. Equation (13.5) defines the adjusted r^2.

ADJUSTED r^2

$$r^2_{adj} = 1 - \left[(1 - r^2) \frac{n-1}{n-k-1} \right] \qquad (13.5)$$

where k is the number of independent variables in the regression equation.

Thus, for the OmniPower data, because $r^2 = 0.7577$, $n = 34$, and $k = 2$,

$$r^2_{adj} = 1 - \left[(1 - r^2) \frac{(34-1)}{(34-2-1)} \right]$$

$$= 1 - \left[(1 - 0.7577) \frac{33}{31} \right]$$

$$= 1 - 0.2579$$

$$= 0.7421$$

Hence, 74.21% of the variation in sales is explained by the multiple regression model—adjusted for number of independent variables and sample size.

Test for the Significance of the Overall Multiple Regression Model

You use the **overall F test** to test for the significance of the overall multiple regression model. This test determines whether there is a significant relationship between the dependent variable and the entire set of independent variables. Because there is more than one independent variable, you use the following null and alternative hypotheses:

$H_0 : \beta_1 = \cdots = \beta_k = 0$ (No linear relationship between the dependent variable and the independent variables.)

H_1: At least one $\beta_j \neq 0$ (Linear relationship between the dependent variable and at least one of the independent variables.)

Equation (13.6) defines the statistic for the overall F test. Table 13.2 presents the associated ANOVA summary table.

OVERALL F-TEST STATISTIC

The F statistic is equal to the regression mean square (MSR) divided by the error mean square (MSE).

$$F = \frac{MSR}{MSE} \qquad (13.6)$$

where F = test statistic from an F distribution with k and $n - k - 1$ degrees of freedom
         k = number of independent variables in the regression model

TABLE 13.2

ANOVA Summary Table for the Overall F Test

Source	Degrees of Freedom	Sum of Squares	Mean Square (Variance)	F
Regression	k	SSR	$MSR = \dfrac{SSR}{k}$	$F = \dfrac{MSR}{MSE}$
Error	$n - k - 1$	SSE	$MSE = \dfrac{SSE}{n - k - 1}$	
Total	$n - 1$	SST		

The decision rule is

Reject H_0 at the α level of significance if $F > F_{U(k,n-k-1)}$;

otherwise, do not reject H_0.

Using a 0.05 level of significance, the critical value of the F distribution with 2 and 31 degrees of freedom found from Table E.5 is approximately 3.32 (see Figure 13.5). From Figure 13.2 or 13.3, the F statistic given in the ANOVA summary table is 48.48. Because 48.48 > 3.32, or because the p-value = 0.000 < 0.05, you reject H_0 and conclude that at least one of the independent variables (price and/or promotional expenditures) is related to sales.

FIGURE 13.5

Testing for the Significance of a Set of Regression Coefficients at the 0.05 Level of Significance with 2 and 31 Degrees of Freedom

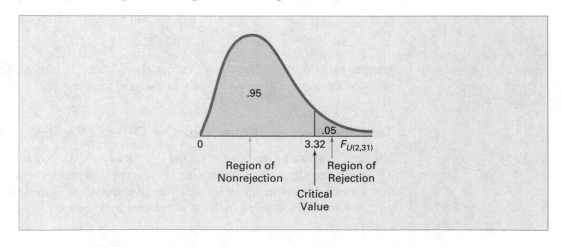

Learning the Basics

 13.9 The following ANOVA summary table is for a multiple regression model with two independent variables.

Source	Degrees of Freedom	Sum of Squares	Mean Squares	F
Regression	2	60		
Error	18	120		
Total	20	180		

a. Determine the mean square that is due to regression and the mean square that is due to error.
b. Compute the F statistic.
c. Determine whether there is a significant relationship between Y and the two independent variables at the 0.05 level of significance.
d. Compute the coefficient of multiple determination r^2 and interpret its meaning.
e. Compute the adjusted r^2.

 13.10 The following ANOVA summary table is for a multiple regression model with two independent variables.

Source	Degrees of Freedom	Sum of Squares	Mean Squares	F
Regression	2	30		
Error	10	120		
Total	12	150		

a. Determine the mean square that is due to regression and the mean square that is due to error.
b. Compute the F statistic.
c. Determine whether there is a significant relationship between Y and the two independent variables at the 0.05 level of significance.
d. Compute the coefficient of multiple determination r^2 and interpret its meaning.
e. Compute the adjusted r^2.

Applying the Concepts

You need to use Microsoft Excel, Minitab, or SPSS to solve problems 13.13–13.17.

13.11 Eileen M. Van Aken and Brian M. Kleiner, professors at Virginia Polytechnic Institute and State University, investigated the factors that contribute to the effectiveness of teams ("Determinants of Effectiveness for Cross-Functional Organizational Design Teams," *Quality Management Journal*, 1997, 4, 51–79). The researchers studied 34 independent variables such as team skills, diversity, meeting frequency, and clarity in expectations. For each of the

teams studied, each of the variables was given a value of 1 through 100 based on the results of interviews and survey data, where 100 represents the highest rating. The dependent variable, team performance, was also given a value of 1 through 100, with 100 representing the highest rating. Many different regression models were explored, including the following:

Model 1

Team Performance $= \beta_0 + \beta_1$ (Team Skills) $+ \varepsilon$,

$$r^2_{adj} = 0.68$$

Model 2

Team Performance $= \beta_0 + \beta_1$ (Clarity in Expectations) $+ \varepsilon$,

$$r^2_{adj} = 0.78$$

Model 3

Team Performance $= \beta_0 + \beta_1$ (Team Skills) $+ \beta_2$ (Clarity in Expectations) $+ \varepsilon$,

$$r^2_{adj} = 0.97$$

a. Interpret the adjusted r^2 for each of the three models.
b. Which of these three models do you think is the best predictor of team performance?

 13.12 In problem 13.3, you predicted the durability of a brand of running shoe based on the forefoot shock-absorbing capability and the change in impact properties over time. The regression analysis resulted in the following ANOVA summary table:

ANOVA	Degrees of Freedom	SS	MS	F	Signifi-cance
Regression	2	12.61020	6.30510	97.69	0.0001
Error	12	0.77453	0.06454		
Total	14	13.38473			

a. Determine whether there is a significant relationship between durability and the two independent variables at the 0.05 level of significance.
b. Interpret the meaning of the p-value.
c. Compute the coefficient of multiple determination r^2 and interpret its meaning.
d. Compute the adjusted r^2.

 13.13 In problem 13.5, you used horsepower and weight to predict gasoline mileage. Using the computer output from that problem, AUTO

a. Determine whether there is a significant relationship between gasoline mileage and the two independent variables (horsepower and weight) at the 0.05 level of significance.

b. Interpret the meaning of the p-value.

c. Compute the coefficient of multiple determination r^2 and interpret its meaning.

d. Compute the adjusted r^2.

 13.14 In problem 13.4, you used sales and number of orders to predict distribution costs at a mail-order catalog business. Using the computer output from that problem, WARECOST

a. Determine whether there is a significant relationship between distribution costs and the two independent variables (sales and number of orders) at the 0.05 level of significance.

b. Interpret the meaning of the p-value.

c. Compute the coefficient of multiple determination r^2 and interpret its meaning.

d. Compute the adjusted r^2.

13.15 In problem 13.7, you used the total staff present and remote hours to predict standby hours. Using the computer output from that problem, STANDBY

a. Determine whether there is a significant relationship between standby hours and the two independent variables (total staff present and remote hours) at the 0.05 level of significance.

b. Interpret the meaning of the p-value.

c. Compute the coefficient of multiple determination r^2 and interpret its meaning.

d. Compute the adjusted r^2.

13.16 In problem 13.6, you used radio advertising and newspaper advertising to predict sales. Using the computer output from that problem, ADVERTISE

a. Determine whether there is a significant relationship between sales and the two independent variables (radio advertising and newspaper advertising) at the 0.05 level of significance.

b. Interpret the meaning of the p-value.

c. Compute the coefficient of multiple determination r^2 and interpret its meaning.

d. Compute the adjusted r^2.

13.17 In problem 13.8, you used the land area of a property and the age of a house to predict appraised value. Using the computer output from that problem, GLENCOVE

a. Determine whether there is a significant relationship between appraised value and the two independent variables (land area of a property and the age of a house) at the 0.05 level of significance.

b. Interpret the meaning of the p-value.

c. Compute the coefficient of multiple determination r^2 and interpret its meaning.

d. Compute the adjusted r^2.

13.3 RESIDUAL ANALYSIS FOR THE MULTIPLE REGRESSION MODEL

In section 12.5, you used residual analysis to evaluate the appropriateness of using the simple linear regression model for a set of data. For the multiple regression model with two independent variables, you need to construct and analyze the following residual plots.

1. Residuals versus $\hat{Y}_i$
2. Residuals versus X_{1i}
3. Residuals versus X_{2i}
4. Residuals versus time

The first residual plot examines the pattern of residuals versus the predicted values of Y. If the residuals show a pattern for different predicted values of Y, there is evidence of a possible quadratic effect in at least one independent variable, a possible violation of the assumption of equal variance (see Figure 12.16), and/or the need to transform the Y variable.

The second and third residual plots involve the independent variables. Patterns in the plot of the residuals versus an independent variable may indicate the existence of a quadratic effect and, therefore, indicate the need to add a quadratic independent variable to the multiple regression model. The fourth plot is used to investigate patterns in the residuals in order to validate the independence assumption when the data are collected in time order. Associated with this residual plot, as in section 12.6, you can compute the Durbin-Watson statistic to determine the existence of positive autocorrelation among the residuals.

You can use statistical and spreadsheet software to plot the residuals. Figure 13.6 illustrates the Microsoft Excel residual plots for the OmniPower sales example. In Figure 13.6, there is very little or no pattern in the relationship between the residuals and the predicted value of Y, the value of X_1 (price), or the value of X_2 (promotional expenditures). Thus, you can conclude that the multiple regression model is appropriate for predicting sales.

FIGURE 13.6

Microsoft Excel Residual Plots for the OmniPower Example: Panel A, Residuals versus Predicted Y, Panel B, Residuals versus Price; Panel C, Residuals versus Promotional Expenditures

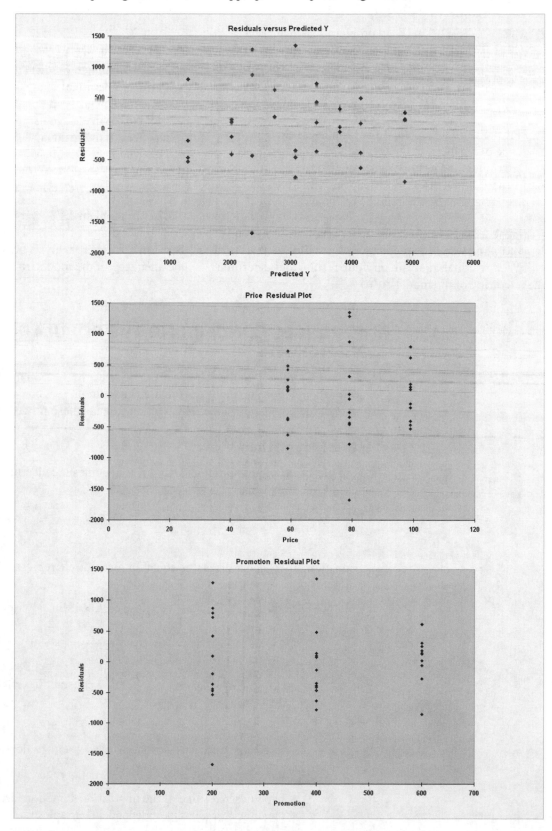

PROBLEMS FOR SECTION 13.3

Applying the Concepts

You need to use Microsoft Excel, Minitab, or SPSS to solve problems 13.18–13.22

  13.18 In problem 13.4, you used sales and number of orders to predict distribution costs at a mail-order catalog business. **WARECOST**
a. Perform a residual analysis on your results and determine the adequacy of the model.
b. Plot the residuals against the months. Is there any evidence of a pattern in the residuals? Explain.
c. Determine the Durbin-Watson statistic.
d. At the 0.05 level of significance, is there evidence of positive autocorrelation in the residuals?

 13.19 In problem 13.5, you used horsepower and weight to predict gasoline mileage. Perform a residual analysis on your results and determine the adequacy of the model. **AUTO**

13.20 In problem 13.6, you used radio advertising and newspaper advertising to predict sales. Perform a residual analysis on your results and determine the adequacy of the model. **ADVERTISE**

13.21 In problem 13.7, you used the total staff present and remote hours to predict standby hours. **STANDBY**
a. Perform a residual analysis on your results and determine the adequacy of the model.
b. Plot the residuals against the weeks. Is there evidence of a pattern in the residuals? Explain.
c. Determine the Durbin-Watson statistic.
d. At the 0.05 level of significance, is there evidence of positive autocorrelation in the residuals?

13.22 In problem 13.8, you used the land area of a property and the age of a house to predict appraised value. Perform a residual analysis on your results and determine the adequacy of the model. **GLENCOVE**

13.4   INFERENCES CONCERNING THE POPULATION REGRESSION COEFFICIENTS

In section 12.7 you tested the slope in a simple linear regression model to determine the significance of the relationship between X and Y. In addition, you constructed a confidence interval estimate of the population slope. This section extends these procedures to multiple regression.

Tests of Hypothesis

In a simple linear regression model, to test a hypothesis concerning the population slope β_1, you used Equation (12.16):

$$t = \frac{b_1 - \beta_1}{S_{b_1}}$$

Equation (13.7) generalizes this equation for multiple regression.

TESTING FOR THE SLOPE IN MULTIPLE REGRESSION

$$t = \frac{b_j - \beta_j}{S_{b_j}} \qquad (13.7)$$

where b_j = slope of variable j with Y, holding constant the effects of all other independent variables

S_{b_j} = standard error of the regression coefficient b_j

t = test statistic for a t distribution with $n - k - 1$ degrees of freedom

k = number of independent variables in the regression equation

β_j = hypothesized value of the population slope for variable j, holding constant the effects of all other independent variables

Microsoft Excel and Minitab output provide the results of the t test for each of the independent variables included in the regression model (see Figure 13.2 or 13.3).

To determine whether variable X_2 (amount of promotional expenditures) has a significant effect on sales, taking into account the price of OmniPower bars, the null and alternative hypotheses are

$$H_0: \beta_2 = 0$$

$$H_1: \beta_2 \neq 0$$

From Equation (13.7), and Figure 13.2 or 13.3,

$$t = \frac{b_2 - \beta_2}{S_{b_2}}$$

$$= \frac{3.6131 - 0}{0.6852} = 5.27$$

If you select a level of significance of 0.05, the critical values of t for 31 degrees of freedom from Table E.3 are -2.0395 and $+2.0395$ (see Figure 13.7).

FIGURE 13.7

Testing for Significance of a Regression Coefficient at the 0.05 Level of Significance with 31 Degrees of Freedom

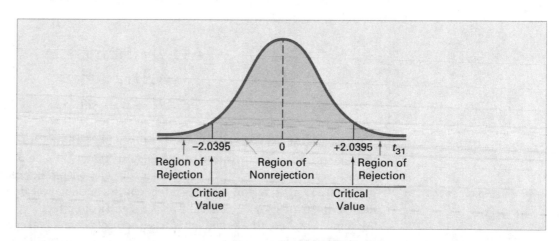

From Figure 13.2 or 13.3, the p-value is 0.00000982 (or 9.82E-06 in scientific notation). Because $t = 5.27 > 2.0395$ or the p-value of 0.00000982 < 0.05, you reject H_0 and conclude that there is a significant relationship between variable X_2 (promotional expenditures) and sales, taking into account the price X_1. This extremely small p-value allows you to strongly reject the null hypothesis that there is no linear relationship between sales and promotional expenditures.

Example 13.1 presents the test for the significance of β_1, the slope of sales with price.

EXAMPLE 13.1

TESTING FOR THE SIGNIFICANCE OF THE SLOPE OF SALES WITH PRICE

At the 0.05 level of significance, is there evidence that the slope of sales with price is different from zero?

SOLUTION From Figure 13.2 or 13.3, $t = -7.766 < -2.0395$ (the critical value for $\alpha = 0.05$) or the p-value = 0.0000000092 < 0.05. Thus, there is a significant relationship between price X_1 and sales, taking into account the promotional expenditures X_2.

As seen with each of these two X variables, the test of significance for a particular regression coefficient is actually a test for the significance of adding a particular variable into a regression model given that the other variable is included. Therefore, the t test for the regression coefficient is equivalent to testing for the contribution of each independent variable.

Confidence Interval Estimation

Instead of testing the significance of a population slope, you may want to estimate the value of a population slope. Equation (13.8) defines the confidence interval estimate for a population slope in multiple regression.

CONFIDENCE INTERVAL ESTIMATE FOR THE SLOPE

$$b_j \pm t_{n-k-1}S_{b_j} \qquad (13.8)$$

For example, if you want to construct a 95% confidence interval estimate of the population slope β_1 (the effect of price X_1 on sales Y, holding constant the effect of promotional expenditures X_2), from Equation (13.8) and Figure 13.2 or 13.3,

$$b_1 \pm t_{n-k-1}S_{b_1}$$

Because the critical value of t at the 95% confidence level with 31 degrees of freedom is 2.0395 (see Table E.3),

$$-53.2173 \pm (2.0395)(6.8522)$$

$$-53.2173 \pm 13.9752$$

$$-67.1925 \le \beta_1 \le -39.2421$$

Taking into account the effect of promotional expenditures, the estimated effect of a 1-cent increase in price is to reduce mean sales by approximately 39.2 to 67.2 bars. You have 95% confidence that this interval correctly estimates the relationship between these variables. From a hypothesis-testing viewpoint, because this confidence interval does not include 0, you conclude that the regression coefficient β_1 has a significant effect.

Example 13.2 constructs and interprets a confidence interval estimate for the slope of sales with promotional expenditures.

EXAMPLE 13.2

CONSTRUCTING A CONFIDENCE INTERVAL ESTIMATE FOR THE SLOPE OF SALES WITH PROMOTIONAL EXPENDITURES

Construct a 95% confidence interval estimate of the population slope of sales with promotional expenditures.

SOLUTION The critical value of t at the 95% confidence level with 31 degrees of freedom is 2.0395 (see Table E.3). Using Equation (13.8)

$$3.6131 \pm (2.0395)(0.6852)$$

$$3.6131 \pm 1.3975$$

$$2.2156 \le \beta_2 \le 5.0106$$

Thus, taking into account the effect of price, the estimated effect of each additional dollar of promotional expenditures is to increase mean sales by approximately 2.2 to 5.0 bars. You have 95% confidence that this interval correctly estimates the relationship between these variables. From a hypothesis-testing viewpoint, because this confidence interval does not include 0, you can conclude that the regression coefficient β_2 has a significant effect.

PROBLEMS FOR SECTION 13.4

Learning the Basics

 13.23 Given the following information from a multiple regression analysis:

$$n = 25, \quad b_1 = 5, \quad b_2 - 10, \quad S_{b_1} = 2, \quad S_{b_2} = 8$$

a. Which variable has the largest slope in units of a t statistic?
b. Construct a 95% confidence interval estimate of the population slope β_1.
c. At the 0.05 level of significance, determine whether each independent variable makes a significant contribution to the regression model. On the basis of these results, indicate the independent variables to include in this model.

13.24 Given the following information from a multiple regression analysis:

$$n = 20, \quad b_1 = 4, \quad b_2 = 3, \quad S_{b_1} = 1.2, \quad S_{b_2} = 0.8$$

a. Which variable has the largest slope in units of a t statistic?
b. Construct a 95% confidence interval estimate of the population slope β_1.
c. At the 0.05 level of significance, determine whether each independent variable makes a significant contribution to the regression model. On the basis of these results, indicate the independent variables to include in this model.

Applying the Concepts

You need to use Microsoft Excel, Minitab, or SPSS to solve problems 13.26–13.30.

 13.25 In problem 13.3, you predicted the durability of a brand of running shoe based on the forefoot shock-absorbing capability (Foreimp) and the change in impact properties over time (Midsole) for a sample of 15 pairs of shoes. Use the following results:

Variable	Coefficients	Standard Error	t stat	p-value
Intercept	−0.02686	0.06905	−0.39	0.7034
Foreimp	0.79116	0.06295	12.57	0.0000
Midsole	0.60484	0.07174	8.43	0.0000

a. Construct a 95% confidence interval estimate of the population slope between durability and forefoot shock-absorbing capability.
b. At the 0.05 level of significance, determine whether each independent variable makes a significant contribution to the regression model. On the basis of these results, indicate the independent variables to include in this model.

  13.26 In problem 13.4, you used sales and number of orders to predict distrib-

ution costs at a mail-order catalog business. Using the computer output from that problem, WARECOST
a. Construct a 95% confidence interval estimate of the population slope between distribution cost and sales.
b. At the 0.05 level of significance, determine whether each independent variable makes a significant contribution to the regression model. On the basis of these results, indicate the independent variables to include in this model.

13.27 In problem 13.5, you used horsepower and weight to predict gasoline mileage. Using the computer output from that problem, AUTO
a. Construct a 95% confidence interval estimate of the population slope between gasoline mileage and horsepower.
b. At the 0.05 level of significance, determine whether each independent variable makes a significant contribution to the regression model. On the basis of these results, indicate the independent variables to include in this model.

13.28 In problem 13.6, you used radio advertising and newspaper advertising to predict sales. Using the computer output from that problem, ADVERTISE
a. Construct a 95% confidence interval estimate of the population slope between sales and radio advertising.
b. At the 0.05 level of significance, determine whether each independent variable makes a significant contribution to the regression model. On the basis of these results, indicate the independent variables to include in this model.

13.29 In problem 13.7, you used the total number of staff present and remote hours to predict standby hours. Using the computer output from that problem, STANDBY
a. Construct a 95% confidence interval estimate of the population slope between standby hours and total number of staff present.
b. At the 0.05 level of significance, determine whether each independent variable makes a significant contribution to the regression model. On the basis of these results, indicate the independent variables to include in this model.

13.30 In problem 13.8, you used the land area of a property and the age of a house to predict appraised value. Using the computer output from that problem, GLENCOVE
a. Construct a 95% confidence interval estimate of the population slope between appraised value and land area of a property.
b. At the 0.05 level of significance, determine whether each independent variable makes a significant contribution to the regression model. On the basis of these results, indicate the independent variables to include in this model.

13.5 USING DUMMY VARIABLES AND INTERACTION TERMS IN REGRESSION MODELS

The multiple regression models discussed in sections 13.1 through 13.4 assumed that each independent variable is numerical. However, in some situations you might want to include categorical variables as independent variables in the regression model. For example, in section 13.1, you used price and promotional expenditures to predict the monthly sales of OmniPower high-energy bars. In addition to these numerical independent variables, you may want to include the effect of the shelf location in the store (e.g., end-aisle display or no end-aisle display) when developing a model to predict OmniPower sales.

The use of **dummy variables** allows you to include categorical independent variables as part of the regression model. If a given categorical independent variable has two categories, then you need only one dummy variable to represent the two categories. A dummy variable X_d is defined as:

$$X_d = 0 \text{ if the observation is in category 1}$$

$$X_d = 1 \text{ if the observation is in category 2}$$

To illustrate the application of dummy variables in regression, consider a model for predicting the assessed value from a sample of 15 houses based on the size of the house (in thousands of square feet) and whether or not the house has a fireplace. To include the categorical variable concerning the presence of a fireplace, the dummy variable X_2 is defined as:

$$X_2 = 0 \text{ if the house does not have a fireplace}$$

$$X_2 = 1 \text{ if the house has a fireplace}$$

In the last column of Table 13.3, you can see how the categorical data are converted to numerical values. HOUSE3

TABLE 13.3

Predicting Assessed Value Based on Size of the House and Presence of a Fireplace

House	$Y =$ Assessed Value ($000)	$X_1 =$ Size of Dwelling (Thousands of Square Feet)	Fireplace	$X_2 =$ Fireplace
1	84.4	2.00	Yes	1
2	77.4	1.71	No	0
3	75.7	1.45	No	0
4	85.9	1.76	Yes	1
5	79.1	1.93	No	0
6	70.4	1.20	Yes	1
7	75.8	1.55	Yes	1
8	85.9	1.93	Yes	1
9	78.5	1.59	Yes	1
10	79.2	1.50	Yes	1
11	86.7	1.90	Yes	1
12	79.3	1.39	Yes	1
13	74.5	1.54	No	0
14	83.8	1.89	Yes	1
15	76.8	1.59	No	0

Assuming that the slope of assessed value with the size of the house is the same for houses that have and do not have a fireplace, the multiple regression model is

$$Y_i = \beta_0 + \beta_1 X_{1i} + \beta_2 X_{2i} + \varepsilon_i$$

where Y_i = assessed value in thousands of dollars for house i

β_0 = Y intercept

X_{1i} = size of the house in thousands of square feet for house i

β_1 = slope of assessed value with size of the house, holding constant the effect of the presence of a fireplace

X_{2i} = dummy variable representing the presence or absence of a fireplace for house i

β_2 = incremental effect of the presence of a fireplace, holding constant the effect of the size of the house

ε_i = random error in Y for house i

Figure 13.8 illustrates the Microsoft Excel output for this model. Figure 13.9 shows Minitab output.

FIGURE 13.8

Microsoft Excel Output for the Regression Model that Includes the Size of the House and the Presence of Fireplace

	A	B	C	D	E	F	G
1	Assessed Value Analysis						
2							
3	Regression Statistics						
4	Multiple R	0.90059					
5	R Square	0.81106					
6	Adjusted R Square	0.77957					
7	Standard Error	2.26260					
8	Observations	15					
9							
10	ANOVA						
11		df	SS	MS	F	Significance F	
12	Regression	2	263.70391	131.85196	25.75565	4.54968E-05	
13	Residual	12	61.43209	5.11934			
14	Total	14	325.136				
15							
16		Coefficients	Standard Error	t Stat	P-value	Lower 95%	Upper 95%
17	Intercept	50.09049	4.351658	11.510668	7.67943E-08	40.60904	59.57194
18	Size	16.18583	2.574442	6.287124	4.02437E-05	10.57661	21.79506
19	Fireplace	3.85298	1.241223	3.104183	0.00912	1.14859	6.55737

FIGURE 13.9

Minitab Output for the Regression Model that Includes the Size of the House and the Presence of Fireplace

```
The regression equation is
Value = 50.1 + 16.2 Size + 3.85 Fireplace


Predictor     Coef    SE Coef       T      P
Constant    50.090      4.352   11.51  0.000
Size        16.186      2.574    6.29  0.000
Fireplace    3.853      1.241    3.10  0.009



S = 2.26260   R-Sq = 81.1%   R-Sq(adj) = 78.0%


Analysis of Variance

Source          DF      SS      MS      F      P
Regression       2  263.70  131.85  25.76  0.000
Residual Error  12   61.43    5.12
Total           14  325.14
```

From Figure 13.8 or 13.9, the regression equation is

$$\hat{Y}_i = 50.09 + 16.186X_{1i} + 3.853X_{2i}$$

For houses without a fireplace, you substitute $X_2 = 0$ into the regression equation

$$\hat{Y}_i = 50.09 + 16.186X_{1i} + 3.853X_{2i}$$

$$= 50.09 + 16.186X_{1i} + 3.853(0)$$

$$= 50.09 + 16.186X_{1i}$$

For houses with a fireplace, you substitute $X_2 = 1$ into the regression equation

$$\hat{Y}_i = 50.09 + 16.186X_{1i} + 3.853X_{2i}$$
$$= 50.09 + 16.186X_{1i} + 3.853(1)$$
$$= 53.943 + 16.186X_{1i}$$

In this model, the regression coefficients are interpreted as follows:

1. Holding constant whether or not a house has a fireplace, for each increase of 1.0 thousand square feet in the size of the house, the mean assessed value is estimated to increase by 16.186 thousand dollars (or $16,186).
2. Holding constant the size of the house, the presence of a fireplace is estimated to increase the mean value of the house by 3.853 thousand dollars (or $3,853).

In Figure 13.8 or 13.9, the t statistic for the slope of the size of the house with assessed value is 6.29 and the p-value is approximately 0.000; the t statistic for presence of a fireplace is 3.10 and the p-value is 0.009. Thus, each of the two variables makes a significant contribution to the model at a level of significance of 0.01. In addition, the coefficient of multiple determination indicates that 81.1% of the variation in assessed value is explained by variation in the size of the house and whether the house has a fireplace.

Interactions

In all the regression models discussed so far, the *effect* an independent variable has on the dependent variable was assumed to be statistically independent of the other independent variables in the model. An **interaction** occurs if the *effect* of an independent variable on the response variable is dependent on the *value* of a second independent variable. For example, it is possible for advertising to have a large effect on the sales of a product when the price of a product is low. However, if the price of the product is too high, increases in advertising will not dramatically change sales. In this case, price and advertising are said to interact. In other words, you cannot make general statements about the effect of advertising on sales. The effect that advertising has on sales is *dependent* on the price. You use an **interaction term** (sometimes referred to as a **cross-product term**) to model an interaction effect in a regression model.

To illustrate the concept of interaction and use of an interaction term, return to the example concerning the assessed values of homes discussed on pages 452–453. In the regression model, you assumed that the effect the size of the home has on the assessed value is independent of whether or not the house has a fireplace. In other words, you assumed that the slope of assessed value with size is the same for houses with fireplaces as it is for houses without fireplaces. If these two slopes are different, an interaction between size of the home and fireplace exists.

To evaluate a hypothesis of equal slopes of a Y variable with X, you first define an interaction term that consists of the product of the independent variable X_1 and the dummy variable X_2. You then test whether this interaction variable makes a significant contribution to a regression model that contains the other X variables. If the interaction is significant, you cannot use the original model for prediction. For the data of Table 13.3, let

$$X_3 = X_1 * X_2$$

Figure 13.10 illustrates Microsoft Excel output for this regression model, which includes the size of the house X_1, the presence of a fireplace X_2, and the interaction of X_1 and X_2 (which is defined as X_3). Figure 13.11 displays Minitab output.

To test for the existence of an interaction, you use the null hypothesis H_0: $\beta_3 = 0$ versus the alternative hypothesis H_1: $\beta_3 \neq 0$. In Figure 13.10 or 13.11, the t statistic for the interaction of size and fireplace is 1.48. Because the p-value = 0.166 > 0.05, you do not reject the null hypothesis. Therefore, the interaction does not make a significant contribution to the model given that size and presence of a fireplace are already included.

FIGURE 13.10

Microsoft Excel Output for a Regression Model that Includes Size, Presence of Fireplace, and Interaction of Size and Fireplace

	A	B	C	D	E	F	G
1	Assessed Value Analysis						
2							
3	Regression Statistics						
4	Multiple R	0.91791					
5	R Square	0.84255					
6	Adjusted R Square	0.79961					
7	Standard Error	2.15727					
8	Observations	15					
9							
10	ANOVA						
11		df	SS	MS	F	Significance F	
12	Regression	3	273.94410	91.31470	19.62150	0.00010	
13	Residual	11	51.19190	4.65361			
14	Total	14	325.136				
15							
16		Coefficients	Standard Error	t Stat	P-value	Lower 95%	Upper 95%
17	Intercept	62.95218	9.61218	6.54921	4.13993E-05	41.79591	84.10845
18	Size	8.36242	5.81730	1.43751	0.17841	-4.44137	21.16621
19	Fireplace	-11.84036	10.64550	-1.11224	0.28975	-35.27007	11.59024
20	Size * Fireplace	9.51800	6.41647	1.48337	0.16605	-4.60456	23.64056

FIGURE 13.11

Minitab Output for a Regression Model that Includes Size, Presence of Fireplace, and Interaction of Size and Fireplace

```
The regression equation is
Value = 63.0 + 8.36 Size - 11.8 Fireplace + 9.52 Size*Fireplace


Predictor         Coef   SE Coef       T      P
Constant        62.952     9.612    6.55  0.000
Size             8.362     5.817    1.44  0.178
Fireplace       -11.84     10.65   -1.11  0.290
Size*Fireplace   9.518     6.416    1.48  0.166


S = 2.15727   R-Sq = 84.3%   R-Sq(adj) = 80.0%


Analysis of Variance

Source          DF      SS      MS      F      P
Regression       3  273.944  91.315  19.62  0.000
Residual Error  11   51.192   4.654
Total           14  325.136
```

PROBLEMS FOR SECTION 13.5

Learning the Basics

 13.31 Suppose X_1 is a numerical variable and X_2 is a dummy variable and the following regression equation for a sample of $n = 20$ is:

$$\hat{Y}_i = 6 + 4X_{1i} + 2X_{2i}$$

a. Interpret the meaning of the slope for variable X_1.
b. Interpret the meaning of the slope for variable X_2.
c. Suppose that the t statistic for testing the contribution of variable X_2 is 3.27. At the 0.05 level of significance, is there evidence that variable X_2 makes a significant contribution to the model?

Applying the Concepts

You need to use Microsoft Excel, Minitab, or SPSS to solve problems 13.32–13.40.

13.32 A real estate association in a suburban community would like to study the relationship between the size of a single-family house (as measured by the number of rooms) and the selling price of the house (in thousands of dollars). Two different neighborhoods are included in the study, one on the east side of the community (=0) and the other on the west side (=1). A random sample of 20 houses was selected with the results given in the file: **NEIGHBOR**

a. State the multiple regression equation.
b. Interpret the meaning of the slopes in this problem.
c. Predict the selling price for a house with nine rooms that is located in an east-side neighborhood, and construct a 95% confidence interval estimate and a 95% prediction interval.
d. Perform a residual analysis on the results, and determine the adequacy of the model.
e. Is there a significant relationship between selling price and the two independent variables (rooms and neighborhood) at the 0.05 level of significance?
f. At the 0.05 level of significance, determine whether each independent variable makes a contribution to the regression model. Indicate the most appropriate regression model for this set of data.
g. Construct 95% confidence interval estimates of the population slope for the relationship between selling price and number of rooms, and between selling price and neighborhood.
h. Interpret the meaning of the coefficient of multiple determination.
i. Compute the adjusted r^2.
j. What assumption do you need to make about the slope of selling price with number of rooms?
k. Add an interaction term to the model, and, at the 0.05 level of significance, determine whether it makes a significant contribution to the model.
l. On the basis of the results of (f) and (k), which model is most appropriate? Explain.

13.33 The marketing manager of a large supermarket chain would like to determine the effect of shelf space and whether the product was placed at the front or back of the aisle on the sales of pet food. A random sample of 12 equal-sized stores is selected with the following results: PETFOOD

Store	Shelf Space (Feet)	Location	Weekly Sales (Hundreds of Dollars)
1	5	Back	1.6
2	5	Front	2.2
3	5	Back	1.4
4	10	Back	1.9
5	10	Back	2.4
6	10	Front	2.6
7	15	Back	2.3
8	15	Back	2.7
9	15	Front	2.8
10	20	Back	2.6
11	20	Back	2.9
12	20	Front	3.1

a. State the multiple regression equation.
b. Interpret the meaning of the slopes in this problem.
c. Predict the weekly sales of pet food for a store with 8 feet of shelf space situated at the back of the aisle, and construct a 95% confidence interval estimate and a 95% prediction interval.
d. Perform a residual analysis on the results and determine the adequacy of the model.
e. Is there is a significant relationship between sales and the two independent variables (shelf space and aisle position) at the 0.05 level of significance?
f. At the 0.05 level of significance, determine whether each independent variable makes a contribution to the regression model. Indicate the most appropriate regression model for this set of data.
g. Construct 95% confidence interval estimates of the population slope for the relationship between sales and shelf space, and between sales and aisle location.
h. Compare the slope in (b) with the slope for the simple linear regression model of problem 12.4. Explain the difference in the results.
i. Interpret the meaning of the coefficient of multiple determination r^2.
j. Compute the adjusted r^2.
k. Compare r^2 with the r^2 value computed in problem 12.16(a).
l. What assumption about the slope of shelf space with sales do you need to make in this problem?
m. Add an interaction term to the model, and at the 0.05 level of significance, determine whether it makes a significant contribution to the model.
n. On the basis of the results of (f) and (m), which model is most appropriate? Explain.

13.34 In mining engineering, holes are often drilled through rock using drill bits. As the drill hole gets deeper, additional rods are added to the drill bit to enable additional drilling to take place. It is expected that drilling time increases with depth. This increased drilling time could be caused by several factors, including the mass of the drill rods that are strung together. A key question relates to whether drilling is faster using dry drilling holes or wet drilling holes. Dry drilling holes involve forcing compressed air down the drill rods to flush the cuttings and drive the hammer. Using wet drilling holes involves forcing water rather than air down the hole. The data file DRILL contains measurements of the time to drill each additional five feet (in minutes), the depth (in feet), and whether the hole was a dry drilling hole or a wet drilling hole for a sample of 50 drill holes. Develop a model to predict additional drilling time based on depth and type of drilling hole (dry or wet).

Source: R. Penner, and D. G. Watts, "Mining Information," The American Statistician, 45, 1991, 4–9.

a. State the multiple regression equation.

b. Interpret the meaning of the slopes in this problem.

c. Predict the additional drilling time for a dry drilling hole at a depth of 100 feet, and construct a 95% confidence interval estimate and a 95% prediction interval.

d. Perform a residual analysis on the results and determine the adequacy of the model.

e. Is there a significant relationship between additional drilling time and the two independent variables (depth and type of drilling hole) at the 0.05 level of significance?

f. At the 0.05 level of significance, determine whether each independent variable makes a contribution to the regression model. Indicate the most appropriate regression model for this set of data.

g. Construct 95% confidence interval estimates of the population slope for the relationship between additional drilling time and depth, and between additional drilling time and type of drilling hole.

h. Interpret the meaning of the coefficient of multiple determination.

i. Compute the adjusted r^2.

j. What assumption about the slope of additional drilling time with depth do you need to make?

k. Add an interaction term to the model and, at the 0.05 level of significance, determine whether it makes a significant contribution to the model.

l. On the basis of the results of (f) and (k), which model is most appropriate? Explain.

13.35 The file COLLEGES2002 contains data on 80 colleges and universities. Among the variables included are the annual total cost (in thousands of dollars), the first quartile score on the Scholastic Aptitude Test (SAT), and whether the school is public or private (0 = public; 1 = private). Develop a model to predict the annual total cost based on first quartile SAT score and whether the school is public or private.

a. State the multiple regression equation.

b. Interpret the meaning of the slopes in this problem.

c. Predict the annual total cost for a school with a first quartile SAT score of 1,000 that is a public institution, and construct a 95% confidence interval estimate and a 95% prediction interval.

d. Perform a residual analysis on the results and determine the adequacy of the model.

e. Is there a significant relationship between annual total cost and the two independent variables (first quartile SAT score and whether the school is public or private) at the 0.05 level of significance?

f. At the 0.05 level of significance, determine whether each independent variable makes a contribution to the regression model. Indicate the most appropriate regression model for this set of data.

g. Construct 95% confidence interval estimates of the population slope for the relationship between annual total cost and first quartile SAT score, and between annual total cost and whether the school is public or private.

h. Interpret the meaning of the coefficient of multiple determination.

i. Compute the adjusted r^2.

j. What assumption about the slope of annual total cost with first quartile SAT score do you need to make?

k. Add an interaction term to the model and, at the 0.05 level of significance, determine whether it makes a significant contribution to the model.

l. On the basis of the results of (f) and (k), which model is most appropriate? Explain.

  13.36 In problem 13.4, you used sales and orders to predict distribution cost. Develop a regression model to predict distribution cost that includes the sales, orders, and the interaction of sales and orders. WARECOST

a. At the 0.05 level of significance, is there evidence that the interaction term makes a significant contribution to the model?

b. Which regression model is more appropriate, the one used in this problem or the one used in problem 13.4? Explain.

13.37 Zagat's publishes restaurant ratings for various locations in the United States. The data file RESTRATE contains the Zagat rating for food, décor, service, and the price per person for a sample of 50 restaurants located in New York City ($X_d = 0$) and 50 restaurants located on Long Island ($X_d = 1$). Develop a regression model to predict the price per person based on a variable that represents the sum of the ratings for food, décor, and service and a dummy variable concerning location (New York City or Long Island).

Source: Extracted from Zagat Survey 2002 New York City Restaurants and Zagat Survey 2001–2002 Long Island Restaurants.

a. State the multiple regression equation.

b. Interpret the meaning of the slopes in this problem.

c. Predict the price for a restaurant with a summated rating of 60 that is located in New York City and construct a 95% confidence interval estimate and 95% prediction interval.

d. Perform a residual analysis on the results and determine the adequacy of the model.

e. Is there a significant relationship between price and the two independent variables (summated rating and location) at the 0.05 level of significance?

f. At the 0.05 level of significance, determine whether each independent variable makes a contribution to the regression model. Indicate the most appropriate regression model for this set of data.

g. Construct 95% confidence interval estimates of the population slope for the relationship between price and summated rating, and between price and location.

h. Compare the slope in (b) with the slope for the simple linear regression model of problem 12.88. Explain the difference in the results.

i. Interpret the meaning of the coefficient of multiple determination.

j. Compute the adjusted r^2.

k. Compare r^2 with the r^2 value computed in problem 12.88(d).

l. What assumption about the slope of price with summated rating do you need to make in this problem?

m. Add an interaction term to the model and, at the 0.05 level of significance, determine whether it makes a significant contribution to the model.

n. On the basis of the results of (f) and (m), which model is most appropriate? Explain.

13.38 In problem 13.6, you used radio advertising and newspaper advertising to predict sales. Develop a regression model to predict sales that includes radio advertising, newspaper advertising, and the interaction of radio advertising and newspaper advertising. ADVERTISE

a. At the 0.05 level of significance, is there evidence that the interaction term makes a significant contribution to the model?

b. Which regression model is more appropriate, the one used in this problem or the one used in problem 13.6? Explain.

PH Grade ASSIST **13.39** In problem 13.5, horsepower and weight were used to predict miles per gallon. Develop a regression model that includes horsepower, weight, and the interaction of horsepower and weight to predict miles per gallon. AUTO

a. At the 0.05 level of significance, is there evidence that the interaction term makes a significant contribution to the model?

b. Which regression model is more appropriate, the one used in this problem or the one used in problem 13.5? Explain.

13.40 In problem 13.7, you used total staff present and remote hours to predict standby hours. Develop a regression model to predict standby hours that includes total staff present, remote hours, and the interaction of total staff present and remote hours. STANDBY

a. At the 0.05 level of significance, is there evidence that the interaction term makes a significant contribution to the model?

b. Which regression model is more appropriate, the one used in this problem or the one used in problem 13.7? Explain.

KEY FORMULAS

Multiple Regression Model with k Independent Variables

$$Y_i = \beta_0 + \beta_1 X_{1i} + \beta_2 X_{2i} + \beta_3 X_{3i} + \cdots + \beta_k X_{ki} + \varepsilon_i \quad (13.1)$$

Multiple Regression Model with Two Independent Variables

$$Y_i = \beta_0 + \beta_1 X_{1i} + \beta_2 X_{2i} + \varepsilon_i \quad (13.2)$$

Multiple Regression Equation with Two Independent Variables

$$\hat{Y}_i = b_0 + b_1 X_{1i} + b_2 X_{2i} \quad (13.3)$$

The Coefficient of Multiple Determination

$$r^2 = \frac{SSR}{SST} \quad (13.4)$$

Adjusted r^2

$$r_{adj}^2 = 1 - \left[(1 - r^2) \frac{n-1}{n-k-1} \right] \quad (13.5)$$

Overall F-Test Statistic

$$F = \frac{MSR}{MSE} \quad (13.6)$$

Testing for the Slope in Multiple Regression

$$t = \frac{b_j - \beta_j}{S_{b_j}} \quad (13.7)$$

Confidence Interval Estimate for the Slope

$$b_j \pm t_{n-k-1} S_{b_j} \quad (13.8)$$

CHAPTER REVIEW PROBLEMS

Checking Your Understanding

13.41 How does the interpretation of the regression coefficients differ in multiple regression and simple regression?

13.42 How does testing the significance of the entire regression model differ from testing the contribution of each independent variable in the multiple regression model?

13.43 How can you evaluate whether the slope of the dependent variable with an independent variable is the same for each level of the dummy variable?

13.44 Under what circumstances do you include an interaction in a regression model?

13.45 When a dummy variable is included in a regression model, what assumption do you need to make concerning the slope between the dependent variable Y and the numerical independent variable X?

Applying the Concepts

You need to use Microsoft Excel, Minitab, or SPSS to solve problems 13.46–13.54.

13.46 Professional basketball has truly become a sport that generates interest among fans around the world. More and more players come from outside the United States to play in the National Basketball Association (NBA). In 2004, nine of the 29 players selected in the first round of the NBA draft were players from outside the United States. You want to develop a regression model to predict the number of wins achieved by each NBA team based on field goal (shots made) percentage for the team and for the opponent. NBA2004

a. State the multiple regression equation.
b. Interpret the meaning of the slopes in this equation.
c. Predict the number of wins for a team that has a field goal percentage of 45% and an opponent field goal percentage of 44%.
d. Perform a residual analysis on your results, and determine the adequacy of the fit of the model.
e. Is there a significant relationship between number of wins and the two independent variables (field goal percentage for the team and for the opponent) at the 0.05 level of significance?
f. Determine the p-value in (e) and interpret its meaning.

g. Interpret the meaning of the coefficient of multiple determination in this problem.
h. Determine the adjusted r^2.
i. At the 0.05 level of significance, determine whether each independent variable makes a significant contribution to the regression model. Indicate the most appropriate regression model for this set of data.
j. Determine the p-values in (i) and interpret their meaning.

13.47 A sample of 30 recently sold single family houses in a small city is selected. Develop a model to predict the selling price (in thousands of dollars) using the assessed value (in thousands of dollars) as well as time period (in months since reassessment). The houses in the city had been reassessed at full value one year prior to the study. The results are contained in the file HOUSE1.

a. State the multiple regression equation.
b. Interpret the meaning of the slopes in this equation.
c. Predict the selling price for a house that has an assessed value of $70,000 and was sold in time period 12.
d. Perform a residual analysis on your results, and determine the adequacy of the model.
e. Determine whether there is a significant relationship between selling price and the two independent variables (assessed value and time period) at the 0.05 level of significance.
f. Determine the p-value in (e) and interpret its meaning.
g. Interpret the meaning of the coefficient of multiple determination in this problem.
h. Determine the adjusted r^2.
i. At the 0.05 level of significance, determine whether each independent variable makes a significant contribution to the regression model. Indicate the most appropriate regression model for this set of data.
j. Determine the p-values in (i) and interpret their meaning.
k. Construct a 95% confidence interval estimate of the population slope between selling price and assessed value. How does the interpretation of the slope here differ from that in problem 12.76?

13.48 Measuring the height of a California redwood tree is a very difficult undertaking because these trees grow to heights of over 300 feet. People familiar with these trees understand that the height of a California redwood tree is

related to other characteristics of the tree, including the diameter of the tree at the breast height of a person, and the thickness of the bark of the tree. The data in the file REDWOOD represent the height, diameter at breast height of a person, and bark thickness for a sample of 21 California redwood trees.
a. State the multiple regression equation.
b. Interpret the meaning of the slopes in this equation.
c. Predict the height for a tree that has a breast diameter of 25 inches and a bark thickness of 2 inches.
d. Interpret the meaning of the coefficient of multiple determination in this problem.
e. Perform a residual analysis on the results and determine the adequacy of the model.
f. Determine whether there is a significant relationship between the height of redwood trees and the two independent variables (breast diameter and the bark thickness) at the 0.05 level of significance?
g. Construct a 95% confidence interval estimate of the population slope between the height of the redwood trees and breast diameter, and between the height of redwood trees and the bark thickness.
h. At the 0.05 level of significance, determine whether each independent variable makes a significant contribution to the regression model. Indicate the independent variables to include in this model.
i. Construct a 95% confidence interval estimate of the mean height for trees that have a breast diameter of 25 inches and a bark thickness of 2 inches along with a prediction interval for an individual tree.

13.49 Develop a model to predict the assessed value (in thousands of dollars) using the size of the houses (in thousands of square feet) and the age of the houses (in years) from the following table: HOUSE2

House	Assessed Value ($000)	Size of Dwelling (Thousands of Square Feet)	Age (Years)
1	84.4	2.00	3.42
2	77.4	1.71	11.50
3	75.7	1.45	8.33
4	85.9	1.76	0.00
5	79.1	1.93	7.42
6	70.4	1.20	32.00
7	75.8	1.55	16.00
8	85.9	1.93	2.00
9	78.5	1.59	1.75
10	79.2	1.50	2.75
11	86.7	1.90	0.00
12	79.3	1.39	0.00
13	74.5	1.54	12.58
14	83.8	1.89	2.75
15	76.8	1.59	7.17

a. State the multiple regression equation.
b. Interpret the meaning of the slopes in this equation.
c. Predict the assessed value for a house that has a size of 1,750 square feet and is 10 years old.
d. Perform a residual analysis on the results and determine the adequacy of the model.
e. Determine whether there is a significant relationship between assessed value and the two independent variables (size and age) at the 0.05 level of significance.
f. Determine the p-value in (e) and interpret its meaning.
g. Interpret the meaning of the coefficient of multiple determination in this problem.
h. Determine the adjusted r^2.
i. At the 0.05 level of significance, determine whether each independent variable makes a significant contribution to the regression model. Indicate the most appropriate regression model for this set of data.
j. Determine the p-values in (i) and interpret their meaning.
k. Construct a 95% confidence interval estimate of the population slope between assessed value and size. How does the interpretation of the slope here differ from that of problem 12.77?
l. The real estate assessor's office has been publicly quoted as saying that the age of a house has no bearing on its assessed value. Based on your answers to (a) through (k), do you agree with this statement? Explain.

13.50 The file COLLEGES2002 contains data on 80 colleges and universities. Among the variables included are the annual total cost (in thousands of dollars), the first-quartile (Q_1) and third-quartile (Q_3) score on the Scholastic Aptitude Test (SAT), and the room-and-board expenses (in thousands of dollars). Develop a model to predict the annual total cost based on first quartile SAT score and room-and-board expenses.
a. State the multiple regression equation.
b. Interpret the meaning of the slopes in this equation.
c. Predict the annual total cost for a school that has a first-quartile SAT score of 1,100 and a room-and-board expense of $5,000.
d. Perform a residual analysis on the results and determine the adequacy of the model.
e. Is there is a significant relationship between annual total cost and the two independent variables (first-quartile SAT score and room-and-board expenses) at the 0.05 level of significance?
f. Determine the p-value in (e) and interpret its meaning.
g. Interpret the meaning of the coefficient of multiple determination in this problem.
h. Determine the adjusted r^2.
i. At the 0.05 level of significance, determine whether each independent variable makes a significant contribution to the regression model. Indicate the most appropriate regression model for this set of data.
j. Determine the p-values in (i) and interpret their meaning.

k. Construct a 95% confidence interval estimate of the population slope between annual total cost and first-quartile SAT score.

l. What other factors that are not included in the model might account for the strong positive relationship between total cost and first quartile SAT score?

13.51 The file AUTO2002 contains data on 121 automobile models from 2002. Among the variables included are the gasoline mileage (in miles per gallon), the length (in inches), and the weight (in pounds) of each automobile. Develop a model to predict the gasoline mileage based on the length and weight of each automobile.

a. State the multiple regression equation.

b. Interpret the meaning of the slopes in this equation.

c. Predict the gasoline mileage for an automobile that has a length of 195 inches and a weight of 3,000 pounds.

d. Perform a residual analysis on the results and determine the adequacy of the model.

e. Is there is a significant relationship between gasoline mileage and the two independent variables (length and weight) at the 0.05 level of significance?

f. Determine the p-value in (e) and interpret its meaning.

g. Interpret the meaning of the coefficient of multiple determination in this problem.

h. Determine the adjusted r^2.

i. At the 0.05 level of significance, determine whether each independent variable makes a significant contribution to the regression model. Indicate the most appropriate regression model for this set of data.

j. Determine the p-values in (i) and interpret their meaning.

k. Construct a 95% confidence interval estimate of the population slope between gasoline mileage and weight.

13.52 Crazy Dave, the well-known baseball analyst, wants to determine which variables are important in predicting a team's wins in a given season. He has collected data related to wins, earned-run average (ERA), and runs scored for the 2003 season (stored in the file **BB2003**). Develop a model to predict the number of wins based on ERA and runs scored.

a. State the multiple regression equation.

b. Interpret the meaning of the slopes in this equation.

c. Predict the number of wins for a team that has an ERA of 4.50 and has scored 750 runs.

d. Perform a residual analysis on the results and determine the adequacy of the model.

e. Is there a significant relationship between number of wins and the two independent variables (ERA and runs scored) at the 0.05 level of significance?

f. Determine the p-value in (e) and interpret its meaning.

g. Interpret the meaning of the coefficient of multiple determination in this problem.

h. Determine the adjusted r^2.

i. At the 0.05 level of significance, determine whether each independent variable makes a significant contribution to the regression model. Indicate the most appropriate regression model for this set of data.

j. Determine the p-values in (i) and interpret their meaning.

k. Construct a 95% confidence interval estimate of the population slope between wins and ERA.

13.53 Referring to problem 13.57, suppose that in addition to using earned run average (ERA) to predict the number of wins, Crazy Dave wants to include the league (American versus National) as an independent variable. Develop a model to predict wins based on ERA and league:
BB2003

a. State the multiple regression equation.

b. Interpret the meaning of the slopes in this problem.

c. Predict the number of wins for a team with an ERA of 4.50 in the American League. Construct a 95% confidence interval estimate for all teams and a 95% prediction interval for an individual team.

d. Perform a residual analysis on the results, and determine the adequacy of the model.

e. Is there a significant relationship between wins and the two independent variables (ERA and league) at the 0.05 level of significance?

f. At the 0.05 level of significance, determine whether each independent variable makes a contribution to the regression model. Indicate the most appropriate regression model for this set of data.

g. Construct 95% confidence interval estimates of the population slope for the relationship between wins and ERA, and between wins and league.

h. Interpret the meaning of the coefficient of multiple determination.

i. Determine the adjusted r^2.

j. What assumption do you have to make about the slope of wins with ERA?

k. Add an interaction term to the model, and, at the 0.05 level of significance, determine whether it makes a significant contribution to the model.

l. On the basis of the results of (f) and (k), which model is most appropriate? Explain.

13.54 You are a real estate broker who wants to compare property values in Glen Cove and Roslyn (which are located approximately 8 miles apart). In order to do so, you will analyze a data set that includes samples for Glen Cove and Roslyn. **GCROSLYN** Making sure to include the dummy variable for location (Glen Cove or Roslyn) in the regression model, develop a regression model to predict appraised value based on the land area of a property, the age of a house, and location. Be sure to determine whether any interaction terms need to be included in the model.

RUNNING CASE: MANAGING THE *SPRINGVILLE HERALD*

In its continuing study of the home-delivery subscription solicitation process, a marketing department team wants to test the effects of two types of structured sales presentations (personal formal and personal informal) and the number of hours spent on telemarketing on the number of new subscriptions. The staff has recorded these data SH13 for the past 24 weeks. You can find this data set at http://www.prenhall.com/HeraldCase/EffectsData.htm and in the **EffectsData.htm** file in the HeraldCase folder on the CD that accompanies this text.

Analyze these data and develop a statistical model to predict the number of new subscriptions for a week based on the number of hours spent on telemarketing and the sales presentation type. Write a report giving detailed findings concerning the regression model used.

WEB CASE

Apply your knowledge of multiple regression models in this Web Case that extends the "Using Statistics" OmniPower scenario from this chapter.

To ensure a successful test-marketing of its OmniPower energy bars, the marketing department of OmniFoods has arranged for the In-Store Placements Group (ISPG), a merchandising consultancy, to work with the grocery store chain conducting the test-market study. Using the same 34-store sample used in the test-market study, ISPG claims that the choice of shelf location and the presence of in-store OmniPower coupon dispensers both increase sale of the energy bars.

Review the ISPG claims and supporting data at OmniFoods internal Web site **www.prenhall.com/Springville/Omni_ISPGMemo.htm** and then answer the following:

1. Are the supporting data consistent to ISPG's claims? Perform an appropriate statistical analysis to confirm (or discredit) the stated relationship between sales and the two independent variables of product shelf location and the presence of in-store OmniPower coupon dispensers.
2. If you were advising OmniFoods, would you recommend using a specific shelf location and in-store coupon dispensers to sell OmniPower bars?
3. What additional data would you advise collecting in order to determine the effectiveness of the sales promotion techniques used by ISPG?

REFERENCES

1. Hocking, R. R., "Developments in Linear Regression Methodology: 1959–1982," *Technometrics* 25 (1983): 219–250.
2. Hosmer, D. W., and S. Lemeshow, *Applied Logistic Regression*, 2nd ed. (New York: Wiley, 2001).
3. Kutner, M., C. Nachtsheim, J. Neter, and W. Li, *Applied Linear Statistical Models*, 5th ed. (New York: McGraw-Hill/Irwin, 2005).
4. *Microsoft Excel 2003* (Redmond, WA: Microsoft Corp., 2002).
5. *Minitab for Windows Version 14* (State College, PA: Minitab, Inc., 2004).
6. *SPSS Base 12.0 Brief Guide* (Upper Saddle River, NJ: Prentice Hall, 2003).

CHAPTER 14

Statistical Applications in Quality and Productivity Management

USING STATISTICS: Service Quality at the Beachcomber Hotel

LEARNING OBJECTIVES

In this chapter, you learn:

- The basic themes of quality management and Deming's 14 points
- The basic aspects of Six Sigma management
- How to construct various control charts
- Which control chart to use for a particular type of data

USING STATISTICS

Service Quality at the Beachcomber Hotel

In the Chapter 11 "Using Statistics" scenario, you were the manager of T. C. Resort Properties. For this scenario, consider that you manage only the Beachcomber Hotel. As the hotel manager, you would want to continually improve the quality of service that your guests receive so that overall guest satisfaction increases. To help you achieve this improvement, T. C. Resort Properties has provided its managers with training in Six Sigma management. In order to meet the business objective of increasing the return rate of guests at your hotel, you have decided to focus on the critical first impressions of the service that your hotel provides. Is the assigned hotel room ready when a guest checks in? Are all expected amenities such as extra towels and a complimentary guest basket in the room when the guest first walks in? Are the video-entertainment center and high-speed Internet access working properly? And, do guests receive their luggage in a reasonable amount of time?

To study these guest satisfaction issues, you have embarked on an improvement project that measures two critical-to-quality (CTQ) measurements, the readiness of the room and the time it takes to deliver luggage. You would like to learn the following:

■ Are the proportion of rooms ready and the time required to deliver luggage to the rooms acceptable?
■ Are the proportion of rooms ready and the luggage delivery time consistent from day to day, or are they increasing or decreasing?
■ On the days when the proportion of rooms that are not ready or the time to deliver luggage is greater than normal, is this due to a chance occurrence or is there a fundamental flaw in the process used to make rooms ready and deliver luggage?

In this chapter the focus is on quality and productivity management. Companies manufacturing products, as well as those providing services, such as the Beachcomber Hotel in the "Using Statistics" scenario, realize that quality and productivity are essential for survival in the global economy. Among the areas in which quality has an impact on our everyday work and personal lives are:

• The design, production, and subsequent reliability of our automobiles
• The services provided by hotels, banks, schools, retailing operations, and mail-order companies
• The continuous improvement in computer chips that makes for faster and more powerful computers
• The ever-expanding capability of communication devices such as data transmission lines, paging devices, facsimile machines, and cellular telephones
• The availability of new technology and equipment that has led to improved diagnosis of illnesses and the improved delivery of health care services

14.1   TOTAL QUALITY MANAGEMENT

During the past twenty-five years, the renewed interest in quality and productivity in the United States followed as a reaction to improvements of Japanese industry that had began as early as 1950. Individuals such as W. Edwards Deming, Joseph Juran, and Kaoru Ishikawa developed an approach that focuses on continuous improvement of products and services through an increased emphasis on statistics, process improvement, and optimization of the total system. This approach, widely known as **total quality management (TQM)**, is characterized by these themes:

- The primary focus is on process improvement.
- Most of the variation in a process is due to the system and not the individual.
- Teamwork is an integral part of a quality management organization.
- Customer satisfaction is a primary organizational goal.
- Organizational transformation must occur in order to implement quality management.
- Fear must be removed from organizations.
- Higher quality costs less not more, but requires an investment in training.

In the 1980s the federal government of the United States increased its efforts to improve quality in American business. Congress passed the Malcolm Baldrige National Improvement Act of 1987 and began awarding the Malcolm Baldrige Award to companies making the greatest strides in improving quality and customer satisfaction. W. Edwards Deming became a prominent consultant to many Fortune 500 companies including Ford, General Motors, and Proctor and Gamble. Through four-day seminars, Deming widely promoted his **"14 points for management"** listed below, and many companies adopted some or all of them.

1. Create constancy of purpose for improvement of product and service.
2. Adopt the new philosophy.
3. Cease dependence on inspection to achieve quality.
4. End the practice of awarding business on the basis of price tag alone. Instead, minimize total cost by working with a single supplier.
5. Improve constantly and forever every process for planning, production, and service.
6. Institute training on the job.
7. Adopt and institute leadership.
8. Drive out fear.
9. Break down barriers between staff areas.
10. Eliminate slogans, exhortations, and targets for the workforce.
11. Eliminate numerical quotas for the workforce and numerical goals for management.
12. Remove barriers that rob people of pride of workmanship. Eliminate the annual rating or merit system.
13. Institute a vigorous program of education and self-improvement for everyone.
14. Put everyone in the company to work to accomplish the transformation.

Point 1, create constancy of purpose, refers to how an organization deals with problems that arise both at present and in the future. The focus is on the constant improvement of a product or service. This improvement process is illustrated by the **Shewhart-Deming cycle** shown in Figure 14.1. The Shewhart-Deming cycle represents a continuous cycle of "plan, do, study, and act." The first step, planning, represents the initial design phase for planning a change in a manufacturing or service process. This step involves teamwork among individuals from different areas within an organization. The second step, doing, involves implementing the change, preferably on a small scale. The third step, studying, involves an analysis of the results using statistical tools to determine what was learned. The fourth step, acting, involves the acceptance of the change, its abandonment, or further study of the change under different conditions.

FIGURE 14.1
Shewhart-Deming Cycle

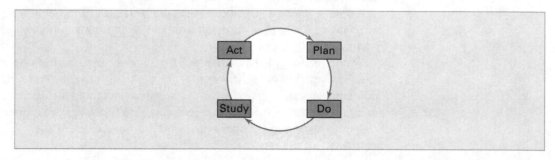

Point 2, adopt the new philosophy, refers to the urgency with which companies need to realize that there is a new economic age of global competition. It is better to be proactive and change before a crisis occurs than to react to some negative experiences that may have occurred. Rather than take the approach "if it's not broke, don't fix it," it is better to continually work on improvement and avoid expensive fixes.

Point 3, cease dependence on inspection to achieve quality, implies that any inspection whose purpose is to improve quality is too late because the quality is already built into the product. It is better to focus on making it right the first time. Among the difficulties involved in inspection (besides high costs) are the failure of inspectors to agree on the operational definitions for nonconforming items, and the problem of separating good and bad items. The following example illustrates the difficulties inspectors face.

Suppose your job involves proofreading the sentence in Figure 14.2 with the objective of counting the number of occurrences of the letter "F." Perform this task and record the number of occurrences of the letter F that you discover.

FIGURE 14.2

An Example of a Proofreading Process

Source: W. W. Scherkenbach, The Deming Route to Quality and Productivity: Road Maps and Roadblocks (Washington, DC: CEEP Press, 1986).

> # FINISHED FILES ARE THE RESULT OF YEARS OF SCIENTIFIC STUDY COMBINED WITH THE EXPERIENCE OF MANY YEARS

People usually see either three Fs or six Fs. The correct number is six Fs. The number you see depends on the method you use to examine the sentence. You are likely to find three Fs if you read the sentence phonetically and six Fs if you count the number of Fs carefully. The point of the exercise is to show that if such a simple process as counting Fs leads to inconsistency of inspectors' results, what will happen when a much more complicated process fails to contain a clear operational definition of nonconforming? Certainly, in such situations, a large amount of variability occurs from inspector to inspector.

Point 4, ending the practice of awarding business on the basis of price tag alone, represents the antithesis of lowest-bidder awards. There is no real long-term meaning to price without knowledge of the quality of the product.

Point 5—improve constantly and forever every process for planning, production and service—reinforces the importance of the continuous focus of the Shewhart-Deming cycle and the belief that quality needs to be built in at the design stage. Attaining quality is a never-ending process in which reduction in variation translates into a reduction in the financial losses resulting from products and services experiencing large fluctuations in quality.

Point 6, institute training, reflects the needs of all employees, including production workers, engineers, and managers. It is critically important for management to understand the differences between special causes and common causes of variation (see section 14.3) so that proper action is taken in each circumstance.

Point 7, adopt and institute leadership, relates to the distinction between leadership and supervision. The aim of leadership should be to improve the system and achieve greater consistency of performance.

Points 8 through 12—drive out fear, break down barriers between staff areas, eliminate slogans, eliminate numerical quotas for the workforce and numerical goals for management, and remove barriers to pride of workmanship (including the annual rating and merit system)—are all related to the evaluation of employee performance. An emphasis on targets and exhortations may place an improper burden on the workforce. Workers cannot produce beyond what the system will allow. It is management's job to *improve* the system, not to raise the expectations on workers beyond the system's capability.

Point 13, encourage education and self-improvement for everyone, reflects the notion that the most important resource of any organization is its people. Efforts that improve the knowledge of people in the organization also serve to increase the assets of the organization. Education and self-improvement can lead to reduced turnover within an organization.

Point 14, take action to accomplish the transformation, again reflects the approach of management as a process in which one continuously strives toward improvement in a never-ending cycle.

Although Deming's points were thought-provoking, some criticized his approach for lacking a formal, objective accountability. Many managers of large organizations, used to seeing financial analyses of policy changes, needed a more prescriptive approach.

14.2   SIX SIGMA MANAGEMENT

Six Sigma management is a quality improvement system originally developed by Motorola in the mid-1980s. Six Sigma offers a more prescriptive and systematic approach to process improvement than TQM, and places a higher emphasis on accountability and bottom-line results. Many companies all over the world are using Six Sigma management to improve efficiency, cut costs, eliminate defects and reduce product variation.

The name Six Sigma comes from the fact that it is a managerial approach designed to create processes that result in no more than 3.4 defects per million.[1] One of the aspects that distinguishes Six Sigma from other approaches is a clear focus on achieving bottom-line results in a relatively short three- to six-month period of time. After seeing the huge financial successes at Motorola, GE, and other early adopters of Six Sigma, many companies worldwide have now instituted Six Sigma programs (see references 1, 8, 9, and 15).

To guide managers in their task of improving short- and long-term results, Six Sigma uses a five-step process known as the **DMAIC model**—named for the five steps in the process: Define, Measure, Analyze, Improve, and Control.

- *Define* The problem is defined along with the costs, benefits, and the impact on the customer.
- *Measure* Operational definitions for each **critical-to-quality (CTQ)** characteristic are developed. In addition, the measurement procedure is verified so that it is consistent over repeated measurements.
- *Analyze* The root causes of *why* defects occur are determined, and variables in the process causing the defects are identified. Data are collected to determine benchmark values for each process variable. This analysis often uses control charts (to be discussed in sections 14.3 and 14.4).
- *Improve* The importance of each process variable on the CTQ characteristic is studied using designed experiments. The objective is to determine the best level for each variable.
- *Control* The objective is to maintain the benefits for the long term by avoiding potential problems that can occur when a process is changed.

Implementation of Six Sigma management requires a data-oriented approach that is heavily based on using statistical tools such as control charts and designed experiments. It also involves training everyone in the organization in the DMAIC model.

[1] *The Six Sigma approach assumes that the process may shift as much as 1.5 standard deviations over the long term. Six standard deviations minus a 1.5 standard deviation shift produces a 4.5 standard deviation goal. The area under the normal curve outside 4.5 standard deviations is approximately 3.4 out of a million (0.0000034).*

14.3   THE THEORY OF CONTROL CHARTS

Both total quality management and Six Sigma management make use of a wide array of statistical tools. One tool widely used in each approach to analyze process data collected sequentially over time is the control chart.

The **control chart** monitors variation in a characteristic of a product or service over time. You can use a control chart to study past performance, to evaluate present conditions, or to predict future outcomes (see reference 7). Information gained from analyzing a control chart forms the basis for process improvement. Different types of control charts allow you to analyze different types of critical-to-quality (CTQ) variables—for categorical variables such as the proportion of hotel rooms that are nonconforming in terms of the availability of amenities and the working order of all appliances in the room, discrete variables such as the number of hotel guests registering a complaint during a week, and continuous variables such as the length of time required for delivering luggage to the room. In addition to providing a visual display of data representing a process, a principal focus of the control chart is the attempt to separate special causes of variation from common causes of variation.

> **Special causes of variation** represent large fluctuations or patterns in the data that are not inherent to a process. These fluctuations are often caused by changes in the process that represent either problems to correct or opportunities to exploit. Some organizations refer to special causes of variation as **assignable causes of variation**.
>
> **Common causes of variation** represent the inherent variability that exists in a process. These fluctuations consist of the numerous small causes of variability that operate randomly or by chance. Some organizations refer to common causes of variation as **chance causes of variation**.

The distinction between the two causes of variation is crucial because special causes of variation are not part of a process and are correctable or exploitable without changing the system. Common causes of variation, however, can be reduced only by changing the system. Such systemic changes are the responsibility of management.

Control charts allow you to monitor a process and identify the presence or absence of special causes. By doing so, control charts help prevent two types of errors. The first type of error involves the belief that an observed value represents special-cause variation when it is due to the common-cause variation of the system. Treating common-cause variation as special-cause variation often results in overadjusting a process. This overadjustment, known as **tampering**, increases the variation in the process. The second type of error involves treating special-cause variation as common-cause variation. This error results in not taking immediate corrective action when necessary. Although both of these types of errors can occur even when using a control chart, they are far less likely.

To construct a control chart, you collect samples from the output of a process over time. The samples used for constructing control charts are known as **subgroups**. For each subgroup (i.e., sample), you calculate the value of a statistic associated with a CTQ variable. Commonly used statistics include the fraction nonconforming and the mean and range of a numerical variable (see section 14.4). You then plot the values versus time and add control limits to the chart. The most typical form of a control chart sets control limits that are within ±3 standard deviations[2] of the statistical measure of interest. Equation (14.1) defines, in general, the upper and lower control limits for control charts.

[2]Recall from section 6.2 that in the normal distribution, $\mu \pm 3\sigma$ includes almost all (99.73%) of the observations in the population.

CONSTRUCTING CONTROL LIMITS

$$\text{Process mean} \pm 3 \text{ standard deviations} \qquad (14.1)$$

so that
Upper control limit (UCL) = process mean +3 standard deviations
Lower control limit (LCL) = process mean −3 standard deviations

When these control limits are set, you evaluate the control chart by trying to find any pattern that might exist in the values over time and by determining whether any points fall outside the control limits. Figure 14.3 illustrates three different situations.

FIGURE 14.3

Three Control Chart
Patterns

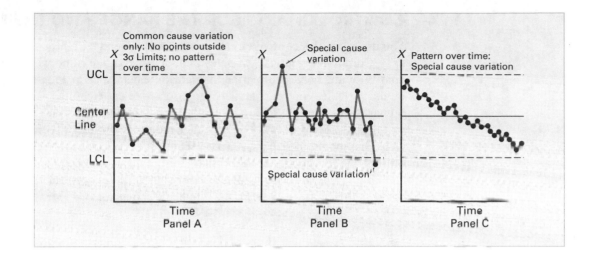

In panel A of Figure 14.3, there is no apparent pattern in the values over time and there are no points that fall outside the 3 standard deviation control limits. The process appears stable and contains only common-cause variation. Panel B, on the contrary, contains two points that fall outside the 3 standard deviation control limits. You should investigate these points to try to determine the special causes that led to their occurrence. Although panel C does not have any points outside the control limits, it has a series of consecutive points above the mean value (the centerline) as well as a series of consecutive points below the mean value. In addition, a long-term overall downward trend is clearly visible. You should investigate the situation to try to determine what may have caused this pattern.

The detection of a trend is not always so obvious. Two other simple rules[3] (see references 7 and 8) that allow you to detect a shift in the mean level of a process are:

- Eight or more *consecutive points* that lie above the center line or eight or more *consecutive points* that lie below the center line.
- Eight or more *consecutive points* move upward in value or eight or more *consecutive points* move downward in value.

A process whose control chart indicates an out-of-control condition (a point outside the control limits or exhibiting a trend) is said to be out of control. An **out-of-control process** contains both common causes of variation and special causes of variation. Because special causes of variation are not part of the process design, an out-of-control process is unpredictable. Once you determine a process is out of control, you must identify the special causes of variation that are producing the out-of-control conditions. If the special causes are detrimental to the quality of the product or service, you need to implement plans to eliminate this source of variation. When a special cause increases quality, you should change the process so that the special cause is incorporated into the process design. Thus, this beneficial special cause now becomes a common-cause source of variation and the process is improved.

A process whose control chart is not indicating any out-of-control conditions is said to be in control. An **in-control process** contains only common causes of variation. Because these sources of variation are inherent to the process itself, an in-control process is predictable. In-control processes are sometimes said to be in a **state of statistical control**. When a process is in control, you must determine whether the amount of common-cause variation in the process is small enough to satisfy the customers of the products or services. If the common-cause variation is small enough to consistently satisfy the customer, you then use control charts to monitor the process on a continuing basis to make sure that the process remains in control. If the common-cause variation is too large, you need to alter the process itself.

[3]Minitab uses different rules—see reference 13.

14.4 CONTROL CHARTS FOR THE RANGE AND THE MEAN

You use **variables control charts** to monitor and analyze a process when you have numerical data. Common numerical variables include time, money, and weight. Because numeric variables provide more information than attribute data such as the proportion of nonconforming items, variables control charts are more sensitive in detecting special-cause variation than the p chart. Variables charts are typically used in pairs. One chart monitors the dispersion (or variability) in a process, and the other monitors the process mean. You must examine the chart that monitors dispersion first because if it indicates the presence of out-of-control conditions, the interpretation of the chart for the mean will be misleading. Although businesses currently use several alternative pairs of charts (see references 7, 8, and 11), this text considers only the control charts for the range and the mean.

The *R* Chart

You can use several different types of control charts to monitor the dispersion (i.e., variability) in a numerically measured characteristic of interest. The simplest and most common is the control chart for the range, the **R chart**. You use the range chart only when the sample size is 10 or less. If the sample size is greater than 10, a standard deviation chart is preferable. Because sample sizes of five or less are typically used in many applications, the standard deviation chart is not illustrated in this text. (For a discussion of standard deviation charts, see references 7, 8, or 11.) The R chart enables you to determine whether the variability in a process is in control or whether changes in the amount of variability are occurring over time. If the process range is in control, then the amount of variation in the process is consistent over time, and you can use the results of the R chart to develop the control limits for the mean.

To develop control limits for the range, you need an estimate of the mean range and the standard deviation of the range. As shown in Equation (14.2), these control limits depend on two constants, the **d_2 factor**, which represents the relationship between the standard deviation and the range for varying sample sizes, and the **d_3 factor**, which represents the relationship between the standard deviation and the standard error of the range for varying sample sizes. Table E.10 contains values for these factors. Equation (14.2) defines the control limits for the R chart.

CONTROL LIMITS FOR THE RANGE

$$\bar{R} \pm 3\bar{R}\frac{d_3}{d_2} \qquad (14.2)$$

$$UCL = \bar{R} + 3\bar{R}\frac{d_3}{d_2}$$

$$LCL = \bar{R} - 3\bar{R}\frac{d_3}{d_2}$$

where

$$\bar{R} = \frac{\sum_{i=1}^{k} R_i}{k}$$

You can simplify the calculations in Equation (14.2) by using the **D_3 factor**, equal to $1 - 3(d_3/d_2)$, and the **D_4 factor**, equal to $1 + 3(d_3/d_2)$, to express the control limits as shown in Equations (14.3a) and (14.3b).

CALCULATING CONTROL LIMITS FOR THE RANGE

$$UCL = D_4\overline{R} \qquad\qquad (14.3a)$$

$$LCL = D_3\overline{R} \qquad\qquad (14.3b)$$

To illustrate the R chart, return to the "Using Statistics" scenario concerning hotel service quality. During the Measure phase of the Six Sigma DMAIC model, the amount of time to deliver luggage was operationally defined as the time from when the guest completes check-in procedures to the time the luggage arrives in the guest's room. During the Analyze phase of the Six Sigma DMAIC model, data were recorded over a 4-week period. Subgroups of five deliveries were selected from the evening shift on each day. Table 14.1 summarizes the results for all 28 days. HOTEL2

TABLE 14.1

Luggage Delivery Times and Subgroup Mean and Range for 28 Days

Day	Luggage Delivery Times in Minutes					Mean	Range
1	6.7	11.7	9.7	7.5	7.8	8.68	5.0
2	7.6	11.4	9.0	8.4	9.2	9.12	3.8
3	9.5	8.9	9.9	8.7	10.7	9.54	2.0
4	9.8	13.2	6.9	9.3	9.4	9.72	6.3
5	11.0	9.9	11.3	11.6	8.5	10.46	3.1
6	8.3	8.4	9.7	9.8	7.1	8.66	2.7
7	9.4	9.3	8.2	7.1	6.1	8.02	3.3
8	11.2	9.8	10.5	9.0	9.7	10.04	2.2
9	10.0	10.7	9.0	8.2	11.0	9.78	2.8
10	8.6	5.8	8.7	9.5	11.4	8.80	5.6
11	10.7	8.6	9.1	10.9	8.6	9.58	2.3
12	10.8	8.3	10.6	10.3	10.0	10.00	2.5
13	9.5	10.5	7.0	8.6	10.1	9.14	3.5
14	12.9	8.9	8.1	9.0	7.6	9.30	5.3
15	7.8	9.0	12.2	9.1	11.7	9.96	4.4
16	11.1	9.9	8.8	5.5	9.5	8.96	5.6
17	9.2	9.7	12.3	8.1	8.5	9.56	4.2
18	9.0	8.1	10.2	9.7	8.4	9.08	2.1
19	9.9	10.1	8.9	9.6	7.1	9.12	3.0
20	10.7	9.8	10.2	8.0	10.2	9.78	2.7
21	9.0	10.0	9.6	10.6	9.0	9.64	1.6
22	10.7	9.8	9.4	7.0	8.9	9.16	3.7
23	10.2	10.5	9.5	12.2	9.1	10.30	3.1
24	10.0	11.1	9.5	8.8	9.9	9.86	2.3
25	9.6	8.8	11.4	12.2	9.3	10.26	3.4
26	8.2	7.9	8.4	9.5	9.2	8.64	1.6
27	7.1	11.1	10.8	11.0	10.2	10.04	4.0
28	11.1	6.6	12.0	11.5	9.7	10.18	5.4
					Sums:	265.38	97.5

For the data in Table 14.1,

$$k = 28, \sum_{i=1}^{k} R_i = 97.5, \text{ and } \overline{R} = \frac{\sum_{i=1}^{k} R_i}{k} = \frac{97.5}{28} = 3.482$$

Using Equation (14.2) and from Table E.10 for $n = 5$, $d_2 = 2.326$ and $d_3 = 0.864$,

$$3.482 \pm 3(3.482)\left(\frac{0.864}{2.326}\right)$$

$$= 3.482 \pm 3.880$$

Thus,

$$UCL = 3.482 + 3.880 = 7.362$$

$$LCL = 3.482 - 3.880 < 0$$

Therefore, the LCL does not exist because it is impossible to get a negative range. Alternatively, using Equation (14.3), and $D_3 = 0$ and $D_4 = 2.114$ from Table E.10,

$$UCL = D_4\overline{R} = (2.114)(3.482) = 7.36$$

and the LCL does not exist.

Figure 14.4 displays the Microsoft Excel R chart for the luggage delivery times. Figure 14.4 does not indicate any individual ranges outside the control limits or any trends.

FIGURE 14.4

Microsoft Excel R Chart for the Luggage Delivery Times

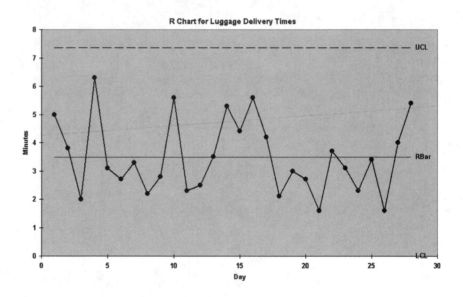

The $\overline{X}$ Chart

Now that you have determined that the control chart shows that the range is in control, you continue by examining the control chart for the process mean, the $\overline{X}$ **chart**.

The control chart for $\overline{X}$ uses subgroups each of size n for k consecutive periods of time. To compute control limits for the mean, you need to compute the mean of the subgroup means (called $\overline{\overline{X}}$) and the standard deviation of the mean (which is called the standard error of the mean $\sigma_{\overline{X}}$ in Chapter 7). The estimate of the standard deviation of the mean is a function of the d_2 factor, which represents the relationship between the standard deviation and the range for varying sample sizes.[6] Equations (14.4) and (14.5) define the control limits for the $\overline{X}$ chart.

[6] $\overline{R}/d_2$ is used to estimate the standard deviation of the population, and $\overline{R}/d_2\sqrt{n}$ is used to estimate the standard deviation of the mean.

CONTROL LIMITS FOR THE $\overline{X}$ CHART

$$\overline{\overline{X}} \pm 3 \frac{\overline{R}}{d_2\sqrt{n}} \qquad \text{(14.4)}$$

$$UCL = \overline{\overline{X}} + 3 \frac{\overline{R}}{d_2\sqrt{n}}$$

$$LCL = \overline{\overline{X}} - 3 \frac{\overline{R}}{d_2\sqrt{n}}$$

where

$$\overline{\overline{X}} = \frac{\sum\limits_{i=1}^{k} \overline{X}_i}{k} \qquad \overline{R} = \frac{\sum\limits_{i=1}^{k} R_i}{k}$$

$\overline{X}_i$ = sample mean of n observations at time i

R_i = range of n observations at time i

k = number of subgroups

You can simplify the calculations in Equation (14.4) by utilizing the A_2 **factor**, equal to $3/\left(d_2\sqrt{n}\right)$. Equations (14.5a) and (14.5b) show the simplified control limits.

CALCULATING CONTROL LIMITS FOR THE MEAN USING THE A_2 FACTOR

$$UCL = \overline{\overline{X}} + A_2\overline{R} \qquad \text{(14.5a)}$$

$$LCL = \overline{\overline{X}} - A_2\overline{R} \qquad \text{(14.5b)}$$

Alternatively, using Equations (14.5a) and (14.5b), and $A_2 = 0.577$ from Table E.10,

$$UCL = 9.478 + (0.577)(3.482) = 9.478 + 2.009 = 11.487$$
$$LCL = 9.478 - (0.577)(3.482) = 9.478 - 2.009 = 7.469$$

These results are the same as those using Equation (14.4), except for rounding error.

Figure 14.5 displays the Microsoft Excel $\overline{X}$ chart for the luggage delivery time data. Figure 14.6 presents Minitab R and $\overline{X}$ charts. Figures 14.5 and 14.6 do not reveal any points outside the control limits or any trend. Although there is a considerable amount of variability among the 28 subgroup means, since both the R chart and the $\overline{X}$ chart are in control, the luggage delivery process is in a state of statistical control. If you want to reduce the variation or lower the mean delivery time, then you need to change the process.

FIGURE 14.5

Microsoft Excel $\overline{X}$ Chart for the Luggage Delivery Times

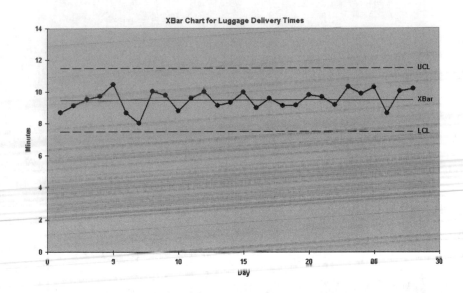

FIGURE 14.6

Minitab $\overline{X}$ and R Charts for the Luggage Delivery Times

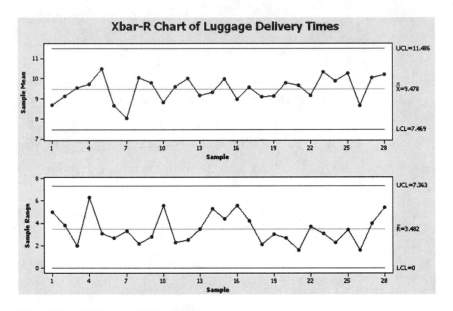

14.5 QUALITY CONTROL CHARTS

We will only be studying two charts, namely X-bar and R charts. Also, the only out-of-control indications that we will be concerned with are:

a. A point above the UCL on the range chart.
b. A point above the UCL or a point below the LCL on the X-bar chart.

In a real life setting, if there is an indication that the process is out-of-control, the people monitoring the process will find an 'Assignable Cause' for this situation. They will then take appropriate steps to make changes in the process so that this instability does not occur again in the future. It is these changes that will result in the improvement of quality.

In order to establish the centre-lines and the upper and lower control limits for the X-bar and R charts we need some initial sample data. Usually the results of from 10 to 30 samples are used. The following two examples will illustrate the formulas and techniques for setting up X-bar and R chart limits. It should be noted that all the formulas shown are based on the assumption that the population of measurements would fit a *normal* distribution.

EXAMPLE 14.1

A chocolate company monitors the weights of its chocolate bars. One particular bar will have a label indicating that it is a 60 gm. Bar. In order to monitor the bar weights, every hour a sample of 4 bars is taken and the bars are weighed. The results of the first 15 samples are shown below.

TABLE 14.2

	Weight of a bar (grams)					
Sample	**Bar 1**	**Bar 2**	**Bar 3**	**Bar 4**	**Mean**	**Range**
1	60.2	60.4	60.1	60.5	60.300	0.4
2	60.6	60.2	60.7	60.6	60.525	0.5
3	60.2	60.2	60.5	60.7	60.400	0.5
4	60.1	60.1	60.6	60.4	60.300	0.5
5	60.3	60.6	60.3	60.1	60.325	0.5
6	60.5	60.4	60.3	60.1	60.250	0.4
7	60.5	60.4	60.5	60.2	60.400	0.3
8	60.3	60.5	60.2	60.3	60.325	0.3
9	60.5	60.1	60.0	60.5	60.275	0.5
10	60.7	60.4	60.4	60.5	60.500	0.3
11	60.0	60.3	60.7	60.3	60.325	0.7
12	60.2	60.7	60.3	60.6	60.450	0.5
13	60.6	60.0	60.6	60.2	60.350	0.6
14	59.9	60.1	60.3	60.6	60.200	0.7
15	60.5	60.2	60.5	60.5	60.425	0.3

First we calculate the R-chart values using the control factors as follows:

$$\bar{R} = 0.47$$
$$UCL_R = D_4\bar{R} = 2.282(0.47) = 1.07$$
$$LCL_R = D_3\bar{R} = 0(0.47) = 0$$

We now check the sample ranges to see if any values are higher than 1.07. There are none. We now proceed to calculate the X-bar chart values.

$$\bar{\bar{X}} = 60.3567$$
$$UCL_{\bar{x}} = \bar{\bar{X}} + A_2\bar{R} = 60.3567 + (0.729)(0.47) = 60.6993$$
$$LCL_{\bar{x}} = \bar{\bar{X}} - A_2\bar{R} = 60.3567 - (0.729)(0.47) = 60.0141$$

We now check the sample means to see if any values are higher than 60.6993 or lower than 60.0141. There are none. This process is **in control**, i.e. stable, and we have established the control chart limits for future samples of this product.

If in the initial samples used to set up the control charts, points are found to be out-of-control, then we will assume that an assignable cause can be found to account for this problem. In the meantime, the sample data for any point that is out-of-control is removed from the calculations, are the control chart values are recalculated. The following example will illustrate the appropriate procedure to follow.

EXAMPLE 14.2

A company is concerned about a particular measurement. The results of 24 samples of 5 items are shown below.

TABLE 14.3

			Sample results				
Sample	Item 1	Item 2	Item 3	Item 4	Item 5	Mean	Range
1	10.65	10.70	10.65	10.65	10.85	10.70	0.20
2	10.75	10.85	10.75	10.85	10.65	10.77	0.20
3	10.75	10.80	10.80	10.70	10.75	10.76	0.10
4	10.60	10.70	10.70	10.75	10.65	10.68	0.15
5	10.70	10.75	10.65	10.85	10.80	10.75	0.20
6	10.60	10.75	10.75	10.85	10.70	10.73	0.25
7	10.60	10.80	10.70	10.75	10.75	10.72	0.20
8	10.75	10.80	10.65	10.75	10.70	10.73	0.15
9	10.65	10.80	10.85	10.85	10.75	10.78	0.20
10	10.60	10.70	10.60	10.80	10.65	10.67	0.20
11	10.80	10.75	10.90	10.50	10.85	10.76	0.40
12	10.85	10.75	10.85	10.65	10.70	10.76	0.20
13	10.70	10.70	10.75	10.75	10.70	10.72	0.05
14	10.65	10.70	10.85	10.75	10.60	10.71	0.25
15	10.75	10.80	10.75	10.80	10.65	10.75	0.15
16	10.90	10.80	10.80	10.75	10.85	10.82	0.15
17	10.75	10.70	10.85	10.70	10.80	10.76	0.15
18	10.75	10.70	10.60	10.70	10.60	10.67	0.15
19	10.65	10.65	10.85	10.65	10.70	10.70	0.20
20	10.55	10.55	10.60	10.50	10.60	10.56	0.10
21	10.50	10.55	10.65	10.80	10.80	10.66	0.30
22	10.80	10.65	10.75	10.65	10.65	10.70	0.15
23	10.65	10.60	10.65	10.60	10.70	10.64	0.10
24	10.65	10.70	10.70	10.60	10.65	10.66	0.10

First calculate the R-chart values:

$$\bar{R} = 0.179$$
$$UCL_R = D_4\bar{R} = 2.114(0.179) = 0.378$$
$$LCL_R = D_3\bar{R} = 0(0.179) = 0$$

Now we look at the sample ranges and find that sample 11 with R = 0.40 is out-of-control. We will assume that an assignable cause for this can be found and in the meantime we **remove** sample 11 and recalculate the R-chart values.

We now get:

$$\bar{R} = 0.170$$
$$UCL_R = D_4\bar{R} = 2.114(0.170) = 0.360$$
$$LCL_R = D_3\bar{R} = 0(0.170) = 0$$

Once again we check the sample ranges and this time there are no ranges that are out-of-control.

Now we calculate the X-bar chart values (with sample 11 having been removed from the data.)

We get:

$$\overline{\overline{X}} = 10.713$$
$$UCL_{\overline{x}} = \overline{\overline{X}} + A_2 \overline{R} = 10.713 + (0.577)(0.170) = 10.811$$
$$LCL_{\overline{x}} = \overline{\overline{X}} - A_2 \overline{R} = 10.713 - (0.577)(0.170) = 10.615$$

We now check the sample means and find that sample 16 with $\overline{X} = 10.82$ and sample 20 with $\overline{X} = 10.56$ are out-of-control. Once again we assume that assignable causes can be found to account for these out-of-control results, and in the meantime we remove samples 16 and 20.

Since the R-chart values above have been calculated including samples 16 and 20, these results are no longer valid. We must recalculate new R-chart values before recalculating new X-bar chart values.

We now get:

$$\overline{R} = 0.174$$
$$UCL_R = D_4 \overline{R} = 2.114(0.174) = 0.368$$
$$LCL_R = D_3 \overline{R} = 0(0.174) = 0$$

We now once again check the sample ranges for any out-of-control points. There are none. We therefore proceed to the X-bar chart values.

We get:

$$\overline{\overline{X}} = 10.715$$
$$UCL_{\overline{x}} = \overline{\overline{X}} + A_2 \overline{R} = 10.715 + (0.577)(0.174) = 10.815$$
$$LCL_{\overline{x}} = \overline{\overline{X}} - A_2 \overline{R} = 10.715 - (0.577)(0.174) = 10.616$$

Once again we check the sample means and find that none of the remaining samples are out-of-control. We now have determined the appropriate X-bar and R-chart control limits

PROBLEMS FOR SECTION 14.5

X-bar and R chart Exercises

(Note: Some of these exercises may not be indicative of real world processes, but are intended to demonstrate the correct procedures for establishing control chart limits.)

14.1 The following results came from samples of size 4. Determine the X-bar and R chart control limits. If any sample results are out-of-control assume an assignable cause can be found and make the necessary adjustments to the control chart values.

Sample	Mean	Range	Sample	Mean	Range
1	75.72	1.0	11	75.80	0.6
2	75.24	0.9	12	75.22	0.2
3	75.18	0.8	13	75.56	1.5
4	75.44	0.4	14	75.22	0.5
5	75.46	0.5	15	75.04	0.8
6	75.32	1.2	16	75.62	1.1
7	75.40	0.9	17	75.92	0.6
8	75.44	0.3	18	75.46	0.5
9	75.08	0.2	19	75.60	0.4
10	75.50	0.6	20	75.74	0.3

14.2 The following results came from samples of size 6. Determine the X-bar and R chart control limits. If any sample results are out-of-control assume an assignable cause can be found and make the necessary adjustments to the control chart values.

Sample	Mean	Range	Sample	Mean	Range
1	35.35	0.34	14	35.41	0.36
2	35.40	0.36	15	35.45	0.24
3	35.36	0.32	16	35.34	0.36
4	35.65	0.26	17	35.42	0.37
5	35.20	0.46	18	35.50	0.58
6	35.40	0.35	19	35.36	0.35
7	35.43	0.31	20	35.31	0.18
8	35.37	0.34	21	35.39	0.73
9	35.48	0.30	22	35.39	0.33
10	35.42	0.37	23	35.40	0.32
11	35.39	0.19	24	35.41	0.34
12	35.38	0.50	25	35.40	0.30
13	35.40	0.33			

14.3 The following results came from samples of size 5. Use the first 20 samples to determine the X-bar and R chart control limits. If any sample results are out-of-control assume an assignable cause can be found and make the necessary adjustments to the control chart values. Are any of the samples 21 to 30 out of control? Explain.

Sample	Mean	Range	Sample	Mean	Range
1	101	22	16	109	12
2	104	17	17	111	38
3	109	36	18	100	30
4	98	19	19	97	19
5	105	23	20	89	31
6	107	16	21	103	27
7	109	16	22	97	36
8	115	30	23	92	25
9	99	20	24	89	23
10	119	29	25	98	18
11	91	14	26	108	24
12	99	20	27	114	19
13	115	39	28	117	51
14	100	30	29	110	21
15	103	26	30	99	30

14.4 The following results came from samples of size 4. Determine the X-bar and R chart control limits. If any sample results are out-of-control assume an assignable cause can be found and make the necessary adjustments to the control chart values.

Sample	Mean	Range	Sample	Mean	Range
1	376.2	32	14	382.7	22
2	366.7	24	15	406.3	23
3	384.3	32	16	396.4	23
4	366.7	26	17	378.7	25
5	370.1	24	18	384.2	24
6	394.2	24	19	406.9	23
7	386.9	28	20	376.4	25
8	396.4	23	21	385.8	29
9	388.0	24	22	390.2	25
10	382.3	26	23	363.5	22
11	398.8	25	24	363.1	27
12	364.6	24	25	374.8	22
13	384.5	24			

14.5 Motel Inn plans to improve service by reducing the mean and variation in time it takes to clean and prepare rooms. In order to study the situation 5 rooms are randomly selected each day and the time required to clean and prepare each room is recorded. The data for the first 10 days is given below.

	Cleaning and Preparation time (minutes)				
Day	Room 1	Room 2	Room 3	Room 4	Room 5
1	14.0	17.7	16.9	14.0	14.9
2	17.6	16.5	15.3	14.5	15.1
3	14.6	14.0	14.7	16.9	14.2
4	14.0	15.5	16.5	15.4	14.7
5	15.3	15.3	15.9	15.0	17.8
6	21.4	14.9	17.7	16.6	13.8
7	18.9	19.9	18.6	17.2	17.9
8	14.8	15.1	16.6	16.3	14.5
9	16.1	14.6	17.5	16.9	17.7
10	14.2	14.7	15.3	15.7	14.3

Determine the X-bar and R chart control limits, assuming that any out-of-control results have assignable causes.

14.6 A chemical company has collected 15 daily samples of measurements of an important chemical property called 'acid value' for one of its products. Each sample consists of six acid value readings, where a single reading is taken every 4 hours during the day. The measurements are shown in the table below.

Acid Value measurements

Day	1	2	3	4	5	6
1	202.1	201.2	196.2	201.6	201.6	201.6
2	202.4	201.9	202.0	201.8	201.9	201.8
3	200.4	200.0	200.8	200.1	198.7	200.4
4	200.4	200.4	200.4	200.8	200.4	201.2
5	203.4	201.6	203.9	201.6	201.4	202.0
6	200.0	200.4	200.8	200.8	199.5	200.4
7	200.4	200.0	200.4	200.4	200.4	200.4
8	200.0	200.8	200.0	200.4	200.0	200.0
9	199.1	200.1	200.4	200.4	200.4	200.0
10	201.2	195.3	197.4	201.2	200.0	201.6
11	201.6	200.8	200.4	201.2	200.4	199.5
12	200.0	199.5	200.4	200.8	200.4	200.8
13	201.2	201.6	200.8	201.2	200.8	200.8
14	200.4	200.0	202.5	200.4	201.2	201.2
15	200.0	200.0	201.6	200.8	200.4	200.0

Determine the X-bar and R chart control limits, assuming that any out-of-control results have assignable causes.

KEY FORMULAS

Constructing Control Limits

Process mean ±3 standard deviations **(14.1)**

Upper control limit (UCL) =
process mean +3 standard deviations

Lower control limit (LCL) =
process mean −3 standard deviations

Control Limits for the Range

$$\overline{R} \pm 3\overline{R}\frac{d_3}{d_2} \qquad \textbf{(14.2)}$$

$$\text{UCL} = \overline{R} + 3\overline{R}\frac{d_3}{d_2}$$

$$\text{LCL} = \overline{R} - 3\overline{R}\frac{d_3}{d_2}$$

Calculating Control Limits for the Range

$$\text{UCL} = D_4\overline{R} \qquad \textbf{(14.3a)}$$

$$\text{LCL} = D_3\overline{R} \qquad \textbf{(14.3b)}$$

Control Limits for the $\overline{X}$ Chart

$$\overline{\overline{X}} \pm 3\frac{\overline{R}}{d_2\sqrt{n}} \qquad \textbf{(14.4)}$$

$$\text{UCL} = \overline{\overline{X}} + 3\frac{\overline{R}}{d_2\sqrt{n}}$$

$$\text{LCL} = \overline{\overline{X}} - 3\frac{\overline{R}}{d_2\sqrt{n}}$$

Calculating Control Limits for the Mean Using the A_2 Factor

$$\text{UCL} = \overline{\overline{X}} + A_2\overline{R} \qquad \textbf{(14.5a)}$$

$$\text{LCL} = \overline{\overline{X}} - A_2\overline{R} \qquad \textbf{(14.5b)}$$

CHAPTER REVIEW PROBLEMS

Checking Your Understanding

14.7 What is the difference between common-cause variation and special-cause variation?

14.8 What should you do to improve a process when special causes of variation are present?

14.9 What should you do to improve a process when only common causes of variation are present?

14.10 What is the difference between attribute control charts and variables control charts?

14.11 Why are the $\overline{X}$ and R charts used together?

14.12 What principles did you learn from the red bead experiment?

Applying the Concepts

You should use Microsoft Excel, Minitab, or SPSS to solve problems 14.13–14.20.

14.13 A producer of cat food constructed control charts and analyzed several quality characteristics. One characteristic of interest is the weight of the filled cans. The data file CATFOOD contains the weights of five cans tested every fifteen minutes during a day's production.
a. Construct a control chart for the range.
b. Construct a control chart for the mean.
c. Is the process in control?

14.14 Researchers at Miami University in Oxford, Ohio, investigated the use of *p* charts to monitor the market share of a product and to document the effectiveness of marketing promotions. Market share is defined as the company's proportion of the total number of products sold in a category. If a *p* chart based on a company's market share indicates an in-control process, then their share in the marketplace is deemed to be stable and consistent over time. In the example given in the article, the RudyBird Diskette Company collected daily sales data from a nationwide retail audit service. The first 30 days of data in the accompanying table indicate the total number of cases of computer diskettes sold and the number of RudyBird diskettes sold. The final 7 days of data were taken after RudyBird launched a major in-store promotion. A control chart was used to see if the in-store promotion would result in special-cause variation in the marketplace.
RUDYBIRD

Cases Sold Before the Promotion

Day	Total	Rudybird	Day	Total	Rudybird
1	154	35	16	177	56
2	153	43	17	143	43
3	200	44	18	200	69
4	197	56	19	134	38
5	194	54	20	192	47
6	172	38	21	155	45
7	190	43	22	135	36
8	209	62	23	189	55
9	173	53	24	184	44
10	171	39	25	170	47
11	173	44	26	178	48
12	168	37	27	167	42
13	184	45	28	204	71
14	211	58	29	183	64
15	179	35	30	169	43

Cases Sold After the Promotion

Day	Total	Rudybird
31	201	92
32	177	76
33	205	85
34	199	90
35	187	77
36	168	79
37	198	97

Source: Extracted from Charles T. Crespy, Timothy C. Krehbiel, and James M. Stearns, "Integrating Analytic Methods into Marketing Research Education: Statistical Control Charts as an Example," Marketing Education Review, *5, Spring 1995, 11–23.*

a. Construct a *p* chart using data from the first 30 days (prior to the promotion) to monitor the market share for RudyBird Diskettes.
b. Is the market share for RudyBird in control before the start of the in-store promotion?
c. On your control chart, extend the control limits generated in (b) and plot the proportions for days 31 through 37. What effect, if any, did the in-store promotion have on RudyBird's market share?

14.15 The manufacturer of "Boston" and "Vermont" asphalt shingles constructed control charts and analyzed several quality characteristics. One characteristic of interest is the strength of the sealant on the shingle. During each day of production, three shingles are tested for their sealant strength. (Thus, a subgroup is operationally defined as one day of production, and the sample size for each subgroup is 3.) Separate pieces are cut from the upper and lower portions of a shingle, and then reassembled to simulate shingles on a roof. A timed heating process is used to simulate the sealing process. The sealed shingle pieces are pulled apart, and the amount of force (in pounds) required to break the sealant bond is measured and recorded. This variable is called the *sealant strength*. The data file SEALANT contains sealant strength measurements on 25 days of production for "Boston" shingles and 19 days for "Vermont" shingles.

For the "Boston" shingles:
a. Construct a control chart for the range.
b. Construct a control chart for the mean.
c. Is the process in control?
d. Repeat (a) through (c) using the 19 production days for "Vermont" shingles.

 14.16 A professional basketball player has embarked on a program to study his ability to shoot foul shots. On each day in which a game is not scheduled, he intends to shoot 100 foul shots. He maintains records over a period of 40 days of practice, with the following results: FOULSPC

Day	Foul Shots Made	Day	Foul Shots Made	Day	Foul Shots Made
1	73	15	73	29	76
2	75	16	76	30	80
3	69	17	69	31	78
4	72	18	68	32	83
5	77	19	72	33	84
6	71	20	70	34	81
7	68	21	64	35	86
8	70	22	67	36	85
9	67	23	72	37	86
10	74	24	70	38	87
11	75	25	74	39	85
12	72	26	76	40	85
13	70	27	75		
14	74	28	78		

a. Construct a *p* chart for the proportion of successful foul shots. Do you think that the player's foul-shooting process is in statistical control? If not, why not?
b. What if you were told that the player used a different method of shooting foul shots for the last twenty days? How might this information change your conclusions in (a)?
c. If you knew the information in (b) prior to doing (a), how might you do the analysis differently?

 14.17 The funds transfer department of a bank is concerned with turnaround time for investigations of funds-transfer payments. A payment may involve the bank as a remitter of funds, a beneficiary of funds, or an intermediary in the payment. An investigation is initiated by a payment inquiry or query by a party involved in the payment or any department affected by the flow of funds. When a query is received, an investigator reconstructs the transaction trail of the payment and verifies that the information is correct and the proper payment is transmitted. The investigator then reports the results of the investigation and the transaction is considered closed. It is important that investigations are closed rapidly, preferably within the same day. The number of new investigations and the number and proportion closed on the same day that the inquiry was made are in the file FUNDTRAN.
a. Construct a control chart for these data.
b. Is the process in a state of statistical control? Explain.
c. Based on the results of (a) and (b), what should management do next to improve the process?

 14.18 A branch manager of a brokerage company is concerned with the number of undesirable trades made by her sales staff. A trade is considered undesirable if there is an error on the trade ticket. Trades with errors are canceled and resubmitted. The cost of correcting errors is billed to the brokerage company. The branch manager wants to know whether the proportion of undesirable trades is in a state of statistical control so she can plan the next step in a quality improvement process. Data were collected for a 30-day period with the following results: TRADE

Day	Undesirable Trades	Total Trades	Day	Undesirable Trades	Total Trades
1	2	74	16	3	54
2	12	85	17	12	74
3	13	114	18	11	103
4	33	136	19	11	100
5	5	97	20	14	88
6	20	115	21	4	58
7	17	108	22	10	69
8	10	76	23	19	135
9	8	69	24	1	67
10	18	98	25	11	77
11	3	104	26	12	88
12	12	98	27	4	66
13	15	105	28	11	72
14	6	98	29	13	118
15	21	204	30	15	138

a. Construct a control chart for these data.

b. Is the process in control? Explain.

c. Based on the results of (a) and (b), what should the manager do next to improve the process?

14.19 As chief operating officer of a local community hospital, you have just returned from a 3-day seminar on quality and productivity. It is your intention to implement many of the ideas that you learned at the seminar. You have decided to maintain control charts for the upcoming month for the proportion of rework in the laboratory (based on 1,000 daily samples) and the time (in hours) between receipt of a specimen at the laboratory and completion of the work (based on a subgroup of 10 specimens per day). The data collected are summarized in the file HOSPADM. You are to make a presentation to the chief executive officer of the hospital and the board of directors. Prepare a report that summarizes the conclusions drawn from analyzing control charts for these variables. In addition, recommend additional variables to measure and monitor using control charts.

14.20 On each morning for a period of 4 weeks, record your pulse rate (in beats per minute) just after you get out of bed and also before you go to sleep at night. Set up $\overline{X}$ and R charts and determine whether your pulse rate is in a state of statistical control. Explain.

CASE STUDY
THE HARNSWELL SEWING MACHINE COMPANY CASE

Phase 1

For almost 50 years, the Harnswell Sewing Machine Company has manufactured industrial sewing machines. The company specializes in automated machines called pattern tackers that sew repetitive patterns on such mass-produced products as shoes, garments, and seat belts. Aside from the sales of machines, the company sells machine parts. Because the company's products have a reputation for being superior, Harnswell is able to command a price premium for its product line.

Recently, the production manager, Natalie York, purchased several books relating to quality at a local bookstore. After reading them, she considered the feasibility of beginning some type of quality program at the company. At the current time, the company has no formal quality program. Parts are 100% inspected at the time of shipping to a customer or installation in a machine, yet Natalie has always wondered why inventory of certain parts (in particular the half-inch cam roller) invariably falls short before a full year lapses, even though 7,000 pieces have been produced for a demand of 5,000 pieces per year.

After a great deal of reflection and with some apprehension, Natalie has decided that she will approach John Harnswell, the owner of the company, about the possibility of beginning a program to improve quality in the company, starting with a trial project in the machine parts area. As she is walking to Mr. Harnswell's office for the meeting, she has second thoughts about whether this is such a good idea. After all, just last month Mr. Harnswell told her, "Why do you need to go to graduate school for your master's degree in business? That is a waste of your time and will not be of any value to the Harnswell Company. All those professors are just up in their ivory towers and don't know a thing about running a business like I do."

As she enters his office, Mr. Harnswell, ever courteous to her, invites Natalie to sit down across from him. "Well, what do you have on your mind this morning?" Mr. Harnswell asks her in an inquisitive tone. She begins by starting to talk about the books that she has just completed reading and about how she has some interesting ideas for making production even better than it is now and improving profits. Before she can finish, Mr. Harnswell has started to answer. "Look, my dear young lady," he says, "everything has been fine since I started this company in 1970. I have built this company up from nothing to one that employs more than 100 people. Why do you want to make waves? Remember, if it ain't broke, don't fix it." With that he ushers her from his office with the admonishment of, "What am I going to do with you if you keep coming up with these ridiculous ideas?"

EXERCISES

HS.1 Based upon what you have read, which of Deming's 14 points of management are most lacking in the Harnswell Sewing Machine Company? Explain.

HS.2 What changes if any, do you think that Natalie York might be able to institute in the company? Explain.

DO NOT CONTINUE UNTIL YOU HAVE COMPLETED THE PHASE 1 EXERCISES

Phase 2

Natalie slowly walks down the hall after leaving Mr. Harnswell's office, feeling rather downcast. He just won't listen to anyone, she thinks. As she walks, Jim Murante, the shop foreman, comes up beside her. "So," he says, "did you really think that he would just listen to you? I've been here more than 25 years. The only way he listens is if he is shown something that worked after it has already been done. Let's see what we can plan out together."

Natalie and Jim decide to begin by investigating the production of the cam rollers that are a precision ground part. The last part of the production process involves the grinding of the outer diameter. After grinding, the part mates with the cam groove of the particular sewing pattern. The half-inch rollers technically have an engineering specification for the outer diameter of the roller of 0.5075 inch (the specifications are actually metric, but in factory floor jargon they are referred to as half-inch), plus a tolerable error of 0.0003 inch on the lower side. Thus, the outer diameter is allowed to be between 0.5072 and 0.5075 inch. Anything larger is reclassified into a different and less costly category, and anything smaller is unusable for anything other than scrap.

The grinding of the cam roller is done on a single machine with a single tool setup and no change in the grinding wheel after initial setup. The operation is done by Dave Martin, the head machinist, who has 30 years of experience in the trade and specific experience producing the cam roller part. Since production occurs in batches, Natalie and Jim sample five parts produced from each batch. Table HS.1 presents data collected over 30 batches.

HARNSWELL

TABLE HS.1

Diameter of Cam Rollers (in inches)

Batch	Cam Roller 1	2	3	4	5
1	.5076	.5076	.5075	.5077	.5075
2	.5075	.5077	.5076	.5076	.5075
3	.5075	.5075	.5075	.5075	.5076
4	.5075	.5076	.5074	.5076	.5073
5	.5075	.5074	.5076	.5073	.5076
6	.5076	.5075	.5076	.5075	.5075
7	.5076	.5076	.5076	.5075	.5075
8	.5075	.5076	.5076	.5075	.5074
9	.5074	.5076	.5075	.5075	.5076
10	.5076	.5077	.5075	.5075	.5075
11	.5075	.5075	.5075	.5076	.5075
12	.5075	.5076	.5075	.5077	.5075
13	.5076	.5076	.5073	.5076	.5074
14	.5075	.5076	.5074	.5076	.5075
15	.5075	.5075	.5076	.5074	.5073
16	.5075	.5074	.5076	.5075	.5075
17	.5075	.5074	.5075	.5074	.5072
18	.5075	.5075	.5076	.5075	.5076
19	.5076	.5076	.5075	.5075	.5076
20	.5075	.5074	.5077	.5076	.5074
21	.5075	.5074	.5075	.5075	.5075
22	.5076	.5076	.5075	.5076	.5074
23	.5076	.5076	.5075	.5075	.5076
24	.5075	.5076	.5075	.5076	.5075
25	.5075	.5075	.5075	.5075	.5074
26	.5077	.5076	.5076	.5074	.5075
27	.5075	.5075	.5074	.5076	.5075
28	.5077	.5076	.5075	.5075	.5076
29	.5075	.5075	.5074	.5075	.5075
30	.5076	.5075	.5075	.5076	.5075

EXERCISE

HS.3 **a.** Is the process in control? Why?

b. What recommendations do you have for improving the process?

DO NOT CONTINUE UNTIL YOU HAVE COMPLETED THE PHASE 2 EXERCISE

Phase 3

Natalie examined the $\overline{X}$ and R charts developed from the data presented in Table HS.1. The R chart indicated that the process is in control, but the $\overline{X}$ chart revealed that the mean for batch 17 was outside the lower control limit. This immediately gave her cause for concern because low values for the roller diameter could mean that parts had to be scrapped. Natalie went down to see Jim Murante, the shop foreman, to try to find out what had happened on batch 17. Jim looked up the production records to determine when this batch was produced. "Aha," He exclaims, "I think I've got the answer! This batch was produced on that really cold morning we had last month. I've been after Mr. Harnswell for a long time to let us install an automatic thermostat here in the shop so that the place doesn't feel so cold when we get here in the morning. All he ever tells me is that people aren't as tough as they used to be."

Natalie stood there almost in shock. What she realized had happened is that, rather than standing idle until the environment and the equipment warmed to acceptable temperatures, the machinist opted to manufacture parts that might have to be scrapped. In fact, Natalie recalled that a major problem had occurred on that same day when several other expensive parts had to be scrapped. Natalie said to Jim, "We just have to do something. We can't let this go on now that we know what problems it is potentially causing." Natalie and Jim decided to take enough money out of petty cash to get the thermostat without having to fill out a requisition requiring Mr. Harnswell's signature. They installed the thermostat and set the heating control so that the heat would turn on a half hour before the shop opened each morning.

EXERCISES

HS.4 What should Natalie now do concerning the cam roller data? Explain.

HS.5 Explain how the actions of Natalie and Jim to avoid this particular problem in the future has resulted in quality improvement.

DO NOT CONTINUE UNTIL YOU HAVE COMPLETED THE PHASE 3 EXERCISES

Phase 4

Because corrective action was taken to eliminate the special cause of variation, the data for batch 17 were removed from the analysis. The control charts for the remaining days indicate a stable system with only common causes of variation operating on the system. Thus, Natalie and Jim sat down with Dave Martin and several other machinists to try to determine all the possible causes for the existence of oversized and scrapped rollers. Natalie was still troubled by the data. After all, she wanted to find out whether the process is giving oversizes (which are downgraded) and undersizes (which are scrapped). She thought about which tables and charts would be most helpful.

EXERCISE

HS.6 **a.** Construct a frequency distribution and a stem-and-leaf display of the cam roller diameters. Which one do you prefer?
b. Based on your results in (a), construct all appropriate graphs of the cam roller diameters.
c. Write a report expressing your conclusions concerning the cam roller diameters. Be sure to discuss the diameters as they relate to the specifications.

DO NOT CONTINUE UNTIL YOU HAVE COMPLETED THE PHASE 4 EXERCISE

Phase 5

Natalie noticed immediately that the overall mean diameter with batch 17 eliminated is 0.507527, which is higher than the allowable value of 0.5075. Thus, the mean diameter of the rollers produced is so high that they would be downgraded in value. In fact, 55 of the 150 rollers sampled (36.67%) were above the specification value. If this percentage is extrapolated to the full year's production, 36.67% of the 7,000 pieces manufactured, or 2,567, could not be sold as half-inch rollers, leaving only 4,433 available for sale. "No wonder we often have shortages that require costly emergency runs," she thought. She also notes that not one diameter is below the lower allowable value of 0.5072, so not one of the rollers had to be scrapped.

Natalie realized that there had to be a reason for all this. Along with Jim Murante, she decided to show the results to Dave Martin, the head machinist. Dave said that the results didn't surprise him that much. "You know," he says "there is only 0.0003 inch in diameter that I'm allowed in variation. If I aim for exactly halfway between 0.5072 and 0.5075, I'm afraid that I'll make a lot of short pieces that will have to be scrapped. I know from way back when I first started here that Mr. Harnswell and everybody else will come down on my head if they start seeing too many of those scraps. I figure that if I aim at 0.5075, the worst thing that will happen will be a bunch of downgrades, but I won't make any pieces that have to be scrapped."

EXERCISES

HS.7 What approach do you think the machinist should take in terms of the diameter he should aim for? Explain.

HS.8 What do you think that Natalie should do next? Explain.

RUNNING CASE
MANAGING THE *SPRINGVILLE HERALD*

Phase 1

An advertising production team is charged with reducing the number and dollar amount of the advertising errors, with initial focus on the ran-in-error category. The team collected data including the number of ads with errors on a Monday to Saturday basis. Table SH14.1 includes the total number of ads and the number containing errors for a period of one month. (Sundays are excluded because a special type of production is used for that day.) SH14-1

TABLE SH14.1

Number of Ads with Errors and Daily Number of Display Ads

Day	Number of Ads with Errors	Number of Ads	Day	Number of Ads with Errors	Number of Ads
1	4	228	14	5	245
2	6	273	15	7	266
3	5	239	16	2	197
4	3	197	17	4	228
5	6	259	18	5	236
6	7	203	19	4	208
7	8	289	20	3	214
8	14	241	21	8	258
9	9	263	22	10	267
10	5	199	23	4	217
11	6	275	24	9	277
12	4	212	25	7	258
13	3	207			

EXERCISES

SH14.1 What is the first thing that the team from the advertising production department should do to reduce the number of errors? Explain.

SH14.2 **a.** Construct the appropriate control chart for these data.

    b. Is the process in a state of statistical control? Explain.

    c. What should the team recommend as the next step to improve the process?

DO NOT CONTINUE UNTIL YOU HAVE COMPLETED THE PHASE 1 EXERCISES

Phase 2

The advertising production team examined the p chart developed from the data of Table SH14.1. Using the rules for determining out-of-control points, they observed that day 8 is above the upper control limit. Upon investigation, they determined that on that day there was an employee from another work area assigned to the processing of the ads because several employees were out ill. The group brainstormed ways of avoiding the problem in the future and recommended that a team of people from other work areas receive training on the work done by this area. Members of this team could then cover the processing of the ads by rotating in one- or two-hour shifts.

EXERCISES

SH14.3 What should the advertising production team now do concerning the data of Table SH14.1? Explain.

SH14.4 Explain how the actions of the team to avoid this particular problem in the future has resulted in quality improvement.

SH14.5 In addition to the number of ads with errors, what other information concerning errors on a daily basis should the team collect?

DO NOT CONTINUE UNTIL YOU HAVE COMPLETED THE PHASE 2 EXERCISES

Phase 3

A print production team also is charged with improving the quality of the *Herald*. The team has chosen as its first project the *blackness* of the print of the newspaper. Each day the print production team determines how "black" the newspaper is printed. Blackness is measured on a densimometer that records the results on a standard scale. Five spots on the first newspaper printed each day are randomly selected and the blackness of each spot is measured. Table SH14.2 presents the results for 25 days. SH14-2

TABLE SH14.2

Newsprint Blackness for 25 Consecutive Days

	Spot				
Day	**1**	**2**	**3**	**4**	**5**
1	0.96	1.01	1.12	1.07	0.97
2	1.06	1.00	1.02	1.16	0.96
3	1.00	0.90	0.98	1.18	0.96
4	0.92	0.89	1.01	1.16	0.90
5	1.02	1.16	1.03	0.89	1.00

	Spot				
Day	**1**	**2**	**3**	**4**	**5**
6	0.88	0.92	1.03	1.16	0.91
7	1.05	1.13	1.01	0.93	1.03
8	0.95	0.86	1.14	0.90	0.95
9	0.99	0.89	1.00	1.15	0.92
10	0.89	1.18	1.03	0.96	1.04
11	0.97	1.13	0.95	0.86	1.06
12	1.00	0.87	1.02	0.98	1.13
13	0.96	0.79	1.17	0.97	0.95
14	1.03	0.89	1.03	1.12	1.03
15	0.96	1.12	0.95	0.88	0.99
16	1.01	0.87	0.99	1.04	1.16
17	0.98	0.85	0.99	1.04	1.16
18	1.03	0.82	1.21	0.98	1.08
19	1.02	0.84	1.15	0.94	1.08
20	0.90	1.02	1.10	1.04	1.08
21	0.96	1.05	1.01	0.93	1.01
22	0.89	1.04	0.97	0.99	0.95
23	0.96	1.00	0.97	1.04	0.95
24	1.01	0.98	1.04	1.01	0.92
25	1.01	1.00	0.92	0.90	1.11

EXERCISE

SH14.6 **a.** Construct the appropriate control charts for these data.
b. Is the process in a state of statistical control? Explain.
c. What should the team recommend as the next step to improve the process?

REFERENCES

1. Arndt, M., "Quality Isn't Just for Widgets," *Business Week*, July 22, 2002, 72–73.
2. Bothe, D. R., *Measuring Process Capability* (New York: McGraw-Hill, 1997).
3. Deming, W. E., *Out of the Crisis* (Cambridge, MA: MIT Center for Advanced Engineering Study, 1986).
4. Deming, W. E., *The New Economics for Business, Industry, and Government* (Cambridge, MA: MIT Center for Advanced Engineering Study, 1993).
5. Friedman, T. L., *The Lexus and the Olive Tree: Understanding Globalization* (New York: Farrar, Straus and Giroux, 1999).
6. Gabor, A., *The Man Who Discovered Quality* (New York: Time Books, 1990).
7. Gitlow, H., A. Oppenheim, R. Oppenheim, and D. Levine, *Quality Management*, 3rd ed. (New York: McGraw-Hill-Irwin, 2005).
8. Gitlow, H. and D. Levine, *Six Sigma for Green Belts and Champions* (Upper Saddle River, NJ: Financial Times-Prentice-Hall, 2005).
9. Hahn, G. J., N. Doganaksoy, and R. Hoerl, "The Evolution of Six Sigma," *Quality Engineering*, 12 (2000): 317–326.
10. Halberstam, D., *The Reckoning* (New York: Morrow, 1986).
11. Levine, D. M., P. P. Ramsey, and R. K. Smidt, *Applied Statistics for Engineers and Scientists Using Microsoft Excel and Minitab* (Upper Saddle River, NJ: Prentice Hall, 2001).
12. *Microsoft Excel* 2003 (Redmond, WA: Microsoft Corp., 2002).
13. *Minitab for Windows Version 14* (State College, PA: Minitab, Inc., 2004).
14. Scherkenbach, W. W., *The Deming Route to Quality and Productivity: Road Maps and Roadblocks* (Washington, DC: CEEP Press, 1987).
15. Snee, R. D., "Impact of Six Sigma on Quality," *Quality Engineering*, 12 (2000): ix–xiv.
16. Walton, M., *The Deming Management Method* (New York: Perigee Books, 1986).

APPENDICES

A. REVIEW OF ARITHMETIC, ALGEBRA, AND LOGARITHMS

A.1   RULES FOR ARITHMETIC OPERATIONS

RULE	EXAMPLE
1. $a + b = c$ and $b + a = c$	$2 + 1 = 3$ and $1 + 2 = 3$
2. $a + (b + c) = (a + b) + c$	$5 + (7 + 4) = (5 + 7) + 4 = 16$
3. $a - b = c$ but $b - a \neq c$	$9 - 7 = 2$ but $7 - 9 = -2$
4. $a \times b = b \times a$	$7 \times 6 = 6 \times 7 = 42$
5. $a \times (b + c) = (a \times b) + (a \times c)$	$2 \times (3 + 5) = (2 \times 3) + (2 \times 5) = 16$
6. $a \div b \neq b \div a$	$12 \div 3 \neq 3 \div 12$
7. $\dfrac{a + b}{c} = \dfrac{a}{c} + \dfrac{b}{c}$	$\dfrac{7 + 3}{2} = \dfrac{7}{2} + \dfrac{3}{2} = 5$
8. $\dfrac{a}{b + c} \neq \dfrac{a}{b} + \dfrac{a}{c}$	$\dfrac{3}{4 + 5} \neq \dfrac{3}{4} + \dfrac{3}{5}$
9. $\dfrac{1}{a} + \dfrac{1}{b} = \dfrac{b + a}{ab}$	$\dfrac{1}{3} + \dfrac{1}{5} = \dfrac{5 + 3}{(3)(5)} = \dfrac{8}{15}$
10. $\dfrac{a}{b} \times \dfrac{c}{d} = \dfrac{a \times c}{b \times d}$	$\dfrac{2}{3} \times \dfrac{6}{7} = \dfrac{2 \times 6}{3 \times 7} = \dfrac{12}{21}$
11. $\dfrac{a}{b} \div \dfrac{c}{d} = \dfrac{a \times d}{b \times c}$	$\dfrac{5}{8} \div \dfrac{3}{7} = \dfrac{5 \times 7}{8 \times 3} = \dfrac{35}{24}$

A.2   RULES FOR ALGEBRA: EXPONENTS AND SQUARE ROOTS

RULE	EXAMPLE
1. $X^a \cdot X^b = X^{a+b}$	$4^2 \cdot 4^3 = 4^5$
2. $(X^a)^b = X^{ab}$	$(2^2)^3 = 2^6$
3. $(X^a / X^b) = X^{a-b}$	$\dfrac{3^5}{3^3} = 3^2$
4. $\dfrac{X^a}{X^a} = X^0 = 1$	$\dfrac{3^4}{3^4} = 3^0 = 1$
5. $\sqrt{XY} = \sqrt{X}\sqrt{Y}$	$\sqrt{(25)(4)} = \sqrt{25}\sqrt{4} = 10$
6. $\sqrt{\dfrac{X}{Y}} = \dfrac{\sqrt{X}}{\sqrt{Y}}$	$\sqrt{\dfrac{16}{100}} = \dfrac{\sqrt{16}}{\sqrt{100}} = 0.40$

A.3   RULES FOR LOGARITHMS

Base-10

LOG is the symbol used for base-10 logarithms:

RULE	EXAMPLE
1. $LOG(10^A) = A$	$LOG(100) = LOG(10^2) = 2$
2. If $LOG(A) = B$, then $A = 10^B$	If $LOG(A) = 2$, then $A = 10^2 = 100$
3. $LOG(A \times B) = LOG(A) + LOG(B)$	$LOG(100) = LOG(10 \times 10)$
	$= LOG(10) + LOG(10) = 1 + 1 = 2$
4. $LOG(A^B) = B \times LOG(A)$	$LOG(1000) = LOG(10^3) = 3 \times LOG(10)$
	$= 3 \times 1 = 3$
5. $LOG(A/B) = LOG(A) - LOG(B)$	$LOG(100) = LOG(1000/10)$
	$= LOG(1000) - LOG(10) = 3 - 1 = 2$

EXAMPLE

Take the base-10 logarithm of each side of the following equation:

$$Y = \beta_0 \beta_1^X \varepsilon$$

SOLUTION Apply rules 3 and 4:

$$LOG(Y) = LOG(\beta_0 \beta_1^X \varepsilon)$$
$$= LOG(\beta_0) + LOG(\beta_1^X) + LOG(\varepsilon)$$
$$= LOG(\beta_0) + X \times LOG(\beta_1) + LOG(\varepsilon)$$

Base-e

LN is the symbol used for base-e logarithms, commonly referred to as natural logarithms. e is Euler's number and $e \cong 2.718282$:

RULE	EXAMPLE
1. $LN(e^A) = A$	$LN(7.389056) = LN(e^2) = 2$
2. If $LN(A) = B$, then $A = e^B$	If $LN(A) = 2$, then $A = e^2 = 7.389056$
3. $LN(A \times B) = LN(A) + LN(B)$	$LN(100) = LN(10 \times 10)$
	$= LN(10) + LN(10)$
	$= 2.302585 + 2.302585 = 4.605170$
4. $LN(A^B) = B \times LN(A)$	$LN(1000) = LN(10^3) = 3 \times LN(10)$
	$= 3 \times 2.302585 = 6.907755$
5. $LN(A/B) = LN(A) - LN(B)$	$LN(100) = LN(1000/10)$
	$= LN(1000) - LN(10)$
	$= 6.907755 - 2.302585 = 4.605170$

EXAMPLE

Take the base-e logarithm of each side of the following equation:

$$Y = \beta_0 \beta_1^X \varepsilon$$

SOLUTION Apply rules 3 and 4:

$$LN(Y) = LN(\beta_0 \beta_1^X \varepsilon)$$
$$= LN(\beta_0) + LN(\beta_1^X) + LN(\varepsilon)$$
$$= LN(\beta_0) + X \times LN(\beta_1) + LN(\varepsilon)$$

B. SUMMATION NOTATION

The symbol Σ, the Greek capital letter sigma, is used to denote "taking the sum of." Consider a set of n values for variable X. The expression $\sum_{i=1}^{n} X_i$ means that these n values are to be added together. Thus:

$$\sum_{i=1}^{n} X_i = X_1 + X_2 + X_3 + \cdots + X_n$$

The following problem illustrates the use of the summation notation. Consider five values of a variable X: $X_1 = 2$, $X_2 = 0$, $X_3 = -1$, $X_4 = 5$, and $X_5 = 7$. Thus:

$$\sum_{i=1}^{5} X_i = X_1 + X_2 + X_3 + X_4 + X_5 = 2 + 0 + (-1) + 5 + 7 = 13$$

In statistics, the squared values of a variable are often summed. Thus:

$$\sum_{i=1}^{n} X_i^2 = X_1^2 + X_2^2 + X_3^2 + \cdots + X_n^2$$

and, in the example above:

$$\sum_{i=1}^{5} X_i^2 = X_1^2 + X_2^2 + X_3^2 + X_4^2 + X_5^2$$
$$= 2^2 + 0^2 + (-1)^2 + 5^2 + 7^2$$
$$= 4 + 0 + 1 + 25 + 49$$
$$= 79$$

$\sum_{i=1}^{n} X_i^2$, the summation of the squares, is *not* the same as $\left(\sum_{i=1}^{n} X_i\right)^2$, the square of the sum.

$$\sum_{i=1}^{n} X_i^2 \neq \left(\sum_{i=1}^{n} X_i\right)^2$$

In the example given earlier, the summation of squares is equal to 79. This is not equal to the square of the sum, which is $13^2 = 169$.

Another frequently used operation involves the summation of the product. Consider two variables, X and Y, each having n values. Then:

$$\sum_{i=1}^{n} X_i Y_i = X_1 Y_1 + X_2 Y_2 + X_3 Y_3 + \cdots + X_n Y_n$$

Continuing with the previous example, suppose there is a second variable, Y, whose five values are $Y_1 = 1$, $Y_2 = 3$, $Y_3 = -2$, $Y_4 = 4$, and $Y_5 = 3$. Then,

$$\sum_{i=1}^{5} X_i Y_i = X_1 Y_1 + X_2 Y_2 + X_3 Y_3 + X_4 Y_4 + X_5 Y_5$$
$$= (2)(1) + (0)(3) + (-1)(-2) + (5)(4) + (7)(3)$$
$$= 2 + 0 + 2 + 20 + 21$$
$$= 45$$

In computing $\sum\limits_{i=1}^{n} X_i Y_i$ realize that the first value of X is multiplied by the first value of Y, the second value of X is multiplied by the second value of Y, and so on. These products are then summed in order to compute the desired result. However, the summation of products is *not* equal to the product of the individual sums.

$$\sum_{i=1}^{n} X_i Y_i \neq \left(\sum_{i=1}^{n} X_i\right)\left(\sum_{i=1}^{n} Y_i\right)$$

In this example, $\sum\limits_{i=1}^{5} X_i = 13$ and $\sum\limits_{i=1}^{5} Y_i = 1 + 3 + (-2) + 4 + 3 = 9$ so that $\left(\sum\limits_{i=1}^{5} X_i\right)\left(\sum\limits_{i=1}^{5} Y_i\right) =$

$(13)(9) = 117$. However $\sum\limits_{i=1}^{5} X_i Y_i = 45$. The following table summarizes these results.

VALUE	X_i	Y_i	$X_i Y_i$
1	2	1	2
2	0	3	0
3	-1	-2	2
4	5	4	20
5	7	3	21
	$\sum\limits_{i=1}^{5} X_i = 13$	$\sum\limits_{i=1}^{5} Y_i = 9$	$\sum\limits_{i=1}^{5} X_i Y_i = 45$

RULE 1 The summation of the values of two variables is equal to the sum of the values of each summed variable.

$$\sum_{i=1}^{n} (X_i + Y_i) = \sum_{i=1}^{n} X_i + \sum_{i=1}^{n} Y_i$$

Thus,

$$\sum_{i=1}^{5} (X_i + Y_i) = (2 + 1) + (0 + 3) + (-1 + (-2)) + (5 + 4) + (7 + 3)$$
$$= 3 + 3 + (-3) + 9 + 10$$
$$= 22$$
$$\sum_{i=1}^{5} X_i + \sum_{i=1}^{5} Y_i = 13 + 9 = 22$$

RULE 2 The summation of a difference between the values of two variables is equal to the difference between the summed values of the variables.

$$\sum_{i=1}^{n} (X_i - Y_i) = \sum_{i=1}^{n} X_i - \sum_{i=1}^{n} Y_i$$

Thus,

$$\sum_{i=1}^{5} (X_i - Y_i) = (2-1) + (0-3) + (-1-(-2)) + (5-4) + (7-3)$$

$$= 1 + (-3) + 1 + 1 + 4$$

$$= 4$$

$$\sum_{i=1}^{5} X_i - \sum_{i=1}^{5} Y_i = 13 - 9 = 4$$

RULE 3 The summation of a constant times a variable is equal to that constant times the summation of the values of the variable.

$$\sum_{i=1}^{n} cX_i = c\sum_{i=1}^{n} X_i$$

where c is a constant.

Thus, if $c = 2$,

$$\sum_{i=1}^{5} cX_i = \sum_{i=1}^{5} 2X_i = (2)(2) + (2)(0) + (2)(-1) + (2)(5) + (2)(7)$$

$$= 4 + 0 + (-2) + 10 + 14$$

$$= 26$$

$$c\sum_{i=1}^{5} X_i = 2\sum_{i=1}^{5} X_i = (2)(13) = 26$$

RULE 4 A constant summed n times will be equal to n times the value of the constant.

$$\sum_{i=1}^{n} c = nc$$

where c is a constant. Thus, if the constant $c = 2$ is summed 5 times,

$$\sum_{i=1}^{5} c = 2 + 2 + 2 + 2 + 2 = 10$$

$$nc = (5)(2) = 10$$

Problem

Suppose there are six values for the variables X and Y such that $X_1 = 2, X_2 = 1, X_3 = 5, X_4 = -3, X_5 = 1, X_6 = -2$, and $Y_1 = 4, Y_2 = 0, Y_3 = -1, Y_4 = 2, Y_5 = 7$, and $Y_6 = -3$. Compute each of the following:

(a) $\sum_{i=1}^{6} X_i$

(b) $\sum_{i=1}^{6} Y_i$

(c) $\sum_{i=1}^{6} X_i^2$

(d) $\sum_{i=1}^{6} Y_i^2$

(e) $\sum_{i=1}^{6} X_i Y_i$

(f) $\sum_{i=1}^{6} (X_i + Y_i)$

(g) $\sum_{i=1}^{6} (X_i - Y_i)$

(i) $\sum_{i=1}^{6} (cX_i)$, where $c = -1$

(h) $\sum_{i=1}^{6} (X_i - 3Y_i + 2X_i^2)$

(j) $\sum_{i=1}^{6} (X_i - 3Y_i + c)$, where $c = +3$

ANSWER
(a) 4   (b) 9   (c) 44   (d) 79   (e) 10   (f) 13   (g) –5   (h) 65   (i) –4   (j) –5

References

1. Bashaw, W. L., *Mathematics for Statistics* (New York: Wiley, 1969).
2. Lanzer, P., *Video Review of Arithmetic* (Hicksville, NY: Video Aided Instruction, 1990).
3. Levine, D., *The MBA Primer: Business Statistics* (Cincinnati, OH: Southwestern Publishing, 2000).
4. Levine, D., *Video Review of Statistics* (Hicksville, NY: Video Aided Instruction, 1989).
5. Shane, H., *Video Review of Elementary Algebra* (Hicksville, NY: Video Aided Instruction, 1990).

C. STATISTICAL SYMBOLS AND GREEK ALPHABET

C.1   STATISTICAL SYMBOLS

+ add   × multiply

− subtract   ÷ divide

= equal to   ≠ not equal to

≅ approximately equal to

> greater than   < less than

≥ greater than or equal to   ≤ less than or equal to

C.2   GREEK ALPHABET

GREEK LETTER		LETTER NAME	ENGLISH EQUIVALENT	GREEK LETTER		LETTER NAME	ENGLISH EQUIVALENT
A	α	Alpha	a	N	ν	Nu	n
B	β	Beta	b	Ξ	ξ	Xi	x
Γ	γ	Gamma	g	O	o	Omicron	ŏ
Δ	δ	Delta	d	Π	π	Pi	p
E	ε	Epsilon	ĕ	P	ρ	Rho	r
Z	ζ	Zeta	z	Σ	σ	Sigma	s
H	η	Eta	ē	T	τ	Tau	t
Θ	θ	Theta	th	Y	υ	Upsilon	u
I	ι	Iota	i	Φ	φ	Phi	ph
K	κ	Kappa	k	X	χ	Chi	ch
Λ	λ	Lambda	l	Ψ	ψ	Psi	ps
M	μ	Mu	m	Ω	ω	Omega	ō

D. CD-ROM CONTENTS

D.1 CD-ROM OVERVIEW

The CD-ROM packaged with this text contains program and data files that support your learning of statistics. This CD-ROM includes the following folders:

PHStat2

Contains the setup program and files for PHStat2 version 2.5. You must run the setup program successfully before you can use PHStat2 inside Microsoft Excel. (Be sure to read the instructions in Appendix F and the contents of the PHStat2 readme file on the CD-ROM, before you run the setup program.)

Excel Data Files

Contains the Microsoft Excel workbook files (with the extension .xls) used in the textbook. A detailed list of the files found in this folder starts at the bottom of this page.

Worksheet Template Examples

Contains the Microsoft Excel workbook files used in the Microsoft Excel appendices. Copies of these files also appear in the Excel Data Files folder.

Minitab

Contains the Minitab worksheet files (with the extension .mtw) used in the textbook. A detailed list of the files found in this folder starts at the bottom of this page.

SPSS

Contains the SPSS data files (with the extension .sav) used in the textbook. A detailed list of the files found in this folder starts at the bottom of this page.

Visual Explorations in Statistics

Contains the files necessary to use the Visual Explorations in Statistics macro workbook. If you are using Microsoft Excel 2000 SR-1 or any later version of Excel, you must first make sure that your Microsoft Office security setting is not **High**. (To check your security setting, select **Tools → Macro → Security** and, if necessary, select the **Medium** option in the Security Level tab and click **OK**. When you finish using Visual Explorations, you can go back and reset the security level to **High**, if desired.)

To use this workbook, you can open the **Visual Explorations.xla** file directly from the CD-ROM in Microsoft Excel. If you prefer to use Visual Explorations without always inserting the CD-ROM, copy the **Visual Explorations.xla** file as well as the **Veshelp.hlp** file, containing the orientation and help files, to the hard disk folder of your choice.

CD-ROM Topics

Contains supplemental textbook sections in Adobe PDF file format. You will need the Adobe Acrobat reader software (available on the CD-ROM) in order to read these sections.

Most likely, you will be using files in the Excel, Minitab, or SPSS folder on a regular basis. You can retrieve those files directly from the CD-ROM or copy them first to a hard disk folder. When you copy the files, the files will likely have read-only status. If you wish, you can change the status of the files to read-write by doing the following:

- Open Windows Explorer to the hard disk folder containing the files.
- Select the files to make read-write. (Select **Edit → Select All** to select every file in list.)
- Select **Files → Properties** and in the Properties dialog box, clear (uncheck) the **Read-only** attribute and click **OK**.

D.2 DATA FILE DESCRIPTIONS

The following is an alphabetical listing and description of the data files stored in Excel, Minitab, and SPSS format. In this text, these names appear in smallcaps (such as MUTUALFUNDS2004. For each data file listed in the text, you will find a corresponding file in .xls, .mtw, and .sav format in the appropriate folder.

ACCESS Coded access read times (in msec), file size, programmer group, and buffer size. (Chapter 10)

ACCRES Processing time in seconds and type of computer jobs (research = 0, accounting = 1). (Chapter 10)

ADVERTISE Sales (in thousands of dollars), radio ads (in thousands of dollars), and newspaper ads (in thousands of dollars) for 22 cities. (Chapter 13)

AIRCLEANERS Name, price, energy cost, and filter cost. (Chapters 2, 3)

ALLOY Lifetime of four different alloys. (Chapter 10)

ANGLE Subgroup number and angle. (Chapter 14)

ANSCOMBE Data sets A, B, C, and D—each with 11 pairs of X and Y values. (Chapter 12)

ASSETS Assets of bond funds (Chapter 3)

AUTO Miles per gallon, horsepower, and weight for a sample of 50 car models. (Chapter 13)

AUTO2002 Name, sports utility vehicle (Yes or No), drive type, horsepower, fuel type, miles per gallon, length, width, weight, cargo volume, and turning circle. (Chapters 2, 3, 10, 13)

BANK1 Waiting time (in minutes) spent by a sample of 15 customers at a bank located in a commercial district. (Chapters 3, 9, 10)

BANK2 Waiting time (in minutes) spent by a sample of 15 customers at a bank located in a residential area. (Chapters 3, 10)

BANKCOST1 Bank name, minimum deposit to open, bounced check fee, foreign ATM fee, and online access. (Chapters 2, 3, 8)

BANKCOST2 Bank name, minimum deposit to open, minimum balance to avoid fees, monthly service charge, bounced check fee, foreign ATM fee, and online access. (Chapters 2, 3, 8)

BANKRETURN Year, one-year certificate of deposit return, thirty-month certificate of deposit return, and money market return. (Chapter 3)

BANKTIME Waiting times of four bank customers per day for 20 days. (Chapter 14)

BATTERIES Time to failure (in hours) for 13 flashlight batteries. (Chapters 3, 9)

BATTERIES2 Name, price, cold-cranking amps (CCA). (Chapters 2, 12)

BB2001 Team, league (0 = American, 1 = National), wins, earned run average, runs scored, hits allowed, walks allowed, saves, errors, average ticket prices, fan cost index, regular season gate receipts, local television radio and cable revenues, other local operating revenue, player compensation and benefits, national and other local expenses, income from baseball operations. (Chapters 2, 12, 13)

BB2003 Team, league (0 = American, 1 = National), wins, earned run average, runs scored, hits allowed, walks allowed, saves, and errors. (Chapters 12, 13)

BBREVENUE Team, revenue, value. (Chapter 12)

BEER Brand, price in dollars, calories, percentage of alcoholic content, type (craft lager = 1, craft ale = 2, imported lager = 3, regular and ice beer = 4, light and no alcohol beer = 5), and country of origin (U.S. = 1, imported = 0). (Chapters 3, 10)

BREAKSTW Breaking strength for machines. (Chapter 10)

BULBS Length of life of 40 lightbulbs from manufacturer A (= 1) and 40 lightbulbs from manufacturer B (= 2). (Chapters 2, 10)

CAMERA Prices of cameras. (Chapter 3)

CANISTER Day and number of nonconforming film canisters. (Chapter 14)

CATFOOD Time period and weight of cat food (Chapter 14)

CELLPHONE Name, type (CDMA or TDMA), price, talk time, battery capacity. (Chapters 2, 3, 12)

CEREALS Name, cost, calories, fiber, and sugar. (Chapter 3)

CHANGE2004 Mutual fund, change in dollars (Chapter 9)

CHEMICAL Viscosity of batches of chemicals. (Chapters 2, 9)

CIRCULATION Magazine, reported newsstand sales, audited newsstand sales. (Chapter 12)

COFFEEDRINK Product, calories, and fat in coffee drinks. (Chapter 3)

COLA Sales for normal and end-aisle locations. (Chapter 10)

COLASPC Day, total number of cans filled, and number of unacceptable cans (over a 22-day period). (Chapter 14)

COLLEGECOST University and change in college cost from 2001–2002 to 2002–2003 (Chapter 3)

COLLEGES2002 School, type (0 = public, 1 = private), first quartile SAT score, third quartile SAT score, room and board, total cost (out-of-state cost for public colleges), and average indebtedness at graduation. (Chapters 10, 13)

COMPTIME Completion time with current market leader and completion time with new software package. (Chapter 10)

CONCRETE1 Compressive strength after two days and seven days. (Chapter 10)

CONTEST2001 Returns for experts, readers, and dart throwers. (Chapter 10)

CRACK Type of crack and crack size. (Chapter 10)

CREDITSCORE City and credit score (Chapter 6)

CUSTSALE Week number, number of customers, and sales (in thousands of dollars) over a period of 15 consecutive weeks. (Chapter 12)

DELIVERY Customer number, number of cases, and delivery time. (Chapter 12)

DISPRAZ Price, price squared, and sales of disposable razors in 15 stores. (Chapter 13)

DOWRETURN Company, ticker symbol, ten-year return. (Chapter 3)

DRILL Time to drill additional five feet, depth, and type of hole. (Chapter 13)

DRINK Amount of soft drink filled in a subgroup of 50 consecutive 2-liter bottles. (Chapters 2, 9)

ELECUSE Electricity consumption (in kilowatts) and mean temperature (in degrees Fahrenheit) over a consecutive 24-month period. (Chapter 12)

ENERGY State and per capita kilowatt hour use. (Chapter 3)

ERRORSPC Number of nonconforming items and number of accounts processed over 39 days. (Chapter 14)

ESPRESSO Tamp (the distance in inches between the espresso grounds and the top of the portafilter) and time (the number of seconds the heart, body, and crema are separated). (Chapter 12)

EXPIMP Country, exports, imports. (Chapter 3)

FASTFOOD Product, type (burger vs. chicken), price, size, total fat, saturated fat, calories, and sodium. (Chapters 2, 3)

FLYASH Fly ash percentage, fly ash percentage squared, and strength. (Chapter 13)

FORCE Force required to break insulator. (Chapters 2, 3, 8, 9)

FOULSPC Number of foul shots made and number taken over 40 days. (Chapter 14)

FUNDTRAN Day, number of new investigations, and number closed over a 30-day period. (Chapter 14)

FURNITURE Days between receipt and resolution of a sample of 50 complaints regarding purchased furniture. (Chapters 2, 3, 8, 9)

GASPRICE Gasoline price in Manhattan, Bronx, Queens, Brooklyn, Nassau, and Suffolk counties (Chapter 10)

GCROSLYN Address, appraised value, location, property size (acres), house size, age, number of rooms, number of bathrooms, and number of cars that can be parked in the garage in Glen Cove and Roslyn, NY. (Chapter 13)

GLENCOVE Address, appraised value, property size (acres), house size, age, number of rooms, number of bathrooms, and number of cars that can be parked in the garage in Glen Cove, NY. (Chapter 13)

GOLFBALL Distance for designs 1, 2, 3, and 4. (Chapter 10)

GPIGMAT GMAT scores and GPI for 20 students. (Chapter 12)

GRANULE Granule loss in Boston and Vermont shingles. (Chapters 3, 8, 9, 10)

HARDNESS Tensile strength and hardness of aluminum specimens. (Chapter 12)

HARNSWELL Day and diameter of cam rollers (in inches) for samples of five parts produced in each of 30 batches. (Chapter 14)

HOSPADM Day, number of admissions, mean processing time (in hours), range of processing times, and proportion of laboratory rework (over a 30-day period). (Chapter 14)

HOTEL1 Day, number of rooms, number of nonconforming rooms per day over a 28-day period, and proportion of nonconforming items. (Chapter 14)

HOTEL2 Day and delivery time for subgroups of five luggage deliveries per day over a 28-day period. (Chapter 14)

HOTEL-CAR City, hotel cost, rental car cost. (Chapters 2, 3, 8)

HOTEL-PRICE City and hotel price. (Chapter 6)

HOTELPRICE2 City, price in 2004, price in 2002. (Chapter 10)

HOUSE1 Selling price (in thousands of dollars), assessed value (in thousands of dollars), type (new = 0, old = 1), and time period of sale for 30 houses. (Chapters 12, 13)

HOUSE2 Assessed value (in thousands of dollars), size (in thousands of square feet), and age (in years) for 15 houses. (Chapters 12, 13)

HOUSE3 Assessed value (in thousands of dollars), size (in thousands of square feet), and presence of a fireplace for 15 houses. (Chapter 13)

HOUSESNY Year, median price, mortgage rate, mortgage payment, mortgage payment in 2002 dollars. (Chapter 2)

HTNGOIL Monthly consumption of heating oil (in gallons), temperature (in degrees Fahrenheit), attic insulation (in inches), and style (0 = not ranch, 1 = ranch). (Chapter 13)

ICECREAM Daily temperature (in degrees Fahrenheit) and sales (in thousands of dollars) for 21 days. (Chapter 12)

INSURANCE Processing time of insurance policies. (Chapters 3, 8, 9)

INTAGLIO Surface hardness of untreated and treated steel plates. (Chapter 10)

INVOICE Number of invoices processed and amount of time (in hours) for 30 days. (Chapter 12)

INVOICES Amount recorded (in dollars) from a sample of 12 sales invoices. (Chapter 9)

KEYBOARD Cause, frequency, and percentage. (Chapter 2)

LARGESTBONDS Five-year return of bond funds. (Chapter 3)

LOCATE Sales volume (in thousands of dollars) for front, middle, and rear locations. (Chapter 10)

MAIL Weight of mail and orders. (Chapters 2, 12)

MEASUREMENT Sample, in-line measurement, and analytical lab measurement. (Chapter 10)

MEDREC Day, number of discharged patients, and number of records not processed for a 30-day period. (Chapter 14)

METALRETURN Year, platinum return, gold return, silver return. (Chapter 3)

MOISTURE Moisture content of Boston shingles and Vermont shingles. (Chapter 9)

MOVING Labor hours and cubic feet of packaged items transported in a sample of 36 clients moved by a particular company. (Chapter 12)

MUTUALFUNDS2004 Fund, category, objective, assets, fees, expense ratio, 2003 Return, three-year return, five-year return, risk, best quarter, and worst quarter. (Chapters 2, 3, 6, 8, 10, 13)

MYELOMA Patient, measurement before transplant, measurement after transplant. (Chapter 10)

NBA2004 Team, number of wins, points per game (for team, opponent, and the difference between team and opponent), field goal (shots made), percentage (for team, opponent, and the difference between team and opponent), turnovers (losing the ball before a shot is taken) per game (for team, opponent, and the difference between team and opponent), offensive rebound percentage, and defensive rebound percentage. (Chapter 13)

NEIGHBOR Selling price (in thousands of dollars), number of rooms, and neighborhood location (east = 0, west = 1) for 20 houses. (Chapter 13)

O-RING Flight number, temperature, and O-ring damage index. (Chapter 12)

OIL-GAS Date, price of gasoline in cents per gallon, price of crude oil in dollars per barrel. (Chapter 12)

OMNI Bars sold, price, and promotion expenses. (Chapter 13)

ONLINEBANKING Year and number of households. (Chapter 2)

ONLINESHOPPING Reason, percentage. (Chapter 2)

PALLET Weight of Boston and weight of Vermont shingles. (Chapters 2, 8, 9, 10)

PARACHUTE Tensile strength of parachutes from suppliers 1, 2, 3, and 4. (Chapter 10)

PEN Gender, ad, and product rating. (Chapter 10)

PERFORM Performance rating before and after motivational training. (Chapter 10)

PETFOOD Shelf space (in feet), weekly sales (in hundreds of dollars), and aisle location (back = 0, front = 1). (Chapters 12, 13)

PETFOOD2 Pet, type of food, cost per serving, cups per can, protein in grams, and fat in grams. (Chapters 3, 10)

PHONE Time (in minutes) to clear telephone line problems and location (I and II) for samples of 20 customer problems reported to the two office locations. (Chapters 3, 6, 10)

PIZZA Product, type (cheese, pepperoni, or chain), cost, calories, and fat. (Chapters 2, 3)

PIZZATIME Time period, delivery time for local restaurant, delivery times for national chain. (Chapter 10)

PRINTERS Name, price, text speed, text cost, color photo time, and color photo cost. (Chapters 2, 3)

PROTEIN Calories (in grams), protein, percentage of calories from fat, percentage of calories from saturated fat, and cholesterol (in mg) for 25 popular protein foods. (Chapter 2)

PTFALLS Month and patient falls. (Chapter 14)

PUMPKIN Circumference and weight of pumpkins. (Chapter 12)

REDWOOD Height, diameter, and bark thickness. (Chapter 13)

REFRIGERATOR Name, price, and energy cost. (Chapters 2, 12)

RENT Monthly rental cost (in dollars) and apartment size (in square footage) for a sample of 25 apartments. (Chapter 12)

RESTRATE Location, food rating, décor rating, service rating, summated rating, coded location (0 = New

York City, 1 = Long Island), and price of restaurants. (Chapters 3, 10, 12, 13)

RETURNS Week and stock price of Microsoft, stock price of General Motors, stock price of Ford, and stock price of International Aluminum. (Chapter 12)

REUSE Percentage of code reused. (Chapter 3)

ROYALS Game, attendance, and whether there was a promotion at Kansas City Royals games. (Chapter 2)

RUBBER Weight of rubber edges. (Chapter 6)

RUDYBIRD Day, total cases sold, and cases of Rudybird sold. (Chapter 14)

SALARIES Job titles, salary for men, and salary for women. (Chapter 10)

SEALANT Sample number, sealant strength for Boston shingles, and sealant strength for Vermont shingles. (Chapter 14)

SECURITY City, turnover rate, and violations per million passengers. (Chapters 2, 3, 12)

SH2 Day and number of calls received at the help desk. (Chapters 2, 3)

SH9 Blackness of newsprint. (Chapter 9)

SH10-1 Length of early calls (in seconds), length of late calls (in seconds), and difference (in seconds). (Chapter 10)

SH10-2 Call, presentation plan (structured = 1, semi-structured = 2, unstructured = 3), and length of call (in seconds). (Chapter 10)

SH12 Hours per month spent telemarketing and number of new subscriptions per month over a 24-month period. (Chapter 12)

SH13 Hours per week spent telemarketing, number of new subscriptions, and type of presentation. (Chapter 13)

SH14-1 Day, number of ads with errors, number of ads, and number of errors over a 25-day period. (Chapter 14)

SH14-2 Day and newsprint blackness measures for each of five spots made over 25 consecutive weekdays. (Chapter 14)

SITE Store number, square footage in thousands of square feet, and sales (in millions of dollars) in 14 stores. (Chapter 12)

SP500 Week, weekly change in the S&P 500, weekly change in the price of Sears, weekly change in the price of Target, and weekly change in the price of Sara Lee. (Chapter 12)

SPONGE Day, number of sponges produced, number of sponges nonconforming over a 32-day period, and proportion of nonconforming sponges. (Chapter 14)

SPORTING Sales, age, annual population growth, income, percentage with high school diploma, and percentage with college diploma. (Chapter 12)

SPORTSTV Year, mean number of viewers in millions for National Football League (NFL), National Basketball Association (NBA), Major League Baseball (MLB), and National Hockey League (NHL). (Chapter 2)

SPWATER Sample number and amount of magnesium. (Chapter 14)

STANDBY Standby hours, staff, remote hours, Dubner hours, and labor hours for 26 weeks. (Chapter 13)

STATES State, commuting time, percentage of homes with more than 8 rooms, median income, percentage of housing that costs more than 30% of family income. (Chapters 2, 3)

STEEL Error in actual length and specified length. (Chapters 2, 6, 8, 9)

STOCKRETURN Year, rate of return of DJIA, S&P 500, Russell 2000, and Wilshire 5000. (Chapter 3)

STOCKS&BONDS Date, closing price of Vanguard Long-Term Bond Index Fund, closing price of the Dow Jones Industrial Average. (Chapter 12)

STOCKS2003 Week, closing weekly stock price for S&P, Sears, Target, Sara Lee. (Chapter 2)

TAX Quarterly sales tax receipts (in thousands of dollars) for all 50 business establishments. (Chapter 3)

TAXES County taxes (in dollars) and age of house (in years) for 19 single-family houses. (Chapter 13)

TEA3 Sample number and weight of tea bags. (Chapter 14)

TEABAGS Weight of tea bags. (Chapters 3, 8, 9)

TELESPC Number of orders and number of corrections over 30 days. (Chapter 14)

TENSILE Sample number and strength. (Chapter 14)

TEXTBOOK Textbook, book store price, and Amazon price. (Chapter 10)

TIMES Times to get ready. (Chapter 3)

TRADE Days, number of undesirable trades, and number of total trades made over a 30-day period. (Chapter 14)

TRADES Day, number of incoming calls, and number of trade executions per day over a 35-day period. (Chapter 12)

TRAINING Assembly time and training program (team-based = 0, individual-based = 1). (Chapter 10)

TRANSMIT Day and number of errors in transmission. (Chapter 14)

TRANSPORT Days and patient transport times (in minutes) for samples of four patients per day over a 30-day period. (Chapter 14)

TRASHBAGS Weight required to break four brands of trashbags. (Chapter 10)

TROUGH Width of trough. (Chapters 2, 3, 8)

TUITION School, tuition in state 2002–03, tuition in state 2003–04, difference in tuition in state 2003–04 and 2002–03, tuition out of state 2002–03, tuition out of state 2003–04, difference in tuition out of state 2003–04 and 2002–03. (Chapter 3)

UERATE Year, month, and monthly unemployment rates. (Chapter 2)

UTILITY Utility charges for 50 one-bedroom apartments. (Chapters 2, 6)

VB Time (in minutes) for nine students to write and run a Visual Basic program. (Chapter 10)

WARECOST Distribution cost (in thousands of dollars), sales (in thousands of dollars), and number of orders for 24 months. (Chapters 12, 13)

WAREHSE Number of units handled per day, and employee number. (Chapter 14)

WHOLEFOODS1 Item, price at Whole Foods, price at Fairway. (Chapter 10)

WIP Processing times for samples of 20 books at each of two plants (A = 1, B = 2). (Chapters 3, 6, 10)

YARN Breaking strength score, pressure (30, 40, or 50 psi), yarn sample, and side-to-side aspect (nozzle = 1, opposite = 2). (Chapter 10)

E. TABLES

E. TABLES

TABLE E.1

Table of Random Numbers

Row	Column 00000 12345	00001 67890	11111 12345	11112 67890	22222 12345	22223 67890	33333 12345	33334 67890
01	49280	88924	35779	00283	81163	07275	89863	02348
02	61870	41657	07468	08612	98083	97349	20775	45091
03	43898	65923	25078	86129	78496	97653	91550	08078
04	62993	93912	30454	84598	56095	20664	12872	64647
05	33850	58555	51438	85507	71865	79488	76783	31708
06	97340	03364	88472	04334	63919	36394	11095	92470
07	70543	29776	10087	10072	55980	64688	68239	20461
08	89382	93809	00796	95945	34101	81277	66090	88872
09	37818	72142	67140	50785	22380	16703	53362	44940
10	60430	22834	14130	96593	23298	56203	92671	15925
11	82975	66158	84731	19436	55790	69229	28661	13675
12	30987	71938	40355	54324	08401	26299	49420	59208
13	55700	24586	93247	32596	11865	63397	44251	43189
14	14756	23997	78643	75912	83832	32768	18928	57070
15	32166	53251	70654	92827	63491	04233	33825	69662
16	23236	73751	31888	81718	06546	83246	47651	04877
17	45794	26926	15130	82455	78305	55058	52551	47182
18	09893	20505	14225	68514	47427	56788	96297	78822
19	54382	74598	91499	14523	68479	27686	46162	83554
20	94750	89923	37089	20048	80336	94598	26940	36858
21	70297	34135	53140	33340	42050	82341	44104	82949
22	85157	47954	32979	26575	57600	40881	12250	73742
23	11100	02340	12860	74697	96644	89439	28707	25815
24	36871	50775	30592	57143	17381	68856	25853	35041
25	23913	48357	63308	16090	51690	54607	72407	55538
26	79348	36085	27973	65157	07456	22255	25626	57054
27	92074	54641	53673	54421	18130	60103	69593	49464
28	06873	21440	75593	41373	49502	17972	82578	16364
29	12478	37622	99659	31065	83613	69889	58869	29571
30	57175	55564	65411	42547	70457	03426	72937	83792
31	91616	11075	80103	07831	59309	13276	26710	73000
32	78025	73539	14621	39044	47450	03197	12787	47709
33	27587	67228	80145	10175	12822	86687	65530	49325
34	16690	20427	04251	64477	73709	73945	92396	68263
35	70183	58065	65489	31833	82093	16747	10386	59293
36	90730	35385	15679	99742	50866	78028	75573	67257
37	10934	93242	13431	24590	02770	48582	00906	58595
38	82462	30166	79613	47416	13389	80268	05085	96666
39	27463	10433	07606	16285	93699	60912	94532	95632
40	02979	52997	09079	92709	90110	47506	53693	49892
41	46888	69929	75233	52507	32097	37594	10067	67327
42	53638	83161	08289	12639	08141	12640	28437	09268
43	82433	61427	17239	89160	19666	08814	37841	12847
44	35766	31672	50082	22795	66948	65581	84393	15890
45	10853	42581	08792	13257	61973	24450	52351	16602
46	20341	27398	72906	63955	17276	10646	74692	48438
47	54458	90542	77563	51839	52901	53355	83281	19177
48	26337	66530	16687	35179	46560	00123	44546	79896
49	34314	23729	85264	05575	96855	23820	11091	79821
50	28603	10708	68933	34189	92166	15181	66628	58599

continued

TABLE E.1

Table of Random Numbers (*Continued*)

	Column							
Row	00000 12345	00001 67890	11111 12345	11112 67890	22222 12345	22223 67890	33333 12345	33334 67890
51	66194	28926	99547	16625	45515	67953	12108	57846
52	78240	43195	24837	32511	70880	22070	52622	61881
53	00833	88000	67299	68215	11274	55624	32991	17436
54	12111	86683	61270	58036	64192	90611	15145	01748
55	47189	99951	05755	03834	43782	90599	40282	51417
56	76396	72486	62423	27618	84184	78922	73561	52818
57	46409	17469	32483	09083	76175	19985	26309	91536
58	74626	22111	87286	46772	42243	68046	44250	42439
59	34450	81974	93723	49023	58432	67083	36876	93391
60	36327	72135	33005	28701	34710	49359	50693	89311
61	74185	77536	84825	09934	99103	09325	67389	45869
62	12296	41623	62873	37943	25584	09609	63360	47270
63	90822	60280	88925	99610	42772	60561	76873	04117
64	72121	79152	96591	90305	10189	79778	68016	13747
65	95268	41377	25684	08151	61816	58555	54305	86189
66	92603	09091	75884	93424	72586	88903	30061	14457
67	18813	90291	05275	01223	79607	95426	34900	09778
68	38840	26903	28624	67157	51986	42865	14508	49315
69	05959	33836	53758	16562	41081	38012	41230	20528
70	85141	21155	99212	32685	51403	31926	69813	58781
71	75047	59643	31074	38172	03718	32119	69506	67143
72	30752	95260	68032	62871	58781	34143	68790	69766
73	22986	82575	42187	62295	84295	30634	66562	31442
74	99439	86692	90348	66036	48399	73451	26698	39437
75	20389	93029	11881	71685	65452	89047	63669	02656
76	39249	05173	68256	36359	20250	68686	05947	09335
77	96777	33605	29481	20063	09398	01843	35139	61344
78	04860	32918	10798	50492	52655	33359	94713	28393
79	41613	42375	00403	03656	77580	87772	86877	57085
80	17930	00794	53836	53692	67135	98102	61912	11246
81	24649	31845	25736	75231	83808	98917	93829	99430
82	79899	34061	54308	59358	56462	58166	97302	86828
83	76801	49594	81002	30397	52728	15101	72070	33706
84	36239	63636	38140	65731	39788	06872	38971	53363
85	07392	64449	17886	63632	53995	17574	22247	62607
86	67133	04181	33874	98835	67453	59734	76381	63455
87	77759	31504	32832	70861	15152	29733	75371	39174
88	85992	72268	42920	20810	29361	51423	90306	73574
89	79553	75952	54116	65553	47139	60579	09165	85490
90	41101	17336	48951	53674	17880	45260	08575	49321
91	36191	17095	32123	91576	84221	78902	82010	30847
92	62329	63898	23268	74283	26091	68409	69704	82267
93	14751	13151	93115	01437	56945	89661	67680	79790
94	48462	59278	44185	29616	76537	19589	83139	28454
95	29435	88105	59651	44391	74588	55114	80834	85686
96	28340	29285	12965	14821	80425	16602	44653	70467
97	02167	58940	27149	80242	10587	79786	34959	75339
98	17864	00991	39557	54981	23588	81914	37609	13128
99	79675	80605	60059	35862	00254	36546	21545	78179
00	72335	82037	92003	34100	29879	46613	89720	13274

Source: Partially extracted from the Rand Corporation, A Million Random Digits with 100,000 Normal Deviates *(Glencoe, IL, The Free Press, 1955).*

TABLE E.2

The Cumulative Standardized Normal Distribution

Entry represents area under the cumulative standardized normal distribution from $-\infty$ to Z

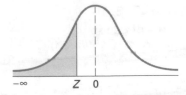

Z	0.00	0.01	0.02	0.03	0.04	0.05	0.06	0.07	0.08	0.09
−6.0	0.000000001									
−5.5	0.000000019									
−5.0	0.000000287									
−4.5	0.000003398									
−4.0	0.000031671									
−3.9	0.00005	0.00005	0.00004	0.00004	0.00004	0.00004	0.00004	0.00004	0.00003	0.00003
−3.8	0.00007	0.00007	0.00007	0.00006	0.00006	0.00006	0.00006	0.00005	0.00005	0.00005
−3.7	0.00011	0.00010	0.00010	0.00010	0.00009	0.00009	0.00008	0.00008	0.00008	0.00008
−3.6	0.00016	0.00015	0.00015	0.00014	0.00014	0.00013	0.00013	0.00012	0.00012	0.00011
−3.5	0.00023	0.00022	0.00022	0.00021	0.00020	0.00019	0.00019	0.00018	0.00017	0.00017
−3.4	0.00034	0.00032	0.00031	0.00030	0.00029	0.00028	0.00027	0.00026	0.00025	0.00024
−3.3	0.00048	0.00047	0.00045	0.00043	0.00042	0.00040	0.00039	0.00038	0.00036	0.00035
−3.2	0.00069	0.00066	0.00064	0.00062	0.00060	0.00058	0.00056	0.00054	0.00052	0.00050
−3.1	0.00097	0.00094	0.00090	0.00087	0.00084	0.00082	0.00079	0.00076	0.00074	0.00071
−3.0	0.00135	0.00131	0.00126	0.00122	0.00118	0.00114	0.00111	0.00107	0.00103	0.00100
−2.9	0.0019	0.0018	0.0018	0.0017	0.0016	0.0016	0.0015	0.0015	0.0014	0.0014
−2.8	0.0026	0.0025	0.0024	0.0023	0.0023	0.0022	0.0021	0.0021	0.0020	0.0019
−2.7	0.0035	0.0034	0.0033	0.0032	0.0031	0.0030	0.0029	0.0028	0.0027	0.0026
−2.6	0.0047	0.0045	0.0044	0.0043	0.0041	0.0040	0.0039	0.0038	0.0037	0.0036
−2.5	0.0062	0.0060	0.0059	0.0057	0.0055	0.0054	0.0052	0.0051	0.0049	0.0048
−2.4	0.0082	0.0080	0.0078	0.0075	0.0073	0.0071	0.0069	0.0068	0.0066	0.0064
−2.3	0.0107	0.0104	0.0102	0.0099	0.0096	0.0094	0.0091	0.0089	0.0087	0.0084
−2.2	0.0139	0.0136	0.0132	0.0129	0.0125	0.0122	0.0119	0.0116	0.0113	0.0110
−2.1	0.0179	0.0174	0.0170	0.0166	0.0162	0.0158	0.0154	0.0150	0.0146	0.0143
−2.0	0.0228	0.0222	0.0217	0.0212	0.0207	0.0202	0.0197	0.0192	0.0188	0.0183
−1.9	0.0287	0.0281	0.0274	0.0268	0.0262	0.0256	0.0250	0.0244	0.0239	0.0233
−1.8	0.0359	0.0351	0.0344	0.0336	0.0329	0.0322	0.0314	0.0307	0.0301	0.0294
−1.7	0.0446	0.0436	0.0427	0.0418	0.0409	0.0401	0.0392	0.0384	0.0375	0.0367
−1.6	0.0548	0.0537	0.0526	0.0516	0.0505	0.0495	0.0485	0.0475	0.0465	0.0455
−1.5	0.0668	0.0655	0.0643	0.0630	0.0618	0.0606	0.0594	0.0582	0.0571	0.0559
−1.4	0.0808	0.0793	0.0778	0.0764	0.0749	0.0735	0.0721	0.0708	0.0694	0.0681
−1.3	0.0968	0.0951	0.0934	0.0918	0.0901	0.0885	0.0869	0.0853	0.0838	0.0823
−1.2	0.1151	0.1131	0.1112	0.1093	0.1075	0.1056	0.1038	0.1020	0.1003	0.0985
−1.1	0.1357	0.1335	0.1314	0.1292	0.1271	0.1251	0.1230	0.1210	0.1190	0.1170
−1.0	0.1587	0.1562	0.1539	0.1515	0.1492	0.1469	0.1446	0.1423	0.1401	0.1379
−0.9	0.1841	0.1814	0.1788	0.1762	0.1736	0.1711	0.1685	0.1660	0.1635	0.1611
−0.8	0.2119	0.2090	0.2061	0.2033	0.2005	0.1977	0.1949	0.1922	0.1894	0.1867
−0.7	0.2420	0.2388	0.2358	0.2327	0.2296	0.2266	0.2236	0.2206	0.2177	0.2148
−0.6	0.2743	0.2709	0.2676	0.2643	0.2611	0.2578	0.2546	0.2514	0.2482	0.2451
−0.5	0.3085	0.3050	0.3015	0.2981	0.2946	0.2912	0.2877	0.2843	0.2810	0.2776
−0.4	0.3446	0.3409	0.3372	0.3336	0.3300	0.3264	0.3228	0.3192	0.3156	0.3121
−0.3	0.3821	0.3783	0.3745	0.3707	0.3669	0.3632	0.3594	0.3557	0.3520	0.3483
−0.2	0.4207	0.4168	0.4129	0.4090	0.4052	0.4013	0.3974	0.3936	0.3897	0.3859
−0.1	0.4602	0.4562	0.4522	0.4483	0.4443	0.4404	0.4364	0.4325	0.4286	0.4247
−0.0	0.5000	0.4960	0.4920	0.4880	0.4840	0.4801	0.4761	0.4721	0.4681	0.4641

continued

TABLE E.2

The Cumulative Standardized Normal Distribution (*Continued*)

Entry represents area under the cumulative standardized normal distribution from $-\infty$ to Z

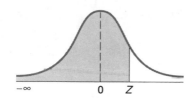

Z	0.00	0.01	0.02	0.03	0.04	0.05	0.06	0.07	0.08	0.09
0.0	0.5000	0.5040	0.5080	0.5120	0.5160	0.5199	0.5239	0.5279	0.5319	0.5359
0.1	0.5398	0.5438	0.5478	0.5517	0.5557	0.5596	0.5636	0.5675	0.5714	0.5753
0.2	0.5793	0.5832	0.5871	0.5910	0.5948	0.5987	0.6026	0.6064	0.6103	0.6141
0.3	0.6179	0.6217	0.6255	0.6293	0.6331	0.6368	0.6406	0.6443	0.6480	0.6517
0.4	0.6554	0.6591	0.6628	0.6664	0.6700	0.6736	0.6772	0.6808	0.6844	0.6879
0.5	0.6915	0.6950	0.6985	0.7019	0.7054	0.7088	0.7123	0.7157	0.7190	0.7224
0.6	0.7257	0.7291	0.7324	0.7357	0.7389	0.7422	0.7454	0.7486	0.7518	0.7549
0.7	0.7580	0.7612	0.7642	0.7673	0.7704	0.7734	0.7764	0.7794	0.7823	0.7852
0.8	0.7881	0.7910	0.7939	0.7967	0.7995	0.8023	0.8051	0.8078	0.8106	0.8133
0.9	0.8159	0.8186	0.8212	0.8238	0.8264	0.8289	0.8315	0.8340	0.8365	0.8389
1.0	0.8413	0.8438	0.8461	0.8485	0.8508	0.8531	0.8554	0.8577	0.8599	0.8621
1.1	0.8643	0.8665	0.8686	0.8708	0.8729	0.8749	0.8770	0.8790	0.8810	0.8830
1.2	0.8849	0.8869	0.8888	0.8907	0.8925	0.8944	0.8962	0.8980	0.8997	0.9015
1.3	0.9032	0.9049	0.9066	0.9082	0.9099	0.9115	0.9131	0.9147	0.9162	0.9177
1.4	0.9192	0.9207	0.9222	0.9236	0.9251	0.9265	0.9279	0.9292	0.9306	0.9319
1.5	0.9332	0.9345	0.9357	0.9370	0.9382	0.9394	0.9406	0.9418	0.9429	0.9441
1.6	0.9452	0.9463	0.9474	0.9484	0.9495	0.9505	0.9515	0.9525	0.9535	0.9545
1.7	0.9554	0.9564	0.9573	0.9582	0.9591	0.9599	0.9608	0.9616	0.9625	0.9633
1.8	0.9641	0.9649	0.9656	0.9664	0.9671	0.9678	0.9686	0.9693	0.9699	0.9706
1.9	0.9713	0.9719	0.9726	0.9732	0.9738	0.9744	0.9750	0.9756	0.9761	0.9767
2.0	0.9772	0.9778	0.9783	0.9788	0.9793	0.9798	0.9803	0.9808	0.9812	0.9817
2.1	0.9821	0.9826	0.9830	0.9834	0.9838	0.9842	0.9846	0.9850	0.9854	0.9857
2.2	0.9861	0.9864	0.9868	0.9871	0.9875	0.9878	0.9881	0.9884	0.9887	0.9890
2.3	0.9893	0.9896	0.9898	0.9901	0.9904	0.9906	0.9909	0.9911	0.9913	0.9916
2.4	0.9918	0.9920	0.9922	0.9925	0.9927	0.9929	0.9931	0.9932	0.9934	0.9936
2.5	0.9938	0.9940	0.9941	0.9943	0.9945	0.9946	0.9948	0.9949	0.9951	0.9952
2.6	0.9953	0.9955	0.9956	0.9957	0.9959	0.9960	0.9961	0.9962	0.9963	0.9964
2.7	0.9965	0.9966	0.9967	0.9968	0.9969	0.9970	0.9971	0.9972	0.9973	0.9974
2.8	0.9974	0.9975	0.9976	0.9977	0.9977	0.9978	0.9979	0.9979	0.9980	0.9981
2.9	0.9981	0.9982	0.9982	0.9983	0.9984	0.9984	0.9985	0.9985	0.9986	0.9986
3.0	0.99865	0.99869	0.99874	0.99878	0.99882	0.99886	0.99889	0.99893	0.99897	0.99900
3.1	0.99903	0.99906	0.99910	0.99913	0.99916	0.99918	0.99921	0.99924	0.99926	0.99929
3.2	0.99931	0.99934	0.99936	0.99938	0.99940	0.99942	0.99944	0.99946	0.99948	0.99950
3.3	0.99952	0.99953	0.99955	0.99957	0.99958	0.99960	0.99961	0.99962	0.99964	0.99965
3.4	0.99966	0.99968	0.99969	0.99970	0.99971	0.99972	0.99973	0.99974	0.99975	0.99976
3.5	0.99977	0.99978	0.99978	0.99979	0.99980	0.99981	0.99981	0.99982	0.99983	0.99983
3.6	0.99984	0.99985	0.99985	0.99986	0.99986	0.99987	0.99987	0.99988	0.99988	0.99989
3.7	0.99989	0.99990	0.99990	0.99990	0.99991	0.99991	0.99992	0.99992	0.99992	0.99992
3.8	0.99993	0.99993	0.99993	0.99994	0.99994	0.99994	0.99994	0.99995	0.99995	0.99995
3.9	0.99995	0.99995	0.99996	0.99996	0.99996	0.99996	0.99996	0.99996	0.99997	0.99997
4.0	0.999968329									
4.5	0.999996602									
5.0	0.999999713									
5.5	0.999999981									
6.0	0.999999999									

TABLE E.3
Critical Values of t

For a particular number of degrees of freedom, entry represents
the critical value of t corresponding to a specified upper-tail
area (α).

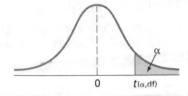

Degrees of Freedom	Upper-Tail Areas					
	0.25	0.10	0.05	0.025	0.01	0.005
1	1.0000	3.0777	6.3138	12.7062	31.8207	63.6574
2	0.8165	1.8856	2.9200	4.3027	6.9646	9.9248
3	0.7649	1.6377	2.3534	3.1824	4.5407	5.8409
4	0.7407	1.5332	2.1318	2.7764	3.7469	4.6041
5	0.7267	1.4759	2.0150	2.5706	3.3649	4.0322
6	0.7176	1.4398	1.9432	2.4469	3.1427	3.7074
7	0.7111	1.4149	1.8946	2.3646	2.9980	3.4995
8	0.7064	1.3968	1.8595	2.3060	2.8965	3.3554
9	0.7027	1.3830	1.8331	2.2622	2.8214	3.2498
10	0.6998	1.3722	1.8125	2.2281	2.7638	3.1693
11	0.6974	1.3634	1.7959	2.2010	2.7181	3.1058
12	0.6955	1.3562	1.7823	2.1788	2.6810	3.0545
13	0.6938	1.3502	1.7709	2.1604	2.6503	3.0123
14	0.6924	1.3450	1.7613	2.1448	2.6245	2.9768
15	0.6912	1.3406	1.7531	2.1315	2.6025	2.9467
16	0.6901	1.3368	1.7459	2.1199	2.5835	2.9208
17	0.6892	1.3334	1.7396	2.1098	2.5669	2.8982
18	0.6884	1.3304	1.7341	2.1009	2.5524	2.8784
19	0.6876	1.3277	1.7291	2.0930	2.5395	2.8609
20	0.6870	1.3253	1.7247	2.0860	2.5280	2.8453
21	0.6864	1.3232	1.7207	2.0796	2.5177	2.8314
22	0.6858	1.3212	1.7171	2.0739	2.5083	2.8188
23	0.6853	1.3195	1.7139	2.0687	2.4999	2.8073
24	0.6848	1.3178	1.7109	2.0639	2.4922	2.7969
25	0.6844	1.3163	1.7081	2.0595	2.4851	2.7874
26	0.6840	1.3150	1.7056	2.0555	2.4786	2.7787
27	0.6837	1.3137	1.7033	2.0518	2.4727	2.7707
28	0.6834	1.3125	1.7011	2.0484	2.4671	2.7633
29	0.6830	1.3114	1.6991	2.0452	2.4620	2.7564
30	0.6828	1.3104	1.6973	2.0423	2.4573	2.7500
31	0.6825	1.3095	1.6955	2.0395	2.4528	2.7740
32	0.6822	1.3086	1.6939	2.0369	2.4487	2.7385
33	0.6820	1.3077	1.6924	2.0345	2.4448	2.7333
34	0.6818	1.3070	1.6909	2.0322	2.4411	2.7284
35	0.6816	1.3062	1.6896	2.0301	2.4377	2.7238
36	0.6814	1.3055	1.6883	2.0281	2.4345	2.7195
37	0.6812	1.3049	1.6871	2.0262	2.4314	2.7154
38	0.6810	1.3042	1.6860	2.0244	2.4286	2.7116
39	0.6808	1.3036	1.6849	2.0227	2.4258	2.7079
40	0.6807	1.3031	1.6839	2.0211	2.4233	2.7045
41	0.6805	1.3025	1.6829	2.0195	2.4208	2.7012
42	0.6804	1.3020	1.6820	2.0181	2.4185	2.6981
43	0.6802	1.3016	1.6811	2.0167	2.4163	2.6951
44	0.6801	1.3011	1.6802	2.0154	2.4141	2.6923
45	0.6800	1.3006	1.6794	2.0141	2.4121	2.6896
46	0.6799	1.3022	1.6787	2.0129	2.4102	2.6870
47	0.6797	1.2998	1.6779	2.0117	2.4083	2.6846
48	0.6796	1.2994	1.6772	2.0106	2.4066	2.6822

continued

TABLE E.3

Critical Values of *t*
(*Continued*)

Degrees of Freedom	Upper-Tail Areas					
	0.25	0.10	0.05	0.025	0.01	0.005
49	0.6795	1.2991	1.6766	2.0096	2.4049	2.6800
50	0.6794	1.2987	1.6759	2.0086	2.4033	2.6778
51	0.6793	1.2984	1.6753	2.0076	2.4017	2.6757
52	0.6792	1.2980	1.6747	2.0066	2.4002	2.6737
53	0.6791	1.2977	1.6741	2.0057	2.3988	2.6718
54	0.6791	1.2974	1.6736	2.0049	2.3974	2.6700
55	0.6790	1.2971	1.6730	2.0040	2.3961	2.6682
56	0.6789	1.2969	1.6725	2.0032	2.3948	2.6665
57	0.6788	1.2966	1.6720	2.0025	2.3936	2.6649
58	0.6787	1.2963	1.6716	2.0017	2.3924	2.6633
59	0.6787	1.2961	1.6711	2.0010	2.3912	2.6618
60	0.6786	1.2958	1.6706	2.0003	2.3901	2.6603
61	0.6785	1.2956	1.6702	1.9996	2.3890	2.6589
62	0.6785	1.2954	1.6698	1.9990	2.3880	2.6575
63	0.6784	1.2951	1.6694	1.9983	2.3870	2.6561
64	0.6783	1.2949	1.6690	1.9977	2.3860	2.6549
65	0.6783	1.2947	1.6686	1.9971	2.3851	2.6536
66	0.6782	1.2945	1.6683	1.9966	2.3842	2.6524
67	0.6782	1.2943	1.6679	1.9960	2.3833	2.6512
68	0.6781	1.2941	1.6676	1.9955	2.3824	2.6501
69	0.6781	1.2939	1.6672	1.9949	2.3816	2.6490
70	0.6780	1.2938	1.6669	1.9944	2.3808	2.6479
71	0.6780	1.2936	1.6666	1.9939	2.3800	2.6469
72	0.6779	1.2934	1.6663	1.9935	2.3793	2.6459
73	0.6779	1.2933	1.6660	1.9930	2.3785	2.6449
74	0.6778	1.2931	1.6657	1.9925	2.3778	2.6439
75	0.6778	1.2929	1.6654	1.9921	2.3771	2.6430
76	0.6777	1.2928	1.6652	1.9917	2.3764	2.6421
77	0.6777	1.2926	1.6649	1.9913	2.3758	2.6412
78	0.6776	1.2925	1.6646	1.9908	2.3751	2.6403
79	0.6776	1.2924	1.6644	1.9905	2.3745	2.6395
80	0.6776	1.2922	1.6641	1.9901	2.3739	2.6387
81	0.6775	1.2921	1.6639	1.9897	2.3733	2.6379
82	0.6775	1.2920	1.6636	1.9893	2.3727	2.6371
83	0.6775	1.2918	1.6634	1.9890	2.3721	2.6364
84	0.6774	1.2917	1.6632	1.9886	2.3716	2.6356
85	0.6774	1.2916	1.6630	1.9883	2.3710	2.6349
86	0.6774	1.2915	1.6628	1.9879	2.3705	2.6342
87	0.6773	1.2914	1.6626	1.9876	2.3700	2.6335
88	0.6773	1.2912	1.6624	1.9873	2.3695	2.6329
89	0.6773	1.2911	1.6622	1.9870	2.3690	2.6322
90	0.6772	1.2910	1.6620	1.9867	2.3685	2.6316
91	0.6772	1.2909	1.6618	1.9864	2.3680	2.6309
92	0.6772	1.2908	1.6616	1.9861	2.3676	2.6303
93	0.6771	1.2907	1.6614	1.9858	2.3671	2.6297
94	0.6771	1.2906	1.6612	1.9855	2.3667	2.6291
95	0.6771	1.2905	1.6611	1.9853	2.3662	2.6286
96	0.6771	1.2904	1.6609	1.9850	2.3658	2.6280
97	0.6770	1.2903	1.6607	1.9847	2.3654	2.6275
98	0.6770	1.2902	1.6606	1.9845	2.3650	2.6269
99	0.6770	1.2902	1.6604	1.9842	2.3646	2.6264
100	0.6770	1.2901	1.6602	1.9840	2.3642	2.6259
110	0.6767	1.2893	1.6588	1.9818	2.3607	2.6213
120	0.6765	1.2886	1.6577	1.9799	2.3578	2.6174
∞	0.6745	1.2816	1.6449	1.9600	2.3263	2.5758

TABLE E.4

Critical Values of χ^2

For a particular number of degrees of freedom, entry represents the critical value
of χ^2 corresponding to a specified upper-tail area (α).

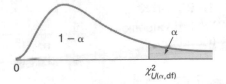

Degrees of Freedom	Upper Tail Areas (α)											
	0.995	0.99	0.975	0.95	0.90	0.75	0.25	0.10	0.05	0.025	0.01	0.005
1			0.001	0.004	0.016	0.102	1.323	2.706	3.841	5.024	6.635	7.879
2	0.010	0.020	0.051	0.103	0.211	0.575	2.773	4.605	5.991	7.378	9.210	10.597
3	0.072	0.115	0.216	0.352	0.584	1.213	4.108	6.251	7.815	9.348	11.345	12.838
4	0.207	0.297	0.484	0.711	1.064	1.923	5.385	7.779	9.488	11.143	13.277	14.860
5	0.412	0.554	0.831	1.145	1.610	2.675	6.626	9.236	11.071	12.833	15.086	16.750
6	0.676	0.872	1.237	1.635	2.204	3.455	7.841	10.645	12.592	14.449	16.812	18.458
7	0.989	1.239	1.690	2.167	2.833	4.255	9.037	12.017	14.067	16.013	18.475	20.278
8	1.344	1.646	2.180	2.733	3.490	5.071	10.219	13.362	15.507	17.535	20.090	21.955
9	1.735	2.088	2.700	3.325	4.168	5.899	11.389	14.684	16.919	19.023	21.666	23.589
10	2.156	2.558	3.247	3.940	4.865	6.737	12.549	15.987	18.307	20.483	23.209	25.188
11	2.603	3.053	3.816	4.575	5.578	7.584	13.701	17.275	19.675	21.920	24.725	26.757
12	3.074	3.571	4.404	5.226	6.304	8.438	14.845	18.549	21.026	23.337	26.217	28.299
13	3.565	4.107	5.009	5.892	7.042	9.299	15.984	19.812	22.362	24.736	27.688	29.819
14	4.075	4.660	5.629	6.571	7.790	10.165	17.117	21.064	23.685	26.119	29.141	31.319
15	4.601	5.229	6.262	7.261	8.547	11.037	18.245	22.307	24.996	27.488	30.578	32.801
16	5.142	5.812	6.908	7.962	9.312	11.912	19.369	23.542	26.296	28.845	32.000	34.267
17	5.697	6.408	7.564	8.672	10.085	12.792	20.489	24.769	27.587	30.191	33.409	35.718
18	6.265	7.015	8.231	9.390	10.865	13.675	21.605	25.989	28.869	31.526	34.805	37.156
19	6.844	7.633	8.907	10.117	11.651	14.562	22.718	27.204	30.144	32.852	36.191	38.582
20	7.434	8.260	9.591	10.851	12.443	15.452	23.828	28.412	31.410	34.170	37.566	39.997
21	8.034	8.897	10.283	11.591	13.240	16.344	24.935	29.615	32.671	35.479	38.932	41.401
22	8.643	9.542	10.982	12.338	14.042	17.240	26.039	30.813	33.924	36.781	40.289	42.796
23	9.260	10.196	11.689	13.091	14.848	18.137	27.141	32.007	35.172	38.076	41.638	44.181
24	9.886	10.856	12.401	13.848	15.659	19.037	28.241	33.196	36.415	39.364	42.980	45.559
25	10.520	11.524	13.120	14.611	16.473	19.939	29.339	34.382	37.652	40.646	44.314	46.928
26	11.160	12.198	13.844	15.379	17.292	20.843	30.435	35.563	38.885	41.923	45.642	48.290
27	11.808	12.879	14.573	16.151	18.114	21.749	31.528	36.741	40.113	43.194	46.963	49.645
28	12.461	13.565	15.308	16.928	18.939	22.657	32.620	37.916	41.337	44.461	48.278	50.993
29	13.121	14.257	16.047	17.708	19.768	23.567	33.711	39.087	42.557	45.722	49.588	52.336
30	13.787	14.954	16.791	18.493	20.599	24.478	34.800	40.256	43.773	46.979	50.892	53.672

For larger values of freedom (df) the expression $Z = \sqrt{2\chi^2} - \sqrt{2(df) - 1}$ may be used and the resulting upper-tail area can be found from the cumulative standardized normal distribution (Table E.2).

TABLE E.5

Critical Values of F

For a particular combination of numerator and denominator degrees of freedom, entry represents the critical values of F corresponding to a specified upper-tail area (α).

$\alpha = 0.05$

$F_{U(\alpha, df_1, df_2)}$

Denominator df_2	Numerator, df_1																		
	1	2	3	4	5	6	7	8	9	10	12	15	20	24	30	40	60	120	∞
1	161.40	199.50	215.70	224.60	230.20	234.00	236.80	238.90	240.50	241.90	243.90	245.90	248.00	249.10	250.10	251.10	252.20	253.30	254.30
2	18.51	19.00	19.16	19.25	19.30	19.33	19.35	19.37	19.38	19.40	19.41	19.43	19.45	19.45	19.46	19.47	19.48	19.49	19.50
3	10.13	9.55	9.28	9.12	9.01	8.94	8.89	8.85	8.81	8.79	8.74	8.70	8.66	8.64	8.62	8.59	8.57	8.55	8.53
4	7.71	6.94	6.59	6.39	6.26	6.16	6.09	6.04	6.00	5.96	5.91	5.86	5.80	5.77	5.75	5.72	5.69	5.66	5.63
5	6.61	5.79	5.41	5.19	5.05	4.95	4.88	4.82	4.77	4.74	4.68	4.62	4.56	4.53	4.50	4.46	4.43	4.40	4.36
6	5.99	5.14	4.76	4.53	4.39	4.28	4.21	4.15	4.10	4.06	4.00	3.94	3.87	3.84	3.81	3.77	3.74	3.70	3.67
7	5.59	4.74	4.35	4.12	3.97	3.87	3.79	3.73	3.68	3.64	3.57	3.51	3.44	3.41	3.38	3.34	3.30	3.27	3.23
8	5.32	4.46	4.07	3.84	3.69	3.58	3.50	3.44	3.39	3.35	3.28	3.22	3.15	3.12	3.08	3.04	3.01	2.97	2.93
9	5.12	4.26	3.86	3.63	3.48	3.37	3.29	3.23	3.18	3.14	3.07	3.01	2.94	2.90	2.86	2.83	2.79	2.75	2.71
10	4.96	4.10	3.71	3.48	3.33	3.22	3.14	3.07	3.02	2.98	2.91	2.85	2.77	2.74	2.70	2.66	2.62	2.58	2.54
11	4.84	3.98	3.59	3.36	3.20	3.09	3.01	2.95	2.90	2.85	2.79	2.72	2.65	2.61	2.57	2.53	2.49	2.45	2.40
12	4.75	3.89	3.49	3.26	3.11	3.00	2.91	2.85	2.80	2.75	2.69	2.62	2.54	2.51	2.47	2.43	2.38	2.34	2.30
13	4.67	3.81	3.41	3.18	3.03	2.92	2.83	2.77	2.71	2.67	2.60	2.53	2.46	2.42	2.38	2.34	2.30	2.25	2.21
14	4.60	3.74	3.34	3.11	2.96	2.85	2.76	2.70	2.65	2.60	2.53	2.46	2.39	2.35	2.31	2.27	2.22	2.18	2.13
15	4.54	3.68	3.29	3.06	2.90	2.79	2.71	2.64	2.59	2.54	2.48	2.40	2.33	2.29	2.25	2.20	2.16	2.11	2.07
16	4.49	3.63	3.24	3.01	2.85	2.74	2.66	2.59	2.54	2.49	2.42	2.35	2.28	2.24	2.19	2.15	2.11	2.06	2.01
17	4.45	3.59	3.20	2.96	2.81	2.70	2.61	2.55	2.49	2.45	2.38	2.31	2.23	2.19	2.15	2.10	2.06	2.01	1.96
18	4.41	3.55	3.16	2.93	2.77	2.66	2.58	2.51	2.46	2.41	2.34	2.27	2.19	2.15	2.11	2.06	2.02	1.97	1.92
19	4.38	3.52	3.13	2.90	2.74	2.63	2.54	2.48	2.42	2.38	2.31	2.23	2.16	2.11	2.07	2.03	1.98	1.93	1.88
20	4.35	3.49	3.10	2.87	2.71	2.60	2.51	2.45	2.39	2.35	2.28	2.20	2.12	2.08	2.04	1.99	1.95	1.90	1.84
21	4.32	3.47	3.07	2.84	2.68	2.57	2.49	2.42	2.37	2.32	2.25	2.18	2.10	2.05	2.01	1.96	1.92	1.87	1.81
22	4.30	3.44	3.05	2.82	2.66	2.55	2.46	2.40	2.34	2.30	2.23	2.15	2.07	2.03	1.98	1.94	1.89	1.84	1.78
23	4.28	3.42	3.03	2.80	2.64	2.53	2.44	2.37	2.32	2.27	2.20	2.13	2.05	2.01	1.96	1.91	1.86	1.81	1.76
24	4.26	3.40	3.01	2.78	2.62	2.51	2.42	2.36	2.30	2.25	2.18	2.11	2.03	1.98	1.94	1.89	1.84	1.79	1.73
25	4.24	3.39	2.99	2.76	2.60	2.49	2.40	2.34	2.28	2.24	2.16	2.09	2.01	1.96	1.92	1.87	1.82	1.77	1.71
26	4.23	3.37	2.98	2.74	2.59	2.47	2.39	2.32	2.27	2.22	2.15	2.07	1.99	1.95	1.90	1.85	1.80	1.75	1.69
27	4.21	3.35	2.96	2.73	2.57	2.46	2.37	2.31	2.25	2.20	2.13	2.06	1.97	1.93	1.88	1.84	1.79	1.73	1.67
28	4.20	3.34	2.95	2.71	2.56	2.45	2.36	2.29	2.24	2.19	2.12	2.04	1.96	1.91	1.87	1.82	1.77	1.71	1.65
29	4.18	3.33	2.93	2.70	2.55	2.43	2.35	2.28	2.22	2.18	2.10	2.03	1.94	1.90	1.85	1.81	1.75	1.70	1.64
30	4.17	3.32	2.92	2.69	2.53	2.42	2.33	2.27	2.21	2.16	2.09	2.01	1.93	1.89	1.84	1.79	1.74	1.68	1.62
40	4.08	3.23	2.84	2.61	2.45	2.34	2.25	2.18	2.12	2.08	2.00	1.92	1.84	1.79	1.74	1.69	1.64	1.58	1.51
60	4.00	3.15	2.76	2.53	2.37	2.25	2.17	2.10	2.04	1.99	1.92	1.84	1.75	1.70	1.65	1.59	1.53	1.47	1.39
120	3.92	3.07	2.68	2.45	2.29	2.17	2.09	2.02	1.96	1.91	1.83	1.75	1.66	1.61	1.55	1.50	1.43	1.35	1.25
∞	3.84	3.00	2.60	2.37	2.21	2.10	2.01	1.94	1.88	1.83	1.75	1.67	1.57	1.52	1.46	1.39	1.32	1.22	1.00

continued

TABLE E.5

Critical Values of F (Continued)

$\alpha = 0.025$

$F_{U(\alpha, df_1, df_2)}$

Denominator df_2	\multicolumn{19}{c}{Numerator, df_1}
	1	2	3	4	5	6	7	8	9	10	12	15	20	24	30	40	60	120	∞
1	647.80	799.50	864.20	899.60	921.80	937.10	948.20	956.70	963.30	968.60	976.70	984.90	993.10	997.20	1,001.00	1,006.00	1,010.00	1,014.00	1,018.00
2	38.51	39.00	39.17	39.25	39.30	39.33	39.36	39.39	39.39	39.40	39.41	39.43	39.45	39.46	39.46	39.47	39.48	39.49	39.50
3	17.44	16.04	15.44	15.10	14.88	14.73	14.62	14.54	14.47	14.42	14.34	14.25	14.17	14.12	14.08	14.04	13.99	13.95	13.90
4	12.22	10.65	9.98	9.60	9.36	9.20	9.07	8.98	8.90	8.84	8.75	8.66	8.56	8.51	8.46	8.41	8.36	8.31	8.26
5	10.01	8.43	7.76	7.39	7.15	6.98	6.85	6.76	6.68	6.62	6.52	6.43	6.33	6.28	6.23	6.18	6.12	6.07	6.02
6	8.81	7.26	6.60	6.23	5.99	5.82	5.70	5.60	5.52	5.46	5.37	5.27	5.17	5.12	5.07	5.01	4.96	4.90	4.85
7	8.07	6.54	5.89	5.52	5.29	5.12	4.99	4.90	4.82	4.76	4.67	4.57	4.47	4.42	4.36	4.31	4.25	4.20	4.14
8	7.57	6.06	5.42	5.05	4.82	4.65	4.53	4.43	4.36	4.30	4.20	4.10	4.00	3.95	3.89	3.84	3.78	3.73	3.67
9	7.21	5.71	5.08	4.72	4.48	4.32	4.20	4.10	4.03	3.96	3.87	3.77	3.67	3.61	3.56	3.51	3.45	3.39	3.33
10	6.94	5.46	4.83	4.47	4.24	4.07	3.95	3.85	3.78	3.72	3.62	3.52	3.42	3.37	3.31	3.26	3.20	3.14	3.08
11	6.72	5.26	4.63	4.28	4.04	3.88	3.76	3.66	3.59	3.53	3.43	3.33	3.23	3.17	3.12	3.06	3.00	2.94	2.88
12	6.55	5.10	4.47	4.12	3.89	3.73	3.61	3.51	3.44	3.37	3.28	3.18	3.07	3.02	2.96	2.91	2.85	2.79	2.72
13	6.41	4.97	4.35	4.00	3.77	3.60	3.48	3.39	3.31	3.25	3.15	3.05	2.95	2.89	2.84	2.78	2.72	2.66	2.60
14	6.30	4.86	4.24	3.89	3.66	3.50	3.38	3.29	3.21	3.15	3.05	2.95	2.84	2.79	2.73	2.67	2.61	2.55	2.49
15	6.20	4.77	4.15	3.80	3.58	3.41	3.29	3.20	3.12	3.06	2.96	2.86	2.76	2.70	2.64	2.59	2.52	2.46	2.40
16	6.12	4.69	4.08	3.73	3.50	3.34	3.22	3.12	3.05	2.99	2.89	2.79	2.68	2.63	2.57	2.51	2.45	2.38	2.32
17	6.04	4.62	4.01	3.66	3.44	3.28	3.16	3.06	2.98	2.92	2.82	2.72	2.62	2.56	2.50	2.44	2.38	2.32	2.25
18	5.98	4.56	3.95	3.61	3.38	3.22	3.10	3.01	2.93	2.87	2.77	2.67	2.56	2.50	2.44	2.38	2.32	2.26	2.19
19	5.92	4.51	3.90	3.56	3.33	3.17	3.05	2.96	2.88	2.82	2.72	2.62	2.51	2.45	2.39	2.33	2.27	2.20	2.13
20	5.87	4.46	3.86	3.51	3.29	3.13	3.01	2.91	2.84	2.77	2.68	2.57	2.46	2.41	2.35	2.29	2.22	2.16	2.09
21	5.83	4.42	3.82	3.48	3.25	3.09	2.97	2.87	2.80	2.73	2.64	2.53	2.42	2.37	2.31	2.25	2.18	2.11	2.04
22	5.79	4.38	3.78	3.44	3.22	3.05	2.93	2.84	2.76	2.70	2.60	2.50	2.39	2.33	2.27	2.21	2.14	2.08	2.00
23	5.75	4.35	3.75	3.41	3.18	3.02	2.90	2.81	2.73	2.67	2.57	2.47	2.36	2.30	2.24	2.18	2.11	2.04	1.97
24	5.72	4.32	3.72	3.38	3.15	2.99	2.87	2.78	2.70	2.64	2.54	2.44	2.33	2.27	2.21	2.15	2.08	2.01	1.94
25	5.69	4.29	3.69	3.35	3.13	2.97	2.85	2.75	2.68	2.61	2.51	2.41	2.30	2.24	2.18	2.12	2.05	1.98	1.91
26	5.66	4.27	3.67	3.33	3.10	2.94	2.82	2.73	2.65	2.59	2.49	2.39	2.28	2.22	2.16	2.09	2.03	1.95	1.88
27	5.63	4.24	3.65	3.31	3.08	2.92	2.80	2.71	2.63	2.57	2.47	2.36	2.25	2.19	2.13	2.07	2.00	1.93	1.85
28	5.61	4.22	3.63	3.29	3.06	2.90	2.78	2.69	2.61	2.55	2.45	2.34	2.23	2.17	2.11	2.05	1.98	1.91	1.83
29	5.59	4.20	3.61	3.27	3.04	2.88	2.76	2.67	2.59	2.53	2.43	2.32	2.21	2.15	2.09	2.03	1.96	1.89	1.81
30	5.57	4.18	3.59	3.25	3.03	2.87	2.75	2.65	2.57	2.51	2.41	2.31	2.20	2.14	2.07	2.01	1.94	1.87	1.79
40	5.42	4.05	3.46	3.13	2.90	2.74	2.62	2.53	2.45	2.39	2.29	2.18	2.07	2.01	1.94	1.88	1.80	1.72	1.64
60	5.29	3.93	3.34	3.01	2.79	2.63	2.51	2.41	2.33	2.27	2.17	2.06	1.94	1.88	1.82	1.74	1.67	1.58	1.48
120	5.15	3.80	3.23	2.89	2.67	2.52	2.39	2.30	2.22	2.16	2.05	1.94	1.82	1.76	1.69	1.61	1.53	1.43	1.31
∞	5.02	3.69	3.12	2.79	2.57	2.41	2.29	2.19	2.11	2.05	1.94	1.83	1.71	1.64	1.57	1.48	1.39	1.27	1.00

continued

TABLE E.5
Critical Values of F (Continued)

$\alpha = 0.01$

$F_{U(\alpha, df_1, df_2)}$

| | Numerator, df_1 | | | | | | | | | | | | | | | | | | |
Denominator df_2	1	2	3	4	5	6	7	8	9	10	12	15	20	24	30	40	60	120	∞
1	4,052.00	4,999.50	5,403.00	5,625.00	5,764.00	5,859.00	5,928.00	5,982.00	6,022.00	6,056.00	6,106.00	6,157.00	6,209.00	6,235.00	6,261.00	6,287.00	6,313.00	6,339.00	6,366.00
2	98.50	99.00	99.17	99.25	99.30	99.33	99.36	99.37	99.39	99.40	99.42	99.43	99.45	99.46	99.47	99.47	99.48	99.49	99.50
3	34.12	30.82	29.46	28.71	28.24	27.91	27.67	27.49	27.35	27.23	27.05	26.87	26.69	26.60	26.50	26.41	26.32	26.22	26.13
4	21.20	18.00	16.69	15.98	15.52	15.21	14.98	14.80	14.66	14.55	14.37	14.20	14.02	13.93	13.84	13.75	13.65	13.56	13.46
5	16.26	13.27	12.06	11.39	10.97	10.67	10.46	10.29	10.16	10.05	9.89	9.72	9.55	9.47	9.38	9.29	9.20	9.11	9.02
6	13.75	10.92	9.78	9.15	8.75	8.47	8.26	8.10	7.98	7.87	7.72	7.56	7.40	7.31	7.23	7.14	7.06	6.97	6.88
7	12.25	9.55	8.45	7.85	7.46	7.19	6.99	6.84	6.72	6.62	6.47	6.31	6.16	6.07	5.99	5.91	5.82	5.74	5.65
8	11.26	8.65	7.59	7.01	6.63	6.37	6.18	6.03	5.91	5.81	5.67	5.52	5.36	5.28	5.20	5.12	5.03	4.95	4.86
9	10.56	8.02	6.99	6.42	6.06	5.80	5.61	5.47	5.35	5.26	5.11	4.96	4.81	4.73	4.65	4.57	4.48	4.40	4.31
10	10.04	7.56	6.55	5.99	5.64	5.39	5.20	5.06	4.94	4.85	4.71	4.56	4.41	4.33	4.25	4.17	4.08	4.00	3.91
11	9.65	7.21	6.22	5.67	5.32	5.07	4.89	4.74	4.63	4.54	4.40	4.25	4.10	4.02	3.94	3.86	3.78	3.69	3.60
12	9.33	6.93	5.95	5.41	5.06	4.82	4.64	4.50	4.39	4.30	4.16	4.01	3.86	3.78	3.70	3.62	3.54	3.45	3.36
13	9.07	6.70	5.74	5.21	4.86	4.62	4.44	4.30	4.19	4.10	3.96	3.82	3.66	3.59	3.51	3.43	3.34	3.25	3.17
14	8.86	6.51	5.56	5.04	4.69	4.46	4.28	4.14	4.03	3.94	3.80	3.66	3.51	3.43	3.35	3.27	3.18	3.09	3.00
15	8.68	6.36	5.42	4.89	4.56	4.32	4.14	4.00	3.89	3.80	3.67	3.52	3.37	3.29	3.21	3.13	3.05	2.96	2.87
16	8.53	6.23	5.29	4.77	4.44	4.20	4.03	3.89	3.78	3.69	3.55	3.41	3.26	3.18	3.10	3.02	2.93	2.81	2.75
17	8.40	6.11	5.18	4.67	4.34	4.10	3.93	3.79	3.68	3.59	3.46	3.31	3.16	3.08	3.00	2.92	2.83	2.75	2.65
18	8.29	6.01	5.09	4.58	4.25	4.01	3.84	3.71	3.60	3.51	3.37	3.23	3.08	3.00	2.92	2.84	2.75	2.66	2.57
19	8.18	5.93	5.01	4.50	4.17	3.94	3.77	3.63	3.52	3.43	3.30	3.15	3.00	2.92	2.84	2.76	2.67	2.58	2.49
20	8.10	5.85	4.94	4.43	4.10	3.87	3.70	3.56	3.46	3.37	3.23	3.09	2.94	2.86	2.78	2.69	2.61	2.52	2.42
21	8.02	5.78	4.87	4.37	4.04	3.81	3.64	3.51	3.40	3.31	3.17	3.03	2.88	2.80	2.72	2.64	2.55	2.46	2.36
22	7.95	5.72	4.82	4.31	3.99	3.76	3.59	3.45	3.35	3.26	3.12	2.98	2.83	2.75	2.67	2.58	2.50	2.40	2.31
23	7.88	5.66	4.76	4.26	3.94	3.71	3.54	3.41	3.30	3.21	3.07	2.93	2.78	2.70	2.62	2.54	2.45	2.35	2.26
24	7.82	5.61	4.72	4.22	3.90	3.67	3.50	3.36	3.26	3.17	3.03	2.89	2.74	2.66	2.58	2.49	2.40	2.31	2.21
25	7.77	5.57	4.68	4.18	3.85	3.63	3.46	3.32	3.22	3.13	2.99	2.85	2.70	2.62	2.54	2.45	2.36	2.27	2.17
26	7.72	5.53	4.64	4.14	3.82	3.59	3.42	3.29	3.18	3.09	2.96	2.81	2.66	2.58	2.50	2.42	2.33	2.23	2.13
27	7.68	5.49	4.60	4.11	3.78	3.56	3.39	3.26	3.15	3.06	2.93	2.78	2.63	2.55	2.47	2.38	2.29	2.20	2.10
28	7.64	5.45	4.57	4.07	3.75	3.53	3.36	3.23	3.12	3.03	2.90	2.75	2.60	2.52	2.44	2.35	2.26	2.17	2.06
29	7.60	5.42	4.54	4.04	3.73	3.50	3.33	3.20	3.09	3.00	2.87	2.73	2.57	2.49	2.41	2.33	2.23	2.14	2.03
30	7.56	5.39	4.51	4.02	3.70	3.47	3.30	3.17	3.07	2.98	2.84	2.70	2.55	2.47	2.39	2.30	2.21	2.11	2.01
40	7.31	5.18	4.31	3.83	3.51	3.29	3.12	2.99	2.89	2.80	2.66	2.52	2.37	2.29	2.20	2.11	2.02	1.92	1.80
60	7.08	4.98	4.13	3.65	3.34	3.12	2.95	2.82	2.72	2.63	2.50	2.35	2.20	2.12	2.03	1.94	1.84	1.73	1.60
120	6.85	4.79	3.95	3.48	3.17	2.96	2.79	2.66	2.56	2.47	2.34	2.19	2.03	1.95	1.86	1.76	1.66	1.53	1.38
∞	6.63	4.61	3.78	3.32	3.02	2.80	2.64	2.51	2.41	2.32	2.18	2.04	1.88	1.79	1.70	1.59	1.47	1.32	1.00

continued

TABLE E.5

Critical Values of F (Continued)

$\alpha = 0.005$

$F_{U(\alpha, df_1, df_2)}$

Denominator df_2	\multicolumn{19}{c}{Numerator, df_1}
	1	2	3	4	5	6	7	8	9	10	12	15	20	24	30	40	60	120	∞
1	16,211.00	20,000.00	21,615.00	22,500.00	23,056.00	23,437.00	23,715.00	23,925.00	24,091.00	24,224.00	24,426.00	24,630.00	24,836.00	24,910.00	25,044.00	25,148.00	25,253.00	25,359.00	25,465.00
2	198.50	199.00	199.20	199.20	199.30	199.30	199.40	199.40	199.40	199.40	199.40	199.40	199.40	199.50	199.50	199.50	199.50	199.50	199.50
3	55.55	49.80	47.47	46.19	45.39	44.84	44.43	44.13	43.88	43.69	43.39	43.08	42.78	42.62	42.47	42.31	42.15	41.99	41.83
4	31.33	26.28	24.26	23.15	22.46	21.97	21.62	21.35	21.14	20.97	20.70	20.44	20.17	20.03	19.89	19.75	19.61	19.47	19.32
5	22.78	18.31	16.53	15.56	14.94	14.51	14.20	13.96	13.77	13.62	13.38	13.15	12.90	12.78	12.66	12.53	12.40	12.27	12.11
6	18.63	14.54	12.92	12.03	11.46	11.07	10.79	10.57	10.39	10.25	10.03	9.81	9.59	9.47	9.36	9.24	9.12	9.00	8.88
7	16.24	12.40	10.88	10.05	9.52	9.16	8.89	8.68	8.51	8.38	8.18	7.97	7.75	7.65	7.53	7.42	7.31	7.19	7.08
8	14.69	11.04	9.60	8.81	8.30	7.95	7.69	7.50	7.34	7.21	7.01	6.81	6.61	6.50	6.40	6.29	6.18	6.06	5.95
9	13.61	10.11	8.72	7.96	7.47	7.13	6.88	6.69	6.54	6.42	6.23	6.03	5.83	5.73	5.62	5.52	5.41	5.30	5.19
10	12.83	9.43	8.08	7.34	6.87	6.54	6.30	6.12	5.97	5.85	5.66	5.47	5.27	5.17	5.07	4.97	4.86	4.75	1.61
11	12.23	8.91	7.60	6.88	6.42	6.10	5.86	5.68	5.54	5.42	5.24	5.05	4.85	4.75	4.65	4.55	4.44	4.34	4.23
12	11.75	8.51	7.23	6.52	6.07	5.76	5.52	5.35	5.20	5.09	4.91	4.72	4.53	4.43	4.33	4.23	4.12	4.01	3.90
13	11.37	8.19	6.93	6.23	5.79	5.48	5.25	5.08	4.94	4.82	4.64	4.46	4.27	4.17	4.07	3.97	3.87	3.76	3.65
14	11.06	7.92	6.68	6.00	5.56	5.26	5.03	4.86	4.72	4.60	4.43	4.25	4.06	3.96	3.86	3.76	3.66	3.55	3.41
15	10.80	7.70	6.48	5.80	5.37	5.07	4.85	4.67	4.54	4.42	4.25	4.07	3.88	3.79	3.69	3.58	3.48	3.37	3.26
16	10.58	7.51	6.30	5.64	5.21	4.91	4.69	4.52	4.38	4.27	4.10	3.92	3.73	3.64	3.54	3.44	3.33	3.22	3.11
17	10.38	7.35	6.16	5.50	5.07	4.78	4.56	4.39	4.25	4.14	3.97	3.79	3.61	3.51	3.41	3.31	3.21	3.10	2.98
18	10.22	7.21	6.03	5.37	4.96	4.66	4.44	4.28	4.14	4.03	3.86	3.68	3.50	3.40	3.30	3.20	3.10	2.89	2.87
19	10.07	7.09	5.92	5.27	4.85	4.56	4.34	4.18	4.04	3.93	3.76	3.59	3.40	3.31	3.21	3.11	3.00	2.89	2.78
20	9.94	6.99	5.82	5.17	4.76	4.47	4.26	4.09	3.96	3.85	3.68	3.50	3.32	3.22	3.12	3.02	2.92	2.81	2.69
21	9.83	6.89	5.73	5.09	4.68	4.39	4.18	4.02	3.88	3.77	3.60	3.43	3.24	3.15	3.05	2.95	2.84	2.73	2.61
22	9.73	6.81	5.65	5.02	4.61	4.32	4.11	3.94	3.81	3.70	3.54	3.36	3.18	3.08	2.98	2.88	2.77	2.66	2.55
23	9.63	6.73	5.58	4.95	4.54	4.26	4.05	3.88	3.75	3.64	3.47	3.30	3.12	3.02	2.92	2.82	2.71	2.60	2.48
24	9.55	6.66	5.52	4.89	4.49	4.20	3.99	3.83	3.69	3.59	3.42	3.25	3.06	2.97	2.87	2.77	2.66	2.55	2.43
25	9.48	6.60	5.46	4.84	4.43	4.15	3.94	3.78	3.64	3.54	3.37	3.20	3.01	2.92	2.82	2.72	2.61	2.50	2.38
26	9.41	6.54	5.41	4.79	4.38	4.10	3.89	3.73	3.60	3.49	3.33	3.15	2.97	2.87	2.77	2.67	2.56	2.45	2.33
27	9.34	6.49	5.36	4.74	4.34	4.06	3.85	3.69	3.56	3.45	3.28	3.11	2.93	2.83	2.73	2.63	2.52	2.41	2.29
28	9.28	6.44	5.32	4.70	4.30	4.02	3.81	3.65	3.52	3.41	3.25	3.07	2.89	2.79	2.69	2.59	2.48	2.37	2.25
29	9.23	6.40	5.28	4.66	4.26	3.98	3.77	3.61	3.48	3.38	3.21	3.04	2.86	2.76	2.66	2.56	2.45	2.33	2.21
30	9.18	6.35	5.24	4.62	4.23	3.95	3.74	3.58	3.45	3.34	3.18	3.01	2.82	2.73	2.63	2.52	2.42	2.30	2.18
40	8.83	6.07	4.98	4.37	3.99	3.71	3.51	3.35	3.22	3.12	2.95	2.78	2.60	2.50	2.40	2.30	2.18	2.06	1.93
60	8.49	5.79	4.73	4.14	3.76	3.49	3.29	3.13	3.01	2.90	2.74	2.57	2.39	2.29	2.19	2.08	1.96	1.83	1.69
120	8.18	5.54	4.50	3.92	3.55	3.28	3.09	2.93	2.81	2.71	2.54	2.37	2.19	2.09	1.98	1.87	1.75	1.61	1.43
∞	7.88	5.30	4.28	3.72	3.35	3.09	2.90	2.74	2.62	2.52	2.36	2.19	2.00	1.90	1.79	1.67	1.53	1.36	1.00

Source: Reprinted from E. S. Pearson and H. O. Hartley, eds., Biometrika Tables for Statisticians, 3rd ed., 1966, by permission of the Biometrika Trustees.

TABLE E.6

Critical Values d_L and d_U of the Durbin-Watson Statistic D (Critical Values are One-Sided)[a]

$\alpha = 0.05$

n	k=1 d_L	k=1 d_U	k=2 d_L	k=2 d_U	k=3 d_L	k=3 d_U	k=4 d_L	k=4 d_U	k=5 d_L	k=5 d_U
15	1.08	1.36	.95	1.54	.82	1.75	.69	1.97	.56	2.21
16	1.10	1.37	.98	1.54	.86	1.73	.74	1.93	.62	2.15
17	1.13	1.38	1.02	1.54	.90	1.71	.78	1.90	.67	2.10
18	1.16	1.39	1.05	1.53	.93	1.69	.82	1.87	.71	2.06
19	1.18	1.40	1.08	1.53	.97	1.68	.86	1.85	.75	2.02
20	1.20	1.41	1.10	1.54	1.00	1.68	.90	1.83	.79	1.99
21	1.22	1.42	1.13	1.54	1.03	1.67	.93	1.81	.83	1.96
22	1.24	1.43	1.15	1.54	1.05	1.66	.96	1.80	.86	1.94
23	1.26	1.44	1.17	1.54	1.08	1.66	.99	1.79	.90	1.92
24	1.27	1.45	1.19	1.55	1.10	1.66	1.01	1.78	.93	1.90
25	1.29	1.45	1.21	1.55	1.12	1.66	1.04	1.77	.95	1.89
26	1.30	1.46	1.22	1.55	1.14	1.65	1.06	1.76	.98	1.88
27	1.32	1.47	1.24	1.56	1.16	1.65	1.08	1.76	1.01	1.86
28	1.33	1.48	1.26	1.56	1.18	1.65	1.10	1.75	1.03	1.85
29	1.34	1.48	1.27	1.56	1.20	1.65	1.12	1.74	1.05	1.84
30	1.35	1.49	1.28	1.57	1.21	1.65	1.14	1.74	1.07	1.83
31	1.36	1.50	1.30	1.57	1.23	1.65	1.16	1.74	1.09	1.83
32	1.37	1.50	1.31	1.57	1.24	1.65	1.18	1.73	1.11	1.82
33	1.38	1.51	1.32	1.58	1.26	1.65	1.19	1.73	1.13	1.81
34	1.39	1.51	1.33	1.58	1.27	1.65	1.21	1.73	1.15	1.81
35	1.40	1.52	1.34	1.58	1.28	1.65	1.22	1.73	1.16	1.80
36	1.41	1.52	1.35	1.59	1.29	1.65	1.24	1.73	1.18	1.80
37	1.42	1.53	1.36	1.59	1.31	1.66	1.25	1.72	1.19	1.80
38	1.43	1.54	1.37	1.59	1.32	1.66	1.26	1.72	1.21	1.79
39	1.43	1.54	1.38	1.60	1.33	1.66	1.27	1.72	1.22	1.79
40	1.44	1.54	1.39	1.60	1.34	1.66	1.29	1.72	1.23	1.79
45	1.48	1.57	1.43	1.62	1.38	1.67	1.34	1.72	1.29	1.78
50	1.50	1.59	1.46	1.63	1.42	1.67	1.38	1.72	1.34	1.77
55	1.53	1.60	1.49	1.64	1.45	1.68	1.41	1.72	1.38	1.77
60	1.55	1.62	1.51	1.65	1.48	1.69	1.44	1.73	1.41	1.77
65	1.57	1.63	1.54	1.66	1.50	1.70	1.47	1.73	1.44	1.77
70	1.58	1.64	1.55	1.67	1.52	1.70	1.49	1.74	1.46	1.77
75	1.60	1.65	1.57	1.68	1.54	1.71	1.51	1.74	1.49	1.77
80	1.61	1.66	1.59	1.69	1.56	1.72	1.53	1.74	1.51	1.77
85	1.62	1.67	1.60	1.70	1.57	1.72	1.55	1.75	1.52	1.77
90	1.63	1.68	1.61	1.70	1.59	1.73	1.57	1.75	1.54	1.78
95	1.64	1.69	1.62	1.71	1.60	1.73	1.58	1.75	1.56	1.78
100	1.65	1.69	1.63	1.72	1.61	1.74	1.59	1.76	1.57	1.78

$\alpha = 0.01$

n	k=1 d_L	k=1 d_U	k=2 d_L	k=2 d_U	k=3 d_L	k=3 d_U	k=4 d_L	k=4 d_U	k=5 d_L	k=5 d_U
15	.81	1.07	.70	1.25	.59	1.46	.49	1.70	.39	1.96
16	.84	1.09	.74	1.25	.63	1.44	.53	1.66	.44	1.90
17	.87	1.10	.77	1.25	.67	1.43	.57	1.63	.48	1.85
18	.90	1.12	.80	1.26	.71	1.42	.61	1.60	.52	1.80
19	.93	1.13	.83	1.26	.74	1.41	.65	1.58	.56	1.77
20	.95	1.15	.86	1.27	.77	1.41	.68	1.57	.60	1.74
21	.97	1.16	.89	1.27	.80	1.41	.72	1.55	.63	1.71
22	1.00	1.17	.91	1.28	.83	1.40	.75	1.54	.66	1.69
23	1.02	1.19	.94	1.29	.86	1.40	.77	1.53	.70	1.67
24	1.04	1.20	.96	1.30	.88	1.41	.80	1.53	.72	1.66
25	1.05	1.21	.98	1.30	.90	1.41	.83	1.52	.75	1.65
26	1.07	1.22	1.00	1.31	.93	1.41	.85	1.52	.78	1.64
27	1.09	1.23	1.02	1.32	.95	1.41	.88	1.51	.81	1.63
28	1.10	1.24	1.04	1.32	.97	1.41	.90	1.51	.83	1.62
29	1.12	1.25	1.05	1.33	.99	1.42	.92	1.51	.85	1.61
30	1.13	1.26	1.07	1.34	1.01	1.42	.94	1.51	.88	1.61
31	1.15	1.27	1.08	1.34	1.02	1.42	.96	1.51	.90	1.60
32	1.16	1.28	1.10	1.35	1.04	1.43	.98	1.51	.92	1.60
33	1.17	1.29	1.11	1.36	1.05	1.43	1.00	1.51	.94	1.59
34	1.18	1.30	1.13	1.36	1.07	1.43	1.01	1.51	.95	1.59
35	1.19	1.31	1.14	1.37	1.08	1.44	1.03	1.51	.97	1.59
36	1.21	1.32	1.15	1.38	1.10	1.44	1.04	1.51	.99	1.59
37	1.22	1.32	1.16	1.38	1.11	1.45	1.06	1.51	1.00	1.59
38	1.23	1.33	1.18	1.39	1.12	1.45	1.07	1.52	1.02	1.58
39	1.24	1.34	1.19	1.39	1.14	1.45	1.09	1.52	1.03	1.58
40	1.25	1.34	1.20	1.40	1.15	1.46	1.10	1.52	1.05	1.58
45	1.29	1.38	1.24	1.42	1.20	1.48	1.16	1.53	1.11	1.58
50	1.32	1.40	1.28	1.45	1.24	1.49	1.20	1.54	1.16	1.59
55	1.36	1.43	1.32	1.47	1.28	1.51	1.25	1.55	1.21	1.59
60	1.38	1.45	1.35	1.48	1.32	1.52	1.28	1.56	1.25	1.60
65	1.41	1.47	1.38	1.50	1.35	1.53	1.31	1.57	1.28	1.61
70	1.43	1.49	1.40	1.52	1.37	1.55	1.34	1.58	1.31	1.61
75	1.45	1.50	1.42	1.53	1.39	1.56	1.37	1.59	1.34	1.62
80	1.47	1.52	1.44	1.54	1.42	1.57	1.39	1.60	1.36	1.62
85	1.48	1.53	1.46	1.55	1.43	1.58	1.41	1.60	1.39	1.63
90	1.50	1.54	1.47	1.56	1.45	1.59	1.43	1.61	1.41	1.64
95	1.51	1.55	1.49	1.57	1.47	1.60	1.45	1.62	1.42	1.64
100	1.52	1.56	1.50	1.58	1.48	1.60	1.46	1.63	1.44	1.65

[a]n = number of observations; k = number of independent variables.

Source: This table is reproduced from Biometrika, 41 (1951): 173 and 175, with the permission of the Biometrika Trustees.

TABLE E.7
Control Chart Factors

Number of Observations in Sample	d_2	d_3	D_3	D_4	A_2
2	1.128	0.853	0	3.267	1.880
3	1.693	0.888	0	2.575	1.023
4	2.059	0.880	0	2.282	0.729
5	2.326	0.864	0	2.114	0.577
6	2.534	0.848	0	2.004	0.483
7	2.704	0.833	0.076	1.924	0.419
8	2.847	0.820	0.136	1.864	0.373
9	2.970	0.808	0.184	1.816	0.337
10	3.078	0.797	0.223	1.777	0.308
11	3.173	0.787	0.256	1.744	0.285
12	3.258	0.778	0.283	1.717	0.266
13	3.336	0.770	0.307	1.693	0.249
14	3.407	0.763	0.328	1.672	0.235
15	3.472	0.756	0.347	1.653	0.223
16	3.532	0.750	0.363	1.637	0.212
17	3.588	0.744	0.378	1.622	0.203
18	3.640	0.739	0.391	1.609	0.194
19	3.689	0.733	0.404	1.596	0.187
20	3.735	0.729	0.415	1.585	0.180
21	3.778	0.724	0.425	1.575	0.173
22	3.819	0.720	0.435	1.565	0.167
23	3.858	0.716	0.443	1.557	0.162
24	3.895	0.712	0.452	1.548	0.157
25	3.931	0.708	0.459	1.541	0.153

Source: Reprinted from ASTM-STP 15D by kind permission of the American Society for Testing and Materials.

TABLE E.8
The Standardized Normal Distribution

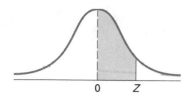

Entry represents area under the standardized normal distribution from the mean to Z

Z	.00	.01	.02	.03	.04	.05	.06	.07	.08	.09
0.0	.0000	.0040	.0080	.0120	.0160	.0199	.0239	.0279	.0319	.0359
0.1	.0398	.0438	.0478	.0517	.0557	.0596	.0636	.0675	.0714	.0753
0.2	.0793	.0832	.0871	.0910	.0948	.0987	.1026	.1064	.1103	.1141
0.3	.1179	.1217	.1255	.1293	.1331	.1368	.1406	.1443	.1480	.1517
0.4	.1554	.1591	.1628	.1664	.1700	.1736	.1772	.1808	.1844	.1879
0.5	.1915	.1950	.1985	.2019	.2054	.2088	.2123	.2157	.2190	.2224
0.6	.2257	.2291	.2324	.2357	.2389	.2422	.2454	.2486	.2518	.2549
0.7	.2580	.2612	.2642	.2673	.2704	.2734	.2764	.2794	.2823	.2852
0.8	.2881	.2910	.2939	.2967	.2995	.3023	.3051	.3078	.3106	.3133
0.9	.3159	.3186	.3212	.3238	.3264	.3289	.3315	.3340	.3365	.3389
1.0	.3413	.3438	.3461	.3485	.3508	.3531	.3554	.3577	.3599	.3621
1.1	.3643	.3665	.3686	.3708	.3729	.3749	.3770	.3790	.3810	.3830
1.2	.3849	.3869	.3888	.3907	.3925	.3944	.3962	.3980	.3997	.4015
1.3	.4032	.4049	.4066	.4082	.4099	.4115	.4131	.4147	.4162	.4177
1.4	.4192	.4207	.4222	.4236	.4251	.4265	.4279	.4292	.4306	.4319
1.5	.4332	.4345	.4357	.4370	.4382	.4394	.4406	.4418	.4429	.4441
1.6	.4452	.4463	.4474	.4484	.4495	.4505	.4515	.4525	.4535	.4545
1.7	.4554	.4564	.4573	.4582	.4591	.4599	.4608	.4616	.4625	.4633
1.8	.4641	.4649	.4656	.4664	.4671	.4678	.4686	.4693	.4699	.4706
1.9	.4713	.4719	.4726	.4732	.4738	.4744	.4750	.4756	.4761	.4767
2.0	.4772	.4778	.4783	.4788	.4793	.4798	.4803	.4808	.4812	.4817
2.1	.4821	.4826	.4830	.4834	.4838	.4842	.4846	.4850	.4854	.4857
2.2	.4861	.4864	.4868	.4871	.4875	.4878	.4881	.4884	.4887	.4890
2.3	.4893	.4896	.4898	.4901	.4904	.4906	.4909	.4911	.4913	.4916
2.4	.4918	.4920	.4922	.4925	.4927	.4929	.4931	.4932	.4934	.4936
2.5	.4938	.4940	.4941	.4943	.4945	.4946	.4948	.4949	.4951	.4952
2.6	.4953	.4955	.4956	.4957	.4959	.4960	.4961	.4962	.4963	.4964
2.7	.4965	.4966	.4967	.4968	.4969	.4970	.4971	.4972	.4973	.4974
2.8	.4974	.4975	.4976	.4977	.4977	.4978	.4979	.4979	.4980	.4981
2.9	.4981	.4982	.4982	.4983	.4984	.4984	.4985	.4985	.4986	.4986
3.0	.49865	.49869	.49874	.49878	.49882	.49886	.49889	.49893	.49897	.49900
3.1	.49903	.49906	.49910	.49913	.49916	.49918	.49921	.49924	.49926	.49929
3.2	.49931	.49934	.49936	.49938	.49940	.49942	.49944	.49946	.49948	.49950
3.3	.49952	.49953	.49955	.49957	.49958	.49960	.49961	.49962	.49964	.49965
3.4	.49966	.49968	.49969	.49970	.49971	.49972	.49973	.49974	.49975	.49976
3.5	.49977	.49978	.49978	.49979	.49980	.49981	.49981	.49982	.49983	.49983
3.6	.49984	.49985	.49985	.49986	.49986	.49987	.49987	.49988	.49988	.49989
3.7	.49989	.49990	.49990	.49990	.49991	.49991	.49992	.49992	.49992	.49992
3.8	.49993	.49993	.49993	.49994	.49994	.49994	.49994	.49995	.49995	.49995
3.9	.49995	.49995	.49996	.49996	.49996	.49996	.49996	.49996	.49997	.49997

Self-Test Solutions and Answers to Selected Problems

The following represent worked-out solutions to Self-Test Problems and brief answers to most of the even-numbered problems in the text. For more detailed solutions including explanations, interpretations, and Excel and Minitab output, see the *Student Solutions Manual*.

CHAPTER 1

1.2 Small, medium and large sizes are categories.

1.4 (a) The number of telephones is a numerical variable that is discrete because the variable is counted. **(b)** The length of the longest long-distance call is a numerical variable that is continuous since any value within a range of values can occur. **(c)** Whether there is a telephone line connected to a computer modem in the household is a categorical variable because the answer can only be yes or no. **(d)** Same answer as in (c).

1.6 (a) categorical; **(b)** numerical, continuous; **(c)** numerical, discrete; **(d)** numerical, discrete.

1.8 (a) numerical, continuous; **(b)** numerical, discrete; **(c)** numerical, continuous; **(d)** categorical.

1.10 The underlying variable, ability of the students, may be continuous but the measuring device, the test, does not have enough precision to distinguish between the two students.

CHAPTER 2

2.3 (b) The Pareto diagram portrays the data best because it allows you to focus on the categories that have the highest percentage of reasons. **(c)** Try to avoid the following mistakes: little or no knowledge of the company, unprepared to discuss career plans, and limited enthusiasm.

2.4 (b) The Pareto diagram is better than the pie chart to portray these data because it not only sorts the frequencies in descending order, it also provides the cumulative polygon on the same scale. **(c)** From the Pareto diagram, it is obvious that "Google" has the largest market share of 32% followed by Yahoo at 25%.

2.6 (b) 88%; **(d)** The Pareto diagram allows you to see which sources account for most of the electricity.

2.8 (b) The bar chart allows you to see that the "have software for all users" category dominates the company use of anti-spam software.

2.10 (b) Rooms dirty, rooms not stocked, and rooms need maintenance have the largest number of complaints, so focusing on these categories can reduce the number of complaints the most.

2.12 Stem-and-leaf of Finance Scores

```
5 | 34
6 | 9
7 | 4
8 | 0
9 | 38
```
$n = 7$

2.14 50 74 74 76 81 89 92

2.16 (a) Ordered array: $15 $15 $18 $18 $20 $20 $20 $20 $20 $21 $22 $22 $25 $25 $25 $25 $25 $26 $28 $29 $30 $30 $30
(b) Stem-and-Leaf Display

```
1 | 5 5 8 8
2 | 0 0 0 0 0 1 2 2 5 5 5 5 5 6 8 9
3 | 0 0 0
```

(c) The stem-and-leaf display provides more information because it not only orders values from the smallest to the largest into stems and leaves, it also conveys information on how the values distribute and cluster in the data set. **(d)** The bounced check fees seem to be concentrated around $20 and $25 since there are five occurences of each of the two values in the sample of 23 banks.

2.18 (a) Ordered array for chicken: 7, 9, 15, 16, 16, 18, 22, 25, 27, 33, 39
Ordered array for burger: 19, 31, 34, 35, 39, 39, 43
(b) Stem-and-leaf display for burgers

```
1 | 9
2 |
3 | 14599
4 | 3
```

Stem-and-leaf display for chicken

```
0 | 79
1 | 5668
2 | 257
3 | 39
```

(c) The stem-and-leaf display provides more information because it not only orders values from the smallest to the largest into stems and leaves, it also conveys information on how the values distribute and cluster in the data set. **(d)** There seems to be higher fat content for burgers because 6 values in the sample of 7 have fat content higher than 30 as compared to only 2 values in the sample of 11 chicken items. Also, there is only 1 value with a fat content lower than 20 for burgers as compared to 6 values in the sample of 11 chicken items.

2.25 (a) 10 but less than 20, 20 but less than 30, 30 but less than 40, 40 but less than 50, 50 but less than 60, 60 but less than 70, 70 but less than 80, 80 but less than 90, 90 but less than 100. **(b)** 10; **(c)** 15, 25, 35, 45, 55, 65, 75, 85, 95

2.27 (a)

Electricity Costs	Frequency	Percentage
$80 up to $100	4	8%
$100 up to $120	7	14
$120 up to $140	9	18
$140 up to $160	13	26
$160 up to $180	9	18
$180 up to $200	5	10
$200 up to $220	3	6

(c)

Electricity Costs	Frequency	Percentage	Cumulative %
$ 99	4	8.00%	8.00%
$119	7	14.00%	22.00%
$139	9	18.00%	40.00%
$159	13	26.00%	66.00%
$179	9	18.00%	84.00%
$199	5	10.00%	94.00%
$219	3	6.00%	100.00%

(d) The majority of utility charges are clustered between $120 and $180.

2.28 (a)

Error	Frequency	Cumulative %	Percentage
−0.00350—−0.00201	13	13%	13%
−0.00200—−0.00051	26	39%	26%
−0.00050— 0.00099	32	71%	32%
0.00100— 0.00249	20	91%	20%
0.00250— 0.00399	8	99%	8%
0.00400— 0.00549	1	100%	1%

(d) Yes, the steel mill is doing a good job at meeting the requirement as there is only one steel part out of a sample of 100 that is as much as 0.005 inches longer than the specified requirement.

2.29 (a)

Width	Frequency	Percentage
8.310—8.329	3	6.12%
8.330—8.349	2	4.08%
8.350—8.369	1	2.04%
8.370—8.389	4	8.16%
8.390—8.409	5	10.20%
8.410—8.429	16	31.65%
8.430—8.449	5	10.20%
8.450—8.469	5	10.20%
8.470—8.489	6	12.24%
8.490—8.509	2	4.08%

(d) All the troughs will meet the company's requirements of between 8.31 and 8.61 inches wide.

2.31 (a)

Bulb Life (hrs)	Percentage, Mfgr A	Percentage, Mfgr B
650— 749	7.5%	0.0%
750— 849	12.5	5.0
850— 949	50.0	20.0
950—1049	22.5	40.0
1050—1149	7.5	22.5
1150—1249	0.0	12.5

(c)

Bulb Life (hrs)	Percentage Less Than, Mfgr A	Percentage Less Than, Mfgr B
650— 749	7.5%	0.0%
750— 849	20.0	5.0
850— 949	70.0	25.0
950—1049	92.5	65.0
1050—1149	100.0	87.5
1150—1249	100.0	100.0

(d) Manufacturer B produces bulbs with longer lives than Manufacturer A. The cumulative percentage for Manufacturer B shows 65% of their bulbs lasted 1,049 hours or less contrasted with 70% of Manufacturer A's bulbs, which lasted 949 hours or less. None of Manufacturer A's bulbs lasted more than 1,149 hours, but 12.5% of Manufacturer B's bulbs lasted between 1,150 and 1,249 hours. At the same time, 7.5% of Manufacturer A's bulbs lasted less than 750 hours, while all of Manufacturer B's bulbs lasted at least 750 hours.

2.51 (c) The publisher gets the largest portion (64.8%) of the revenue. About half (32.2%) of the revenue received by the publisher covers manufacturing costs. Publisher's marketing and promotion account for the next larger share of the revenue at 15.4%. Author, bookstore employee salaries and benefits, and publisher administrative costs and taxes each accounts for around 10% of the revenue while the publisher after-tax profit, bookstore operations, bookstore pretax profit and freight constitute the "trivial few" allocations of the revenue.

2.53 (b) From 1999 to 2003, payment by cash and check had declined while payment by debit and other type of payment had increased. The percentage of payment by credit had remained more or less constant.

2.55 (a) The Pareto diagram is most appropriate because it not only sorts the frequencies in descending order, it also provides the cumulative polygon on the same scale. From the Pareto diagram, USA and Brazil make up more than half of the coffee consumption in major markets in 2000. **(b)** The Pareto diagram is most appropriate because it not only sorts the frequencies in descending order, it also provides the cumulative polygon on the same scale. From the Pareto diagram, no single major corporation dominates the coffee market in Brazil. The corporation that owns the largest share of the market, Sara Lee owned brands, captures less than 30% of the market share.

CHAPTER 3

3.35 (a) mean = 7, median = 7, mode = 7; **(b)** range = 9, interquartile range = 5, $S^2 = 10.8$, $S = 3.286$, $CV = 46.943\%$; **(c)** Z scores: 0, −0.913, 0.609, 0, −1.217, 1.521. None of the Z scores is larger than 3.0 or smaller than −3.0. There is no outlier. **(d)** symmetric since mean = median

3.37 (a) mean = 2, median = 7, mode = 7; **(b)** range = 17, interquartile range = 14.5, $S^2 = 62$, $S = 7.874$, $CV = 393.7\%$; **(c)** left skewed since mean < median

3.39 (a)

	Grade X	Grade Y
Mean	575	575.4
Median	575	575
Standard deviation	6.40	2.07

(b) If quality is measured by central tendency, Grade X tires provide slightly better quality because X's mean and median are both equal to the expected value, 575 mm. If, however, quality is measured by consistency, Grade Y provides better quality because, even though Y's mean is only slightly larger than the mean for Grade X, Y's standard deviation is much smaller. The range in values for Grade Y is 5 mm compared to the range in values for Grade X, which is 16 mm.

(c)

	Grade X	Grade Y, Altered
Mean	575	577.4
Median	575	575
Standard deviation	6.40	6.11

When the fifth Y tire measures 588 mm rather than 578 mm, Y's mean inner diameter becomes 577.4 mm, which is larger than X's mean inner diameter, and Y's standard deviation increases from 2.07 mm to 6.11 mm. In this case, X's tires are providing better quality in terms of the mean inner diameter with only slightly more variation among the tires than Y's.

3.40 (a) For the burgers: $\bar{X} = \dfrac{240}{7} = 34.2857$ Median $= (7+1)/2 = 4^{th}$ ranked value $= 35$ $Q_1 = (7+1)/4 = 2^{nd}$ ranked value $= 31$ $Q_3 = 3(7+1)/4 = 6^{th}$ ranked value $= 39$

For chicken items: $\bar{X} = \dfrac{227}{11} = 20.6364$ Median $= (11+1)/2 = 6^{th}$ ranked value $= 18$ $Q_1 = (11+1)/4 = 3^{rd}$ ranked value $= 15$ $Q_3 = 3(11+1)/4 = 9^{th}$ ranked value $= 27$

(b) For the burgers: Range $= 43 - 19 = 24$, Interquartile range $= 39 - 31 = 8$

Total Fat(X)	X – Mean	(X – Mean)^2
19	-15.2857	233.653061
31	-3.28571	10.7959184
34	-0.28571	0.08163265
35	0.714286	0.51020408
39	4.714286	22.2244898
39	4.714286	22.2244898
43	8.714286	75.9387755
34.285714 Mean		Sum: 365.428571

$S^2 = \dfrac{365.428571}{6} = 60.904761; S = \sqrt{60.904761} = 7.804$

$C.V. = \dfrac{7.804}{34.28571} \times 100\% = 22.761\%$

For the chicken items: Range $= 39 - 7 = 32$; Interquartile range $= 27 - 15 = 12$

Total Fat(X)	(X –Mean)	(X –Mean)^2
7	-13.6364	185.950413
9	-11.6364	135.404959
15	-5.63636	31.768595
16	-4.63636	21.4958678
16	-4.63636	21.4958678
18	-2.63636	6.95041322
22	1.363636	1.85950413
25	4.363636	19.0413223
27	6.363636	40.4958678
33	12.36364	152.859504
39	18.36364	337.22314
20.636364 Mean		Sum: 954.545455

$S^2 = \dfrac{954.54545}{10} = 95.454545; S = \sqrt{95.454545} = 9.77$

$C.V. = \dfrac{9.77}{20.636} \times 100\% = 47.344\%$

(c) The data for chicken items are skewed to the right and the data for burgers are skewed to the left. **(d)** In general, burgers have more total fat than chicken items. The lowest total fat among burgers is still higher than 50% of the total fat among chicken items. About 25% of the burgers have higher total fat than the highest total fat among the chicken items.

3.41 (a) The distribution of family incomes will most likely be skewed to the right due to the presence of a few millionaires and billionaires. As a result, the median income is a better measure of central tendency than the mean income. **(b)** The article reports the median home price and not the mean home price because the median is a better measure of central tendency in the presence of some extremely expensive homes that will drive the mean home price upward.

3.43 (a) Calories: mean $= 380$, median $= 350$, 1st quartile $= 260$, 3rd quartile $= 510$. Fat: mean $= 15.79$, median $= 19$, 1st quartile $= 8$, 3rd quartile $= 22$ **(b)** Calories: variance $= 12,800$, standard deviation $= 113.14$, range $= 290$, interquartile range $= 250$, CV $= 29.77\%$. None of the Z scores are less than -3 or greater than 3. There is no outlier in calories. Fat: variance $= 52.82$, standard deviation $= 7.27$, range $= 18.5$, Interquartile range $= 14$, CV $= 46.04\%$. None of the Z scores are less than -3 or greater than 3. There is no outlier in fat. **(c)** Calories are slightly right-skewed while fat is slightly left-skewed. **(d)** The mean calories are 380 while the middle ranked calorie is 350. The average scatter of calories around the mean is 113.14. The middle 50% of the calories are scattered over 250 while the difference between the highest and the lowest calories is 290. The mean fat is 15.79 grams while the middle ranked fat is 19 grams. The average scatter of fat around the mean is 7.27 grams. 50% of the values are scattered over 14 grams while the difference between the highest and the lowest fat is 18.5 grams.

3.45 (a) mean $= \$347.86$, median $= \$340$, 1st quartile $= \$290$, 3rd quartile $= \$400$. **(b)** variance $= 4,910.44$, standard deviation $= \$70.07$, range $= \$230$, interquartile range $= \$110$, CV $= 20.14\%$. None of the Z scores are less than -3 or greater than 3. There is no outlier in the price. **(c)** The price of 3-megapixel cameras is symmetrical. **(d)** The mean price is $\$347.86$ while the middle ranked price is $\$340$. The average scatter of price around the mean is $\$70.07$. The middle 50% of the prices are scattered over $\$110$ while the difference between the highest and the lowest price is $\$230$.

3.47 (a) Mean = 473.46, Median = 451. There is no mode. The median seems to be a better descriptive measure, since the data are not symmetric. **(b)** Range = 785, Variance = 44,422.44, Standard deviation = 210.77. **(c)** From the manufacturer's viewpoint, the worst measure would be to compute the proportion of batteries that last over 400 hours (8/13 = 0.61). The median (451) and the mean (473.5) are both over 400, and would be better measures for the manufacturer to use in advertisements. **(d)** Mean = 550.38, Median = 492, Mode = none, Range = 1,078, Variance = 99,435.26, Standard deviation =315.33. From the manufacturer's viewpoint, the worst measure remains the proportion of batteries that last over 400 hours (9/13 = 0.69). The median (492) and the mean (550.38) are both well over 400, and would be better measures for the manufacturer to use in advertisements. The shape of the distribution of the altered data set is right-skewed, since its mean is larger than its median.

3.49 (a) Mean = 7.11, Median = 6.68, Q_1 = 5.64, Q_3 = 8.73. **(b)** Variance = 4.336, Standard deviation = 2.082, Range = 6.67, Interquartile range = 3.09, Coefficient of variation = 29.27%. **(c)** Since the mean is greater than the median, the distribution is right-skewed. **(d)** The mean and median are both more than 5 minutes. The distribution is right-skewed, meaning that there are more unusually high values than low values. Further, 13 of the 15 bank customers sampled (or 86.7%) had waiting times in excess of 5 minutes. So, the customer is more likely to experience a waiting time in excess of 5 minutes. The manager overstated the bank's service record in responding that the customer would "almost certainly" not wait longer than 5 minutes for service.

3.51 (a) Population Mean μ = 6 **(b)** Population Standard deviation, σ = 1.673, Population Variance, σ^2 = 2.8
3.52 (a) $\mu = \dfrac{514}{50} = 10.28$, $\sigma^2 = \dfrac{204.92}{50} = 4.0984$, $\sigma = \sqrt{4.0984} = 2.02445$
(b) 64%, 94%, 100% **(c)** These percentages are lower than the empirical rule would suggest.

3.53 (a) 68%; **(b)** 95%; **(c)** not calculable, 75%, 88.89%. **(d)** $\mu - 4\sigma$ to $\mu + 4\sigma$ or −2.8 to 19.2

3.55 (a) mean = 12,999.2158, variance = 14,959,700.52, std. dev. = 3,867.7772. **(b)** 64.71%, 98.04% and 100% of these states have mean per capita energy consumption within 1, 2, and 3 standard deviation of the mean, respectively. **(c)** This is consistent with the 68%, 95%, and 99.7% according to the empirical rule. **(d)** (a)mean = 12,857.7402, variance = 14,238,110.67, std. dev. = 3,773.3421. **(b)** 66%, 98%, and 100% of these states have a mean per capita energy consumption within 1, 2, and 3 standard deviations of the mean, respectively. **(c)** This is consistent with the 68%, 95% and 99.7% according to the empirical rule.

3.61 (a) 3,4,7,9,12; **(b)** The distances between the median and the extremes are close, 4 and 5, but the differences in the sizes of the whiskers are different (1 on the left and 3 on the right) so this distribution is slightly right-skewed. **(c)** In 3.2(c) since the mean = median, the distribution was said to be symmetric. The box part of the graph is symmetric, but the whiskers show right skewness.

3.63 (a) −8, −6.5, 7, 8, 9; **(b)** The shape is left-skewed. **(c)** This is consistent with the answer in 3.4(c).

3.65 (a) Five-number summary: 309 593 895.5 1,425 1,720. **(b)** right-skewed

3.67 (a) Bounced-check fee: Five-number summary: 15 20 22 26 30. Monthly service fee: Five-number summary: 0 5 7 10 12. **(b)** The distribution of bounced-check fees is skewed slightly to the right. The

distribution of monthly service charges is skewed to the left. **(c)** The central tendency of the bounced-check fee is substantially higher than that of monthly service fees. While the distribution of the bounced-check fees is symmetrical, the distribution of monthly service fees is skewed more to the left with a few banks charging very low or no monthly service fee.

3.69 (a) Commercial district: Five-number summary: 0.38 3.2 4.5 5.55 6.46. Residential area: Five-number summary: 3.82 5.64 6.68 8.73 10.49. **(b)** Commercial district: The distribution is skewed to the left. Residential area: The distribution is skewed slightly to the right. **(c)** The central tendency of the waiting times for the bank branch located in the commercial district of a city is lower than that of the branch located in the residential area. There are a few longer-than-normal waiting times for the branch located in the residential area whereas there are a few exceptionally short waiting times for the branch located in the commercial area.

3.87 (a) mean = 43.89, median = 45, 1st quartile = 18, 3rd quartile - 63. **(b)** range = 76, interquartile range = 45, variance = 639.2564, standard deviation = 25.28, coefficient of variation = 57.61%. **(c)** The distribution is skewed to the right because there are a few policies that require an exceptionally long period to be approved. **(d)** The mean approval process takes 43.89 days with 50% of the policies being approved in less than 45 days. 50% of the applications are approved between 18 and 63 days. About 67% of the applications are approved between 18.6 to 69.2 days.

3.89 (a) mean = 8.421, median = 8.42, range = 0.186, S = 0.0461. The mean and median width are both 8.42 inches. The range of the widths is 0.186 inches, and the average scatter around the mean is 0.0461 inches. **(b)** 8.312, 8.404, 8.42, 8.459, 8.498; **(c)** Even though the mean = median, the left whisker is longer so the distribution is left-skewed. **(d)** All the troughs in this sample meet the specifications.

3.91 (a) Office I: mean = 2.214, median = 1.54; Office II: mean = 2.011, median = 1.505; Office I: Q_1 = 0.93, Q_3 = 3.93; Office II: Q_1 = 0.6, Q_3 = 3.75; **(b)** Office I: Range = 5.80, IQR = 3.00, S^2 = 2.952, S = 1.718, CV = 77.597%; Office II: Range = 7.47, IQR = 3.15, S^2 = 3.579, S = 1.892, CV = 94.04%; **(c)** Yes, they are both right-skewed. **(d)** Office II has more variability in times to clear problems, with a wider range and a larger standard deviation. Office II has a lower mean time to clear problems.

3.93 (a) Cost: mean = 0.171; median = 0.17; Calories: mean = 165.758, median = 190; Fiber: mean = 6.909, median = 6; Sugar: mean = 11.394, median = 11; Cost: Q_1 = 0.13, Q_3 = 0.20; Calories: Q_1 = 135, Q_3 = 200; Fiber: Q_1 = 5, Q_3 = 8; Sugar: Q_1 = 6, Q_3 = 17.5; **(b)** Cost: Range = 0.17, IQR = 0.07, S^2 = 0.00220, S = 0.0469, CV = 27.49%; Calories: Range = 160, IQR = 65, S^2 = 2,681.439, S = 51.783, CV = 31.240%; Fiber: Range = 8, IQR = 3, S^2 = 5.773, S = 2.403, CV = 34.781%; Sugar: Range = 23, IQR = 11.50, S^2 = 44.246, S = 6.652, CV = 58.382%; **(c)** Cost: right-skewed, calories: left skewed, fiber: right skewed, sugar: approximately symmetric; **(d)** Cost: The mean cost is about 17 cents per ounce. Most cereals cluster around this cost with a few high-priced cereals. The average scatter around the mean is about 5 cents per ounce. Calories: The mean calories is about 166 and a middle value of 190, with an average scatter around the mean of about 52. Since the data are left-skewed, most of the calories are clustered at the high end with a few lower-calorie cereals. Fiber: The mean amount of fiber is about 6.9 grams with a middle value of 6 grams, with an average scatter around the mean of about 2.4 grams. Since the fiber is right-skewed, the cereals tend to cluster around the lower fiber numbers. Three cereals increase the fiber mean. Sugar: The mean amount of sugar is 11.4 grams with a middle value of 11 grams. The average scatter around the middle is 6.65 grams. The data are fairly symmetric.

CHAPTER 4

4.2 (a) Simple events include selecting a red ball. **(b)** Selecting a white ball

4.4 (a) 60/100 = 3/5 = 0.6 **(b)** 10/100 = 1/10 = 0.1 **(c)** 35/100 = 7/20 = 0.35 **(d)** 9/10 = 0.9

4.6 (a) Mutually exclusive, not collectively exhaustive **(b)** Not mutually exclusive, not collectively exhaustive **(c)** Mutually exclusive, not collectively exhaustive **(d)** Mutually exclusive, collectively exhaustive

4.8 (a) "Is a homeowner." **(b)** "A homeowner who drives himself/herself to work." **(c)** "Does not drive self to work." **(d)** "A person can drive himself/herself to work and is also a homeowner."

4.10 (a) "A wafer is good." **(b)** "A wafer is good and no particle was found on the die." **(c)** "bad wafer." **(d)** A wafer can be a "good wafer" and was produced by a die "with particles."

4.12 (a) 83/369 = 0.2249; **(b)** 137/369 = 0.3713; **(c)** 220/369 = 0.5962; **(d)** The probability of "small-to-midsized or offered stock options" includes the probability of "small-to-midsized and offered stock options," the probability of "small-to-midsized but did not offer stock options" and the probability of "large and offered stock options."

4.14 (a) 360/500 = 18/25 = 0.72; **(b)** 224/500 = 56/125 = 0.448; **(c)** 396/500 = 99/125 = 0.792 **(d)** 500/500 = 1.00

4.16 (a) 10/30 = 1/3 = 0.33; **(b)** 20/60 = 1/3 = 0.33; **(c)** 40/60 = 2/3 = 0.67; **(d)** Since $P(A \mid B) = P(A) = 1/3$, events A and B are statistically independent.

4.18 $\frac{1}{2} = 0.5$

4.20 Since $P(A \text{ and } B) = 0.20$ and $P(A) P(B) = 0.12$, events A and B are not statistically independent.

4.21 (a) P (a homeowner | drives to work) = 824/1505 = 0.5475; **(b)** P (drives to work | a homeowner) = 824/1000 = 0.8240 **(c)** The conditional events are reversed. **(d)** Since P (a homeowner) = 1000/2000 = 0.50 is not equal to P (a homeowner | drives to work) = 824/1505 = 0.5475, driving to work and whether the respondent is a homeowner or a renter are not statistically independent.

4.22 (a) 36/116 = 0.3103; **(b)** 14/334 = 0.0419; **(c)** 320/334 = 0.9581 P (no particles) = 400/450 = 0.8889. Since P (no particles | good) $\neq$ P (no particles), "a good wafer" and "a die with no particle" are not statistically independent.

4.24 (a) 29/56 = 0.5179; **(b)** 29/155 = 0.1871; **(c)** The conditional events are reversed. **(d)** Since P (white | claim bias) = 0.1871 is not equal to P (white) = 0.1210, being white and claiming bias are not statistically independent.

4.26 (a) 0.025/0.6 = 0.0417; **(b)** 0.015/0.4 = 0.0375; **(c)** Since P (needs warranty repair | manufacturer based in U.S.) = 0.0417 and P (needs warranty repair) = 0.04, the two events are not statistically independent.

4.28 (a) 0.0045; **(b)** 0.012; **(c)** 0.0059; **(d)** 0.0483

4.30 0.095

4.32 (a) 0.736; **(b)** 0.997

4.33 (a) H = husband watching; W = wife watching

$$P(H \mid W) = \frac{P(W \mid H) \cdot P(H)}{P(W \mid H) \cdot P(H) + P(W \mid H') \cdot P(H')}$$

$$= \frac{(0.4)(0.6)}{(0.4)(0.6) + (0.3)(0.4)} = \frac{0.24}{0.36}$$

$$= \frac{2}{3} = 0.667$$

(b) $P(W) = 0.24 + 0.12 = 0.36$

4.34 (a) 0.4615; **(b)** 0.325

4.36 (a) P (huge success | favorable review) = 0.099/0.459 = 0.2157, P (moderate success | favorable review) = 0.14/0.459 = 0.3050; P (break even | favorable review) = 0.16/0.459 = 0.3486; P (loser | favorable review) = 0.06/0.459 = 0.1307; **(b)** P (favorable review) = 0.459.

4.38 $3^{10} = 59,049$

4.40 (a) $2^7 = 128$; **(b)** $6^7 = 279,936$ **(c)** There are two mutually exclusive and collectively exhaustive outcomes in (a) and six in (b).

4.41 (7)(3)(3) = 63

4.42 (8)(4)(3)(3) = 288

4.43 $n! = 4! = (4)(3)(2)(1) = 24$

4.44 $5! = (5)(4)(3)(2)(1) = 120$. Not all these orders are equally likely because the players are different in each team.

4.46 $n! = 6! = 720$

4.47 $\frac{n!}{(n-X)!} = \frac{12!}{9!} = (12)(11)(10) = 1,320$

4.48 28

4.49 $\frac{n!}{X!(n-X)!} = \frac{7!}{4!(3!)} = \frac{(7)(6)(5)}{(3)(2)(1)} = 35$

4.50 4,950

4.62 (a) 0.035, **(b)** 0.49, **(c)** 0.975, **(d)** 0.02, **(e)** 0.2857, **(f)** The conditions are switched. Part (d) answers $P(A \mid B)$ and part (e) answers $P(B \mid A)$.

4.64 (a) A simple event can be "a firm that has a transactional public web site" and a joint event can be "a firm that has a transactional public web site and has sales greater than \$10 billion." **(b)** 0.3469, **(c)** 0.1449, **(d)** Since P (transactional public web site) $\cdot$ P (sales in excess of \$10 billion) $\neq P$ (transactional public web site and sales in excess of \$10 billion), the two events, "sales in excess of ten billion dollars" and "has a transactional public web site" are not independent.

4.66 (a) 0.0225; **(b)** 3,937.5 $\cong$ 3,938 can be expected to read the advertisement and place an order. **(c)** 0.03; **(d)** 5,250 can be expected to read the advertisement and place an order.

4.68 (a) 0.4712; **(b)** Since the probability that a fatality involved a rollover given that the fatality involved an SUV, van, or pickup is 0.4712, which is almost twice the probability that a fatality involved a rollover with any vehicle type at 0.24, SUV's, vans, or pickups are generally more prone to rollover accidents.

CHAPTER 5

5.2 (a) C: $\mu = 2$, D: $\mu = 2$; **(b)** C: $\sigma = 1.414$, D: $\sigma = 1.095$; **(c)** Distribution C is uniform and symmetric; distribution D is symmetric and has a single mode.

5.4 (a) $\mu = 2$; **(b)** $\sigma = 1.183$

5.5 (a)–(b)

X	P(x)	X*P(X)	$(X - \mu)^2$	$(X - \mu)^2*P(X)$
0	0.32	0	1.6129	0.516128
1	0.35	0.35	0.0729	0.025515
2	0.18	0.36	0.5329	0.095922
3	0.08	0.24	2.9929	0.239432
4	0.04	0.16	7.4529	0.298116
5	0.02	0.10	13.9129	0.278258
6	0.01	0.06	22.3729	0.223729
	(a) Mean =	1.27	variance =	1.6771
			(b) Stdev =	1.29503

5.6 (a)

X	P(X)
$ – 1	21/36
$ + 1	15/36

(b)

X	P(X)
$ – 1	21/36
$ + 1	15/36

(c)

X	P(X)
$ – 1	30/36
$ + 4	6/36

(d) $ – 0.167 for each method of play

5.17 (a) 0.5997; **(b)** 0.0016; **(c)** 0.0439; **(d)** 0.4018

5.19 (a) 0.0778; **(b)** 0.6826; **(c)** 0.0870; **(d)(a)** $P(X = 5) = 0.3277$
(b) $P(X \geq 3) = 0.9421$; **(c)** $P(X < 2) = 0.0067$

5.21 Given $p = 0.90$ and $n = 3$,

(a) $P(X = 3) = \dfrac{n!}{X!(n-X)!} p^X (1-p)^{n-X} = \dfrac{3!}{3!0!}(0.9)^3(0.1)^0 = 0.729$

(b) $P(X = 0) = \dfrac{n!}{X!(n-X)!} p^X (1-p)^{n-X} = \dfrac{3!}{0!3!}(0.9)^0(0.1)^3 = 0.001$

(c) $P(X \geq 2) = P(X = 2) + P(X = 3) = \dfrac{3!}{2!1!}(0.9)^2(0.1)^1 + \dfrac{3!}{3!0!}(0.9)^3(0.1)^0 = 0.972$

(d) $E(X) = np = 3(0.9) = 2.7$ $\sigma_X = \sqrt{np(1-p)} = \sqrt{3(0.9)(0.1)} = 0.5196$

5.23 (a) $P(X = 0) =$ approximately 0; **(b)** $P(X = 1) =$ approximately 0; **(c)** $P(X \leq 2) = 0.000000374$; **(d)** $P(X \geq 3) = 1.0$

5.25 (a) Since 68% and 24% come from the survey results conducted by the networks, they are best classified as empirical classical probability. **(b)** 0.000014; **(c)** 0.9721; **(d)** 0.000447

5.32 (a) 0.2565; **(b)** 0.1396; **(c)** 0.3033; **(d)** 0.0247

5.34 (a) 0.0337; **(b)** 0.0067; **(c)** 0.9596; **(d)** 0.0404

5.36 (a) $P(X < 5) = P(X = 0) + P(X = 1) + P(X = 2) + P(X = 3) + P(X = 4)$

$= \dfrac{e^{-6}(6)^0}{0!} + \dfrac{e^{-6}(6)^1}{1!} + \dfrac{e^{-6}(6)^2}{2!} + \dfrac{e^{-6}(6)^3}{3!} + \dfrac{e^{-6}(6)^4}{4!}$

$= 0.002479 + 0.014873 + 0.044618 + 0.089235 + 0.133853 = 0.2851$

(b) $P(X = 5) = \dfrac{e^{-6}(6)^5}{5!} = 0.1606$

(c) $P(X \geq 5) = 1 - P(X < 5) = 1 - 0.2851 = 0.7149$

(d) $P(X = 4 \text{ or } X = 5) = P(X = 4) + P(X = 5) = \dfrac{e^{-6}(6)^4}{4!} + \dfrac{e^{-6}(6)^5}{5!} = 0.2945$

5.38 (a) 0.0404; **(b)** 0.9596; **(c)** 0.8301; **(d)** Because Delta has a higher mean rate of mishandled bags per 1,000 passengers than Jet Blue, its probability of mishandling at least a certain number of bags is higher than that of Jet Blue.

5.40 (a) 0.0176; **(b)** 0.9093; **(c)** 0.9220

5.42 (a) 0.0062; **(b)** 0.1173; **(c)** Because Kia has a higher mean rate of problems per car, the probability that a randomly selected Kia will have no more than 2 problems is lower than that of a randomly chosen Lexus. Likewise, the probability that a randomly selected Kia will have zero problems is lower than that of a randomly chosen Lexus.

5.44 (a) 0.2165; **(b)** 0.8013; **(c)** Because Kia has a lower mean rate of problems per car in 2004 compared to 2003, the probability that a randomly selected Kia has zero problems and the probability of no more than 2 problems are both higher than their values in 2003.

5.56 (a) 0.74; **(b)** 0.74; **(c)** 0.3898; **(d)** 0.0012; **(e)** The assumption of independence may not be true.

5.58 (a) 0.0547; **(b)** 0.3828; **(c)** 0.9298; **(d)** If the indicator is a random event, the probability that it will make a correct prediction in 8 or more times out of 10 is virtually zero. If one is willing to accept the argument that the amount of campaign expenditures spent during an election year exerts some multiplying impact on the stock market, the probability that the Dow Jones Industrial Average will increase in a U.S. presidential election year is likely to be near 0.90 based on the result of (a)–(c).

5.60 (a) 0.018228; **(b)** 0.089782; **(c)** 0.89199; **(d)** mean = 3.3, standard deviation = 1.486943

5.62 (a) 0.0000; **(b)** 0.04924; **(c)** 0.909646; **(d)** 0.49578

5.64 (a) 0.0003; **(b)** 0.2289; **(c)** 0.4696; **(d)** 0.5304; **(e)** 0.469581; **(f)** 4.4 so about 4 people on average will refuse to participate

5.66 (a) $\mu = 17.6$, **(b)** $\sigma = 1.453$, **(c)** 0.0776, **(d)** 0.5631, **(e)** 0.9740

5.68 (a) 0.0000192791; **(b)** 0.0334; **(c)** 0.8815; **(d)** Based on the results in (a)–(c), the probability that the Standard & Poor's 500 index will increase if there is an early gain in the first five trading days of the year is very likely to be close to 0.90 because that yields a probability of 88.15% that at least 29 of the 34 years the Standard & Poor's 500 index will increase the entire year. However, you should be aware that a high correlation between two events does not always imply a causal relationship.

5.70 (a) The assumptions needed are (i) the probability that a golfer loses a golf ball in a given interval is constant, (ii) the probability that a golfer loses more than one golf ball approaches 0 as the interval gets smaller, (iii) the probability that a golfer loses a golf ball is independent from interval to interval. **(b)** 0.0111; **(c)** 0.70293; **(d)** 0.29707

CHAPTER 6

6.8 (a) 0.9089, **(b)** 0.0911, **(c)** + 1.96, **(d)** – 1.00 and + 1.00.

6.10 (a) 0.1401, **(b)** 0.4168, **(c)** 0.3918, **(d)** + 1.00

6.12 (a) 0.9599, **(b)** 0.0228, **(c)** 43.42, **(d)** 46.64 and 53.36

6.14 (a) $P(34 < X < 50) = P(-1.33 < Z < 0) = 0.4082$, **(b)** $P(X < 30) + P(X > 60) = P(Z < -1.67) + P(Z > 0.83) = 0.0475 + (1.0 - 0.7967) = 0.2508$; **(c)** $P(Z < -0.84) \cong 0.20$, $Z = -0.84 = \dfrac{X - 50}{12}$

$X = 50 - 0.84(12) = 39.92$ thousand miles or 39,920 miles **(d)** The smaller standard deviation makes the Z-values larger. **(a)** $P(34 < X < 50) = P(-1.60 < Z < 0) = 0.4452$ **(b)** $P(X < 30) + P(X > 60) = P(Z < -2.00) + P(Z > 1.00) = 0.0228 + (1.0 - 0.8413) = 0.1815$ **(c)** $X = 50 - 0.84(10) = 41.6$ thousand miles or 41,600 miles

6.16 (a) 0.9878; **(b)** 0.8185; **(c)** 86.16%; **(d)** <u>Option 1:</u> Since your score of 81% on this exam represents a Z-score of 1.00, which is below the minimum Z-score of 1.28, you will not earn an "A" grade on the exam under this grading option. <u>Option 2:</u> Since your score of 68% on this exam represents a Z-score of 2.00, which is well above the minimum Z-score of 1.28, you will earn an "A" grade on the exam under this grading option. You should prefer Option 2.

6.18 (a) 0.9772; **(b)** 0.1587, **(c)** 0.0038; **(d)** 0.9962

6.25 (a) 0.4772, **(b)** 0.9544, **(c)** 0.0456, **(d)** 1.8835, **(e)** 1.8710 and 2.1290

6.27 (a) 0.2734, **(b)** 0.2038, **(c)** 4.404 ounces, **(d)** 4.188 ounces and 5.212 ounces

6.29 (a) 0.7273, **(b)** 0.2884, **(c)** 0.0426, **(d)** 0.0386, **(e)** The common stocks have higher mean annual returns than the long-term government bonds. But they also have higher volatility as reflected by their larger standard deviation. This is the usual trade-off between high return and high volatility in an investment instrument. *Note:* The above answers are computed using Microsoft Excel. They may be slightly different when Table E.2 is used.

6.31 (a) 0.8413; **(b)** 0.9330; **(c)** 0.9332; **(d)** 0.3347; **(e)** 0.4080 and 1.1920

CHAPTER 7

7.2 (a) virtually zero; **(b)** 0.1587; **(c)** 0.0139; **(d)** 50.195

7.4 (a) Both means are equal to 6. This property is called unbiasedness. **(c)** The distribution for $n = 3$ has less variability. The larger sample size has resulted in sample means being closer to μ.

7.6 (a) Since $\bar{X} >$ median, the shape of the sampling distribution of $\bar{X}$ for samples of size 2 will be right skewed. **(b)** When the sample size is 100, the sampling distribution of $\bar{X}$ will be very close to a normal distribution as a result of the central limit theorem. **(c)** 0.1333

7.8 (a) $P(\bar{X} > 3) = P(Z > -1.00) = 1.0 - 0.1587 = 0.8413$ **(b)** $P(Z < 1.04) = 0.85$ $\bar{X} = 3.10 + 1.04(0.1) = 3.204$ **(c)** To be able to use the standardized normal distribution as an approximation for the area under the curve, you must assume that the

population is approximately symmetrical. **(d)** $P(Z < 1.04) = 0.85$ $\bar{X} = 3.10 + 1.04(0.05) = 3.152$

7.10 (a) 0.9969, **(b)** 0.0142, **(c)** 2.3830 and 2.6170, **(d)** 2.6170. *Note:* These answers are computed using Microsoft Excel. They may be slightly different when Table E.2 is used.

7.40 (a) 0.30, **(b)** 0.0693

7.42 (a) $\mu = 0.501$, $\sigma = \sqrt{\dfrac{\pi(1-\pi)}{n}} = \sqrt{\dfrac{0.501(1-0.501)}{100}} = 0.05$

$P(p > 0.55) = P(Z > 0.98) = 1.0 - 0.8365 = 0.1635$

(b) $\mu = 0.60$, $\sigma = \sqrt{\dfrac{\pi(1-\pi)}{n}} = \sqrt{\dfrac{0.6(1-0.6)}{100}} = 0.04899$

$P(p > 0.55) = P(Z > -1.021) = 1.0 - 0.1539 = 0.8461$

(c) $\mu = 0.49$, $\sigma_P = \sqrt{\dfrac{\pi(1-\pi)}{n}} = \sqrt{\dfrac{0.49(1-0.49)}{100}} = 0.05$

$P(p > 0.55) = P(Z > 1.20) = 1.0 - 0.8849 = 0.1151$ **(d)** Increasing the sample size by a factor of 4 decreases the standard error by a factor of 2. **(a)** $P(p > 0.55) = P(Z > 1.96) = 1.0 - 0.9750 = 0.0250$ **(b)** $P(p > 0.55) = P(Z > -2.04) = 1.0 - 0.0207 = 0.9793$ **(c)** $P(p > 0.55) = P(Z > 2.40) = 1.0 - 0.9918 = 0.0082$

7.44 (a) 0.50, **(b)** 0.5717, **(c)** 0.9523, **(d) (a)** 0.50, **(b)** 0.4246, **(c)** 0.8386

7.46 (a) 0.5926, **(b)** 0.7211 and 0.8189, **(c)** 0.7117 and 0.8283

7.48 (a) 0.6314, **(b)** 0.0041, **(c)** $P(p > .35) = P(Z > 1.3223) = 0.0930$. If the population proportion is 29%, the proportion of the samples with 35% or more who do not intend to work for pay at all is 9.3%, an unlikely occurrence. Hence, the population estimate of 29% is likely to be an underestimation. **(d)** When the sample size is smaller in (c) compared to (b), the standard error of the sampling distribution of sample proportion is larger.

7.50 (a) 0.3626, **(b)** 0.9816, **(c)** 0.0092. *Note:* These answers are computed using Microsoft Excel. They may be slightly different when Table E.2 is used.

7.52 Sample without replacement: Read from left to right in 3-digit sequences and continue unfinished sequences from end of row to beginning of next row.

Row 05: 338 505 855 551 438 855 077 186 579 488 767 833 170
Rows 05–06: 897
Row 06: 340 033 648 847 204 334 639 193 639 411 095 924
Rows 06–07: 707
Row 07: 054 329 776 100 871 007 255 980 646 886 823 920 461
Row 08: 893 829 380 900 796 959 453 410 181 277 660 908 887
Rows 08–09: 237
Row 09: 818 721 426 714 050 785 223 801 670 353 362 449
Rows 09–10: 406

Note: All sequences above 902 are discarded.

7.54 A simple random sample would be less practical for personal interviews because of travel costs (unless interviewees are paid to attend a central interviewing location).

7.56 Here all members of the population are equally likely to be selected and the sample selection mechanism is based on chance. But selection of two elements is not independent; for example, if *A* is in the sample, we know that *B* is also, and that *C* and *D* are not.

7.57 (a) Since a complete roster of full-time students exists, a simple random sample of 200 students could be taken. If student satisfaction with the quality of campus life randomly fluctuates across the student body, a systematic 1-in-20 sample could also be taken from the population frame. If student satisfaction with the quality of life may differ by gender and by experience/class level, a stratified sample using eight strata, female freshmen through female seniors and male freshmen through male seniors, could be selected. If student satisfaction with the quality of life is thought to fluctuate as much within clusters as between them, a cluster sample could be taken. **(b)** A simple random sample is one of the simplest to select. The population frame is the registrar's file of 4,000 student names. **(c)** A systematic sample is easier to select from the registrar's records than a simple random sample, since an initial person is selected at random and then every 20th person thereafter would be sampled. The systematic sample would have the additional benefit that the alphabetic distribution of sampled students' names would be more comparable to the alphabetic distribution of student names in the campus population. **(d)** If rosters by gender and class designations are readily available, a stratified sample should be taken. Since student satisfaction with the quality of life may indeed differ by gender and class level, the use of a stratified sampling design will not only ensure all strata are represented in the sample, it will generate a more representative sample and produce estimates of the population parameter that have greater precision. **(e)** If all 4,000 full-time students reside in one of 20 on-campus residence halls, which fully integrate students by gender and by class, a cluster sample should be taken. A cluster could be defined as an entire residence hall, and the students of a single randomly selected residence hall could be sampled. Since the dormitories are fully integrated by floor, a cluster could alternatively be defined as one floor of one of the 20 dormitories. Four floors could be randomly sampled to produce the required 200 student sample. Selection of an entire dormitory may make distribution and collection of the survey easier to accomplish. In contrast, if there is some variable other than gender or class that differs across dormitories, sampling by floor may produce a more representative sample.

7.58 (a) Row 16: 2323 6737 5131 8888 1718 0654 6832 4647 6510 4877
Row 17: 4579 4269 2615 1308 2455 7830 5550 5852 5514 7182
Row 18: 0989 3205 0514 2256 8514 4642 7567 8896 2977 8822
Row 19: 5438 2745 9891 4991 4523 6847 9276 8646 1628 3554
Row 20: 9475 0899 2337 0892 0048 8033 6945 9826 9403 6858
Row 21: 7029 7341 3553 1403 3340 4205 0823 4144 1048 2949
Row 22: 8515 7479 5432 9792 6575 5760 0408 8112 2507 3742
Row 23: 1110 0023 4012 8607 4697 9664 4894 3928 7072 5815
Row 24: 3687 1507 7530 5925 7143 1738 1688 5625 8533 5041
Row 25: 2391 3483 5763 3081 6090 5169 0546

Note: All sequences above 5,000 are discarded. There were no repeating sequences.
(b) 089 189 289 389 489 589 689 789 889 989
1089 1189 1289 1389 1489 1589 1689 1789 1889 1989
2089 2189 2289 2389 2489 2589 2689 2789 2889 2989
3089 3189 3289 3389 3489 3589 3689 3789 3889 3989
4089 4189 4289 4389 4489 4589 4689 4789 4889 4989

(c) With the single exception of invoice #0989, the invoices selected in the simple random sample are not the same as those selected in the systematic sample. It would be highly unlikely that a simple random sample would select the same units as a systematic sample.

7.78 (a) 0.4999; **(b)** 0.00009; **(c)** 0; **(d)** 0; **(e)** 0.7518

7.80 (a) 0.8944; **(b)** 4.617, 4.783; **(c)** 4.641

7.82 (a) 0.0092; **(b)** 0.9823; **(c)** 0.0000

7.84 Even though Internet polling is less expensive, faster, and offers higher response rates than telephone surveys, it may lead to more coverage error since a greater proportion of the population may have telephones than have Internet access. It may also lead to nonresponse bias since a certain class and/or age group of people may not use the Internet or may use the Internet less frequently. Due to these errors, the data collected are not appropriate for making inferences about the general population.

7.86 (a) With a response rate of only 15.5%, nonresponse error should be the major cause of concern in this study. Measurement error is a possibility also. **(b)** The researchers should follow up with the nonrespondents. **(c)** The step mentioned in (b) could have been followed to increase the response rate to the survey, thus increasing its worthiness.

7.88 (a) What was the comparison group of "other workers"? Were they another sample? Where did they come from? Were they truly comparable? What was the sampling scheme? What was the population from which the sample was selected? How was salary measured? What was the mode of response? What was the response rate? **(b)** Various answers are possible.

CHAPTER 8
8.2 $114.68 \leq \mu \leq 135.32$

8.4 In order to have 100% certainty, the entire population would have to be sampled.

8.6 Yes, it is true since 5% of intervals will not include the true mean.

8.8 (a) $\bar{X} \pm Z \cdot \dfrac{\sigma}{\sqrt{n}} = 350 \pm 1.96 \cdot \dfrac{100}{\sqrt{64}}$; $325.50 \leq \mu \leq 374.50$. **(b)** No. The manufacturer cannot support a claim that the bulbs have a mean of 400 hours. Based on the data from the sample, a mean of 400 hours would represent a distance of 4 standard deviations above the sample mean of 350 hours. **(c)** No. Since σ is known and $n = 64$, from the Central Limit Theorem, you know that the sampling distribution of $\bar{X}$ is approximately normal. **(d)** The confidence interval is narrower based on a population standard deviation of 80 hours rather than the original standard deviation of 100 hours.
(a) $\bar{X} \pm Z \cdot \dfrac{\sigma}{\sqrt{n}} = 350 \pm 1.96 \cdot \dfrac{80}{\sqrt{64}}$, $330.4 \leq \mu \leq 369.6$. **(b)** Based on the smaller standard deviation, a mean of 400 hours would represent a distance of 5 standard deviations above the sample mean of 350 hours. No, the manufacturer cannot support a claim that the bulbs have a mean life of 400 hours.

8.10 (a) 2.2622; **(b)** 3.2498; **(c)** 2.0395; **(d)** 1.9977; **(e)** 1.7531

8.12 $38.95 \leq \mu \leq 61.05$

8.14 $-0.12 \leq \mu \leq 11.84$, $2.00 \leq \mu \leq 6.00$. The presence of the outlier increases the sample mean and greatly inflates the sample standard deviation.

8.15 (a) $\bar{X} \pm t\left(\dfrac{s}{\sqrt{n}}\right) = 1.67 \pm 2.0930\left(\dfrac{0.32}{\sqrt{20}}\right)$, $\$1.52 \leq \mu \leq \$1.82$. **(b)** The store owner can have 95% confidence that the population mean retail value of greeting cards that it has in its inventory is between \$1.52 and

$1.82. The store owner could multiply the ends of the confidence interval by the number of cards to estimate the total value of her inventory.

8.16 (a) $29.44 \leq \mu \leq 34.56$. **(b)** The quality improvement team can be 95% confident that the population mean turnaround time is between 29.44 hours and 34.56 hours. **(c)** The project was a success because the initial turnaround time of 68 hours does not fall into the interval.

8.18 (a) $\$21.01 \leq \mu \leq \$24.99$. **(b)** You can be 95% confident that the population mean bounced-check fee is between $21.01 and $24.99.

8.20 (a) $31.12 \leq \mu \leq 54.06$; **(b)** The number of days is approximately normally distributed. **(c)** Yes, the outliers skew the data. **(d)** Since the sample size is fairly large at $n = 50$, the use of the t distribution is appropriate.

8.22 (a) $\bar{X} \pm t \left(\dfrac{S}{\sqrt{n}} \right) = 182.4 \pm 2.0930 \left(\dfrac{44.2700}{\sqrt{20}} \right)$, $\$161.68 \leq \mu \leq \$203.12$

(b) $\bar{X} \pm t \left(\dfrac{S}{\sqrt{n}} \right) = 45 \pm 2.0930 \left(\dfrac{10.0263}{\sqrt{20}} \right)$, $\$40.31 \leq \mu \leq \$49.69$

(c) The population distribution needs to be normally distributed. **(d)** Both the normal probability plot and the box-and-whisker plot show that the population distributions for hotel cost and car rental are not normally distributed and are skewed to the right.

8.24 $0.19 \leq \pi \leq 0.31$

8.26 (a) $p = \dfrac{X}{n} = \dfrac{135}{500} = 0.27$

$p \pm Z \cdot \sqrt{\dfrac{p(1-p)}{n}} = 0.27 \pm 2.58 \sqrt{\dfrac{0.27(0.73)}{500}}$ $0.2189 \leq \pi \leq 0.3211$

(b) The manager in charge of promotional programs concerning residential customers can infer that the proportion of households that would purchase an additional telephone line if it were made available at a substantially reduced installation cost is somewhere between 0.22 and 0.32 with 99% confidence.

8.28 (a) $0.74 \leq \pi \leq 0.80$; **(b)** $0.75 \leq \pi \leq 0.79$; **(c)** The 95% confidence interval is wider. The loss in precision results in a wider confidence interval is the price you pay to achieve a higher level of confidence.

8.30 (a) $0.416 \leq \pi \leq 0.504$; **(b)** $0.074 \leq \pi \leq 0.126$

8.32 (a) $0.419 \leq \pi \leq 0.481$; **(b)** You estimate with 95% confidence that between 41.9% and 48.1% of all working women in North America believe that companies should hold positions for those on maternity leave for more than 6 months.

8.34 $n = 35$

8.36 $n = 1,041$

8.38 (a) $n = \dfrac{Z^2 \sigma^2}{e^2} = \dfrac{(1.96^2)(400^2)}{50^2} = 245.86$ Use $n = 246$

(b) $n = \dfrac{Z^2 \sigma^2}{e^2} = \dfrac{(1.96^2)(400^2)}{25^2} = 983.41$ Use $n = 984$

8.40 $n = 97$

8.42 (a) $n = 167$; **(b)** $n = 97$

8.44 $n = 62$

8.46 (a) $n = 2,377$; **(b)** $n = 1,978$; **(c)** The sample sizes differ because the estimated population proportions are different. **(d)** Since purchasing groceries at wholesale clubs and purchasing groceries at convenience stores are not necessary mutually exclusive events, it is appropriate to use one sample and ask the respondents both questions.

8.48 (a) $0.9017 \leq \pi \leq 0.9572$; **(b)** You are 95% confident that the population proportion of business men and women who have their presentations disturbed by cell phones is between 0.9017 and 0.9572. **(c)** $n = 158$; **(d)** $n = 273$

8.56 (a) People visiting the *Redbook* Web site. **(b)** no; **(c)** no

8.58 (a) $0.512 \leq \pi \leq 0.648$; **(b)** $0.431 \leq \pi \leq 0.569$; **(c)** $0.163 \leq \pi \leq 0.277$; **(d)** $0.136 \leq \pi \leq 0.244$; **(e)** $n = 2,401$

8.60 (a) $14.085 \leq \mu \leq 16.515$; **(b)** $0.530 \leq \pi \leq 0.820$; **(c)** $n = 25$; **(d)** $n = 784$; **(e)** If a single sample were to be selected for both purposes, the larger of the two sample sizes ($n = 784$) should be used.

8.62 (a) $8.049 \leq \mu \leq 11.351$; **(b)** $0.284 \leq \pi \leq 0.676$; **(c)** $n = 35$; **(d)** $n = 121$; **(e)** If a single sample were to be selected for both purposes, the larger of the two sample sizes ($n = 121$) should be used.

8.64 (a) $\$25.80 \leq \mu \leq \$31.24$; **(b)** $0.3037 \leq \pi \leq 0.4963$; **(c)** $n = 97$; **(d)** $n = 423$; **(e)** If a single sample were to be selected for both purposes, the larger of the two sample sizes ($n = 423$) should be used.

8.66 (a) $\$36.66 \leq \mu \leq \$40.42$; **(b)** $0.2027 \leq \pi \leq 0.3973$; **(c)** $n = 110$; **(d)** $n = 423$; **(e)** If a single sample were to be selected for both purposes, the larger of the two sample sizes ($n = 423$) should be used.

8.68 (a) $8.41 \leq \mu \leq 8.43$; **(b)** With 95% confidence, the population mean width of troughs is somewhere between 8.41 and 8.43 inches.

8.70 (a) $0.2425 \leq \mu \leq 0.2856$; **(b)** $0.1975 \leq \mu \leq 0.2385$; **(c)** The amount of granule loss for both brands are skewed to the right. **(d)** Since the two confidence intervals do not overlap, you can conclude that the mean granule loss of Boston shingles is higher than that of Vermont shingles.

8.72 (a) NY, Food: $19.51 \leq \mu \leq 20.69$; LI, Food: $19.73 \leq \mu \leq 21.35$; NY, Décor: $16.35 \leq \mu \leq 17.89$; LI, Décor: $16.65 \leq \mu \leq 18.63$; NY Services: $17.74 \leq \mu \leq 19.06$; LI Services: $18.37 \leq \mu \leq 19.71$; NY Price: $\$37.00 \leq \mu \leq \$42.48$; LI Price: $\$31.55 \leq \mu \leq \$35.93$.

CHAPTER 9

9.2 H_1 denotes the alternative hypothesis.

9.4 β

9.6 α is the probability of making a Type I error.

9.8 The power of the test is $1 - \beta$.

9.10 It is possible to not reject a null hypothesis when it is false, since it is possible for a sample mean to fall in the nonrejection region even if the null hypothesis is false.

9.12 All else being equal, the closer the population mean is to the hypothesized mean, the larger β will be.

9.14 H_0: defendant is guilty, H_1: defendant is innocent. A Type I error would be not convicting a guilty person. A Type II error would be convicting an innocent person.

9.16 H_0: $\mu = 20$ minutes. 20 minutes is adequate travel time between classes.
H_1: $\mu \neq 20$ minutes. 20 minutes is not adequate travel time between classes.

9.18 H_0: $\mu = 1.00$. The mean amount of paint per one-gallon can is one gallon.
H_1: $\mu \neq 1.00$. The mean amount of paint per one-gallon can differs from one gallon.

9.20 Since $Z_{calc} = +2.21 > 1.96$, reject H_0.

9.22 Reject H_0 if $Z_{calc} < -2.58$ or if $Z_{calc} > 2.58$.

9.24 p-value $= 0.0456$

9.26 p-value $= 0.1676$

9.28 (a) H_0: $\mu = 70$ pounds. H_1: $\mu \neq 70$ pounds.
Decision rule: Reject H_0 if $Z < -1.96$ or $Z > +1.96$.

Test statistic: $Z = \dfrac{\overline{X} - \mu}{\sigma/\sqrt{n}} = \dfrac{69.1 - 70}{3.5/\sqrt{49}} = -1.80$

Decision: Since $-1.96 < Z_{calc} = -1.80 < 1.96$, do not reject H_0. There is insufficient evidence to conclude that the cloth has a mean breaking strength that differs from 70 pounds. **(b)** p-value $= 2(0.0359) = 0.0718$. Interpretation: The probability of getting a sample of 49 pieces that yield a mean strength that is farther away from the hypothesized population mean than this sample is 0.0718 or 7.18%.
(c) Decision rule: Reject H_0 if $Z < -1.96$ or $Z > +1.96$.

Test statistic: $Z = \dfrac{\overline{X} - \mu}{\sigma/\sqrt{n}} = \dfrac{69.1 - 70}{1.75/\sqrt{49}} = -3.60$. Decision: Since $Z_{calc} =$

$-3.60 < -1.96$, reject H_0. There is enough evidence to conclude that the cloth has a mean breaking strength that differs from 70 pounds.
(d) Decision rule: Reject H_0 if $Z < -1.96$ or $Z > +1.96$. Test statistic:

$Z = \dfrac{\overline{X} - \mu}{\sigma/\sqrt{n}} = \dfrac{69 - 70}{3.5/\sqrt{49}} = -2.00$. Decision: Since $Z_{calc} = -2.00 < -1.96$,

reject H_0. There is enough evidence to conclude that the cloth has a mean breaking strength that differs from 70 pounds.

9.30 (a) Since $Z_{calc} = -2.00 < -1.96$, reject H_0. **(b)** p-value $= 0.0456$; **(c)** $325.5 \leq \mu \leq 374.5$; **(d)** The conclusions are the same.

9.32 (a) Since $-1.96 < Z_{calc} = -0.80 < 1.96$, do not reject H_0; **(b)** p-value $= 0.4238$; **(c)** Since $Z_{calc} = -2.40 < -1.96$, reject H_0; **(d)** Since $Z_{calc} = -2.26 < -1.96$, reject H_0.

9.34 $Z = +2.33$

9.36 $Z = -2.33$

9.38 p-value $= 0.0228$

9.40 p-value $= 0.0838$

9.42 p-value $= 0.9162$

9.44 (a) Since $Z_{calc} = -1.75 < -1.645$, reject H_0; **(b)** p-value $= 0.0401$ < 0.05, reject H_0; **(c)** The probability of getting a sample mean of 2.73 feet or less if the population mean is 2.8 feet is 0.0401. **(d)** They are the same.

9.46 (a) H_0: $\mu \leq 5$ H_1: $\mu > 5$; **(b)** A Type I error occurs when you conclude that children take a mean of more than 5 trips a week to the store, when in fact they take a mean of no more than 5 trips a week to the store. A Type II error occurs when you conclude that children take a mean of no more than 5 trips a week to the store, when in fact they take a mean of more than 5 trips a week to the store. **(c)** Since $Z_{calc} = 2.9375 > 2.3263$ or the p-value of 0.0017 is less than 0.01, reject H_0. There is enough evidence to conclude the population mean number of trips to the store is greater than 5 per week. **(d)** The probability that the sample mean is 5.47 trips or more when the null hypothesis is true is 0.0017.

9.48 $t = 2.00$

9.50 (a) $t_{crit} = \pm 2.1315$; **(b)** $t_{crit} = +1.7531$

9.52 No, you should not use a t test, since the original population is left-skewed, and the sample size is not large enough for the t to be influenced by the Central Limit Theorem.

9.54 (a) H_0: $\mu \leq \$300$. H_1: $\mu > \$300$.
Decision rule: $df = 99$. If $t > 1.2902$, reject H_0.

Test statistic: $t = \dfrac{\overline{X} - \mu}{S/\sqrt{n}} = \dfrac{\$315.40 - \$300.00}{\$43.20/\sqrt{100}} = 3.5648$. Decision:

Since $t_{calc} = 3.5648 > 1.2902$, reject H_0. There is enough evidence to conclude that the mean cost of textbooks per semester at a large university is more than $300.
(b) Decision rule: $df = 99$. If $t > 1.6604$, reject H_0.

Test statistic: $t = \dfrac{\overline{X} - \mu}{S/\sqrt{n}} = \dfrac{\$315.40 - \$300.00}{\$75.00/\sqrt{100}} = 2.0533$

Decision: Since $t_{calc} = 2.0533 > 1.6604$, reject H_0. There is enough evidence to conclude that the mean cost of textbooks per semester at a large university is more than $300. **(c)** Decision rule: $df = 99$. If $t > 1.2902$, reject H_0.

Test statistic: $t = \dfrac{\overline{X} - \mu}{S/\sqrt{n}} = \dfrac{\$305.11 - \$300.00}{\$43.20/\sqrt{100}} = 1.1829$. Decision:

Since $t_{calc} = 1.1829 < t = 1.2902$, do not reject H_0. There is not enough evidence to conclude that the mean cost of textbooks per semester at a large university is more than $300.

9.56 Since $t_{calc} = -1.30 > -1.6694$ and the p-value of 0.0992 > 0.05, do not reject H_0. There is not enough evidence to conclude that the mean waiting time is less than 3.7 minutes.

9.58 (a) Since $t = 1.2567 < 1.7823$, do not reject H_0. There is not enough evidence to conclude that the mean life of the batteries is more than 400 hours. **(b)** p-value $= 0.1164$. The probability that a sample of 13 batteries results in a sample mean of 473.46 or more is 11.64% if the population mean life is 400 hours. **(c)** Allowing for only 5% probability of making a Type I error, the manufacturer should not say in advertisements that these batteries should last more than 400 hours.
(d) (a) Since $t = 1.7195 < 1.7823$, do not reject H_0. There is not enough evidence to conclude that the mean life of the batteries is more than 400 hours. **(b)** p-value $= 0.0556$. The probability that a sample of 13 batteries results in a sample mean of 550.38 or more is 5.56% if the population

mean life is 400 hours. **(c)** Allowing for only 5% probability of making a Type I error, the manufacturer should not say in advertisements that these batteries should last more than 400 hours. They can make the claim that these batteries should last more than 400 hours only if they are willing to raise the level of significance to more than 0.0556. The extremely large value of 1,342 raises the sample mean and sample standard deviation and, hence, results in a higher measured t statistic of 1.7195. This is, however, still not enough to offset the lower hours in the remaining sample to the degree that the null hypothesis can be rejected.

9.60 (a) Since $-2.0096 < t = 0.114 < 2.0096$, do not reject H_0; **(b)** p-value = 0.9095; **(c)** Yes, the data appear to have met the normality assumption. **(d)** The amount of fill is decreasing over time. Therefore, the t test is invalid.

9.62 (a) Since $t = -5.684 < -2.6178$, reject H_0. There is enough evidence to conclude that the mean viscosity has changed from 15.5. **(b)** The population distribution needs to be normal. **(c)** The normal probability plot indicates that the distribution is slightly skewed to the right.

9.64 (a) Since $-2.68 < t = 0.094 < 2.68$, do not reject H_0; **(b)** $5.462 \le \mu \le 5.542$; **(c)** The conclusions are the same.

9.66 $p = 0.22$

9.68 Do not reject H_0.

9.69 (a) H_0: $\pi \le 0.5$; H_1: $\pi > 0.5$.
Decision rule: If $Z > 1.645$, reject H_0.

Test statistic: $Z = \dfrac{p - \pi}{\sqrt{\dfrac{\pi(1 - \pi)}{n}}} = \dfrac{0.5702 - 0.5}{\sqrt{\dfrac{0.5(0.5)}{1040}}} = 4.5273$

Decision: Since $Z_{calc} = 4.5273 > 1.645$, reject H_0. There is enough evidence to show that more than half of all Americans would rather have $100 than a day off from work. **(b)** p-value = 0.00. The probability is approximately 0 of observing a sample of 593 or more out of 1,040 Americans who will rather have the $100 than a day off from work, if the population proportion is 0.5.

9.70 Since $Z_{calc} = 2.6902 > 1.645$ and the p-value of $0.0036 < 0.05$, reject H_0. There is enough evidence to show that the proportion of employers that planned to hire new employees in 2004 is larger than the 2003 proportion of 0.43.

9.72 (a) Since $-1.96 < Z_{calc} = 0.6381 < 1.96$, do not reject H_0 and conclude that there is not enough evidence to show that the percentage of people who trust energy-efficiency ratings differs from 50%. **(b)** p-value = 0.5234. Since the p-value of $0.5234 > 0.05$, do not reject H_0

9.74 (a) $p = 0.7112$. **(b)** Since $Z_{calc} = 5.7771 > 1.6449$, reject H_0. There is enough evidence to conclude that more than half of all successful women executives have children. **(c)** Since $Z_{calc} = 1.2927 < 1.6449$, do not reject H_0. There is not enough evidence to conclude that more than two-thirds of all successful women executives have children. **(d)** The random sample assumption is not likely to be valid because the criteria used in defining "successful women executives" is very likely to be quite different than those used in defining the "most powerful women in business" who attended the summit.

9.84 (a) buying a site that is not profitable; **(b)** not buying a profitable site; **(c)** Type I; **(d)** If the executives adopt a less stringent rejection criterion by

buying sites for which the computer model predicts moderate or large profit, the probability of committing a Type I error will increase. Many more of the sites the computer model predicts that will generate moderate profit may end up not being profitable at all. On the other hand, the less stringent rejection criterion will lower the probability of committing a Type II error, since now, more potentially profitable sites will be purchased.

9.86 (a) Since $t = 3.248 > 2.0010$, reject H_0. **(b)** p-value = 0.0019; **(c)** Since $Z = -0.32 > -1.645$, do not reject H_0. **(d)** Since $-2.0010 < t = 0.75 < 2.0010$, do not reject H_0. **(e)** Since $t = -1.61 > -1.645$, do not reject H_0.

9.88 (a) Since $t = -1.69 > -1.7613$, do not reject H_0. **(b)** The data are from a population that is normally distributed.

9.90 (a) Since $t = -1.47 > -1.6896$, do not reject H_0; **(b)** p-value = 0.0748; **(c)** Since $t = -3.10 < -1.6973$, reject H_0; **(d)** p-value = 0.0021; **(e)** The data in the population are assumed to be normally distributed.

9.92 (a) $t = -21.61$, reject H_0; **(b)** p-value = 0.0000; **(c)** $t = -27.19$, reject H_0; **(d)** p-value = 0.0000

CHAPTER 10

10.2 Since $-2.58 \le Z = 1.73 \le 2.58$, do not reject H_0.

10.4 (a) $t = 3.8959$; **(b)** $df = 21$; **(c)** 2.5177; **(d)** Since $3.8959 > 2.5177$, reject H_0.

10.6 $3.73 \le \mu_1 - \mu_2 \le 12.27$

10.8 (a) Since $5.20 > 2.33$, reject H_0. **(b)** p-value < 0.00003.

10.10 (a) Since $-2.0117 < t_{calc} = 0.1023 < 2.0117$, do not reject H_0. There is no evidence of a difference in the two means for the Age 8 group. Since $t_{calc} = 3.375 > 1.9908$, reject H_0. There is evidence of a difference in the two means for the Age 12 group. Since $t_{calc} = 3.3349 > 1.9966$, reject H_0. There is evidence of a difference in the two means for the Age 16 group. **(b)** The test results show that children in the United States begin to develop preferences for brand name products as early as Age 12.

10.12 (a) H_0: $\mu_1 = \mu_2$ where Populations: 1 = Males, 2 = Females
H_1: $\mu_1 \ne \mu_2$
Decision rule: $df = 170$. If $t < -1.974$ or $t > 1.974$, reject H_0.
Test statistic:

$$S_p^2 = \frac{(n_1 - 1)(S_1^2) + (n_2 - 1)(S_2^2)}{(n_1 - 1) + (n_2 - 1)}$$

$$= \frac{(99)(13.35^2) + (71)(9.42^2)}{99 + 71} = 140.8489$$

$$t = \frac{(\bar{X}_1 - \bar{X}_2) - (\mu_1 - \mu_2)}{\sqrt{S_p^2\left(\dfrac{1}{n_1} + \dfrac{1}{n_2}\right)}}$$

$$= \frac{(40.26 - 36.85) - 0}{\sqrt{140.8489\left(\dfrac{1}{100} + \dfrac{1}{72}\right)}} = 1.859$$

Decision: Since $-1.974 < t_{calc} = 1.859 < 1.974$, do not reject H_0. There is not enough evidence to conclude that the mean computer anxiety experienced by males and females is different. **(b)** p-value = 0.0648. **(c)** In order to use the pooled-variance t test, you need to assume that the populations are normally distributed with equal variances.

10.14 (a) Since $-4.1343 < -2.0484$, reject H_0. **(b)** p-value = 0.0003; **(c)** The original populations of waiting times are approximately normally distributed. **(d)** $-4.2292 \leq \mu_1 - \mu_2 \leq -1.4268$

10.16 (a) Since the $-2.024 < t = 0.354 < 2.024$ or p-value = 0.725 > 0.05, do not reject the null hypothesis. There is not enough evidence to conclude that the mean time to clear problems in the two offices is different. **(b)** p-value = 0.725. The probability that a sample will yield a t-test statistic more extreme than 0.3544 is 0.725 if the mean waiting time between Office 1 and Office 2 is the same. **(c)** You need to assume that the two populations are normally distributed. **(d)** $-0.9543 \leq \mu_1 - \mu_2 \leq 1.3593$

10.18 (a) Since $t_{calc} = 4.10 > 2.024$, reject H_0. There is evidence of a difference in the mean surface hardness between untreated and treated steel plates. **(b)** p-value = 0.0002. The probability that two samples have a mean difference of 9.3634 or more is 0.02% if there is no difference in the mean surface hardness between untreated and treated steel plates. **(c)** You need to assume that the population distribution of hardness of both untreated and treated steel plates is normally distributed. **(d)** $4.7447 \leq \mu_1 - \mu_2 \leq 13.9821$

10.20 (a) Since $t_{calc} = -2.1522 < -2.0211$, reject H_0. There is enough evidence to conclude that the mean assembly times in seconds are different between employees trained in a computer-assisted, individual-based program and those trained in a team-based program. **(b)** You must assume that each of the two independent populations is normally distributed. **(c)** Since $t = -2.152 < -2.052$ or p-value = 0.041 < 0.05, reject H_0. **(d)** The results in (a) and (c) are the same. **(e)** $-4.52 \leq \mu_1 - \mu_2 \leq -0.14$. You are 95% confident that the difference between the population means of the two training methods is between -4.52 and -0.14.

10.22 $df = 19$

10.24 (a) Since $t = -6.8672 < -2.1098$, reject H_0. There is a difference in the mean daily hotel rate in March 2004 and June 2002. **(b)** You must assume that the distribution of the differences between the daily hotel rate in March 2004 and June 2002 is approximately normally distributed. **(c)** p-value is virtually zero. The probability that the t statistic for the mean difference in daily hotel rate is 6.8672 or more in either direction is virtually zero, if there is no difference in the mean daily hotel rate in March 2004 and June 2002. **(d)** $-102.86 \leq \mu_D \leq -54.51$. You are 95% confident that the mean difference in the hotel rate between March 2004 and June 2002 is somewhere between $-\$102.86$ and $-\$54.51$.

10.26 (a) $H_0: \mu_D = 0$ $H_1: \mu_D \neq 0$
Decision rule: $df = 14$. If $t < -2.9768$ or $t > 2.9768$, reject H_0.

Test statistic: $t = \dfrac{\overline{D} - \mu_D}{S_D / \sqrt{n}} = \dfrac{3.5307 - 0}{13.8493 / \sqrt{15}} = 0.9874$

Decision: Since $-2.9768 < t_{calc} = 0.9874 < 2.9768$, do not reject H_0. There is insufficient evidence to conclude that there is a difference in the mean price of textbooks between the local bookstore and Amazon.com.

(b) You must assume that the distribution of the differences between the mean price of business textbooks between the local bookstore and Amazon.com is approximately normally distributed.

(c) $\overline{D} \pm t\left(\dfrac{S_D}{\sqrt{n}}\right) = 3.5307 \pm 2.9768\left(\dfrac{13.8493}{\sqrt{15}}\right), -7.1141 \leq \mu_D \leq 14.1755$

You are 99% confident that the mean difference between the price is somewhere between -7.1141 and 14.1755. **(d)** The results in (a) and (c) are the same. The hypothesized value of 0 for the difference in the mean price for textbooks between the local bookstore and Amazon.com is inside the 99% confidence interval.

10.28 (a) Since $t = 1.8425 < 1.943$, do not reject H_0. There is not enough evidence to conclude that the mean bone marrow microvessel density is higher before the stem cell transplant than after the stem cell transplant. **(b)** p-value = 0.0575. The probability that the t statistic for the mean difference in density is 1.8425 or more is 5.75% if the mean density is not higher before the stem cell transplant than after the stem cell transplant. **(c)** $-28.26 \leq \mu_D \leq 200.55$. You are 95% confident that the mean difference in bone marrow microvessel density before and after the stem cell transplant is somewhere between -28.26 and 200.55.

10.30 (a) Since $t = -9.3721 < -2.4258$, reject H_0. **(b)** The population of differences in strength is approximately normally distributed. **(c)** $p = 0.000$.

10.32 (a) Since $-2.58 \leq Z = -0.58 \leq 2.58$, do not reject H_0; **(b)** $-0.273 \leq \pi_1 - \pi_2 \leq 0.173$

10.34 (a) Since $Z = -13.53 < -1.96$, reject H_0. **(b)** p-value < 0.00003; **(c)** $-0.2841 \leq \pi_1 - \pi_2 \leq -0.2165$

10.36 (a) Since $Z_{calc} = 5.8019 > 1.645$, reject H_0. There is sufficient evidence to conclude that the proportion of adults online who use the Internet to gather data about products/services is higher in December 2003 than in 2000. **(b)** The p-value is virtually 0. The probability that the difference in two sample proportions is 0.16 or larger is virtually zero when the null hypothesis is true.

10.38 (a) $H_0: \pi_1 \leq \pi_2$ $H_1: \pi_1 > \pi_2$
Decision rule: If $Z > 1.645$, reject H_0.

Test statistic: $\overline{p} = \dfrac{X_1 + X_2}{n_1 + n_2} = \dfrac{29 + 126}{56 + 407} = 0.3348$

$$Z = \frac{(p_1 - p_2) - (\pi_1 - \pi_2)}{\sqrt{(\overline{p})(1 - \overline{p})\left(\dfrac{1}{n_1} + \dfrac{1}{n_2}\right)}}$$

$$= \frac{(0.5179 - 0.3096) - 0}{\sqrt{(0.3348)(1 - 0.3348)\left(\dfrac{1}{56} + \dfrac{1}{407}\right)}}$$

$$= 3.0965$$

Decision: Since $Z_{calc} = 3.0965 > 1.645$, reject H_0. There is sufficient evidence to conclude that white workers are more likely to claim bias than black workers. **(b)** The p-value is 0.00098. The probability that the difference in two sample proportions is 0.20828 or larger is 0.00098 when the null hypothesis is true.

10.42 (a) 0.429; **(b)** 0.362; **(c)** 0.297; **(d)** 0.258

10.44 $df_{\text{numerator}} = 24$, $df_{\text{denominator}} = 24$.

10.46 Since $0.4405 < F = 0.8258 < 2.27$, do not reject H_0.

10.48 (a) Since $0.3378 < F = 1.2995 < 3.18$, do not reject H_0. **(b)** Since $F = 1.2995 < 2.62$, do not reject H_0. **(c)** Since $F = 1.2995 > 0.4032$, do not reject H_0.

10.50 (a) $H_0 : \sigma_1^2 = \sigma_2^2$ $H_1 : \sigma_1^2 \neq \sigma_2^2$
Decision rule: If $F > 1.556$ or $F < 0.653$, reject H_0.

Test statistic: $F = \dfrac{S_1^2}{S_2^2} = \dfrac{(13.35)^2}{(9.42)^2} = 2.008$

Decision: Since $F_{\text{calc}} = 2.008 > 1.556$, reject H_0. There is enough evidence to conclude that the two population variances are different. **(b)** p-value $= 0.0022$. **(c)** The test assumes that each of the two populations are normally distributed. **(d)** Based on (a) and (b), a separate variance t test should be used.

10.52 (a) Since $0.3958 < F = 0.8248 < 2.5265$, do not reject H_0; **(b)** 0.6789; **(c)** The test assumes that the populations of times are approximately normally distributed; **(d)** yes

10.54 Since $F = 5.76 > 2.54$, reject H_0.

10.56 (a) $SSW = 150$; **(b)** $MSA = 15$; **(c)** $MSW = 5$; **(d)** $F = 3$

10.58 (a) 2; **(b)** 18; **(c)** 20

10.60 (a) Reject H_0 if $F > 2.95$, otherwise do not reject H_0. **(b)** Since $F = 4 > 2.95$ reject H_0. **(c)** The table does not have 28 degrees of freedom in the denominator so use the next larger critical value, $Q_U = 3.90$. **(d)** Critical range $= 6.166$

10.62 (a) Since $F = 10.99 > F_{0.05,2,9} = 4.26$, reject H_0. **(b)** Critical range $= 40.39$. The experts and darts are not different from each other, but they are both different from the readers. **(c)** It is not valid to infer that the dartboard is better than the professionals since their means are not significantly different. **(d)** Since $F = 0.101 < 4.26$, do not reject H_0. There is no evidence of a significant difference in the variation in the return for the three categories.

10.64 (a) $H_0 : \mu_A = \mu_B = \mu_C = \mu_D$ H_1: At least one mean is different.

$$MSA = \frac{SSA}{c-1} = \frac{1986.475}{3} = 662.1583$$

$$MSW = \frac{SSW}{n-c} = \frac{495.5}{36} = 13.76389$$

$$F = \frac{MSA}{MSW} = \frac{662.1583}{13.76389} = 48.1084$$

$$F_{\alpha,c-1,n-c} = F_{0.05,3,36} = 2.8663$$

Since the p-value is approximately zero and $F = 48.1084 > 2.8663$, you reject H_0. There is sufficient evidence of a difference in the mean strength of the four brands of trash bags.

(b) Critical range $= Q_u \sqrt{\dfrac{MSW}{2}\left(\dfrac{1}{n_j}+\dfrac{1}{n_{j'}}\right)} = 3.79\sqrt{\dfrac{13.7639}{2}\left(\dfrac{1}{10}+\dfrac{1}{10}\right)}$

$= 4.446$

From the Tukey-Kramer procedure, there is a difference in mean strength between Kroger and Tuffstuff, Glad and Tuffstuff, and Hefty and Tuffstuff. **(c)** ANOVA output for Levene's test for homogeneity of variance:

$$MSA = \frac{SSA}{c-1} = \frac{24.075}{3} = 8.025$$

$$MSW = \frac{SSW}{n-c} = \frac{198.2}{36} = 5.5056$$

$$F = \frac{MSA}{MSW} = \frac{8.025}{5.5056} = 1.4576$$

$$F_{\alpha,c-1,n-c} = F_{0.05,3,36} = 2.8663$$

Since the p-value $= 0.2423 > 0.05$ and $F = 1.458 < 2.866$, do not reject H_0. There is insufficient evidence to conclude that the variances in strength among the four brands of trash bags are different. **(d)** From the results in (a) and (b), Tuffstuff has the lowest mean strength and should be avoided.

10.66 (a) Since $F = 12.56 > F_{0.05,4,25} = 2.76$, reject H_0. **(b)** Critical range $= 4.67$. Advertisements A and B are different from Advertisements C and D. Advertisement E is only different from Advertisement D. **(c)** Since $F = 1.927 < 2.76$, do not reject H_0. There is no evidence of a significant difference in the variation in the ratings among the 5 advertisements. **(d)** The advertisement underselling the pen's characteristics had the highest mean ratings and the advertisements overselling the pen's characteristics had the lowest mean ratings. Therefore, use an advertisement that undersells the pen's characteristics and avoid advertisements that oversell the pen's characteristics.

10.68 (a) Since $F = 53.03 > F_{0.05,3,30} = 2.92$, reject H_0. **(b)** Critical range $= 5.27$ (using 30 degrees of freedom). Designs 3 and 4 are different from designs 1 and 2. Designs 1 and 2 are different from each other. **(c)** The assumptions are that samples are randomly and independently selected (or randomly assigned), the original populations of distances are approximately normally distributed, and the variances are equal. **(d)** Since $F = 2.093 < F_{3,30} = 2.92$, do not reject H_0. There is no evidence of a significant difference in the variation in the distance among the 4 designs. **(e)** The manager should choose design 3 or 4.

10.80 (a) $H_0 : \sigma_1^2 \geq \sigma_2^2$ $H_1 : \sigma_1^2 < \sigma_2^2$
(b) Type I error: Rejecting the null hypothesis that price variance on the Internet is no lower than the price variance in the brick-and-mortar market when the price variance on the Internet is no lower than the price variance in the brick-and-mortar market. Type II error: Failing to reject the null hypothesis that price variance on the Internet is no lower than the price variance in the brick-and-mortar market when the price variance on the Internet is lower than the price variance in the brick-and-mortar market. **(c)** An F test for differences in two variances can be used. **(d)** You need to assume that each of the two populations are normally distributed. **(e) (a)** $H_0 : \mu_1 \geq \mu_2$ $H_1 : \mu_1 < \mu_2$
(b) Type I error: Rejecting the null hypothesis that the mean price in electronic market is no lower than the mean price in physical market when the mean price in the electronic market is no lower than the mean price in the physical market. Type II error: Failing to reject the null hypothesis that the mean price in the electronic market is no lower than the mean price in the physical market when the mean price in the electronic market is lower than the mean price in the physical market. **(c)** A paired t test for the mean difference can be used. **(d)** You must assume that the distribution of the difference between the mean price in the electronic market and the physical market is approximately normally distributed.

10.82 (a) The researchers can ask the teenagers, after viewing each ad, to rate the dangers of smoking using a scale from 0 to 10 with 10 representing the most dangerous.
(b) $H_0: \mu_T \geq \mu_S$ $H_1: \mu_T < \mu_S$; **(c)** Type I error is the error made by concluding that ads produced by the state are more effective than those produced by Philip Morris while it is not true. The risk of Type I error here is that teenagers can miss the opportunity from the better ads produced by Philip Morris to recognize the true dangers of smoking and the additional expenses the state will have to incur to produce and run the ads. Type II error is the error made by concluding that ads produced by Philip Morris is no less effective than those produced by the state while ads produced by the state are more effective. The risk of Type II error here is that more teenagers will miss the opportunity to recognize the true dangers of smoking from the ads produced by the state. **(d)** Since both ads are shown to the same group of teenagers, a paired t test for the mean difference is most appropriate. **(e)** Statistically reliable here means the conclusions drawn from the test are reliable because all the assumptions needed for the test to be valid are fulfilled.

10.84 (a) Since $t_{calc} = 4.5826 > 2.528$, reject H_0. There is sufficient evidence to conclude that the mean monthly electric bill is more than \$80 for single-family homes in County II during the summer season. **(b)** Since $0.3265 < F_{calc} = 2.78 < 3.2220$, do not reject H_0. There is not enough evidence to conclude that County I and II have different population variances for monthly electric bills. **(c)** Since $t = 2.273 < 2.414$ or p-value $= 0.0140 > 0.01$, do not reject H_0. There is not enough evidence to conclude that the mean monthly bill is higher in County I than in County II. **(d)** $-3.1323 \leq \mu_1 - \mu_2 \leq 37.1323$

10.86 (a) Since $t_{calc} = 3.3282 > 1.8595$, reject H_0. There is enough evidence to conclude that the introductory computer students required more than a mean of 10 minutes to write and run a program in Visual Basic. **(b)** Since $t_{calc} = 1.3636 < 1.8595$, do not reject H_0. There is not enough evidence to conclude that the introductory computer students required more than a mean of 10 minutes to write and run a program in Visual Basic. **(c)** Although the mean time necessary to complete the assignment increased from 12 to 16 minutes as a result of the increase in one data value, the standard deviation went from 1.8 to 13.2, which reduced the t-value. **(d)** Since $0.2328 < F_{calc} = 0.8125 < 3.8549$, do not reject H_0. There is not enough evidence to conclude that the population variances are different for the Introduction to Computers students and computer majors. Hence, the pooled-variance t test is a valid test to determine whether computer majors can write a Visual Basic program in less time than introductory students, assuming that the distributions of the time needed to write a Visual Basic program for both the Introduction to Computers students and the computer majors are approximately normally distributed. Since $t_{calc} = 4.0666 > 1.7341$, reject H_0. There is enough evidence that the mean time is higher for Introduction to Computers students than for computer majors. **(e)** p-value $= 0.000362$. If the true population mean amount of time needed for Introduction to Computer students to write a Visual Basic program is no more than 10 minutes, the probability for observing a sample mean greater than the 12 minutes in the current sample is 0.0362%. Hence, at a 95% level of confidence, you can conclude that the population mean amount of time needed for Introduction to Computer students to write a Visual Basic program is more than 10 minutes. As illustrated in part (d) in which there is not enough evidence to conclude that the population variances are different for the Introduction to Computers students and computer majors, the pooled-variance t test performed is a valid test to determine whether computer majors can write a Visual Basic program in less time than introductory students, assuming that the distribution of the time needed to write a Visual Basic program for both the Introduction

to Computers students and the computer majors are approximately normally distributed.

10.88 (a) Since $t_{calc} = 7.8735 > 2.3598$, reject H_0. There is enough evidence to conclude that the mean salary for men is greater than the mean salary for women.
(b) The p-value is approximately zero.

10.90 From the box-and-whisker plot and the summary statistics, both distributions are approximately normally distributed. $0.5289 < F = 0.947 < 1.89$ There is insufficient evidence to conclude that the two population variances are significantly different at 5% level of significance. $t = -5.084 < -1.99$ At 5% level of significance, there is sufficient evidence to reject the null hypothesis of no difference in the mean life of the bulbs between the two manufacturers. You can conclude that there is significant difference between the mean life of the bulbs between the two manufacturers.

10.96 (a) Since $F = 3.339 > 1.9096$ or p-value $= 0.000361 < 0.05$, reject H_0. There is evidence of a difference between the variances in the attendance at games with promotions and games without promotions.
(b) Since the variances cannot be assumed to be equal, you should use a separate-variance t test for the difference in two means. Since $t = 4.745 > 1.996$ or since the p-value is approximately zero, you reject H_0. **(c)** There is evidence that there is a difference in the mean attendance at games with promotions and games without promotions at the 5% level of significance.

10.98 The normal probability plots suggest that the two populations are not normally distributed. An F test is inappropriate for testing the difference in two variances. The sample variances for Boston and Vermont shingles are 0.0203 and 0.015, respectively, which are not very different. It appears that a pooled-variance t test is appropriate for testing the difference in means. Since $t = 3.015 > 1.967$ or the p-value $= 0.0028 < \alpha = 0.05$, reject H_0. There is sufficient evidence to conclude that there is a difference in the mean granule loss of Boston and Vermont shingles.

10.100 (a) Since $F = 0.075 < F_{0.05,2,15} = 3.68$, do not reject H_0. **(b)** Since $F = 4.09 > F_{0.05,2,15} = 3.68$, reject H_0. **(c)** Critical range $= 1.489$. Breaking strength is significantly different between 30 and 50 psi.

CHAPTER 11

11.2 (a) For $df = 1$ and $\alpha = 0.95$, $\chi^2 = 0.004$. **(b)** For $df = 1$ and $\alpha = 0.975$, $\chi^2 = 0.00098$. **(c)** For $df = 1$ and $\alpha = 0.99$, $\chi^2 = 0.000157$.

11.4 (a) All $f_e = 25$; **(b)** Since $\chi^2 = 4.00 > 3.841$, reject H_0.

11.6 (a) Since $\chi^2 = 1.0 < 3.841$, do not reject H_0. There is not enough evidence to conclude that there is a significant difference between males and females in the proportion who make gas mileage a priority. **(b)** Since $\chi^2 = 10.0 > 3.841$, reject H_0. There is enough evidence to conclude that there is a significant difference between males and females in the proportion who make gas mileage a priority. **(c)** The larger sample size in (b) increases the difference between the observed and expected frequencies and, hence, results in a larger test statistic value.

11.8 (a) $H_0: \pi_1 = \pi_2$ $H_1: \pi_1 \neq \pi_2$

f_o	f_e	$(f_o - f_e)$	$(f_o - f_e)^2/f_e$
370	395	−25	1.58227
130	105	25	5.95238
420	395	25	1.58227
80	105	−25	5.95238
			15.06932

Decision rule: $df = 1$. If $\chi^2 > 3.841$, reject H_0.

Test statistic: $\chi^2 = \sum\limits_{\text{all cells}} \dfrac{(f_0 - f_e)^2}{f_e} = 15.0693$

Decision: Since $\chi^2_{\text{calc}} = 15.0693 > 3.841$, reject H_0. There is enough evidence to conclude that there is a significant difference in the proportion of African Americans and whites who invest in stocks. **(b)** p-value = 0.0001. The probability of a test statistic as large as 15.0693 or larger when the null hypothesis is true is 0.0001. **(c)** The results of (a) and (b) are exactly the same as those of problem 10.39. The χ^2_{calc} in (a) and the Z_{calc} in problem 10.39 (a) satisfy the relationship that $\chi^2_{\text{calc}} = 15.0693 = (Z_{\text{calc}})^2 = (-3.8819)^2$ and the p-value in problem 10.39 (b) is exactly the same as the p-value in (b).

11.10 (a) Since $\chi^2 = 33.333 > 3.841$, reject H_0. **(b)** p-value < 0.001.

11.12 (a) The expected frequencies for the first row are 20, 30, and 40. The expected frequencies for the second row are 30, 45, and 60. **(b)** Since $\chi^2 = 12.5 > 5.991$, reject H_0. **(c)** A vs. B: $0.20 > 0.196$, therefore A and B are different, A vs. C: $0.30 > 0.185$, therefore A and C are different, B vs. C: $0.10 < 0.185$, therefore B and C are not different.

11.14 Since the calculated test statistic $742.3961 > 9.4877$, reject H_0 and conclude that there is a difference in the proportion of people who eat out at least once a week in the various countries. **(b)** p-value is virtually zero. The probability of a test statistic greater than 742.3961 or more is approximately zero if there is no difference in the proportion of people who eat out at least once a week in the various countries. **(c)** At the 5% level of significance, there is no significant difference between the proportions in Germany and France, while there is significant difference between all the remaining pairs of countries.

11.16 (a) $H_0 : \pi_1 = \pi_2 = \pi_3$ H_1: at least one proportion differs

f_o	f_e	$(f_o - f_e)$	$(f_o - f_e)^2/f_e$
48	42.667	5.333	0.667
152	157.333	−5.333	0.181
56	42.667	13.333	4.167
144	157.333	−13.333	1.130
24	42.667	−18.667	8.167
176	157.333	18.667	2.215
			16.5254

Decision rule: $df = (c - 1) = (3 - 1) = 2$. If $\chi^2 > 5.9915$, reject H_0.

Test statistic: $\chi^2 = \sum\limits_{\text{all cells}} \dfrac{(f_0 - f_e)^2}{f_e} = 16.5254$

Decision: Since $\chi^2_{\text{calc}} = 16.5254 > 5.9915$, reject H_0. There is a significant difference in the age groups with respect to major grocery shopping day. **(b)** p-value = 0.0003. The probability that the test statistic is greater than or equal to 16.5254 is 0.03%, if the null hypothesis is true.

(c)

Pairwise Comparisons	Critical Range	$\lvert p_{S_j} - p_{S_{j'}} \rvert$
1 to 2	0.1073	0.04
2 to 3	0.0959	0.16*
1 to 3	0.0929	0.12*

There is a significance difference between the 35–54 and over 54 groups, and between the under 35 and over 54 groups. **(d)** The stores can use this information to target their marketing on the specific group of shoppers on Saturday and the days other than Saturday.

11.18 (a) Since $\chi^2_{\text{calc}} = 128.24 > 5.9915$, reject H_0. There is enough evidence to show that there is a significant difference in the proportion of people who object to their medical records being shared with the three organizations. **(b)** There is a significant difference between each pair of organizations.

11.20 Since $\chi^2_{\text{calc}} = 3.50 < 5.991$, do not reject the null hypothesis. There is insufficient evidence to conclude that there is a difference in the proportion of hotels that correctly post minibar charges among the three cities. **(b)** The p-value is 0.174. The probability of a test statistic larger than 3.5 is 0.174 if the null hypothesis is true.

11.22 Since the null hypotheses are not rejected for any of the three items, it is not necessary to perform the Marascuilo procedure.

11.24 $df = (r - 1)(c - 1) = (3 - 1)(4 - 1) = 6$.

11.26 (a) and **(b)** Since the $\chi^2_{\text{calc}} = 20.680 > 12.592$, reject H_0. There is evidence of a relationship between the quarter of the year in which draft-aged men were born and the numbers assigned as their draft eligibilities during the Vietnam War. It appears that the results of the lottery drawing are different from what would be expected if the lottery were random. **(c)** Since $\chi^2_{\text{calc}} = 9.803 < 12.592$, do not reject H_0. There is not enough evidence to conclude there is any relationship between the quarter of the year in which draft-aged men were born and the numbers assigned as their draft eligibilities during the Vietnam War. It appears that the results of the lottery drawing are consistent with what would be expected if the lottery were random.

11.28 (a) H_0: There is no relationship between the commuting time of company employees and the level of stress-related problems observed on the job. H_1: There is a relationship between the commuting time of company employees and the level of stress-related problems observed on the job.

f_o	f_e	$(f_o - f_e)$	$(f_o - f_e)^2/f_e$
9	12.1379	−3.1379	0.8112
17	20.1034	−3.1034	0.4791
18	11.7586	6.2414	3.3129
5	5.2414	−0.2414	0.0111
8	8.6810	−0.6810	0.0534
6	5.0776	0.9224	0.1676
18	14.6207	3.3793	0.7811
28	24.2155	3.7845	0.5915
7	14.1638	−7.1638	3.6233
			9.8311

(a) Decision rule: If $\chi^2 > 13.277$, reject H_0.

Test statistic: $\chi^2 = \sum\limits_{\text{all cells}} \dfrac{(f_0 - f_e)^2}{f_e} = 9.8311$

Decision: Since the $\chi^2_{\text{calc}} = 9.8311 < 13.277$, do not reject H_0. There is not enough evidence to conclude that there is a relationship between the commuting time of company employees and the level of stress-related problems observed on the job. **(b)** Since $\chi^2_{\text{calc}} = 9.831 > 9.488$, reject H_0. There is enough evidence at the 0.05 level to conclude that there is a relationship.

11.30 Since $\chi^2 = 129.520 > 21.026$, reject H_0.

11.34 (a) Since the $\chi^2_{\text{calc}} = 0.412 < 3.841$, do not reject H_0. There is not enough evidence to conclude that there is a relationship between a student's gender and their pizzeria selection. **(b)** Since the $\chi^2_{\text{calc}} = 2.624 < 3.841$, do not reject H_0. There is not enough evidence to conclude that there is a relationship between a student's gender and their pizzeria selection. **(c)** Since the $\chi^2_{calc} = 4.956 < 5.991$, do not reject H_0. There is not enough evidence to conclude that there is a relationship between price and pizzeria selection. **(d)** p-value = 0.0839. The probability of a sample that gives a test statistic equal to or greater than 4.956 is 8.39% if the null hypothesis of no relationship between price and pizzeria selection is true. **(e)** Since there is no evidence that price and pizzeria selection are related, it is inappropriate to determine which prices are different in terms of pizzeria preference.

11.36 (a) Since $\chi^2 = 3.3084 < 3.8415$, do not reject H_0 and conclude that there is insufficient evidence of a difference between the proportion of boys and girls who worry about having enough money. **(b)** p-value = 0.0689. The probability of a test statistic larger than 3.3084 is 6.89% if there is not a significant difference between the proportion of boys and girls who worry about having enough money.

11.38 (a) Since $\chi^2_{calc} = 12.026 > 3.841$, reject H_0. There is enough evidence to conclude there is a relationship between the type of user and the seriousness of concern over the first statement. **(b)** The p-value = 0.000525. The probability of a test statistic of 12.026 or larger is 0.000525 if there is no relationship between type of user and the seriousness of concern over the first statement. **(c)** Since $\chi^2_{calc} = 7.297 > 3.841$, reject H_0. There is enough evidence to conclude there is a relationship between type of user and the seriousness of concern over the second statement. **(d)** The p-value = 0.00691. The probability of a test statistic of 7.297 or larger is 0.00691 if there is no relationship between type of user and the seriousness of concern over the second statement.

11.40 (a) Since $\chi^2_{calc} = 11.895 < 12.592$, do not reject H_0. There is not enough evidence to conclude that there is a relationship between the attitudes of employees toward the use of self-managed work teams and employee job classification. **(b)** Since $\chi^2_{calc} = 3.294 < 12.592$, do not reject H_0. There is not enough evidence to conclude that there is a relationship between the attitudes of employees toward vacation time without pay and employee job classification.

11.42 Since $\chi^2_{calc} = 160.38 > 5.991$, reject H_0. There is enough evidence to conclude that there is a relationship between the type of incident and the type of model.

CHAPTER 12

12.2 (a) yes; **(b)** no; **(c)** no; **(d)** yes.

12.4 (b) $b_1 = \dfrac{SSXY}{SSX} = \dfrac{27.75}{375} = 0.074$

$b_0 = \bar{Y} - b_1\bar{X} = 2.375 - 0.074(12.5) = 1.45$
For each increase in shelf space of an additional foot, weekly sales are estimated to increase by 0.074 hundreds of dollars, or $7.40. **(c)** $\hat{Y} = 1.45 + 0.074X = 1.45 + 0.074(8) = 2.042$, or $204.20

12.6 (b) $b_0 = -2.37$, $b_1 = 0.0501$; **(c)** For every cubic foot increase in the amount moved, labor hours are estimated to increase by 0.0501. **(d)** 22.67 labor hours

12.8 (b) $b_0 = -246.2599$, $b_1 = 4.1897$ **(c)** For each additional million dollar increase in revenue, the mean value is estimated to increase by 4.1897 million dollars. **(d)** 382.2005 million dollars.

12.10 (b) $b_0 = 6.048$, $b_1 = 2.019$; **(c)** For every one Rockwell E unit increase in hardness, the mean tensile strength is estimated to increase by 2,019 pounds per square inch. **(d)** 147,382 pounds per square inch

12.12 $r^2 = 0.90$. 90% of the variation in the dependent variable can be explained by the variation in the independent variable.

12.14 $r^2 = 0.75$. 75% of the variation in the dependent variable can be explained by the variation in the independent variable.

12.16 (a) $r^2 = \dfrac{SSR}{SST} = \dfrac{2.0535}{3.0025} = 0.684$.

68.4% of the variation in sales can be explained by the variation in shelf space.

(b) $S_{YX} = \sqrt{\dfrac{SSE}{n-2}} = \sqrt{\dfrac{\sum_{i-1}^{n}(Y_i - \hat{Y}_i)^2}{n-2}} = \sqrt{\dfrac{0.949}{10}} = 0.308$ **(c)** Based on (a) and (b), the model should be very useful for predicting sales.

12.18 (a) $r^2 = 0.8892$. 88.92% of the variation in labor hours can be explained by the variation in cubic feet moved. **(b)** $S_{YX} = 5.0314$; **(c)** Based on (a) and (b), the model should be very useful for predicting the labor hours.

12.20 (a) $r^2 = 0.9424$. 94.24% of the variation in value of a baseball franchise can be explained by the variation in its annual revenue. **(b)** $S_{YX} = 33.7876$ **(c)** Based on (a) and (b), the model should be very useful for predicting value of a baseball franchise.

12.22 (a) $r^2 = 0.4613$. 46.13% of the variation in the tensile strength can be explained by the variation in the hardness. **(b)** $S_{YX} = 9.0616$ **(c)** Based on (a) and (b), the model is only marginally useful for predicting tensile strength.

12.24 A residual analysis of the data indicates a pattern, with sizeable clusters of consecutive residuals that are either all positive or all negative. This pattern indicates a violation of the assumption of linearity. A quadratic model should be investigated.

12.26 (a) There does not appear to be a pattern in the residual plot. **(b)** The assumptions of regression do not appear to be seriously violated.

12.28 (a) Based on the residual plot, there appears to be a nonlinear pattern in the residuals. A quadratic model should be investigated. **(b)** The assumptions of normality and equal variance do not appear to be seriously violated.

12.30 (a) Based on the residual plot, there appears to be a nonlinear pattern in the residuals. A quadratic model should be investigated. **(b)** The assumptions of normality and equal variance do not appear to be seriously violated.

12.32 (a) An increasing linear relationship exists. **(b)** There is evidence of a strong positive autocorrelation among the residuals.

12.34 (a) No, because the data were not collected over time. **(b)** If a single store had been selected, then studied over a period of time, you would compute the Durbin-Watson statistic.

12.36 (a) $b_1 = \dfrac{SSXY}{SSX} = \dfrac{201399.05}{12495626} = 0.0161$

$b_0 = \bar{Y} - b_1\bar{X} = 71.2621 - 0.0161(4393) = 0.458$ **(b)** $\hat{Y} = 0.458 + 0.0161X = 0.458 + 0.0161(4500) = 72.908$ or $72,908 **(c)** There is no evidence of a pattern in the residuals over time.

(d) $D = \dfrac{\sum_{i=2}^{n}(e_i - e_{i-1})^2}{\sum_{i=1}^{n}e_i^2} = \dfrac{1243.2244}{599.0683} = 2.08 > 1.45$. There is no

evidence of positive autocorrelation among the residuals. **(e)** Based on a residual analysis, the model appears to be adequate.

12.38 (a) $b_0 = -2.535$, $b_1 = .06073$; **(b)** \$2,505.40; **(d)** $D = 1.64 > d_U = 1.42$ so there is no evidence of positive autocorrelation among the residuals. **(e)** The plot does show some nonlinear pattern suggesting that a nonlinear model might be better. Otherwise, the model appears to be adequate.

12.40 (a) 3.00; **(b)** $t_{16} = \pm 2.1199$; **(c)** Reject H_0. There is evidence that the fitted linear regression model is useful. **(d)** $1.32 \le \beta_1 \le 7.68$.

12.42 (a) $t = \dfrac{h_1 - \beta_1}{S_{b_1}} = \dfrac{0.074}{0.0159} = 4.65$, $t_{10} = 2.2281$ with 10 degrees of freedom for $\alpha = 0.05$. Reject H_0. There is evidence that the fitted linear regression model is useful. **(b)** $b_1 \pm t_{n-2} S_{b_1} = 0.074 \pm 2.2281(0.0159)$ $0.0386 \le \beta_1 \le 0.1094$

12.44 (a) $t = 16.52 > 2.0322$, reject H_0; **(b)** $0.044 \le \beta_1 \le 0.0562$

12.46 (a) Since the p-value is approximately zero, reject H_0 at 5% level of significance. There is evidence of a linear relationship between annual revenue and franchise value. **(b)** $3.7888 \le \beta_1 \le 4.5906$

12.48 (a) p-value is virtually $0 < 0.05$, reject H_0; **(b)** $1.246 \le \beta_1 \le 2.792$

12.50 (b) If the S&P gains 30% in a year, the ULPIX is expected to gain an estimated 60%. **(c)** If the S&P loses 35% in a year, the ULPIX is expected to lose an estimated 70%.

12.52 (a) -0.401; **(b)** p-value $= 0.0885 > 0.05$, do not reject H_0; **(c)** At the 0.05 level of significance, there is no relationship between turnover rate of preboarding screeners and the security violations detected.

12.54 (a) 0.484; **(b)** p-value $= 0.017 < 0.05$, reject H_0; **(c)** At the 0.05 level of significance, there is a relationship between cold-cranking amps and price. **(d)** Yes, there is a positive linear relationship indicating that as cold-cranking amps increase so does the price.

12.56 (a) $15.95 \le \mu_{Y|X=400} \le 18.05$; **(b)** $14.651 \le Y_{X=400} \le 19.349$

12.58 (a) $\hat{Y}_i \pm t_{n-2} S_{YX} \sqrt{h_i}$
$= 2.042 \pm 2.2281(0.3081)\sqrt{0.1373}$
$1.7876 \le \mu_{Y|X=8} \le 2.2964$

(b) $\hat{Y}_i \pm t_{n-2} S_{YX} \sqrt{1 + h_i}$
$= 2.042 \pm 2.2281(0.3081)\sqrt{1 + 0.1373}$
$1.3100 \le Y_{X=8} \le 2.7740$

(c) Part (b) provides a prediction interval for the individual response given a specific value of the independent variable and part (a) provides an interval estimate for the mean value given a specific value of the independent variable. Since there is much more variation in predicting an individual value than in estimating a mean value, a prediction interval is wider than a confidence interval estimate.

12.60 (a) $20.799 \le \mu_{Y|X=500} \le 24.542$; **(b)** $12.276 \le Y_{X=500} \le 33.065$

12.62 (a) $367.0757 \le \mu_{Y|X=150} \le 397.3254$; **(b)** $311.3562 \le Y_{X=150} \le 453.0448$

12.74 (a) $b_0 = 24.84$, $b_1 = 0.14$ **(b)** For each additional case, the predicted delivery time is estimated to increase by 0.14 minutes. **(c)** 45.84; **(d)** No, 500 is outside the relevant range of the data used to fit the regression equation. **(e)** $r^2 = 0.972$; **(f)** There is no obvious pattern in the residuals so the assumptions of regression are met. The model appears to be adequate. **(g)** $t = 24.88 > 2.1009$, reject H_0; **(h)** $44.88 \le \mu_{Y|X=150} \le 46.80$; **(i)** $41.56 \le Y_{X=150} \le 50.12$; **(j)** $0.128 \le \beta_1 \le 0.152$

12.76 (a) $b_0 = -44.172$, $b_1 = 1.782$; **(b)** For each additional dollar in assessed value, the predicted selling price is estimated to increase by

\$1.78. **(c)** \$80,458; **(d)** $r^2 = 0.926$; **(e)** There is no obvious pattern in the residuals so the assumptions of regression are met. The model appears to be adequate. **(f)** $t = 18.66 > 2.0484$, reject H_0; **(g)** $78.707 \le \mu_{Y|X=70} \le 82.388$; **(h)** $73.195 \le Y_{X=70} \le 87.900$; **(i)** $1.586 \le \beta_1 \le 1.977$

12.78 (a) $b_0 = 0.30$, $b_1 = 0.00487$; **(b)** For each additional point on the GMAT score, the predicted GPI is estimated to increase by 0.00487. **(c)** 3.2225; **(d)** $r^2 = 0.798$ **(e)** There is no obvious pattern in the residuals so the assumptions of regression are met. The model appears to be adequate. **(f)** $t = 8.43 > 2.1009$, reject H_0; **(g)** $3.144 \le \mu_{Y|X=600} \le 3.301$; **(h)** $2.886 \le Y_{X=600} \le 3.559$; **(i)** $0.00366 \le \beta_1 \le .00608$

12.80 (a) There is no clear relationship shown on the scatterplot. **(c)** Looking at all 23 flights, when the temperature is lower, there is likely to be some O-ring damage, particularly if the temperature is below 60 degrees. **(d)** 31 degrees is outside the relevant range so a prediction should not be made. **(e)** predicted $Y = 18.036 - 0.240X$ where $X =$ temperature and $Y =$ O-ring damage; **(g)** A nonlinear model would be more appropriate. **(h)** The appearance on the residual plot of a nonlinear pattern indicates a nonlinear model would be better

12.82 (a) $b_0 = -2629.222$, $b_1 = 82.472$; **(b)** For each additional centimeter in circumference, the mean weight is estimated to increase by 82.472 grams. **(c)** 2,319.08 grams; **(e)** $r^2 = 0.937$; **(f)** There appears to be a nonlinear relationship between circumference and weight. **(g)** p-value is virtually $0 < 0.05$, reject H_0; **(h)** $72.787 \le \beta_1 \le 92.156$; **(i)** $2186.959 \le \mu_{Y|X=60} \le 2451.202$; **(j)** $1726.551 \le Y_{X=60} \le 2911.610$

12.84 (b) $\hat{Y} = 931,626.16 + 21,782.76X$ **(c)** $b_1 = 21,782.76$ means that as the median age of the customer base increases by one year, the latest one-month sales total is estimated to increase by \$21,782.76. **(d)** $r^2 = 0.0017$. Only 0.17% of the total variation in the franchise's latest one-month sales total can be explained by using the median age of customer base. **(e)** The residuals are very evenly spread out across different range of median age. **(f)** Since $-2.4926 < t = 0.2482 < 2.4926$, do not reject H_0. There is not enough evidence to conclude that there is a linear relationship between the one-month sales total and the median age of the customer base. **(g)** $-156,181.50 \le \beta_1 \le 199,747.02$.

12.86 (a) There is a positive linear relationship between total sales and the percentage of customer base with a college diploma. **(b)** $\hat{Y} = 789,847.38 + 35,854.15X$ **(c)** $b_1 = 35,854.15$ means that for each increase of one percent of the customer base having received a college diploma, the latest one-month sales total is estimated to increase by \$35,854.15. **(d)** $r^2 = 0.1036$. So, 10.36% of the total variation in the franchise's latest one-month sales total can be explained by the percentage of the customer base with a college diploma. **(e)** The residuals are quite evenly spread out around zero. **(f)** Since $t = 2.0392 > 2.0281$, reject H_0. There is enough evidence to conclude that there is a linear relationship between one-month sales total and percentage of customer base with a college diploma. **(g)** $b_1 \pm t_{n-2} S_{b_1} = 35,854.15 \pm 2.0281(17,582.269)$ $195.75 \le \beta_1 \le 71,512.60$

12.88 (a) $b_0 = -24.247$, $b_1 = 1.046$; **(b)** For each additional unit increase in summated rating, the price per person is estimated to increase by \$1.05. Since no restaurant will receive a summated rating of 0, it is inappropriate to interpret the Y-intercept. **(c)** \$28.07; **(d)** $r^2 = 0.658$; **(e)** There is no obvious pattern in the residuals so the assumptions of regression are met. The model appears to be adequate. **(f)** p-value is virtually $0 < 0.05$, reject H_0; **(g)** $26.55 \le \mu_{Y|X=50} \le 29.59$; **(h)** \$16.00 $\le Y_{X=50} \le$ \$40.15; **(i)** $0.895 \le \beta_1 \le 1.198$

12.90 (a) MSFT and Ford 0.167; MSFT and GM 0.157; MSFT and IAL -0.232; Ford and GM 0.867; Ford and IAL 0.697; and GM and IAL 0.629; **(b)** There is a strongly positive linear relationship between the stock price of Ford and GM, a moderately strong positive linear relationship between the stock price of Ford and IAL and between GM and IAL, a very weak positive linear relationship between the stock price of Ford and Microsoft, between GM and Microsoft, and a rather weak negative linear relationship between Microsoft and IAL. **(c)** It is not a good idea to have all the stocks in an individual's portfolio be strongly, positively correlated among each other because the portfolio risk can be reduced when a pair of stock prices is negatively related in a portfolio.

CHAPTER 13

13.2 (a) For each one unit increase in X_1, you estimate that Y will decrease 2 units, holding X_2 constant. For each one unit increase in X_2, you estimate that Y will increase 7 units, holding X_1 constant. **(b)** The Y-intercept equal to 50, estimates the predicted value of Y when both X_1 and X_2 are zero.

13.4 (a) $\hat{Y} = -2.72825 + 0.047114X_1 + 0.011947 X_2$; **(b)** For a given number of orders, for each increase of \$1,000 in sales, distribution cost is estimated to increase by \$47.114. For a given amount of sales, for each increase of one order, distribution cost is estimated to increase by \$11.95. **(c)** The interpretation of b_0 has no practical meaning here because it would represent the estimated distribution cost when there were no sales and no orders. **(d)** $\hat{Y} = -2.72825 + 0.047114(400) + 0.011947(4500)$ $= 69.878$ or \$69,878; **(e)** \$66,419,93 $\leq \mu_{Y|X} \leq$ \$73,337.01; **(f)** \$59,380.61 $\leq Y_X \leq$ \$80,376.33

13.6 (a) $\hat{Y} = 156.4 + 13.081X_1 + 16.795X_2$; **(b)** For a given amount of newspaper advertising, each increase by \$1,000 in radio advertising is estimated to result in a mean increase in sales of \$13,081. For a given amount of radio advertising, each increase by \$1,000 in newspaper advertising is estimated to result in a mean increase in sales of \$16,795. **(c)** When there is no money spent on radio advertising and newspaper advertising, the estimated mean sales is \$156,430.44. **(d)** $\hat{Y} = 156.4 + 13.081(20) + 16.795(20) = 753.95$ or \$753,950; **(e)** \$623,038.31 $\leq \mu_{Y|X}$ $\leq$ \$884,860.93; **(f)** \$396,522.63 $\leq Y_X \leq$ \$1,111,376.60

13.8 (a) $\hat{Y} = 400.8057 + 456.4485X_1 - 2.4708X_2$ where $X_1 = $ Land, $X_2 = $ age; **(b)** For a given age, each increase by one acre in land area is estimated to result in a mean increase in appraised value by \$456.45 thousands. For a given acreage, each increase of one year in age is estimated to result in the mean decrease in appraised value by \$2.47 thousands. **(c)** The interpretation of b_0 has no practical meaning here because it would represent the estimated appraised value of a new house that has no land area. **(d)** $\hat{Y} = 400.8057 + 456.4485(0.25) - 2.4708(45) =$ \$403.73 thousands. **(e)** $372.7370 \leq \mu_{Y|X} \leq 434.7243$; **(f)** $235.1964 \leq Y_X \leq 572.2649$

13.10 (a) $MSR = 15$, $MSE = 12$; **(b)** 1.25; **(c)** $F = 1.25 < 4.10$, do not reject H_0; **(d)** 0.20; **(e)** 0.04

13.12 (a) $F = 97.69 > F_{U(2,15-2-1)} = 3.89$. Reject H_0. There is evidence of a significant linear relationship with at least one of the independent variables. **(b)** The p-value is 0.0001. **(c)** $r^2 = 0.9421$. 94.21% of the variation in the long-term ability to absorb shock can be explained by variation in forefoot absorbing capability and variation in midsole impact. **(d)** $r_{adj}^2 = 0.93245$

13.14 (a) $F = 74.13 > 3.467$, reject H_0; **(b)** p-value = 0; **(c)** $r^2 = 0.8759$. 87.59% of the variation in distribution cost can be explained by variation in sales and variation in number of orders. **(d)** $r_{adj}^2 = 0.8641$

13.16 (a) $F = 40.16 > F_{U(2,22-2-1)} = 3.522$. Reject H_0. There is evidence of a significant linear relationship. **(b)** The p-value is less than 0.001. **(c)** $r^2 = 0.8087$. 80.87% of the variation in sales can be explained by

variation in radio advertising and variation in newspaper advertising. **(d)** $r_{adj}^2 = 0.7886$

13.18 (a) Based upon a residual analysis, the model appears adequate. **(b)** There is no evidence of a pattern in the residuals versus time. **(c)** $D = \dfrac{1,077.0956}{477.0430} = 2.26$; **(d)** $D = 2.26 > 1.55$. There is no evidence of positive autocorrelation in the residuals.

13.20 There appears to be a quadratic relationship in the plot of the residuals against both radio and newspaper advertising. Thus, quadratic terms for each of these explanatory variables should be considered for inclusion in the model.

13.22 There is no particular pattern in the residual plots and the model appears to be adequate.

13.24 (a) Variable X_2 has a larger slope in terms of the t statistic of 3.75 than variable X_1, which has a smaller slope in terms of the t statistic of 3.33. **(b)** $1.46824 \leq \beta_1 \leq 6.33176$; **(c)** For X_1: $t = 4/1.2 = 3.33 > 2.1098$ with 17 degrees of freedom for $\alpha = 0.05$. Reject H_0. There is evidence that X_1 contributes to a model already containing X_2. For X_2: $t = 3/0.8 = 3.75 > 2.1098$ with 17 degrees of freedom for $\alpha = 0.05$. Reject H_0. There is evidence that X_2 contributes to a model already containing X_1. Both X_1 and X_2 should be included in the model.

13.26 (a) 95% confidence interval on β_1: $b_1 \pm t_{n-k-1} S_{b_1}$, $0.0471 \pm 2.0796 \cdot 0.0203$, $0.00488 \leq \beta_1 \leq 0.08932$; **(b)** For X_1: $t = b_1/S_{b_1} = 0.0471/0.0203 = 2.32 > 2.0796$. Reject H_0. There is evidence that X_1 contributes to a model already containing X_2. For X_2: $t = b_2/S_{b_2} = 0.01195/0.00225 = 5.31 > 2.0796$ with 21 degrees of freedom for $\alpha = 0.05$. Reject H_0. There is evidence that X_2 contributes to a model already containing X_1. Both X_1 (sales) and X_2 (orders) should be included in the model.

13.28 (a) $9.398 \leq \beta_1 \leq 16.763$; **(b)** For X_1: $t = 7.43 > 2.093$. Reject H_0. There is evidence that X_1 contributes to a model already containing X_2. For X_2: $t = 5.67 > 2.093$. Reject H_0. There is evidence that X_2 contributes to a model already containing X_1. Both X_1 (radio advertising) and X_2 (newspaper advertising) should be included in the model.

13.30 (a) $227.5865 \leq \beta_1 \leq 685.3104$; **(b)** For X_1: $t = 4.0922$ and p-value = 0.0003. Since p-value < 0.05, reject H_0. There is evidence that X_1 contributes to a model already containing X_2. For X_2: $t = -3.6295$ and p-value = 0.0012. Since p-value < 0.05, reject H_0. There is evidence that X_2 contributes to a model already containing X_1. Both X_1 (land area) and X_2 (age) should be included in the model.

13.32 (a) predicted Price = 43.737 + 9.219 Rooms + 12.697 west; **(b)** Holding constant the effect of neighborhood, for each additional room, the mean selling price is estimated to increase by 9.219 thousands of dollars, or \$9,219. For a given number of rooms, the mean selling price in the west neighborhood is estimated to be 12.697 thousand dollars (\$12,697) greater than the east neighborhood. **(c)** \$126,710; \$121,470 $\leq \mu_{Y|X} \leq$ \$131,940; \$109,560 $\leq Y_X \leq$ \$143,860; **(d)** the model appears adequate; **(e)** $F = 55.39 > 3.59$, reject H_0; **(f)** $t = 8.95 > 2.1098$, reject H_0. $t = 3.59 > 2.1098$, reject H_0. include both variables; **(g)** $7.0466 \leq \beta_1 \leq 11.392$; $5.239 \leq \beta_2 \leq 20.155$; **(h)** 86.7% of the variation in selling price is explained by the variation in number of rooms and location. **(i)** 85.1%; **(j)** The slope of selling price with number of rooms is the same regardless of location. **(k)** p-value = 0.330, do not reject H_0, do not include the interaction term; **(l)** the model developed in part (a) should be used.

13.34 (a) predicted Time = 8.01 + 0.00523 Depth − 2.105 Dry;
(b) Holding constant the effect of type of drilling, for each foot increase in depth of the hole, the drilling time is estimated to increase by 0.0052 minutes. For a given depth, a dry drilling is estimated to reduce the drilling time over wet drilling by 2.1052 minutes. **(c)** 6.428 minutes, $6.210 \leq \mu_{Y|X} \leq 6.646$; $4.923 \leq Y_X \leq 7.932$; **(d)** The model appears adequate. **(e)** $F = 111.11 > 3.09$, reject H_0; **(f)** $t = 5.03 > 1.9847$, reject H_0. $t = -14.03 < -1.9847$, reject H_0. include both variables; **(g)** $0.0032 \leq \beta_1 \leq 0.0073$; $-2.403 \leq \beta_2 \leq -1.807$; **(h)** 69.6% of the variation in drill time is explained by the variation of depth and variation in type of drilling, **(i)** 69.0%; **(j)** The slope of the additional drilling time with the depth of the hole is the same regardless of the type of drilling method used. **(k)** The p-value of the interaction term = 0.462 > 0.05, so the term is not significant and should not be included in the model. **(l)** The model in part (a) should be used.

13.36 (a) $\hat{Y} = 31.5594 + 0.0296X_1 + 0.0041X_2 + 0.000017159X_1X_2$, where X_1 = sales, X_2 = orders, the p-value is 0.3249 > 0.05. Do not reject H_0. There is not enough evidence that the interaction term makes a contribution to the model. **(b)** Since there is not enough evidence of any interaction effect between sales and orders, the model in problem 14.4 should be used.

13.38 (a) The p-value of the interaction term = 0.002 < .05, so the term is significant and should be included in the model. **(b)** Use the model developed in this problem.

13.40 (a) For X_1X_2: the p-value is 0.2353 > 0.05. Do not reject H_0. There is not enough evidence that the interaction term makes a contribution to the model. **(b)** Since there is not enough evidence of an interaction effect between total staff present and remote hours, the model in problem 14.7 should be used.

13.47 (a) predicted Price = −44.988 + 1.751 Value + 0.368 Time; **(c)** $81,969; **(d)** The model is adequate; **(e)** $F = 223.46 > 3.35$, reject H_0; **(f)** p-value = 0 so the model is significant. **(g)** 94.3% of the variation in selling price is explained by the variation in assessed value and time since reassessment. **(h)** 93.9%; **(i)** Since $t = 20.41 > 2.0518$, reject H_0. Since $t = 2.87 > 2.0518$, reject H_0. Use a model that includes both variables. **(j)** 0.000 and 0.008 < 0.05, so both variables are significant; **(k)** $1.574 \leq \beta_1 \leq 1.927$

13.49 (a) predicted Value = 63.775 + 10.725 Size − 0.284 Age; **(c)** $79,702; **(d)** The residual plot against age indicates a potential pattern. **(e)** $F = 28.58 > 3.89$, reject H_0. **(f)** p-value = 0 indicating the model is significant. **(g)** 82.6% of the variation in assessed value is explained by the variation in size and the age of the home. **(h)** 79.8%; **(i)** Since $t = 3.56 > 2.1788$, reject H_0. Since $t = -3.40 < -2.1788$, reject H_0. **(j)** p-values = 0.004 and 0.005 < 0.05, so both variables are significant. **(k)** $4.158 \leq \beta_1 \leq 17.292$; **(l)** no

13.51 (a) predicted MPG = 40.877 − 0.0121 Length − 0.00495 Weight; **(c)** 23.66 miles per gallon; **(d)** A quadratic model should be fit. There is some evidence of unequal variance. **(e)** $F = 92.93 > 3.07$, reject H_0.

(f) p-value = 0 indicating a significant model. **(g)** 61.2% of the variation in miles per gallon is explained by the variation in car length and weight. **(h)** 60.5%; **(i)** Since $t = -0.46 > -1.9799$, do not reject H_0. Since $t = -10.24 < -1.9799$, reject H_0. Use only weight in the model. **(j)** Length is not significant since the p-value for length = 0.647. Weight is significant since the p-value for weight = 0; **(k)** $-0.00591 \leq \beta_2 \leq -0.00400$

13.55 (a) $\hat{Y} = 152.0316 - 2.4587X_1 - 15.8687X_2$, where X_1 = league dummy (0 = American, 1 = National) and X_2 = ERA. **(b)** Holding constant the effect of ERA, the estimated number of wins for a team in the American league is 2.4587 above that of the National league. Holding constant the effect of league, for each unit increase in ERA, the number of wins is estimated to decrease by 15.8687. **(c)** 81 wins. **(d)** Based on the residual analysis, the model appears adequate. **(e)** $F = 11.1784$ and p-value = 0.00025 < 0.05. Reject H_0. There is evidence of a relationship between number of wins and the two independent variables. **(f)** For X_1: $t = -0.6447$. p-value = 0.5246 > 0.05. Do not reject H_0. Which league the team is in does not make a significant contribution and should not be included in the model. For X_2: $t = -4.7763$. p-value is virtually zero < 0.05. Reject H_0. ERA makes a significant contribution and should be included in the model. The model should include ERA but not the league. **(g)** $-10.2842 \leq \beta_1 \leq 5.3668$, $-22.6856 \leq \beta_2 \leq -9.0518$; **(h)** $r^2_{Y.12} = 0.4595$. 45.95% of the variation in number of wins can be explained by variation in type of league and variation in ERA. **(i)** $r^2_{adj} = 0.4195$; **(j)** The slope of number of wins with ERA is the same regardless of whether the team is in the American or National league. **(k)** $\hat{Y} = 162.6777 - 21.8842X_1 - 18.2211X_2 + 4.4027X_1X_2$. For X_1X_2: the p-value is 0.5189. Do not reject H_0. There is no evidence that the interaction term makes a contribution to the model. **(l)** The model with only ERA should be used.

CHAPTER 14

14.14 (a) $\bar{p} = 0.2702$, LCL = 0.1700, UCL = 0.3703; **(b)** Yes, RudyBird's market share is in control before the in-store promotion. **(c)** All 7 days of the in-store promotion are above the UCL. The promotion increased market share.

14.16 (a) $\bar{p} = 0.75175$, LCL = 0.62215, UCL = 0.88135. Although none of the points are outside the control limits there is a clear pattern over time with the last 13 points above the center line. Therefore, this process is not in control. **(b)** Since the increasing trend begins around day 20, this change in method would be the assignable cause. **(c)** The control chart would have been developed using the first 20 days and then, using those limits, the additional proportions could have been plotted.

14.18 (a) $\bar{p} = 0.1198$, LCL = 0.0205, UCL = 0.2191; **(b)** Day 24 is below the LCL, therefore, the process is out of control. **(c)** Special causes of variation should be investigated to improve the process. Next the process should be improved to decrease the proportion of undesirable trades.